PHILADELPHIA ORDNANCE DISTRICT
IN WORLD WAR II

PHILADELPHIA ORDNANCE DISTRICT IN WORLD WAR II

A RECORD OF THE PHILADELPHIA ORDNANCE DISTRICT AND
INDUSTRY OF THE DISTRICT DURING THE WAR YEARS 1941–1945

Compiled by

ROBERT T. GEBLER

HISTORIAN

Philadelphia Ordnance District

1942-1946

WESTBROOK PUBLISHING COMPANY, INC.
PHILADELPHIA, PA.
1949

COPYRIGHT, 1949
by
ROBERT T. GEBLER
PHILADELPHIA, PA.

This is Number .690. of a
Limited Edition of 1,000 copies

AN EXPLANATION

THIS history of the Philadelphia Ordinance District in World War II was written to please three persons—or for one person who might have an occasional change of reading, or investigational mood.

The key to this, what may appear an unusual technique, is revealed in the repetition of names and developments which appear and reappear throughout this volume—repetitions which were inevitable if the reading tastes and reference needs of our readers were squarely to be met.

Our first reader, if not our most frequent browser, will find much "meat to his liking" in Part I, which affords a comprehensive background history of the District—its early developments, its subsequent expansion with the increasing demands of global war, together with intimate glimpses of the men who shaped and directed the destiny of the District. This reader will perhaps wish to explore no further.

Part II of this work is pointed for the reader who will have nothing short of the full, sweeping, chronological accounting of war's impact upon Ordinance, upon Industry, upon life and living throughout the District, the "tumult and the shouting," the events and eventualities—a panorama graphically recalling for this reader the color, the movement, the cross-currents of the war as we saw and felt it here.

Follows, a very practical Part III, designed for the reader or researcher who would know intimately the internal operations of the District offices; of the shifts, of the changes, of obsoletions, mergers and additions of units and activities which made the production of organization charts something akin to a major industry hereabouts.

To please three persons—

That is how it happens that certain repetitions found their way into our narrative. However, these repetitions have an importance that may not first appear. Usually they express a similar fact, or thought, each time from a different point of view and possibly toward a different end, all together providing a thoroughness of accounting or appraisal that otherwise might have been lacking.

It need further to be explained that it obviously was impossible to include the names, and references to the accomplishments of all those who served the Industry-Ordinance Team during the War. More than 8,000 persons, military and civilian, passed through the District Offices from 1938 to VJ-Day; the number of prime contractors, sub-contractors, suppliers and others add many more thousands of names to the honor roll. The names and events which do appear are those which fell into the sweep of the narrative as this record unfolded.

While the official history of the Philadelphia Ordnance District has been freely drawn upon in preparation of this volume, this version is the author's and any opinions expressed herein are his own and do not necessarily reflect those of the War Department.

CONTENTS

By Way of Preface

HOW IT ALL BEGAN

HAD not young Dave Hauseman suddenly developed back in 1917 a yen for soda crackers and gargantuan libations of H_2O this baring of P. O. D. past might never have been written.

You see, it was this way: Dave, who then was a Wharton school student, wanted, along with eighty-two of his classmates, to get into the European fracas. "Easy," he thought. "Just sign up, and there you are!" But the course of patriotism, like true love, "never runs smooth," as Dave soon learned. There was that little matter of weight. Eighty-two lads made the grade, hands down; but Dave, as the legend runs, because of a critical lack of avoirdupois, was "sent to the showers."

Undaunted, our young man bethought him of certain boyhood legends anent soda crackers and water, and forthwith proceeded to stow away vast quantities of both. Days later, water logged and heavier by pounds, he returned to the enlistment center where he quickly was given a triple A-1 priority. He was in the Army! And he stayed put! That too is history!

But let us suppose that the soda cracker and water diet had not occurred to the future General; suppose, if you will, there had been no World War I, or even suppose that David N. Hauseman—who was first to suggest a history such as this—had never been born! Do you think, then, the Historian never would have been assigned the task of putting a revealing pen to paper?

No such good fortune. There still would have been, as it later developed, a certain C. Jared Ingersoll with whom the Historian would have to contend.

"Make it about eighty pages," he said, recalling a brief history of the District published by the War Department following World War I. The Historian knew that a history of P. O. D. would run to many times eighty pages; but higher echelon had spoken, and cheerful assent immediately became a virtue.

And that is how this history was born.

The hope of the compiler is that when this work shall have been completed, it will bring to the reader pleasant memories, refreshing recollection of the events which took place here, of associates long since scattered the length and breadth of private industry. What more?

Above all, it is the historian's earnest prayer that when he shall have read it, A. Donald Kelso, well-remembered industrialist, scholar, poet, and one time District Chief, may say as was his custom when he was well pleased:

"I think that is wonderful!"

ROBERT T. GEBLER
Philadelphia, Pa.

1 July 1949

War Time Leaders
of P. O. D.

C. JARED INGERSOLL

Reported for Duty as District Chief, 7 September 1940. Named Deputy Chief in shift in organization in January 1942 when it became necessary to have a military officer in charge. Was renamed Chief 3 January 1944, following re-assignment of Colonel Fred A. McMahon. Resigned because of ill health, 4 June 1945

BRIGADIER GENERAL DAVID N. HAUSEMAN

Promoted from Deputy Chief in January 1942. Transferred to Washington 1 December 1943 to head Redistribution Branch, A.S.F. Office Chief of Ordnance

COLONEL A. DONALD KELSO

Named District Chief, 4 June 1945. Separated 19 December 1945

PART ONE

Chapter I

ORDNANCE, 'WAY BACK WHEN

IF ANYONE believes that "Ordnance" is a modern phenomenon, tell him to "look again"! There was an Ordnance Department as far back as 1812, set up by Congress, 14 May of that year, with the passing of an act reorganizing the Army. Dr. William Eustis, then Secretary of War, called to the job of heading the newly created Office of Commissary General of Ordnance, one Decius Wadsworth who had at one time served the Nation as Second Chief of Engineers and, again, as Second Superintendent of the Military Academy.

Since the days of Decius, and to World War II, the Ordnance Department had been pretty much a "touch and go" affair, marked by a waxing and and waning from sudden war to confused peace, and from war to war. This is not a criticism of Army policy or method; it is simply one phase of Democracy at work. Here, when we have peace, we spread on the butter, thickly: Comes war, we are "all-out" for guns, ships and planes—and fast; and we get them!

However, we have learned many vital lessons, and it is doubted that ever again some swift Pearl Harbor will catch us with our preparedness pants down. We now have, for instance, the full record of what we did here, what were our problems and the steps taken to meet them, and it was to be expected that the record would be maintained through the peace years, noting developments of material, progress in manufacturing and the integration of new techniques—all to the end that we shall know in a sudden moment of danger who can make what, how much, and how soon.

It would be tragic if what we had learned of organization, our kind of organization, soon should be forgotten, for not only did we build in Phila-delphia, from "scratch," and in a few brief years what was then the equivalent of a three billion dollar enterprise; but we accomplished this amazing result in the face of odds which under normal conditions would have appeared insurmountable.

The story, when written, of the part of the Philadelphia Ordnance District, will be, beyond its more glamorous aspects, a story of sudden and great mobilizations of manpower, and of technical and industrial skills; a story of incredibly swift conversions of plants, of machines; and of inventive genius creating new things "to order," magicians at work!

And beyond all that, another story, a story of men, men who long will be remembered for what they did here, many putting aside opportunities for larger financial gains, stepping willingly into the very vortex of a new, strange, cruelly demanding occupation; such men as those whose names shall be noted in this feeble record of their magnificent contributions—Ingersoll, Hauseman, Kelso, Gant, Allen, Seiler, Guernsey, Hamilton, Wolfe, Broberg, Gadsden, Disney, Kelley, Shaeffer, Beyer, Wexlin, Target, Baxter, Sandler, Farrington, Fleitas, Stokes, Conger, Dennison, Langham, Fox, Carlson, Lafean, Allison, Harvey, Jefferies, Fred Smith, Lew Smith, Vic Smith, Miller, Van Deusen, Whelan, Wexlin, Andrews, Hoffman, Potts, Ogden, Gilmer, Minnier, Feustel, Denny, Gilbert, La Rue, Snyder, Wilmsen, Clark, Buerger, Schmid, Uhler, O'Rourke, Press, Klair, Lafferty—the list goes on and on, rocketing from a total in mid-1938 of less than forty persons, to more than forty-one hundred at the peak in 1942. And that, too, is history!

A story of men?

Great men! Great women!

P. O. D.!

Top row, L to R: Lt. John J. Geraghty, Lt. Edward S. Tinley, Captain David H. McIlvaine, Lt. Howard S. Gallaher. Second row: Lt. Robert O. Watson, Captain Fred E. Smith, Lt. Rupert G. Getzer, Lt. Neal W. Slack. Third row: Captain John C. Pyle, Jr., Major Edw. N. Lafferty, Captain Welles H. Denney, Captain John Stevens. Bottom: Lt. E. C. Petterson, M. H. Miller, Dan C. Bell, H. Paul Gant

Chapter II

PROCUREMENT WORLD WAR I STYLE

AS INTERESTING a spot as any at which to begin this story of P. O. D. in World War I is right here at 150 South Broad Street—say, almost any Wednesday forenoon of the year 1917. Had you dropped by at that time, you would have found the "Ordnance Bourse" in session. Men—manufacturers of various kinds of equipment and commodities, milling about among officers of the District Office, groups engaged in earnest discussion or examining the various items of materiel on exhibit. This was procurement in action and, "on the spot!"

Near the end of the long room, which had been provided for Ordnance Department use by the Manufacturers' Club, you would have observed a returned soldier, megaphone in hand, mounting an improvised platform. He is reading from an official looking form, his voice rises clearly above the hum of inquiry and negotiation before him:

"Attention, ple-e-e-a-se!" he is calling. "Does anyone here make box shooks—box shooks? Does anyone here make box shooks?"

Or the call might have been for "bolas," or "drop bombs" or helmets of which latter the District produced 2,700,000 during the course of the war. Whatever the item, hands were raised as capacity was found. Officers and civilian specialists were watching and ready. The prospective war contractor was taken in tow and the machinery of procurement began to roll.

The idea of an "Ordnance Bourse," or the Ordnance Manufacturers' Exchange, as it officially was named, came from Captain F. S. Guerber, Manager of Ammunition, Explosives and Loading. He had it from an earlier peacetime, commercial experience in Belgium, where he found that many trips throughout Flanders to see producers in the iron trade could be eliminated by means of the establishment of a central strategic display, or bourse, for convenient meeting.

Crude as the method was, as compared to World War II procedure, it no doubt was effective in bringing together at one point, and at one time, all persons who might be interested in a particular allocation. Too, the Philadelphia Ordnance District was smaller. The most remote facility was no more than a few hours away.

Opposed to the conveniences of the Ordnance Bourse and related activities in World War I, of the Philadelphia Ordnance District, there was an offsetting and greater cost per dollar of production than in World War II. For instance, allotments to cover payment on contracts placed in the District approximated $750,000,000.00 of which $250,000,000.00 were expended between the months of April and December, 1918. On 1 November, 1918, there were outstanding 1,119 contracts, calling for payments of $484,897,000.00. As of 1 November, 1944, by way of comparison, there were outstanding, 1,992 contracts, held by 614 contractors, and to a dollar value of $2,009,912,145.93. However, although working to smaller dollar totals, personnel of the District during World War I, was, at all points of comparison, at higher levels than during World War II. In the former instance, the personnel peak was reached in June, 1918, five months before the Armistice. At that time, the payroll carried the names of 4,475 civilians. At the highest point in World War II, the civilian personnel total of P. O. D. stood at 4,149 persons; and from that point, began a steady decline, stimulated by consolidation of units and activities, establishment of routines, and by occasional directives.

Back in World War I days the District was pretty much what the word implied, a convenient geographical division. The various District functions were assigned to individuals who worked directly with Washington. Offices were scattered. One office was located in the then Vulcanite Building, 1710 Market Street, one in the Middle City Post Office Building, at 34 South 17th Street, another at 1726 Ludlow Street, and one at 1712 Ludlow Street.

Something resembling unification appeared with the apointment 13 March, 1918, as District Chief, of John C. Jones, President, Harrison Safety Boiler Works, of Philadelphia. His was a turbulent administration. He saw the end of the war and, out of a rich industrial experience, was able to bring a degree of order out of the chaos, as far as the District was concerned. Mr. Jones remained at his post through the inevitable period of Claims and Salvage, into 1919 when the "books were closed" and personnel disbanded. Part of his task following declaration of the peace was the transfer from the Rochester and New York Ordnance Districts to the Philadelphia Ordnance District of remaining personnel who subsequently were assigned by Mr. Jones to the Frankford Arsenal. Files of the three Districts were sent to Frankford and Washington.

From mid-1919 to the reactivation of the District in 1922, and for some time after that, the District could boast but one employee, Miss Helen V. Meehan who, at this writing, July, 1949, bears the distinction of being the oldest employee in point of service, in the District. Signal honors came to Miss Meehan on 11 November, 1944, Armistice anniversary, when she was presented by Mr. C. Jared Ingersoll, District Chief, with a "diploma" testifying to her twenty-five years of loyal service, a Civilian Ribbon, and an armful of chrysanthemums from Chief Ingersoll's Fort Washington, Pennsylvania, gardens.

Reactivation, a consequence of the National Defense Act of 1920 again brought John C. Jones to the post of District Chief, and with him, in the capacity of Executive Assistant, Captain Walter F. Vander Hyden, who officially assumed his duties 13 November of that year following completion in Washington of special duties in connection with industrial mobilization.

Through this period and well into the administration of the late Philip H. Gadsden, which followed, tentative schedules of production were assigned, and survey operations firmly established as a District function.

In January, 1924, Captain Vander Hyden was transferred to Washington. He was succeeded by Captain Walter E. Ditmars, Ordnance Department, who resigned in October, 1925, to be followed by Captain F. C. Shaffer.

The Philadelphia Ordnance District must have had from the start a fine collection of four-leafed clovers, horseshoes and hind feet of rabbits shot under dark moons in cemetery lots. In no other way could the District have obtained its succession of top-flight, topside men.

Colonel David N. Hauseman, District Chief awards decorations to boys in recognition of successes in War Stamp Sales

Chapter III

EARLY PEACE YEARS

SURVEYING of plants and placing of schedules continued at a rising tempo through the '20s. Captain Shaffer was able, out of his earlier Ordnance experience, to make substantial contribution. It was during the Shaffer era, 1925, that the training program for Reserve Officers was got under way, the full benefits of which were not to be felt until almost fifteen years later when the country was practically "fist-to-nose" with the implications of war.

Under the training program, conferences were held once each week from October to May. Discussions were informal and were largely for the purpose of having the embryo officers become acquainted with each other. Social aspects were not overlooked.

Once each year, and this went on for some time, there were required, when funds should be available, fifteen days of active duty at Aberdeen Proving Grounds and the District Office. With development of the Reserve Officer organization, meeting discussions turned to manufacturing methods, particularly in reference to ammunition, artillery items, forgings for gun tubes for the "75 mm. Field Gun and the 155 mm. Howitzer." Drawings and specifications were explained and reviewed. World War I officers turned up to cover realistic phases of battle requirements.

Not much talk of terminations in those days. Interest was in what might be around the corner. In June, 1930, Captain Shaffer was relieved by the late Major Walter L. Clark and District head-quarters were moved from the Widener Building to the Gimbel Building at Ninth and Chestnut Streets. Training now embraced study of material and review of procurement planning, organization and contract method and procedures. Recruitment was of qualified civilians, ex-officers and of ROTC graduates. Promotion was on the basis of length of service, satisfactory completion of three hundred hours of Army Extension School Courses, and a tour of active duty.

The whole idea was good, but something went haywire in 1931 and into 1932, with the performance. Interest lagged. Attendance ebbed. Substantial pickup did not come until September 1933 when Major Clark was reassigned and the Executive Assistant's baton was passed along to Major R. L. Maxwell.

It was under the new incumbent that interest in officer training reached what Captain, later Major, Charles T. "Encyclopedia" Michener was pleased to name the "all-time high." "Largely due," he wrote, "to the Maxwellian personality, his organizing ability, assignments to officers of definite duties, visits to nearby Army installations, and talks by such Army notables as the then Secretary of War, Mr. Dern, then Lt. Colonel L. H. Campbell, Jr., of Frankford Arsenal, and others. And, O, yes! there was a fairly comprehensive Ordnance exhibit set up in the District Office."

One among the numerous activities of Major Maxwell was to convene from time to time, with the co-operation of the Chief of Staff of the First Military Area, all local boards, and have appear all candidates for promotion and those qualified civilians who were believed to be good material for commissions.

Midway of 1934 Major Maxwell moved on to wider fields, subsequently to rise to the rank of Major General. Major Walter C. Hamilton was assigned. The Major, so the record reads, had, among other sterling qualifications, a keen sense of organization. This was made manifest in the "Production Mobilization Plan of 1939" also known as "Philadelphia Ordnance District in Time of War," which Major Hamilton developed with the cooperation of Otho V. Kean, who had come to the District in June 1939 as Senior Engineer, absorbing at the same time the duties of Chief Inspector.

A sidelight on Otho V. Kean at this point will not be amiss. Prior to World War I, he had been a Captain of Ordnance, retiring in 1915 to enter private business. In 1938, no longer able to resist the old interest, he returned to the District, plunging into the job of reorganizing functions and procedures. The Senior Engineer was later to prove an able assistant to Brigadier General, then Major D. N. Hauseman. As a matter of fact, Major Hauseman, while Chief of the Procurement Planning Section, Office of the Chief of Ordnance, had had a voice in the selection of Otho V. Kean. The presence in the District of so capable an assistant was no doubt one of the factors which gave Major Hauseman the heart to tackle the job he found here. Unfortunately, however, Kean already had, through intensity of purpose and his willingness to assume every duty large or small that came his way, given speed to the illness which lead to his untimely death in September, 1940, just four month's following Major Hauseman's arrival in Philadelphia.

Display and Bond Sales Booth in front of P.O.D. headquarters during 2nd Bond Drive with James P. McCue of the guards in command

Chapter IV

P.O.D. SEEKS WISE COUNSEL

NINETEEN twenty-five—that was the year Advisory Boards were set up in the thirteen Ordinance Districts. The first panel in the Philadelphia Ordnance District of the Advisory Board was got together under the direction of the then Executive Assistant, Captain Walter E. Ditmars.

"The individuals comprising the Advisory Boards," wrote Secretary of the Navy Wilbur, in 1925, "are key men in the Nation's scheme of National defense. Voluntarily they give the Philadelphia District, and the United States, services which the Government could not secure on a salary at any cost, however high . . ."

On the first panel appeared the names of such local notables as John C. Jones, Chairman, President, Harrison Safety Boiler Works; Samuel M. Vauclain, President, Baldwin Locomotive Works; W. W. Atterbury, President, Pennsylvania Railroad Company; A. Atwater Kent, President, A. Atwater Kent Manufacturing Company; George Horace Lorimer, Editor, Saturday Evening Post; Eugene G. Grace, President, Bethlehem Steel Company; Charles R. Richards, President, Lehigh University; Josiah Penniman, Provost, University of Pennsylvania; Eldridge R. Johnson, President, Victor Talking Machine Company; Leonard H. Kinnard, President, Bell Telephone Company of Pennsylvania; Irenee DuPont, President, E. I. DuPont de Nemours & Company; John E. Zimmerman, President, United Gas Improvement Company; Edward T. Stotesbury, President, Drexel & Company.

Among dignitaries to serve their time were, Dr. Henry B. Allen, Director, Franklin Institute; W. L. Batt, President, S. K. F. Industries; Quincy Bent, Vice President, Bethlehem Steel Company; Charles E. Brinley, President, Baldwin Locomotive Works; Walter S. Carpenter, President, E. I. DuPont de Nemours & Company; M. W. Clement, President, Pennsylvania Railroad Company; Wm.

D. Disston, Vice President, Henry Disston & Sons, Inc.; Arthur Dorrance, President, Campbell Soup Company; Jacob France, Chairman, Equitable Trust Company of Baltimore; Dr. H. L. Frevert, President, Midvale Company; James E. Gowen, President, Girard Trust Company; P. Blair Lee, President, Western Savings Fund Company; Hudson W. Reed, Vice President, United Gas Improvement Company; John S. Zinsser, President, Sharpe & Dohme Company; Colonel D. K. Bullens, President, New England Auto Products Company.

Many great personalities have come and gone in Advisory Board history, each to leave the imprint of his character, and to make important contributions to the Board's usefulness. For instance, James W. Rawle, Vice President, J. G. Brill Company; James Elverson, Jr., President, Philadelphia Inquirer Company; Arthur W. Thompson, President, United Gas Improvement Company; Dr. W. C. L. Eglin, President, Franklin Institute, Vice President, Philadelphia Electric Company, and George H. Houston, President, Baldwin Locomotive Works.

"The Advisory Board through training and experience of its members," says Department Circular No. 6, dated April 1926, 'Notes on Industrial Mobilization, New York Ordnance District,' "brings to bear upon problems of general policy, comprehensive knowledge of industrial organization, basic raw and semi-finished materials, manufacturing, merchandising, law, finance, power, publishing, communication, construction and transportation, as well as Government requirements and procedures. Its principal functions are to consider questions of general policy effecting the interests of the District as a whole, to recommend such courses of action as will most effectively utilize the District's total resources toward meeting the Government's total requirements allocated to the District, and to advise the District Chief in such other instances as may from time to time appear necessary or desirable."

Army Ordnance Association

The Army Ordnance Association, now, under the Unification plan, the American Ordnance Association, provided one more means of tapping, for military application, the vast industrial experience of the nation. The A. O. A. was launched in the still troubled waters of the World War I period—1919. A lesson had been well learned; that the military could not live apart from industry; nor industry from the military; and that the partnership forged by the urgencies of war must be extended through the Peace if national readiness should be made a fact. "Preparedness," of course, was to be the objective.

"Membership," so stated the Constitution of the Army Ordnance Association, "shall be open to all men who are American citizens and who are interested in promoting the cause of industrial preparedness, particularly in connection with the design, procurement, production, manufacture, inspection, test or supply of Ordnance Material."

The Philadelphia Post of the Army Ordnance Association was established 9 December 1925, with the following named officers and directors:

Major John Q. MacDonald, Ordnance Reserve, President.
Lt. Colonel Archibald B. Hubbard, Ordnance Reserve, Vice President.
Captain F. F. Shaffer, Executive Assistant, Philadelphia Ordnance District, Treasurer.
Lieutenant T. R. Snyder, Ordnance Reserve, Secretary.

Directors:
Major Joseph Steinmetz, Ordnance Reserve
Charles Z. Tryon
Samuel Shoemaker
Edward T. Longstreth
E. M. Chance
J. H. Robbins

Others to serve from time to time were, C. Jared Ingersoll, District Chief, President; William D. Disston, Vice President; George W. Elliott, Vice President; Lt. Phillip J. Fields, Secretary-Treasurer; and Directors—Edward G. Budd, D. K. Bullens, R. A. Cannon, W. D. Disston, G. W. Elliott, L. E. Hess, E. J. Longstreth, Walter F. Perkins, W. Wear, H. W. Prentis, Jr., Ralph Kelly, R. P. Page, Jr., and C. W. Woolworth.

The Army Ordnance Association released in July 1920 the first issue of the Association's official publication, the Army Ordnance Magazine.

The subscriber-membership had climbed slowly in the Philadelphia District to a total as of 1 December 1943, of 1,470 persons. Membership subsequently spiraled to 3,923, taking in its sweep the Regional and Inspection Office areas and their contractors.

The peace saw an expected dwindling. The low in membership was reached in 1948—at 1640.

Taking a long jump, to 26 March 1935, we find P. O. D. still actively plugging for preparedness, with an impressive exhibit and demonstration on Reyburn Plaza of Army vehicles—even a mobile shop, field pieces, small arms and a miscellany of combat equipment. Thus did the District, for one glorious day, celebrate its seventeenth birthday anniversary.

And just about everybody with a uniform was there: reserves, soldiers from Raritan Arsenal, Frankford Arsenal and Aberdeen Proving Ground who came along with the equipment from those installations, the colorful Philadelphia City Troop, organized in 1774, detachments of the National Guard. The Hon. George H. Dern, Secretary of War, Colonel U. S. Grant, 3rd, Rear Admiral William C. Watts and a train load of dignitaries were up from Washington. There was a parade, speeches.

The next day, however, was the payoff. Not to be outdone by the preparedness prestidigitators, student groups and other well-meaning but very very badly informed citizens, and a sprinkling of out-and-out "peace-at-any-pricers," swarmed down like a cloud of seventeen-year locusts upon Reyburn Plaza, devouring in their wrath, to the extent which they could manage, the harvest of the previous day.

The effects of the locustian onslaught were made evident in many ways. Protestation was carried to a point where any laudatory mention in the press of preparedness or its associate activities in Ordnance was forthwith cried down by the dissenters. As a result, there were years during which little of news value was released by the Philadelphia Post of the Ordnance Association; and who can say that this paucity of constructive publicity did not have its effect in "dampening down," to some extent, the earlier war effort in Philadelphia.

It took a Pearl Harbor to show some of our population how wrong it had been.

Chapter V

THEY HAD TO BE GOOD

THE history of the Philadelphia Ordnance District runs rife with the names of men and women of signal ability. Never at any time did the records reveal an emergency or sudden need for which there was not at hand an individual eminently qualified to meet the need.

Commenting upon that observation, O. Howard Wolfe, Chief of the General Office Division, from his appointment, February 1942, to the time of his transfer, November 1943, to the Chairmanship of the Philadelphia Branch of the War Finance Committee, wrote in a memorandum to the District historian:

"The Philadelphia Ordnance District was fortunate in its leadership. Its period of major growth and achievement, certainly in the critical phase of organization, was under the direction of two rare leaders ideally not only qualified to solve what seemed unsurmountable problems, but having that rare quality of coordination and well nigh perfect team work.

"In choosing the supporting staff of key personnel, certain tests were applied in which social position, "pull," or political prestige were given little or no weight. Men who had given evidence of necessary experience or other qualifications were sought out and persuaded to accept appointment. Others—and there were literally hundreds of them—who came voluntarily to seek assignments were interviewed carefully and tactfully. If it was found that the intention was primarily a desire to be useful in contributing to the "war effort" the applicant was given every opportunity to be heard by Section and Division Chiefs to determine if his particular training or experience could be used.

Not much time was wasted on "topside" applicants who were obviously just looking for honors, a commission, or just a job, unless they had particular talents that could be turned to good use. The inefficient, or those who could not or would not adjust themselves to the rigorous discipline imposed by Army or Civil Service regulations and the day-to-day pressure of responsibility were transferred or eased out. This policy was followed both with the military and civilian personnel."

All of which is by way of setting the stage for the succession of "brilliants" who were to make history in P. O. D.

Take the earlier Executive Officers for instance. Their responsibility was largely that of plant surveys and of finding contractors willing to accept schedules. As the District expanded, more and more of this work which continued in constantly increasing volume was absorbed by other officers and the incoming civilian personnel while the Executive Officers found themselves assuming more and more of the executive functions of the District.

However, the "heat" was not yet on in March 1939 when Captain W. S. Broberg was assigned here from Rock Island Arsenal to act as Chief of the Industrial Division and to double as Executive Assistant to Major Hamilton. Veterans of the District, among them the later Major John H. Beyer, Major W. L. Lafean, Jr., Samuel "Sid" S. Horner, aide to Major W. L. Stephens, Jr., Sam McClenahan, successor to Captain J. F. Carson, as Chief of Civilian Personnel Branch, Thomas S. Potts who in his time "played many parts," Helen V. Meehan, Louise Evenson and their co-workers of the old days, voted Captain, later Major, Broberg, one of the most colorful personalities ever to come to the District. For here, they pointed out, was one of those rare individuals who combined in happy measure a high degree of executive ability with a decided flair for the creative. That he was an artist of note there never was a doubt. Several of his paintings long graced the walls of 150 South Broad Street, bearing silent testimony to his artistic attainments.

Playwriting and play directing were other of Major Broberg's accomplishments, and he was able to express himself with vividness and certainty of direction, both on paper and vocally.

The Major was a West Pointer, graduated in 1918. He attended the Coast Guard Artillery School, Massachusetts Institute of Technology, Ordnance School and Army Industrial College.

On 1 July 1940, Captain Broberg was promoted to the grade of Major. During the interim following the departure from the District in April 1940 of Major Hamilton, and preceding Brigadier General then Major, David N. Hauseman's arrival 26 June 1940 in the District, as Executive Officer, Captain Broberg occupied that berth—and to good purpose, as the record reveals.

Several stories in the Broberg tradition still were being told through the "forties" in the District. One, of which young William H. Hickson was the hero, or the victim, depending upon how you look at it, concerned the request by Major Broberg for a fresh desk blotter. Bill, not being wise in the way of majors, admirals or maharajas, and moved by a deep urge to save money for the Government, replied—but innocently:

"Turn it over, Major, it's all right on the other side."

According to Louise Evenson, a bystander, the Major opened wide the flood-gates of his wrath. P. O. D. workers nearby stood not upon the order of their going, leaving Hickson, his ears burning, to face alone the deluge which threatened his very existence.

"Then there's the story of the man who came in one day looking for business. He had been in the doghouse," explained John J. Target of Ammunition, "and was required to give evidence to the effect that he was actually a contractor." It had developed that the man's interest was only that of a salesman. Major Broberg was familiar with the situation, and had invited the man to come in for a talk.

"I had no sooner announced my visitor," continued John, "when the Major let loose with both barrels, and outlined in no uncertain terms his opinion of the visitor, which, of course, the visitor, on the other side of the partition, heard to the end.

"When I came out of Major Broberg's office, the visitor took one look at my very red face, and managed to stammer, 'I think I know where I stand,'—and left."

The 1,000th 13-Ton Tank to leave the assembly line at American Car & Foundry Company, Berwick, Pa. heads big parade, 2 August 1941, painted white for the event

Chapter VI

"BUILD UP FOR WAR ... "

THE year 1944 carried an earlier date line. Wartime production results in P. O. D. were underwritten as far back as 1938, 1939, 1940. What happened, what was planned, what was done—and who did it—during that earlier period accounted in good measure for the end result further down the years.

The problem through the late 1930's and well into the 1940's, and one which, as a matter of fact, was constantly present, was the selection of men and the conception and integration of methods which, together, would bring the desired end result. There was not time for studied approach. The need was becoming increasingly great, and at an ever increasing tempo.

Topside of those days had of necessity to be men who could see beyond their noses. That they succeeded so well under the difficulties they faced is one of the amazing performances of modern industry. Topside of the early days were often required to make hair-line decisions with one eye on the clock. Too much praise cannot be accorded those men, nor to those who maintained the tradition after them.

An important problem was the one of welding into a "single minded" group a large number of men and women coming to P. O. D. from practically every field of technological, scientific, manufacturing and administrational activity. There were differences in temperament, in quality and degree of training. Square pegs were to be matched with square holes; Ordnance ideas, techniques and procedures indoctrinated.

All of which, in 1938, was a comparatively simple matter. As of 13 May of that year, civilian personnel of the District Office, then in the Mitten Building, stood at just ten civilians—officers. By November, under the stimulation of production surveys, the total of personnel had climbed to twenty-three; by 10 March 1939, to thirty-three civilian employees and two officers.

It is interesting at this late date to read down the list of those who made up the District staff as of March 1939. It was a compact group. There were no exclusive duties. Planning and Surveys were directed by the Reserve Officers. The civilian personnel did the "foot" work. Administration tasks were distributed without regard for Commodity or other type of set-ups.

The greater number of those who saw service in P. O. D. in early 1939 had, before VJ Day, departed to other fields. Those remaining with the District deep into the war years. The list follows:

Maj. W. C. Hamilton	Samuel S. Horner
Capt. P. L. Deylitz	Harry L. Koenig
Eva L. Beermen	William J. Landherr
John H. Beyer	Samuel McClenahan
Michael M. Bigger	R. R. D. McCullough
William J. Bright	Helen V. Meehan
William H. Crown, Jr.	Elsie V. Mugnier
Richard S. Edmonds	D. H. Murphy, Jr.
Louise C. Evenson	Ambrose L. Naughton
Frederick S. Feldheim	John W. Ogden
William J. Flood	Thomas S. Potts
Carl T. Gohn	William F. Rathgeber
Charles C. Gray	William J. Scott
Granville S. Hart	Samuel R. Shadel
William C. Hickson	Nelson E. Spurling
Hugh L. Hilferty	Elizabeth E. Tucker
Maynard L. Hodgson	Walter G. Vernon
Harry J. Voltz	

Others coming into the District later during the year included:

Arthur B. Allison	Joseph C. Imperatice
Harry J. Boertzel, Jr.	Charles F. Kemper
Archibald F. Borbeck	William Kinsler
Cyril P. Cosgrove	W. H. Lownsbury
Lucy M. Deeney	Raymond F. Meyers
Nora M. Daugherty	Matthew A. Newman
Harry E. Genther	Helen F. Sherrick
Ralph L. Hawkins	Howard H. Stock
Fred Van Sant, Jr.	John J. Target

"Our duty during the early days," explained Thomas S. Potts, "was to plan for the procurement of Ordnance material with the view of a possible emergency. This involved contact of manufacturing plants, listing of equipment, physical property, study of contractors' organization, and generally passing upon the "know how" of the executive personnel."

"There were hurdles to be got over, of course; some of the contractors, remembering the confusion attending World War I cancellations, were reluctant to cooperate. Others were prejudiced against Government agencies. However, the greater number were willing to lend a hand."

If we read the record aright, the early surveyors for Ordnance, all new to the procedures, approached contractor-prospects in timidity and with misgiving. However, fortified with Major Hamilton's card bearing an introduction, they experienced little difficulty in reaching the proper executives. The interviewing technique went about like this: The surveyor would aim to impress upon the contractor the importance of preparing for "M" Day. He then would open a "picture book" of Ordnance material and components, point to an item and ask, "Can you make this?" What was inside the item or what made it "tick" was the "great unknown" to all concerned. The little matter of tolerances was not given a thought. Drawings were not available.

One of the earlier officers, Captain Paul L. Deylitz, then living at Frankford Arsenal and riding each day on the "El" to the District Office, had a procurement technique all his own. Rolling along, he would note the names on factory buildings which he passed en route. These names he would turn over to the surveyors to be followed up. On one occasion, a listed facility turned out to be a manufacturer of burial caskets.

The surveyors "cast wide their nets," often making a prize catch. Two such catches were the Warren Webster Company, Camden, New Jersey, manufacturers of Steam Specialties, and the Ocean City Manufacturing Company, Philadelphia, Pennsylvania, manufacturers of fishing reels. The first named company was contacted on the second day out, and due to the fact that it had a small group of automatic screw machines, company officials were urged to consider the manufacture of the M20 Booster. The Ocean City Manufacturing Company, while willing to undertake production of Percussion Primers, argued unsuccessfully what they feared might be their inability to turn out a satisfactory result. At any rate, both firms later received Educational Orders.

In June 1939 the Planning Section received a setback. Appropriation needed to hire engineers for periods of three months had run out, and seven of the eleven employees were dropped. However, the 1939–1940 appropriations were made available in July 1939, no doubt encouraged by the President's request, 1939, for five billions of dollars. At any rate the surveying force was augmented, and the work accelerated. A subsequent stimulus to defence appropriations was the signing, 22 July 1940, of the French Armistice.

An amusing incident of the period, and it was not too merry at the moment, was provided by a short, mysterious appearing gentleman wearing a movie villain goatee and carrying a little black bag. He had requested to see Major Hamilton in reference to a new bomb. He did not carry his bag into the Major's office, but left it on the settee outside the inclosure. It was a jittery fifteen minutes, old timers report. Nerves were taut; eyes bulging. When the visitor had departed, taking his bag, the staff breathed a sigh of relief and dashed downstairs for black coffee.

Surveyors, or inspectors, had much to learn of Ordnance. The Ordnance nomenclature was as strange to them as Ordnance Material and processes. Fuze was spelled "f-u-z-e" or "f-u-s-e" as suited the convenience of the inspector. P.D., B.D. or B.N. designating a fuze was utterly without significance. One man, boasting "some" engineering background, asked for a list of Non-Ferocious (for non-ferrous) Foundries. And later in the war effort, an inspector was to ask William J. Jefferies, then Chief Inspector, the difference between Ferrous and Non-ferrous scrap—and that man was employed for the purpose of investigating the availability of just those types of scrap.

"One inspector had been reading the O. P. M.," reported Bill, "and had come up to look over my bookcase. He told me he would like to obtain information concerning brass. Spreading out an auto map he turned to me and said, 'Tell me, Mr. Jeffries, where the principal brass mines are located.' However, his heart was in the right place, and once he had caught on he did a good job. There were many of his kind."

One important hurdle to the employment, during the period, of capable men was the limitations of Civil Service, imposing a hardship which dragged deep into the "forties." Civil Service rules and rulings, classifications and rates of pay admitted of little argument. Ordnance now was dealing with top flight men of broad technical, scientific and managerial ability. The need for these men was critical, and Civil Service would not bend. The idea of adjusting pay to the "measure of the man" or the scope of the job was not in the book.

Chapter VII

TOPSIDE AT THE TOP

THE year 1940 was one to remember. Not only had life really begun for P. O. D., but organization was well under way, and portents were beginning to appear in the District sky.

Midway of the year came from Washington a young Lochinvar to take up the reins of Executive Officer of the Philadelphia Ordnance District. Office Order No. 3, bearing the date of 26 June 1940, and signed Fred E. Smith, Captain, Ordnance Department, Adjutant, Philadelphia Ordnance District, announced the significant event somewhat in this fashion:

> "Effective this date Major D. N. Hauseman reporting as Executive Officer of this District."

Whether by accident or custom, or by deliberate choice, a no more prophetic word than "effective" could have been chosen to head up any announcement concerning this young officer. When he came here, the Defense Program still had to be sold to industry in the District: He sold it! An "effective" organization had of necessity to be recruited and welded into a thoroughly unified, "effective" whole: He did it! A new philosophy, a new economy had to be integrated, in industry and in his own organization: He accomplished that!

David Nathaniel Hauseman, a native of Pottstown, Pennsylvania, has had a long and distinguished military career serving in both World War I and World War II. In military service he rose from private to brigadier general. He lived in Philadelphia following his early schooling, and until his graduation in 1917 from the University of Pennsylvania. Some time following his enlistment for service during World War I, he was commissioned a second lieutenant in the Ordnance Department and stationed at the Ordnance Training Camp, Augusta Arsenal, Augusta, Georgia, from June 1917 to September of that year, when he was transferred to Fort McClellan, Alabama, where he remained until his assignment in December 1917,

to the Bartlett-Hayward Company, Baltimore, Maryland.

The following summer found Lieutenant Hauseman in Washington and in charge of the Distribution Section, Field Service, Ammunition Division, Office of the Chief of Ordnance. Later in the year he was made Assistant Commanding Officer of Morgan Ordnance Depot, South Amboy, New Jersey. From September 1921 to June 1922 he was in attendance at Field Artillery School. The course here marked the initiation of eight hour equitation periods. From June to December of 1922, he was Ordnance Officer at Fort Knox, Kentucky, closing the Ordnance Cantonment there which subsequently was set up as a regular Army base.

During the first six months of 1924 Lieutenant Hauseman served as Commanding Officer, 84th Ordnance Company, Erie Ordnance Depot, Erie, Pennsylvania. Following this assignment he signed up for three years of graduate work at the Massachusetts Institute of Technology. In 1927 he was appointed Executive Officer, Birmingham Ordnance District, Birmingham, Alabama. In September 1935 he was back in school; this time, the Graduate School of Business Administration at Harvard. Upon completion of his studies, he was recalled to Washington and placed in charge of the Procurement Planning Section, Office of the Chief of Ordnance. Came another round of studies, at the Army Industrial College; then, once more to Procurement Planning where he remained until his departure in 1940 for Philadelphia.

Philadelphia Ordnance was big business even as far back as 1940, an eight million dollar business, in fact. By the end of that year the total had topped one hundred and three million dollars, and before the end of Major Hauseman's first full year in the District, the total had crossed the two hundred million mark with more than three hundred contracts in force. Among his honors were the Legion of Merit Award and the Distinguished Service

Medal. He also received both the Army and the Navy Commendation Awards.

No one now doubts that Major David N. Hauseman was the man for the job. The record on that is clear—and emphatic. Greatest among his assets was his ability to attract men of large calibre; to see the job and fit the right man into it. C. Jared Ingersoll, who was to be three times named District Chief, is a case in point.

While the then Major Hausman was not wholly responsible for the selection of C. Jared Ingersoll for the top post, a post made vacant by the retirement of the late Phillip H. Gadsden, however, Major Hauseman's appraisal of Mr. Ingersoll's fitness for the job, and his persistence in winning him to Philadelphia Ordnance District are to be given credit. The incentive came down from Brigadier General Wesson, then Chief of Ordnance, who had been trying to smoke out, as Mr. Gadsden's successor, a man who measured up to the need, as he saw it. Word came along the grapevine that C. Jared Ingersoll was just the man—IF. Not dismayed by the size of the "IF," and with the pattern clearly in mind, David Hauseman set forth on his mission. The pattern was about like this, "We need a good man. He must be a proved man, an able man. He needs to be a successful man, of outstanding executive ability, widely known and highly regarded in the worlds of business and finance. He must have no axes to grind. No embarrassing alliances. His name and his public utterances must be good newspaper copy.

"It was just about this time," Jared Ingersoll was to say months later, "that I had been deeply stirred by the activities of the late William Allen White who, irritated by the 'peace-at-any-pricers' and realizing that we sooner or later should find ourselves in the midst of this war, had come all-out for full preparation and readiness. That was an Idea I could crusade for, and I did—on the radio and in interviews with representatives of the press. All of which, I think, had some small part in turning the quest in my direction.

"At any rate, Major Hausman called around to see me one day early in August of 1940 on the eve of my departure for a vacation. When my secretary announced his presence, I had no idea whom this major might be. I had never heard of a Major Hauseman. My reaction was, that he conceivably might be someone I had met during World War I and that he was 'moving in for a touch.' I refused to see him. That didn't stop him. He came again and again. Finally, pretty much annoyed, I asked that he be sent in. That was the end. In ten minutes I knew I was sunk!

"The Major told me that he had been having some trouble in swinging some important manufacturers into line for defense production. They didn't want any part of Government business. He thought that through my contacts I would be able to change that picture. I told him I would be glad to do what I could, and here I am.

"Too, being a civilian, I could cut red tape and cross-cut channels as the occasion might demand. I should never be in the position of cooling my heels in a reception room because of difference of military status."

So, C. Jared Ingersoll came into the District as its head. He reported for duty 7 September 1940. His appointment was made 29 September; and he was administered the oath of office 8 October 1940, just one month and one day following his first day of active service.

At this time Educational Orders and Production Studies were very much to the fore. Machine tool shortages already were being felt. Gages were at a premium. Surveys and resurveys of industry were being intensified. Arsenals had recently been directed to call on the District for Assistance in negotiating contracts. Office Memorandum No. 1 came along 10 August, setting up six Commodity Divisions— Ammunition, Artillery, Automotive, Miscellaneous Machinery, Raw Materials, and Explosives. During the year, Regional Offices, then known as Sub-Offices, formally were set up in Bethlehem, Berwick, Baltimore, Eddystone, Reading and York. (The Philadelphia Regional Office did not come into existence until the Fall of 1941.) Priorities had gone into effect by joint action of the Army and Navy Defense Commission. Personnel operations were divorced from the Progress and Statistics Section and established as a separate unit. Increasing demand for personnel forced relaxation by Executive Order No. 8564, of Civil Service rules and regulations. On the whole, it was a year of great decisions, for clear thinking, incisive action. Fortunately the District had at the helm two such stalwarts as Chief Ingersoll and his Deputy, Major Hauseman.

Like his associate, Major Hauseman, C. Jared Ingersoll emerged from college in 1917; and following in the path of the Chief of Ordnance, Lt. General Levin H. Campbell, Jr., whom he later was to serve, he had his first contact with the Services via the Navy. Princeton was his school; civil engineering, the subject of his studies, was a fitting preparation for his life in railroading, a field in which he has distinguished himself.

"Serving his country" was in line with Ingersoll tradition. Long before, another Jared Ingersoll had put aside personal interest and opportunity to give himself to a national emergency. This was recalled in a tribute paid 9 October 1944 by Lt. Howard L. Burns, a young officer-lawyer of the District Legal Branch, addressing employees at the presentation to Mr. Ingersoll of a silver plaque marking completion of his fourth year of service to the District. Lieutenant Burns noted upon that occasion—"It is interesting to observe history come full turn. About one hundred and fifty years ago, a few blocks down Chestnut Street, certain men, equal to the crises of the times, set themselves to the task of guaranteeing in this country the dignity of the individual. The result of their efforts, the Constitution of the United States, described by Gladstone as the most wonderful work ever struck off at a given time by the brain and purpose of man, was in part created by a man who signed his name Jared Ingersoll. Today his namesake has emerged in this crisis to strike his blow for liberty and to further guarantee the dignity of the individual through his efforts toward the successful prosecution of this war. Yes, the Ingersolls are still in the same old business of protecting the rights of man, just not at the same old stand. They have only moved up the street a bit!"

That plaque, incidentally, truly represented the affection of the District for its Chief. Everyone had made contribution to the cost. "Not more than a dime from anyone!" said Chairman H. Paul Gant, "This is everybody's affair!"

The job of Master of Ceremonies was ably handled by John Swartley of the Tank-Automotive Branch. A congratulatory letter from Lt. General Campbell was read. Louis C. Purdy of the Purchase Branch spoke for the civilian personnel.

Mr. Ingersoll continued at his post of District Chief until sometime early in 1942 when a shift of organization made necessary by military considerations found Major Hauseman, now Lieutenant Colonel Hauseman (he had been raised to that rank, 15 October 1941, and to a full Colonel, 9 February 1942), in the role of District Chief; Mr.

Ingersoll moving to the post of Deputy Chief, but no less energetic because of this shift. This arrangement held until early in January 1944, when he was renamed District Chief. It happened this way: In October 1943 Colonel Hauseman had been named to the post of Chief, Redistribution Division, Office Chief of Ordnance in Washington. He was succeeded by Colonel Fred A. McMahon, assigned here from the Cincinnati Ordnance District where he had occupied a similar berth. Mr. Ingersoll remained as Deputy Chief in the new administration. Early in January 1944 Colonel McMahon was transferred to Washington for other duties, and Mr. Ingersoll was moved back to the No. 1 assignment.

In the words inscribed upon the silver plaque: "Great emergencies beget great men, and these, delaying not upon personal interest or private gain, rise to the obligations placed upon them and grow stronger in the faithful performance of their tasks. And when shall be written the names of those who stood high in the councils of the Nation in its dark hour, none shall echo a larger devotion to duty, a more unstinted adherence to high principle, and none shall be remembered with greater affection than that of C. Jared Ingersoll, District Chief."

But Jared Ingersoll was to pay for this "larger devotion to duty," pay as all men must who dare beyond limits of endurance. In the Spring of 1945 the break came. This tireless leader, the very symbol of robust health, had over-expended himself, and the physicians took over. A long rest was ordered. In due time the Chief was back at his desk, but just long enough to select his successor.

On 4 June, Lieutenant Colonel A. Donald Kelso, who had arrived in P. O. D. less than three years before, a civilian, was named Chief of ASF, Philadelphia Ordnance District. On 9 August he was promoted to the rank of Colonel, and just one day before his separation, 18 December 1945, he received from Lieutenant General Levin H. Campbell Jr., the award of the Legion of Merit and Citation.

The new Chief was first assigned to the District 12 October 1942, on the recommendation of Colonel Hauseman. He later was assigned to the post of Chief, Sub-Office (Regional Office) Administration Branch, succeeding Captain Joseph B. Anderson. The duties of the post now were such that the Chief had of necessity to be an officer, and of a rank no lower than that of Major.

While awaiting arrival of his commission, which came along 9 January 1943, he made the circuit of the offices which soon were to be his responsibility, to survey procedures, routines and current problems.

Born in the zero belt of New York State, Don Kelso stopped long enough on his way to his Utopia to gather in at Harvard an A.B. in Literature and, as student pilot, to do a stint of training at the Ground School of the Massachusetts Institute of Technology.

In industry, following a turn with the American Glue Company, the embryo Chief moved on to the then newly formed Durex Corporation, occupying in turn the assignments of Factory Superintendent, General Manager, Managing Director and Vice President. Early in 1942 he obtained his temporary release by the Durex Company for a tour of duty with the War Production Board, Facilities Division.

The result of his first effort in P. O. D. was the correction in Sub-Offices and Inspection Offices, of inconsistencies in management wherever they existed, cutting out duplications of effort, establishing harmonious and more productive relationships between the Sub-Offices and Commodity and other Branches of the District. There was much of this to be done during the growing stage of P. O. D. Manouvering personnel into positions where they could make best use of their abilities was another responsibility.

There is much to be said for this fine officer— his spearheading of attacks upon the problems of all-out production; his efforts, beside his able henchmen, Majors Langham and Lafferty, and others, during the expanded Ammunition Programs in May and December of 1944 and into 1945; in cutting back in June 1945, schedules which, earlier, as Chief of the Industrial Division of P. O. D. he had had a hand in setting up; and, his generalship in the Terminations campaign, and it was a campaign, with Lieutenant Colonel Albert W. Gilmer, Terminations head, drawing kudos from higher echelon and industry all along the line.

With December 1945 came the time to say farewell to Don Kelso, the last of our wartime leaders. Three great commanders—Hauseman, Ingersoll and Kelso, a team which in any great industry or in any cause would have been unbeatable—and beyond price. Each in his time met head-on emergencies, achieved many goals, crossed deadlines that often appeared impossible. These men will live long in the memories of those whose privilege it was to work with them. You will learn more of them as you proceed with this narrative.

A fine gentleman came to take the place of Colonel Kelso—Colonel John P. Harris of Powder-Explosive-Propellant fame. Within a few short months even he was gone and P. O. D. as we had known it not so long ago was no more.

Chapter VIII

MEET THE EXECUTIVE OFFICERS

THE years from 1938 through the early 1940's have sometimes been lightly mentioned as the Cro-Magnon period of P. O. D., the years during which the first of the latter-day P. O. Ders appeared over the Philadelphia horizon. Earlier traces of the Cro-Magnon type had been noted but it remained for the distant rumble of impending conflict to bring them out of their caves in numbers.

For instance, there was John W. Ogden who arrived in the District as far back as February 1937, signing up as an Ordnance Engineer, following five years with the Reading Railroad as a Supervising Field Engineer on the electrification of suburban lines. Prior to that John Ogden had spent three years with the Liquor Control Board as a store manager, a position he obtained as the result of a "mental agility test," coming out in the top ten of 838 selectees taking the examination. It is also on record that he did a bit of teaching in local high schools—blueprint reading and shop mathematics.

Beyond all that was Cornell and the University of Pennsylvania, with a resulting B.S. in Civil Engineering. Jack Ogden was not long in the District before he was shifted to the Engineering-Production post under Major W. S. Broberg, then Chief of the Industrial Division. The major had many irons in the early Ordnance fires, to the end that the young engineer might properly have been labeled Chief of Production.

It was about this time that Educational Orders and Production Studies came into the picture to engage the talents of this early comer in the District. By 1 March 1941 he received his commission of 1st Lieutenant. On 5 January 1942 he was assigned by Lt. Colonel Hauseman to the post of Executive Officer, the responsibilities of which office earlier had been served by Major Broberg, Lt. Colonel, then Captain, Fred Smith and, later, Captain Joseph B. Anderson.

Came December 1942 and the now Captain Ogden was moved down to the Richmond Regional Office where there had suddenly developed a need for an administrator of Ogden-mental dimension. Serving his turn in Richmond as Officer-in-Charge, he was reassigned to Pentagon to take over the office of Chief, Smaller War Plants, Legal Division, Office, Chief of Ordnance. While deep in this task he contrived to crash *Ordnance Magazine* with a smaller war plants story (page 453, vol. XXVII, No. 147, November-December 1944). It was during his tenure at Pentagon that his well-earned majority caught up with him.

Succeeding the dynamic "Jack" by seconds, Colonel, then Major Robert G. Allen, who arrived in P. O. D. in July 1942, as Chief of the Tank and Automotive Branch, came downstairs to take the helm.

In civilian life Robert G. Allen was one of Pennsylvania's ablest and most progressive public men. He served two terms in the U. S. Congress, 1937–1939 and 1940–1941. As one of the leaders in the young progressive group in the Lower House he was a member of the Foreign Affairs Committee, becoming prominent for his introduction of legislation to modify and to eventually scrap the Neutrality Bill. He was also responsible, in no small measure, according to *Time Fuze*, May 1943, for the first legislation to prohibit the shipment of high octane gasoline and scrap iron to Japan.

The Colonel left Congress voluntarily to assume the presidency of the Duff-Norton Company at Pittsburgh where he remained until the call came from P. O. D. Beyond his immediate duties, Bob Allen took an active part in the public relations program of P. O. D. He participated in many Army and Navy "E" Award ceremonies, and frequently was called upon to turn his oratory upon civic, social and business groups.

Colonel Allen was born in Winchester, Massachussetts, taking in his stride Phillips Andover, Harvard College and a very convincing assortment of athletic trophies. Bob Allen early learned to win—in college, in politics, in business, which was all by way of preparation for the winning job he did in the District, to say nothing of his Vermont farm and cheese factory.

On 30 August 1943 came the moment for the Colonel to move to other parts, as noted elsewhere. He was next heard from while moving in the general direction of Hawaii on another assignment from Uncle Sam.

The quality of leadership in the Executive post seemed never to subside. Come what would the high level of performance remained equal to the need, in line always with the rising tempo of war and its critical demands. To fill the difficult post of Executive Officer came Henry W. Gadsden, the second of his name to importantly serve the District. Lieutenant Colonel, then Captain Gadsden was brought in from his assignment as Officer-in-Charge, Philadelphia Mobile Shop Depot, to fill the vacant post. He had been assigned on 1 June 1943 to the Depot. What he accomplished there is another story. The record will turn up in a subsequent chapter.

Topside of the District knew what it was doing when it set its sights on Henry Gadsden, and his firm, Sharp and Dohme, Philadelphia drug and pharmaceutical manufacturers, knew what they were doing in trying to hold on to him. However, his people saw the need and in due course granted him his release. So, on 24 March 1942 he reported for active duty as 1st Lieutenant and as assistant to the Executive Officer. He received his majority 1 November 1943, and his lieutenant colonelcy 9 April 1945. In June he was assigned the additional duty of Administrator, Cressona Ordnance Plant, Cressona, Pennsylvania, and shortly thereafter, Administrator, Pottstown Ordnance Plant, Pottstown, Pennsylvania, as well.

The interests of Lt. Colonel Gadsden touched at one time and another practically every major activity of the District. Because of his earlier administrative and industrial experience he was able, although one of our younger officers, to carry many responsibilities. He was frequently consultant to Commodity Branches, and directed or had a part in many special programs. Notable among the latter were the expanded ammunition programs; recruitment in a tight labor market and a subsequent reduction in force accomplished without disturbance to the rest of the Ordnance program and without effect upon morale. As a result of his participation the District was enabled to accept a very large share of the June and December 1944 procurements, particularly the heavy shell and fuze schedules. Approximately 40 per cent of the increased requirements on these items had been secured to the District.

The District set up an enviable record following VJ Day in conforming to the restricted budget and the required economical use of personnel for contract termination work. Here again we see the hand of Lt. Colonel Gadsden.

In his time, in Ordnance, Henry played many parts. In addition to duties which specifically were those of the Executive Officer, he appears on the charts as Chairman, Board of Sales; Chairman, Board of Terminations; Administration Officer, Attached Organizations; Assistant to District Chief on Procurement, and Member, Committee on Meritorious Awards, upon each of which he left his mark.

And upon the eve of another year he was gone; the last of the wartime Executive Officers. There were others to follow in the settling-down months, each doing his part according to the needs of the hour.

Chapter IX

MORE OF THE CRO-MAGNONS, 1939-1942

ANTEDATING by five days the arrival of John W. Ogden, came to P. O. D. one John H. Beyer, Michigan 1936, to sign up as Junior Inspector. Two years with General Electric Company, following college, proved an excellent tune-up for the Ordnance ordeal. On 17 July 1939, "Johnny" Beyer was commissioned a 2nd Lieutenant, continued until 27 May 1940, his duties as an inspector, and on that day, with release in hand, found high priority responsibility on the payroll of the Read Machinery Company of York, Pennsylvania, which company later was to fabricate for Ordnance doodads such as, among others, the 60 mm. Mortar, M2 and Mount M2 and M5, and Shell H. E., 105 mm., M1.

However, "Johnny" Beyer was not long destined to warm stools in the Read Cafeteria for, along about 12 November 1940, in the words of a boogey-woogey song popular in the middle "forties," "Sam Got Him!" He was brought back for extended duty in P. O. D. and groomed for top berth in the Artillery Branch, continuing as Chief through the consolidation, 17 March 1944. of the Artillery and Small Arms Branches, his majority coming on apace.

Among Major Beyer's claims to fame was his ability to make records, particularly in reference to Accuracy Predictions; for note that during the nineteen months the Accuracy of Predictions procedure had been in effect (beginning in March 1943 when this standard of efficiency was established by the Office of the Chief of Ordnance), "Johnny" Beyer's team hit top score ten times, second place five times, third place three times, and on another occasion, a good fifth.

"A miss is always as good as a mile, as far as I am concerned," commented the major; or did he?

So much for Major John. But before we can leave him there is something to be said for that other luminary of the Artillery-Small Arms Branch, the Major's good right bower, Captain Josef H. Buerger, Princeton 1940, Beaver High School, Kiski and all that sort of thing.

Having absorbed by June 1940 a large share, if not all that Princeton had to offer, "Joe" set out to put the world in order, beginning with the Sales Department of the Carnegie-Illinois Steel Corporation, and working out of Pittsburgh and Philadelphia. Approximately one year, seven months and several days later, this young Reserve officer found himself suddenly with new problems to lick, and signing himself "2nd Lieutenant J. H. Buerger, Ord. Dept."

That "Joe" early had a flair for the tougher assignments, taking to them as a duck to water, was borne out by a little Ordnance affair dating from the Spring of 1942. It was like this. There had developed among mortar manufacturers a critical shortage of seamless tubing. It was made the responsibility of the lieutenant to expedite from the steel suppliers to the mortar facilities the purchase orders for the tubings. It became evident in July 1942 that the constantly increasing demands registered for the item by the Navy, Air Corps and Lend-Lease would leave very little tubing for the mortar program. Nothing to do under the circumstances but investigate the possibilities of manufacture from bar stock and forgings. However, zero for progress in that direction! Raw materials also were practically out of circulation. But Joe wasn't. He bethought himself of centrifugally cast barrels, and forthwith betook himself to the U. S. Pipe and Foundry Company, Burlington, New Jersey, manufacturers of centrifugally cast iron pipes, where he learned from the company's Research Director, Dr. A. E. Schuh, that the idea had its merits.

Development work was begun 16 July 1942, with limited laboratory equipment, including a twenty-five pound induction furnace. The first experimental casting, in a sand mold, centrifugally spun, was rolled off just four days later. During the three weeks following, there was cast and rough-machined a number of tubes sufficient to enable mortar manufacturers to finish, machine and observe the characteristics of this new type tube. Finally 18 August 1942, at Aberdeen Proving

Ground, the Joe Buerger tube was put through its paces, performing so well that it was pronounced in many respects better than mortars fabricated from seamless tubing.

Lieutenant Buerger, being Lieutenant Buerger, promptly wrote off his achievement, and turned his ingenuity to other matters. His surprise, to say nothing of his delight, can well be imagined when, early in March 1944, he received from Lt. General L. H. Campbell, Jr., Chief of Ordnance, a commendation upon his fine work.

> "By the exercise of your initiative and ingenuity you have made a marked contribution to the vital war production program to conserve critical materials and machines. It is with pleasure that I commend you for this outstanding service which you have rendered your country."

At this point the trail crosses that of other of the Cro-Magnon period Ordnance men. Hatchet marks and other signs of an inspectional character cut into nearby rocks revealed, when interpreted, the date 16 August 1938, and the name, John J. Target. With this evidence, and aided by subsequent exploration, the historian was able to piece together the following story:

John, as we already have noted, joined up in August of 1938, just seven years out of Penn from whose ancient halls he emerged in 1931, a full fledged industrial engineer, followed later with evening study, at Temple University, of metallurgy.

John met all problems standing up and head on. When it was reported back to P. O. D. that H.E. shells and A.P. shot manufactured in this and in other districts were dropping their damage short of German marks on the Italian front, John went to work. Micrometer measuring of diameters already had proved inadequate. There was a lack of uniformity in the manner of taking readings. Too, bands would register expansion following removal from shell bodies.

There was a toughie, and time was short. Every clue to a solution was followed. All, save one, missed; and that one turned the trick. Nitric acid! Application of the acid, it was discovered, quickly revealed the presence under the band of openings caused by etching irregularities and minute burrs of excess metal.

Thanks to John Target, the shootin' now was bringing down "heavier bags," and was safer going for all concerned, except the enemy. All of which was accomplished by reducing dispersion,

through increased band tightness, and holding tolerance within .004 the opening on the side of the band.

The curtain falls, then rises, bringing to the stage, front center, another star performer in the drama of war's implementing—Samuel McClenahan, born to P. O. D. 7 February 1939.

Seems if everything Sam did during his pre-Ordnance days contributed something to the experience which later was to stand him in such good stead as a Junior Inspector—the task for which he signed up.

According to the record, Sam McClenahan, or Mac, as he frequently was hailed, early launched himself upon a vigorous and never-to-be-satisfied search for "know how." No barrier too high, no task too stiff, no day too long for Sam McClenahan. Mathematics, metallurgy, Columbia, Temple University, weighty tomes, technical journals—all was grist that came to the McClenahan mill.

In 1933 Sam McClenahan joined forces with the mechanical refrigeration firm of P. E. Oetzel Company. Later, in 1936 he moved on to the Leeds & Northrup Company where he was able further to display his assortment of skills.

Then, Ordnance . . . inspection, during those days when method had not been too well developed, and organization was inadequate; selection and hiring of inspection personnel; assistant to the Chief of the then Sub-Office Administration Division of P. O. D.—and early in 1944, appointment as Chief of the Civilian Personnel Branch succeeding Captain John F. Carson who had held that post from the inception of the Branch to his assignment 22 May 1944, to Aberdeen Proving Ground for special training.

The Spring of 1944 was not a propitious time for a new man to take over. The reclassification job had just been completed. There were complaints and mutterings aplenty by those personnel who had not been upgraded. It was a time for the patient, understanding, thorough-going approach. But Sam McClenahan proved, overwhelmingly, the man for the moment as he later was to demonstrate during the expanded ammunition programs of June and December 1944 to which reference was made in the preceding chapter. Then it was that he was found a capable ally in the recruitment of personnel needed to meet the critical schedules, and again to assist the Executive Officer, Lieutenant Colonel, then Major, Gadsden, in restoring personnel to the former level.

Chapter X

THE COORDINATORS MOVE IN

DECIDING early in 1942 that every up-and-coming Ordnance District should have the sound counsel of a group of well chosen elders, the Chief of Ordnance passed on to Colonel Hauseman the urge that he go forth, find five wise men, each a shining light in his particular field, and lure him into the District Office. These men were to be known as the Coordinators' Group. The five members would be drawn from as many fields. There would be a banker, an engineer, a manufacturer, a representative from heavy industry and so on. The purpose, to bring to bear upon organizational problems and procedures a broad background of diverse experience, thus assisting the District Chief, and expediting the activities of the District generally.

"The problem of building an organization," wrote the then Deputy Chief, C. Jared Ingersoll, back in January, 1943, "was and is a difficult one and involved trying to obtain effective personnel from industry. The greatest single element in accomplishing this was an appeal to the individual's patriotism or to the patriotism of the head of a corporation, therein he would release some very able individual for service with the P. O. D."

But let it be said to the everlasting glory of the members of the Coordinations' Group that very little urging was necessary. To a man, they quickly saw the need and as quickly rose to the opportunity and its responsibilities.

The five offices to be filled were those of Administrative Coordinator, Procurement Coordinator, Purchase Coordinator, Production Coordinator and Coordinator of Inspection. The men selected were O. Howard Wolfe for the Administrative Post, Walter C. Pew (subsequently commissioned a Major), for the Procurement assignment, Martin Sandler for Purchase, Charles O. Guernsey for Inspection, and Malcolm R. White for Coordinator of Production.

The banking phase, represented by O. Howard Wolfe, Vice-President, Philadelphia National Bank, brought to bear upon his assignment as Administration Coordinator a broad experience of internal management and personnel, acquired both as a bank executive and as A. E. F.-Y. M. C. A. Personnel Officer during World War I. At that time,

operating from his Paris headquarters, he was in general charge of an office staff consisting of some 700 persons, plus a field staff of 6,000 persons. In 1932 he again was loaned by his bank to organize and manage the Philadelphia Loan Agency of the Reconstruction Finance Corporation. At the time of his appointment 2 February 1942, to his Ordnance post, he was Chief Administrative Officer of his bank.

Coordinator Wolfe had been President of the Pennsylvania Bankers Association, the Association of Reserve City Bankers and other craft groups. For eight years he had been a member of the faculty of the Graduate School of Banking, Rutgers University, of which School he was one of the organizers.

Prior to his appointment, there had been no definite plan of organization for handling the many administrative and general office functions arising in an organization such as that of the Philadelphia Ordnance District. To this point the work had been carried on by the Chief and the Deputy Chief. Mr. Wolfe began at once to set up a more comprehensive system of personnel practice and organization, and relieved the District Chief of much of the work of interviewing business executives and industrialists who were then being considered for key positions in the District.

The units of the District organization assigned for administration to Branch Chief Wolfe were, according to a chart prepared shortly after his appointment, and dated 14 March 1942, Civilian Personnel Branch with Captain John F. Carson as Chief; Property Branch under the then Captain, later Major W. L. Stephens, Jr., Fiscal Branch, piloted by Captain, later Major Robert H. Andrews; Mail and Record Section under Lt. Phillip J. Fields. Later in the year the Legal Branch, with Lt. Colonel Joseph A. Whelan at the head post, the Security Branch, with Captain Robert H. Merz as Chief, and the Censorship Branch under Captain L. H. Van Dusen, Jr., were added to Mr. Wolfe's responsibilities.

The General Office Division prospered under Howard Wolfe. His associates, respecting his judgements and the soundness of his philosophy, gave him their best. He was one of the few bankers that recognized the existence of a world beyond the bank; one of that rare race of top executives who believed that other men could possess ability, generate ideas. Little wonder he was missed in the District when he answered the call in late 1943, to head up the Philadelphia War Finance Committee, a post which he later resigned to return to his bank.

The departure from P. O. D. of Administrative Coordinator Wolfe marked the demise, insofar as the District was concerned, of a "shade" that had haunted these halls from the hour of the Coordinator's first appearance. That this "shade" had a very definite personality, no one can deny. Though no one had ever seen it, no one who ever had business with O. Howard Wolfe was permitted for a moment to overlook the fact that this "shade" was right there all the time, waiting its opportunity to plunge into every conference, to inject itself into every meeting, to "steal the show" on the slightest encouragement.

Mysterious? A devil's-broth of a thing? By no means! It was "Joe Zilch"—the original "Joe Zilch"—and no figment of the Coordinator's imagination, either. "Joe" was O. H. W.'s alter ego. He was a whipping-boy, straw-man, horrible example, mouth-piece or whatever seemed best at a particular moment to suit the Wolfesian polemics.

Days on end, it was "Joe Zilch this . . ." and "Joe Zilch that . . ." As O. H. W. went so went Joe Zilch, or vice versa. What Joe thought clinched all argument, for who can joust with a wraith? And if you should batter down Joe's verbal defenses, there still was O. Howard Wolfe. You were licked before you started!

WALTER C. PEW

It was Hail and Farewell! in the District for Walter C. Pew. You saw him and then you didn't. He was here and gone with the alacrity of a bat out of Tophet and it seemed only weeks later he was in Europe with the rank of Colonel. This high-octane young man—and he was young; actually the youngest of the Coordinator Group—came into P. O. D. 10 April 1942, as Coordinator of Procurement, gave many impressive demonstrations of his great ability, and just about the time the District began fully to appreciate him, he met up with Destiny in the form of Robert H. Johnson, President of Johnson & Johnson, New Brunswick, New Jersey, manufacturers of pharmaceutical supplies, and Chief of District Office Ad-

ministration Division, Office, Chief of Ordnance, who was sweeping around the country prying loose information and inspiration whenever he could find either.

So Johnson met Pew, and that was that. In June, Walter C. Pew, who had been spot-commissioned a Major, almost on the heels of his advent in the District, was kidnapped by Johnson and planted as runner-up in the Administration Branch. Later, when Robert H. Johnson moved over to Smaller War Plants, the Major took on Administration, and from thence, over the "big water."

Major Pew, a Pennsylvanian— his birthplace Pittsburgh—came at an early age to Philadelphia where he received primary education, after which he attended Hill Preparatory School, Pottstown, Pa. Later he matriculated in Massachusetts Institute of Technology for special work in geology, mining and mineralogy. Completing his studies, he obtained a position with the Sun Oil Company. Upon completion of this assignment he returned to Philadelphia to the yards of Sun Shipbuilding and Dry Dock Company at Chester, Pa., a subsidiary of Sun Oil Company. There he learned much in Marine construction and installation. This led to a position as Assistant Marine Superintendent at Marcus Hook, Pa. While working in this capacity, trips were made to the company's affiliated plants in France, Belgium, England and Germany. When the Company began marketing motor fuel through filling stations he became General Supervisor of Stations. Development in those spheres beyond the company's actual boundaries brought the additional assignment of General Manager and it was from that position that Walter C. Pew was commissioned a Major, Ordnance Reserve.

MARTIN SANDLER

"The time has come," the Chief has said,
"To talk of these and those;
Of catalysts, Suppliers' Lists,
And synthesis, analysis,
Awards and L. P. O.'s;
Of acetates, percipitates,
Colloids and A. S. P.'s;
Of chicken soup and O. P. I.'s
And yarn and manganese:
And so we might go on and on
To find no greater glory
Than in the tasks that punctuate
The Sandler repertory.

All of which is by way of saying that when Martin Sandler, one time Navy Chemist, later Yarn Mill executive and eventually braumeister, came into P. O. D. 16 April 1941, he brought along as complete a collection of well-rounded abilities as could be packed into one man's experience, and no one now doubts that he was able to find full use for every one of them. The record is pretty clear on this; for note you that to the end of his natal year in P. O. D. contracts placed in the District just about topped $492,600,000 (a tidy bit of change for that time), and before 1946 was to pass into history, the total would ease beyond the $3,000,000,000 mark; and all this, mind you, in four short years. A heap of purchasing! A heap of know-how!

And this was Martin Sandler's second war, and his third tour of duty under "Uncle Sugar." He received an honorable discharge from the Army late in 1918. He is a native Philadelphian, holds degrees of B.S. and M.S. in chemistry from the University of Pennsylvania. During 1922 he served the Navy as an analytical chemist. The following year found him in the chemical laboratory of the Campbell Soup Company, Camden, N. J. In 1925 he went into business, becoming part owner, as well as General Manager, of the Clifton Yarn Mills, of Clifton Heights, Pa., from whence, in April 1941, he signed up with the District, following almost by hours the establishment in P. O. D. of an independent Purchase Section which marked the separation of Procurement Planning and Purchase activities; a move made necessary by the rapid and substantial increase in Ordnance procurement.

With the formation of the Coordinators' Group, Martin Sandler logically was assigned the Purchase post; and again, 17 January 1942, when the Board of Awards convened for the first time, Martin Sandler moved in to represent Purchase, sharing honors with H. Paul Gant, Planning Director, and Lt Colonel Joseph A. Whelan, of the Legal Branch.

Late in 1943 there was set up in the District under the impetus of Colonel Fred A. McMahon, then District Chief, a Control Board consisting of eight members. These included H. Paul Gant, the then Major A. J. Seiler, New Chief Industrial Division; Lt. Colonel Joseph A. Whelan, Chief of Legal Branch; Major W. L. Lafean, ,Jr. Control Officer; Major Henry W. Gadsden, Executive Officer; Major Joseph C. Hoffman, Chief of Fiscal Branch; Major W. L. Stephens, Jr., Property

Branch Chief; Captain J. F. Carson, then Chief of Civilian Personnel; Malcolm R. White of Procurement Liaison and, if you haven't guessed it—Martin Sandler, who remained on the Board through strife, storm and change.

Came the "hot spot" era in Terminations—that was along in December 1945—and there was established a Purchase-Terminations Division, embracing the Termination Branch, Property Disposal Branch, Purchase Branch and Price Analysis Branch. And for Division Chief—Martin Sandler.

Martin Sandler made many important contributions to P. O. D. operations. Most important to the historian, because of its possibilities in the compilation of records, as well as one dependable means toward always being sure was what Martin Sandler had himself labeled: "Fortified Folders." Just to enlighten the class, a "Fortified Folder" is "all there is; there isn't any more." In it, the complete, unexpurgated, unabridged story of a given transaction, omitting not one iota of the record, and all in good order, promising rather disappointing reading for nosey congressmen and such five, ten, twenty, thirty years hence.

On the lighter side, P. O. Ders long will remember, among other Sandler analecta, the now famous fanfare that so often heralded words of wisdom dispensed at staff meetings and upon provocation, anytime; it went something like this . . . "If I may be permitted to interject a remark at this point . . ."; and borrowing that announcement, the historian grasps the opportunity to move on to the dissection of another District luminary.

MALCOLM R. WHITE

Not content with honors earned as a Captain in Ordnance, World War I, "Mal" White came out of retirement, 21 April 1942, to join up as Co-ordinator of Production Graduating in 1902, from Purdue University, with his degree in mechanical engineering, he followed his bent which landed him as President, Liberty Electric Company of New York and, later, the presidency of the United Beryllium Corporation.

It was learned early in 1942 that one of the things required for better production was better planning. With this end in view, the post of Procurement Liaison Director was created and authority placed with Malcolm White. It was the duty of this office to assure the closest cooperation between the Commodity Branches and the Procurement Planning Section Representatives on all planning matter. This procedure saw many changes with the progress of the war. At the time it met all needs. "Mal" White was also, during those early days, Director of Defense Plant Corporation Facilities in the District. He continued in the District until January 1944 when he transferred to Washington to assist Colonel D. N. Hauseman, who had been named Chief of the Readjustment Division, OCO.

CHARLES O. GUERNSEY

The District might have searched far and wide yet never have found a man better equipped by training, experience and temperament for the post of Co-Ordinator of Inspection than "Charley" Guernsey, borrowed in April 1942, from the J. G. Brill Company (later to be known as ACF, Brill Motors Company) where he had been Vice President in charge of Engineering.

Establishment in the Industrial Division of the District of an Inspection Section was almost coincidental with "Charley" Guernsey's appointment as the Inspection Co-ordinator. Shortly thereafter he was named Technical Director, his office becoming a consulting agency on all technical matters. French E. Dennison, Chief Inspector, reported to the Technical Director, the two working as a team, and following the policy of delegating authority whenever practicable, and limiting their own activities to exceptional difficulties and overall matters of policy.

Speaking of those days, Director Guernsey once said: "At the inception of the War Program most manufacturers started on material with which they were not familiar and which, in some instances they were not equipped to handle. This, combined with difficulties with untrained personnel in the Ordnance inspection organization, lead to delay in launching the program. Most items of material then were new to industry or, at best, were the type made in small quantities on general purpose machines under shop or laboratory conditions. In many cases, and into 1940, drawings were inadequate as to tolerances and finish required. Of even greater importance, designs were not adequate to mass production. On new developments, dimensions and tolerances were established on the basis of engineers' judgment. But in practice, considerable development and experimental work had to be done by the contractors and Ordnance inspectors. Inspection forces were, of a consequence, compelled to act in both an engineering and experimental capacity to make production designs workable."

Modest to a fault, "Charley" Guernsey closed like a clam when one sought to uncover and appraise his many accomplishments in the war production effort. "Just tell them," he said, "when we see a head we hit it." One thing he did do was to draw Daniel H. Bell into the fray, as Conversion Engineer.

"Charley" Guernsey is remembered for not only his cheerful readiness to roll up his sleeves and jump into anybody's problem but, as well, for his effortless humor which he so often employed in sizing up a situation. It is recalled that on one occasion when he had been asked by Malcolm White, Major Arthur J. Seiler, Chief of the Industrial Division, and H. Paul Gant, Planning Director, to pass judgment on an engineering candidate, he reported, "Yes, this man knows a lot about engineering but most of the things he knows aren't so." At another time he said of an applicant who appeared very much confused in his thinking, "He reminds me of the Japanese general who mounted his horse and rode off in all directions."

In January 1944 "Charley" sang his swan song and returned to his old love at Brill's, taking back with him Arthur "Jack-be-nimble" Le Bon. Later came word that both had moved on to Indianapolis and into new fields.

To go back for a moment: It originally was planned that the Coordinators should be superimposed upon the then (early 1942) District Organization. The appointees, however, were not definitely assigned duties, and what they should do had not at once been made clear by the Office, Chief of Ordnance.

However, these men did not long remain inactive. They soon were absorbed into the fabric of the Organization, becoming in the process the "Special Assistants," and so they were indicated on the District Charts. As the duties of this group were expanded with war's increasing demand, new members were added. They were:

Lt. Colonel, then Major Arthur J. Seiler, Chief, Industrial Service; Colonel, then Major A. D. Kelso, Chief, Sub-Office Division; Charles P. Stokes, Chief, Advance Payments Section Fiscal Branch.

Already Major Walter C. Pew, transferred to Office, Chief of Ordnance, had been replaced by H. Paul Gant. M. T. "Dusty" Miller had replaced Malcolm R. White, upon the latter's appointment as Procurement Liaison Director.

You have already heard something of Lt. Colonel Seiler, neighbor of Carey Grant, Colonel Kelso of Durex fame, and Charles P. Stokes, financial mystic; now for a word concerning H. Paul Gant, who played so important a part in District Affairs.

Paul Gant was once cited as the "meetingest" man in all P. O. D. history. He once boasted his weekly average meetings at fifteen, to say nothing of his pertaining duties as Chairman of the Board of Awards, the Board of Sales, and the Control Board, his membership on the Board of Terminations (1945), Chairmanship of the Board for Recommending Army and Navy "E" Awards, and membership of the Civilian Efficiency Rating Board.

Many in P. O. D. expressed amazement that any individual could have accomplished so much in so little time after four years of retirement to a Chester County farm—or any farm. The fact that Paul Gant could direct such a diversity of work with apparently effortless precision imposed upon the District something of a "$64.00 question."

Paul Gant, often spoken of as the "Mr. Anthony of P. O. D." as a result of his ability to assist District personnel in adjusting their differences and in ironing their peeves, came to the District, in January 1942. During the following month he set up a Special Projects Section to conduct special investigations and handle the various problems involving engineering and business judgment.

And the end is not yet, for note you, he also was in the records as, in addition to Special Assistant to the District Chief, Director of Planning, the duties of the latter named embracing the co-ordination and overall supervision of the Planning Section, and the Conservation Section, which included fuel conservation, scrap salvage and transportation. In the same year, 1942, he organized and set up for business the Smaller War Plants Section to co-operate with the Smaller War Plants Section of the War Production Board in spreading work to distressed industries.

In June 1943 Paul Gant organized a Procurement Statistics Section to develop and maintain complete statistics covering all statistics covering all procurements of the District from 1940 forward for duration. Opinion of the Office of the Chief of Ordnance was that the system developed by this Section was head and shoulders over any other in use among the Ordnance Districts.

Now a Pennsylvanian, Paul Gant acquired this distinction by adoption, for he was born in the unreconstructed State of Mississippi. Heading East

and North by way of the University of Tennessee, where he stopped long enough to receive a B.S. in electrical engineering, he arrived in New York as Manager of Power Sales for the Western Electric Company after two years' sojourn in Chicago for the same firm. In 1912 he forsook Manhattan for the more restful atmosphere of Philadelphia of that period and a partnership in the engineering firm of Lewis, Robinson and Gant. Six years later came World War I. Young Gant enlisted his services as a Captain of Ordnance, first in the construction division in Washington; then from November 1918 to March 1919, as Depot Ordnance Officer at Pig Point, Virginia.

Upon his honorable discharge from the Army, Paul Gant resumed his former connection in Philadelphia, remaining with Lewis, Robinson and Gant until 1927 when he became Vice President in Charge of Sales for the York Heating and Ventilating Corporation. From 1931 to his retirement in 1938 he was Vice President and Regional Manager of the Carrier Corporation, with headquarters in Philadelphia.

Director Gant's department easily might have been termed the nerve-center of the District. On him and his associates fell the responsibility for determining what contractors were best suited to perform specific manufacturing functions. Their detailed knowledge of the capacity, equipment, personnel, efficiency, stability and background of every plant within the District's boundaries enabled them, in consultation with representatives of the departments concerned, to recommend the firms which should be invited to bid on Ordnance contracts.

And always one to place credit where credit was due, Paul Gant generously passed the laurel to his faithful crew—and here they are:

Major, then Captain Eugene H. Uhler, Chief of the Procurement Planning Section
Major, then Captain W. C. Canning, Chief, Transportation Section
Captain Dan H. Pletta, Chief, Scrap Salvage Section
Mr. Thomas S. Potts, Chief, Fuel Conservation Section
Mr. Blythe J. Minnier, Chief, Procurement Statistics Section
Mr. Warren Webster, Jr., Chief, Smaller War Plants Section

In reminiscent mood, Paul Gant, like Hamlet, "could a tale unfold that would harrow thy young soul, freeze your blood, and make every hair stand on end like the quills upon the fretful porcupine"— and his are tales of political chiselers and itinerant industrialists come to carve out liberal portions of Uncle Sam's war appropriations; and usually as thoroughly innocent of equipment, plant and "know-how" as a ring-tailed rincus, whatever that might be.

"They were great days, back there," said Captain Gene Uhler, one afternoon in Director Gant's Office, in an effort to draw the Director into discussion.

"I recall one small machine shop operator who came in to see me, demanding that he be put on the District's Suppliers' List. I told him we would oblige, and he promised he would check in on us a few weeks later. However, we didn't get around during the ensuing two weeks to putting him on the List; so I thought I would put him down for subcontracting. About three weeks later he came in with all guns blazing because he had not meanwhile been given a chance to bid.

"I thought the man had been taken care of on the Suppliers' List for one of the Shell items. At this point I turned the case over to Captain Louis F. Unger, requesting that the visitor wait outside the office for ten minutes. Captain Unger explained the case to the man, who shortly left in a considerable huff, threatening "to see his Congressman"—which he did.

"Upon investigation it developed that the man had been after us for a contract for some Engineering Corps work. Actually he had been on a Supplier's List, but not that of Ordnance. As a result of this disagreement we did receive a blast from the Congressman, and since the Congressman also had written Mr. Ingersoll, we received a peppering from that quarter.

At this point Director Gant broke down, and with a hearty "That reminds me," he was off:

"At one point back in 1942," the Director began, "I was asked to act as a buffer for politicos when they came in to needle Brigadier General, then Colonel Hauseman, for war business. Not being in uniform I could get away with insulting them as occasion might demand. One man, I recall, came in with a letter of introduction from a Congressman. He said he was in the textile business and wanted us to give him a list of all the materials we were going to buy as it was his purpose to

locate small manufacturers and help them get the business in return for which he would get commissions.

"Of course, I turned him down, telling him we didn't do business that way—so he left. However, he was back two weeks later with another scheme. This time he asked for a list of the contractors with whom we already had done business. Upon receipt of this information he said, he would make a deal with some real estate outfit, and then try to sell the war contractors property for plant expansion, and thus draw commissions from both contractor and real estate agent! Again I turned him down. Then he told me it might be worth my while if I cooperated with him. In other words, 'cut me in' on his deals. At this point I not too politely ordered him out and threatened to have him put in jail.

"We have had many very narrow escapes in the District," Paul Gant continued, "but somehow or other we have always managed to avoid getting into trouble. For instance, one day a man came in from upstate who wanted to make some money by manufacturing ammunition items. If I remember correctly, it was the 75 mm. Shell. However, he had a friend in Washington who was a Senator and through whom he obtained a letter of introduction to the Ordnance Department. I sent him with the letter to Colonel Hauseman. It turned out that he didn't have a plant, didn't have any machinery, and didn't have any available personnel. In fact, all he had was a desire to make money. He explained to the Colonel that what he proposed to do was to have the Government put up the money to lease a plant and pay his employees—and he would make the ammunition.

"We refused, of course. The visitor left, assuring me he would see the Senator. Not stopping there, he went all the way to the President's Secretarial Staff. We told him, upon the occasion of his next visit to the District Office that he would have to go back home and prepare a letter setting forth how he proposed to produce these shells. He prepared the letter, in view of which we had to give him an opportunity to submit an estimate, as we had bids from other people. Fortunately for Ordnance his price was higher than the others so we crossed him off the List. From the very beginning it looked like a political set-up. Some time later on we learned that the same man had been indicted.

"In several instances, one a request from Washington for investigation, lead to a discovery which caused me to oppose the awards. In both instances the fears of this office were justified. In one instance a New Jersey pair wanted the Government to set up, at its own expense, a six million dollar project which they would operate. With the New York Ordnance District we investigated the project and its backers. One man was too slick, too oily to be safe, we reasoned. Within the year he was indicted on a fraud charge.

"So it went," the Director concluded and he might have given the story a Durante ending by exclaiming, "I got a million of 'em—a million of 'em!"—and he would have been very close to being right: He had!

And those other members of the Special As-sistants—Charles P. Stokes, who made a record for the District and added to his own laurels by reclaiming to the Government a sum of money of astronomical dimension; of M. E. "Dusty" Miller, who set up noteworthy highs in Production; of Lt. Colonel Arthur J. Seiler who was to repeat as Industrial Chief the records he made at Eddystone Sub (Regional) Office and to go overseas to cover himself with more honors—of all these men who were where their talents were most needed—and when they were most needed—follow their activities through subsequent chapters.

The Office, Chief of Ordnance, through the Philadelphia Ordnance District, had much for which it could be thankful; not least of which was its manpower—topside and all sides.

1st 240 mm. Howitzer, en route to Aberdeen Proving Ground, halts before the Budd Company plant to "look pretty" for news camera men

Chapter XI

THE "SPECIALISTS" HAVE GROWING PAINS

THE expansion late in 1942 of the "Special Assistants" group brought into action, and in a most critical period, three "good soldiers" who knew their targets and how to hit them: Lieutenant Colonel, then Major Arthur J. Seiler, Chief, Industrial Division, then named the Industrial Service; Major, then plain Mr. A. Donald Kelso, and Charles P. Stokes, retired banker, and Chief of the Advance Payments Section, who deserted his Maryland model farm to hoe a different kind of row in Ordnance.

ARTHUR J. SEILER

Out of the West came this young Lochinvar, his steed a modern airplane which he flew with consumate skill. Born in Helena, Montana, he attended Montana State College and enrolled in ROTC, in which he set up records, and earned his B.S. Thence to Massachusetts State College to pick up his M.S. on the way to his first major league job, with York Ice Machinery Company, where he was made manager in the Development and Research Department. His next move was to the York Oil Burner Company, and subsequently he was named president of the company. Meanwhile, he had been commissioned a second lieutenant in the Ordnance Reserve.

In November 1940, "Art" came to the District and was promptly placed in charge of the Baldwin Locomotive Works Inspection Office, which office later became known as the Eddystone Sub-Office and, still later, the Eddystone Regional Office, supervising Powder, Explosives and Propellant Inspection Offices at Carney's Point, New Jersey, and Elkton, Maryland.

On 19 April 1941, "Art" Seiler was commissioned first lieutenant, and shortly thereafter brought to the District office to fill the post of Chief, Industrial Service. On 22 October 1941, he was promoted to Captain. He was made a Major, 29 April 1942, and Lieutenant Colonel, 11 May 1943. On 14 December, following, he was named Director of Production and Inspection, and on 17 January 1944 he was transferred to the Detroit Ordnance District, from whence, after his

tour of duty, he was assigned to Ordnance duties in Australia and the Philippines.

Born next door to Gary Cooper and at about the same time, kibitzers of the period marvelled that, unlike his now famous neighbor, Art did not take his better-than-six-feet of good looks and geniality to Hollywood. At any rate, he learned while at college to beat the stuffings out of a drum, "which he played loud, if not good." Later, he learned in Yellowstone Park to navigate a sight-seeing bus, acquiring in the process a familiarity with the Park that stamped him an ace tourist guide. Again, later, this time on behalf of the National Guards' Rifle Team of which he was a member, he knocked down no end of cups, ribbons and other high honors.

Art, in Ordnance didn't do half-bad—not half-bad. He was an excellent example of the right man in the right job at the right time. He was succeeded in the Industrial Service responsibility by Major A. D. Kelso, who moved up from the post of Chief of the Sub-Office Administration Branch.

A. DONALD KELSO

The addition to the panel of Special Assistants of Arthur J. Seiler, A. Donald Kelso and Charles P. Stokes, coming on the heels of the appointment of H. Paul Gant, recently named Director of Planning, brought to peak strength the "know how" group backing up the District Chief, giving the Chief a hard hitting, fast moving team that would have been hard, if not impossible, to equal. Here was experience and ability acquired over wide and varying areas, and over a period of years, which could, at a moment's notice, be brought to bear upon some current problem or opportunity.

A. Donald Kelso is a fair example of what the group could provide. You have read of him in an earlier chapter, of his accomplishments in the ammunition programs and later in pointing the termination program. Perhaps it would not be amiss at this point to recall his first assignment upon coming into P. O. D. You will remember that he could not be immediately assigned to the post for which he was selected, for the reason that it was required that the incumbent of necessity be an officer of a rank no lower than that of major.

Pending arrival of his commission "Mr." Kelso was delegated by Colonel Hauseman to go into the field, look into the Sub-Office, or field service, a personnel of thirty officers, fifty production engineers, one thousand and three hundred inspection personnel and seven hundred and fifty office personnel of various classifications; a formidable prospect for a newcomer, however well qualified. Anything could happen under the stress of war in an organization as large and as far flung as this.

There were hurdles to be got over. Duplication of effort, overlapping of authority, confusion. Of course, all was not gloomy, but there was enough, and with enough ramifications, to jeopardize the whole program. "Mr." Kelso never hesitated in moving square pegs into square holes, in putting his people where they could best express their particular abilities. Officers were shown how better to acquaint themselves with contractors' problems through properly frequent contact. Administrational routines were simplified; economies in reporting methods were affected; and all measures of a corrective measure were made effective without interruption to the increasing demands then being placed upon the Sub-Offices.

It is unfortunate that there is no means of measuring in time, or dollars, or other medium, the economies in operation, or other end values of the work of this officer and his associates.

CHARLES P. STOKES

"Give us men, more and more men to direct the swiftly increasing activities of P. O. D.!" was the cry back in 1941 and well into 1942. "Men who have demonstrated in a big way their ability to get over tough hurdles. Proved leaders who could direct and inspire others in the accomplishment of impossible goals."

So, armed to the teeth, with sub-machine guns, dirks, bear traps and much logic, C. Jared Ingersoll, District Chief, Colonel D. W. Hauseman, the Deputy Chief, and O. Howard Wolfe, Administrative Officer, set out to bag what was to be heralded one of the greatest aggregations of fighting minds ever to be herded into one organization.

An early victim was the suave Charles P. Stokes. If he made any resistance or ran to cover, it is not on record, for on one fair morning in January 1942 he turned up at the District Office mentally stripped

for action and rarin' to go—and the archives reveal he went!

Charley Stokes was, and is, a Philadelphian of the "first water." He knew his Philadelphia—knew its industry—knew his way around—vitally important knowledge of those days when it was highly essential that Ordnance get to industry topside and swing it quickly into line regardless of the difficulties involved—and he came out of a well-earned retirement dating back to 1928, to do his part of the job.

Industry, reluctant at first, soon saw the light and switched over, willing to go all out for war production, but now beginning to discover that production on the basis Ordnance wanted ran into more money than many firms had at hand or readily could obtain to meet greatly expanded payrolls, purchase huge amounts of materials, provide and equip increased and new plants. As a consequence, Ordnance now found itself in the banking business.

And that's where Charley Stokes came in right handy: He knew finance; had lived it, breathed it and had distinguished himself in that field. He was the man for the job. From 1909, just a few years out of the University of Pennsylvania, until his retirement in 1928, he had been a partner in the investment banking firms of Wistar & Stokes and Janney & Company of Philadelphia—and his subsequent record, after 1928, as a farmer and a cattle breeder leaves no doubts that his financial experience had been acquired to good purpose.

His first assignment was that of Chief, Advance Payments and Special Investigations Section of the Fiscal Branch, of which Colonel, then Captain, Robert H. Andrews was Chief. Some few months later he was given the additional assignment of Chief, Price Adjustment Section, established 28 August 1942, succeeding Major Brendan D. Walsh, transferred. In this capacity he reported to the District Chief. The Price Adjustment Section was charged with the responsibility for statutory price and voluntary reductions of contracts. Public Law 528, Section 403, under which the Price Adjustment work was authorized, required the Secretaries of War, Navy and Maritime Commissions to insert in government contracts and subcontracts in excess of $100,000 renegotiation clauses; actually to renegotiate government contracts, and to recover excessive profits for the government when found.

Charles P. Stokes retained both his assignments

until his resignation in June 1945. In April 1943, in view of the broadened scope of the Advanced Payments Section which now was, in addition to its original function, administering partial payments, financing continuity contracts and making advances against contract termination claims, the name of the Section was changed to the Contract Financing Section as more accurately descriptive.

As the war program grew contractors were encouraged to obtain financing through their own banks and bankers continually were urged to investigate and seek this type of business, with success. However, even with the relief thus provided, the Advance Payment Section, from its inception in January 1942 to the end of 1945 had advanced to contractors a total of $228,005,367.49, representing 163 contracts in the hands of 81 contractors in the District. All of these advances were repaid. Nor did C. P. and his economists do badly in renegotiating money back into the Treasury cash-register. From the birth of the Price Adjustment Section to Charles P. Stokes' mustering out in June 1945 there was recovered, including voluntary payments, the rather neat sum of $200,000,000.00.

Charley's going took from the P. O. D. clan its ace raconteur and ready wit, its top-flight satirist, and its standout manipulator of words. His was the distinction of never having been verbally outdistanced, vocally beaten to the punch or oratorically outsmarted. Typical of his artistry was a letter he wrote to Major Joe Baxter of the Purchase Branch, in response to that officer's invitation to a farewell dinner for the departing Martin Sandler. He wrote:

My dear Joe:

Many thanks for asking me to the dinner and I am sorry beyond expression that I cannot foregather and with you pay tribute to that silent, shrinking man, the noblest Roman of them all. I am unfortunately, however, otherwise committed.

Viewing in retrospect this almost monastic figure, I am amazed at the quirk of destiny that projected him into the hurly-burly of Ordnance procurement in wartime. With his simple, trusting nature, his childlike faith in others, his long spells of lethargy and above all his complete indifference to money, he was indeed a strange figure in his field.

That these qualities may not some day be his undoing is my fervent prayer. Despite the urging of all that loved him, he continued to function entirely by word of mouth with never a written record of anything he did or why he did it. His folders, entirely unfortified by any supporting memoranda, may some day, I fear, arise to haunt him. Republics are notoriously ungrateful and it may well be that Martin should never have left the ivory tower in which he dwelt before he came with us.

Say to him for me please, "Well done and hail and farewell."

Yours faithfully,
Charlie Stokes

Upon his retirement command of the Price Adjustment Section passed over to his worthy assistant chief, Major W. Fred Feustel. The Contract Financing Section, its larger responsibilities having been discharged, was at about the same time dropped from the District organizational chart and its remaining responsibilities were assumed by Captain W. F. Rathgeber, Chief of the Accounting Section of the Fiscal Branch of which he was also Assistant Chief, under Captain R. G. Palmer.

Charles P. Stokes, like others of District topside, saw service in World War I, entering in 1917 as a private and emerging the following year a second lieutenant in the Army Air Corps.

It is a matter of record that the special assistants more than earned their salt.

Chapter XII

IT WAS THUS WITH INSPECTION

When I joined P. O. D. in January 1939," wrote Louise C. Evenson of the Ammunition Branch, "a three by five-inch wood box held all of our inspection records. One drawer of a filing cabinet held all the inspection folders. I often have compared this with the hundreds of Kardex files and filing cabinets later required to maintain the inspection records. There were about twelve inspectors. The greater volume of inspection work centered at Midvale Company, J. G. Brill Company, Henry Disston & Sons, Inc., Baldwin Locomotive Works, Bethlehem Steel Company, and several plants in the York area.

"An innovation that startled us at the time (1940) was the introduction in Ordnance of women inspectors. This was the cause of much hilarity. Sam McClenahan took a good-natured ribbing when it was announced that it would be his job to interview the girls. As to Sam's success, deponents sayeth not. The girls, however, accomplished the unexpected: They made good on the job! Some advanced in short order to the post of Chief Inspector in the plants to which they had been assigned."

"Just the same," reported John Target, "we had some interesting experiences with ladies. I recall one particular girl who had been a school teacher, a bright appearing person, who was working as a shell inspector in a Pennsylvania plant. I had gone up there to check on inspection activity, particularly in reference to one-hundred-percent-inspection. I asked the ex-school marm if she was striving to attain one-hundred-percent inspection. She of course replied that she was.

"However, I noticed as I watched her, she did not inspect each shell. Inasmuch as this work required checking to .003 of an inch I asked her whether she put the gage on for each and every shell, to which she replied, "O, no! I just look at the shells and I can tell by just looking whether they are in tolerance. If I am in doubt, I pick them up and feel them."

On another occasion, John Target and Ray Meyers visited an Inspection Office to check the inspection of the M9 Grenade. Ray noticed that one of the girls was not using her gage. When

asked to explain, she told Ray, "I don't use the gage because when I did use it, I only had to reject a lot of the material."

When asked what she was doing, a female inspector in another plant, replied, "I'm merely putting them on and sending them through." There was no thought to the end use of the item she was handling. All this girl knew was that she had something to do, and she was doing it. Much of this sort of thing was observed by French E. Dennison, Inspection Director, on his "swing around the circuit" on an inspectional check-up early during the war.

The Director hinted that he had worked on that trip about "thirty-six hours a day and nine days a week." Anyway, the need for "jacking up" of inspection was critical. Groups were gathered in Regional Offices and in some plants to get the inspection story first hand. There were seventy-seven meetings attended by more than one thousand inspection personnel. On one plant "Denny" was called upon to talk to a group of Negro girl inspectors. Only a few in the group gave any facial indication of interest. The rest listened in respectful silence. Nothing to do but turn on the heat.

The Director bore down on the why of one hundred per cent inspection, the meaning of major, minor and incidental items, and what might happen if an end item should go wrong somewhere along the line—a rocket exploding in the tube of a bazooka, for instance, or falling short and exploding among our own troops; and there were records of just such disasters. Denny's talk was stiff and straight and as a consequence the girls soon were sitting on the edges of their chairs. One girl demanded to know if he was trying to accuse her of killing American soldiers. When the many possibilities of disaster were further pointed out to her, and her duties and responsibilities emphasized, the girl broke down and wept.

It was not that the girls did not care, that they were totally indifferent, or that instructions were lacking, or that they were less dependable than men workers, for they were not, as the record reveals; but rather that instructions were not always too rigidly enforced. For instance, an item might have been considered correct if it checked with gages, but momentary inattention, or improper handling in passing from one inspector to another, or in disposition could easily be cause for error.

A case in point was a critical ammunition component. The final check was a small opening of a required tolerance. The girl selected for this check was above average of intelligence. She was careful, conscientious and knew the importance of her assignment. Yet, faults had occured in the end item which had caused the death of some of our own boys. These faults were traced to the component which was her responsibility.

Checking up at the plant, the Inspection Director stopped at the table of the inspector. The girl met him in tears. "Am I doing something wrong?" she asked. Denny watched her at work. Her performance was well nigh perfect. "But," he asked, "how do you dispose of these units when you have made your inspection?"

"What do you mean, Mr. Dennison?"

"I mean, what do you do with them?"

"Why, I put the perfect ones in this pile at my right, and the imperfect ones in this pile at my left."

"Has it ever occurred to you that something might happen after that? You might leave your work for a moment and give some saboteur his opportunity. Several units could fall on the floor and be replaced, accidentally, in the wrong pile."

Distracting for a moment the attention of the girl, the Director switched several components from one pile to the other, then asked the girl to repeat the inspection. She was amazed. Denny gave the implication time to sink in before continuing his talk. Meanwhile, the plant manager, standing nearby, said:

"You are exactly right, Mr. Dennison. You have hit the nail on the head. Tell you what I'm going to do: I am going to have a hole cut in that table and put a box underneath, with a lock, if you'd like. Then I'll put a brush, dipped in red paint at the opening in the table, so that every defective unit dropped into the "morgue" will carry it's stain of guilt along with it."

Thus had French E. Dennison and his predecessors run to earth each and every material failure. One faulty rocket exploding in a bazooka easily could kill a soldier, and by the same token, shatter

all confidence of an entire company in the weapon. And one faulty operation on the least component could have brought about this tragic result.

Eternal vigilance was the price of success in inspectional procedure, as well as in other phases of Ordnance activity. Men and women inspectors alike imposed problems. Ordnance found itself working unceasingly toward two chief objectives. They were (1), development in inspectors of adequate skills, and (2), the maintenance of a state of mind: The most efficient inspectors were those who knew what they were doing, and why, and who had clearly in mind the end use of their respective components or parts. That was the whole problem. It was never a problem of sex. The women as well as the men responded wholeheartedly to the need once the way was made clear. The women have featured this chapter for the reason that, as Louise Evenson suggested at the beginning, they were an innovation, and it became the historian's wish to show how far they had come against early prejudices, lack of previous industrial experience and, in some instances, natural handicaps.

Recruitment during the early days had its headaches—Sam McClenahan will recall a one-day trip which he made with Captain F. Carson and Miss Helen V. Meehan into Northeastern Pennsylvania for the purpose of rounding up good inspectional material. Headquarters were established in Scranton, in the Hotel Casey.

Recruiting started at 8:00 A. M. and continued through the day to 8:30 P. M. Hotel officials estimated that within that period more than fifteen hundred persons had visited the headquarters. Of that number, one hundred and fifty applicants were signed up; and of these, one hundred put in an appearance at Miss Meehan's office the first morning back in Philadelphia, as requested. However, only a few were in condition to talk business. A visit to the moister regions of the Hotel Benjamin Franklin had put them in a mood for nothing short of some more Benjamin Franklin. Besides being nicely lubricated, they were "broke" and had to be supplied with funds to carry them through to the first pay day. By three o'clock in the afternoon Sam had passed out all the money he had in bank, plus fifty dollars borrowed from Colonel Hauseman.

"And the lending went on for a period of eight months," said Sam in recalling that experience.

"We needed inspectors and stopped at nothing to get them."

"More trouble from there on," C. O. Guernsey later was to report. "Charley" came to P. O. D. as a member of the Co-ordinators' Group, which was set up in 1942 in the District at the instance of the Secretary of War.

"We sent a large number of our inspectors to the Arsenals for special training " he said. "We had as many as thirty-two persons at one time receiving Arsenal instruction—and many of these were lost to us either because of the draft or to higher salaried jobs in private industry. Some of the steps taken to improve the latter situation were to secure a more generous and a more prompt policy of promotions; to provide the proper levelling off of ratings and pay for equivalent work and to strengthen the inspection organization by means of suitable promotions and transfers of inspection personnel.

"It was felt in the District at the time that improvement could be made in the overall policy of reducing inspection at source and substituting inspection at destination where feasible; also by requiring the contractor to carry his fair share of the inspection load; and again by proper levelling off or equalization of inspection."

And what was done to keep up with inspection problems and how, must remain for a later chapter.

Lieutenant General Levin H. Campbell, Jr. who succeeded Major General C. M. Wesson as Chief of Ordnance, 31 May 1942

Robert P. Patterson was appointed Assistant Secretary of War, July 1940, moving to the Secretaryship which he held to his resignation in July 1947

Chapter XIII

MAINLY SMITH

SMITHS, Smiths everywhere, but not a Pocahontas in sight! Not so much even as a Captain John among them. But no matter; those of the Clan Smith gravitating into P. O. D., beginning with Captain Fred E., who entered these portals 5 July 1939, made history enough and gloriously.

Cap'n. Fred's first assignment was that of Adjutant. He was twice Executive Officer. In June 1941 he was appointed to the No. 1 job in the then newly formed Plant Protection Service continuing at his station through the transfer of jurisdiction 22 September 1942 of his Section to the Third Service Command with headquarters in the Fidelity-Philadelphia Building, 123 South Broad Street.

From January 1939 the F. B. I. had been making very thorough inspections of certain vital plants, emphasizing in their recommendations protection against sabotage, but it was early discovered that proper coverage of the thousands of important plants in the United States would require added facilities. It therefore was directed 12 May 1941 by the Under Secretary of War that responsibility for the functioning of plant protection should be delegated to the procurement districts to the maximum extent consistent with proper control and efficient operation. As plant protection had never existed in the military service considerable flexibility in the selection of personnel as well as in the procedure to be followed was permitted.

Survey was immediately made by Captain Smith and his capable staff of all causes of delay to production. It was found that fire was the explanation of approximately 90 per cent of the cases then under review. It was also found that in 95 per cent of the cases the destroying agency employed by saboteurs was fire or explosions contributing to fire. Acting on this premise an officer of one of the largest fire insurance companies was selected to head the inspection personnel. The official—Joseph M. Creedon.

High type personnel comprising engineers of extended experience of insurance rating boards procedures were selected. These men were required, before assigned to inspections, to complete a special course of instruction covering generally fire pre-vention and sabotage prevention, personnel systems, guard forces, fences and identification systems.

The service later was expanded to include greater assistance to the facilities, to the end that interruptions from any cause to production might be minimized. Anticipating opposition by the facilities, there was initiated the procedure of delegating an officer to introduce the plant protection engineer, who would explain on his first visit the necessity for and the methods of plant protection.

The *Bulletin*, No. 1, of the Ordnance Department Plant Protection Inspection Service, issued 9 July 1941, establishing the Plant Protection Service, placed all matters of lighting and fencing, guards, investigation of employees, aliens, subversive activities, labor relations, control of visitors, under this Service. The *Bulletin* was prepared, either accidentally or purposely, in accordance with the procedure set up in P. O. D.

The acceptance of the program by District contractors had been underestimated by P. O. D., for it developed that, possibly because of its well-planned presentation, the plan was readily accepted in every instance, lock, stock and barrel.

As of 8 December 1941 jurisdiction of the Plant Protection Service was extended to cover facilities holding British contracts; and a few weeks later, 31 December 1941, came the edict of the Under Secretary of War, assigning the Service joint responsibility with the Federal Power Commission for inspection of all electrical utilities in the Philadelphia Ordnance District. Personnel at this time of the Service stood at two officers, fourteen inspectors and five clerical assistants.

Fred and his Commandos were informed 21 February 1942 that expansion to implement the Finger Print Program would have to be got under way. Time was short. The deadline was 1 June. Four hundred thousand facilities' employees in the District were involved. However, instructions were not received until late in March. "So what?" mumbled the new Lt. Colonel, "we'll do it." And he did! Fortunately, forty thousand persons already had been printed; but there were by actual count, three hundred twenty-one thousand more of the same. With the assistance of the American Red Cross, Emergency Aid and volunteer groups, the deadline was met—and another wartime Indian "bit the dust."

And just to show that its heart was in the right place, the Ordnance Department turned over to Fred, 10 April 1942, one hundred Navy plants.

The need for the Plant Protection began, in the Spring of 1943, to taper off. The Intelligence Section, with Captain Morton H. Fetterolf in charge, moved back to the Philadelphia Ord. Dist. Office 1 April. Colonel Smith was assigned to overseas duty, leaving Major, then Captain, Arthur H. Boyer in charge of the remaining Sections of the Service which were terminated, in February 1944.

On 1 June 1944, Captain Fetterolf, who had entered the Service from the investment banking house of Carstairs & Company, was released on inactive duty status. He was succeeded by Captain Richard A. Line, who came to the District with Colonel Fred A. McMahon, 1 December 1943.

Fred Smith was born in Flemington, New Jersey, and early acquired a flair for wooden soldiers, popguns and tin swords. Graduating in 1910 from Reading Academy, he entered the Wharton School of the University of Pennsylvania. Three years of this, and the rumble of war filtered through to

capture his imagination. Nothing to do but sign up, which he did, with the Red Cross where he trained for service in the Ambulance Corps.

However, Fred's plans were changed by the President's declaration of war. Fred Eugene Smith became suddenly Private Smith, 12,624. He embarked in October for France, where he was attached to a Base Hospital Unit, spent two years overseas, rose to the rank of top sergeant, returning 19 May 1919 to U. S. A. and civilian life.

Came 30 July 1927, and a second lieutenant's commission in the 315th Infantry Reserve, which he resigned early during the Summer of 1928. However, he was recommissioned in October, this time a first lieutenant, Specialist Reserve, Army Ordnance, receiving on 10 December of the same year his assignment to the Philadelphia Ordnance District. On 17 September, 1940 he was promoted to the rank of major and on 17 July 1942 lieutenant colonel.

And from the European theatre there came, early in November 1944, word that the Colonel had received the Bronze Star, a recognition of meritorious service in connection with the storing and delivery to the Normandy beach-head and other invasion points of Ordnance material.

In war after war it is always the same . . . the Smiths come to the top.

ℰ≈℧

Chapter XIV

PROCUREMENT MOVES AHEAD

IT IS difficult to know exactly at this late day when a distinct Planning Section came into being in P. O. D. It is recorded in the basic history of the District: "A Planning Section was not set up as a separate department of the District; but the District was activated as a separate part of Procurement Planning. This unique situation arose from the fact that the decentralized Ordnance District originally was a Planning Department in the Field for the Office of the Chief of Ordnance administered from Washington . . ."

At any rate a separate Planning activity was in the making in the District as far back as 1933; its background the Mobilization Plan of that year. This was chiefly a system of apportionments for each District based upon data earlier drawn from industrial surveys. Other Mobilization Plans came with the passing years. On 1 July 1939, the Procurement Planning Section, such as it was at the time, became the responsibility of the Assistant District Chief Captain, later Major, W. S. Broberg, who continued in his supervisory capacity until 1 January 1941, when a separate Procurement Planning Section was set up with Lieutenant, later Captain, Eugene H. Uhler in charge.

The principal procurement planning activities to November 1939 had been (1) visits to plants which had received invitations to bid on Educational Orders and (2) a complete recheck of all Acceptable Schedules of Production. The object of the latter was to reduce machine tool deficiencies. Survey of work was continued, but at a decreased pace, in order to expedite the revision work on schedules. To this point three hundred and sixty-two plants in the Philadelphia Ordnance District had been surveyed; sixty others in the Philadelphia Ordnance District had been surveyed; sixty others in the Baltimore Ordnance District which, on 30 June 1937, had been consolidated with the now expanding Philadelphia Ordnance District.

A program embracing Educational Orders and Production Studies was conceived and advocated by the Army Ordnance Association as far back as 1931. However, Congress did not see fit to appropriate funds for this purpose until the fiscal year 1938. Pleas for preparedness in any form received scant consideration during the interval. "The purpose of the program," wrote Captain Corbit S. Hoffman, Jr., from the Edward G. Budd Company, where he was stationed in 1944 as Inspector-in-Charge, "was to provide funds to the Army to enable industry to acquire a working knowledge of the manufacture of military material. The appropriated funds were allotted to the various services and the services placed contracts with facilities possessing engineering and manufacturing qualifications."

The Production Studies were contracts awarded to manufacturers who, having the manufacturing ability and a nucleus of machine tools for the production of critical Ordnance items (but without actually producing anything) would make up for Ordnance, for general use, a description of manufacture and a report enumerating the steps they would take in production.

Reports of all surveys in reference to Educational Orders and Production Studies were submitted through the Office of the Chief of Ordnance to the Army and Navy Munitions Board.

District participation in the program dated from February and March 1939, when plants having Educational Orders and Production Studies in were begun. Contracts were awarded during the early months of 1940. They were:

300—1000# Demolition Bombs, American Car & Foundry Company, Berwick, Pa.

5075—75 mm. H.E., Shells, M48, Armstrong Cork Company, Lancaster, Pa.

10—Light Tanks, M2A4, Baldwin Locomotive Works, Eddystone, Pa.

40—Power Trains, Baldwin Locomotive Works, Eddystone, Pa.

5000—155 mm. Shell Forging, M101, Baldwin Locomotive Works, Eddystone, Pa.

5000—75 mm. H.E., Shells, M48, Darling Valve & Mfg. Company, Williamsport, Pa.

5000—Fuzes, P.D., M48, Philco Corporation, Philadelphia, Pa.

11—Mount Telescope, M18, Precision Mfg. Co., Philadelphia, Pa.

5000—105 mm. Shell Forgings, M101, Taylor-Wharton Steel Company, Easton, Pa.

1000—Red Star Cluster, Ground, Signals, M6A , Triumph Explosives, Inc., Elkton, Md.

10,000—Booster, M20, Warren Webster Company, Camden, New Jersey.

The Production Studies, of which there were six, were placed September 1939, as follows:

Karl Lieberknecht, Inc., Reading, Pa.—Range Quadrant, M3—Telescope Mount M16.

Darling Valve & Manufacturing Company, Williamsport, Pa.—75 mm. Shell, M48.

Revere Copper & Brass Company, Baltimore, Md. —.30 Cal. and .50 Cal. Cartridge Case.

Black & Decker Manufacturing Company, Townson, Md.—Booster, M20.

Harrisburg Steel Company, Harrisburg, Pa.—300 # Demolition Bomb.

Eastern Rolling Mill Company, Baltimore, Md.— 105 mm. Cartridge Case.

Gages were a principal bottleneck in the performance of these contracts—gages and machine tool shortages, factors which caused the delay to well into 1942 of the completion of the last of the contracts assigned under the program, which finally was terminated 30 June 1942.

Early impetus had no doubt been a reflection of the National Defense Act of 3 April 1939, increasing Educational Orders from $2,000,000 annually, to $34,000,000 for the ensuing three years; and the Strategic War Materials Act of 7 June 1939, ordering War, Navy and Interior Secretaries to determine what such materials were, and authorizing the expenditure from 1939 through 1943 of $100,000,000.00.

The general effect of the Educational Order and Production Study Program was good. Here was schooling on the practical side for both Ordnance and industry. All the companies participating in the program became important factors in Ordnance production in the District, although not always on the item upon which they had tried their teeth.

The Warren Webster Company, for instance, through its Educational Order as a "starter" became the indispensable producer of Boosters. The Baldwin Locomotive Works never became a volume producer of Light Tanks, but the Educational Order was, again, the "starter" whereby Spicer Manufacturing Company became a key producer of Light Tank Transmissions. Revere Copper & Brass, Inc., Baltimore, Maryland, did not follow the lead indicated by its Production Study Order, but this same Production Study served as a study for the neighboring Eastern Rolling Mill Company to start its work, which made it eventually one of the country's leading producers of 105 mm. cartridge cases. The Precision Manufacturing Company, while meeting up with Ordnance via Mount, Telescope, M18, soon was in a fair way to become one of the District's top producers of gages—and did.

And P. O. D. was fortunate in retaining through the war the services of many of the men whose names illumine the old record . . . men who at one time and another worked on Educational Orders and Production Studies. During a major part of the period, survey and production headed up under then First Lieutenant John W. Ogden, serving under Captain, later (July 1940) Major W. S. Broberg. Others working on the Orders and Studies included John H. Beyer, later to become Artillery Branch Chief, Thomas S. Potts, William E. Eadie, Jr., Procurement Plans Chief, who left the District 31 January 1943, a first lieutenant, and returned 18 February 1945, after active service in England, a major; Corbit S. Hoffman, Jr., joining up in February 1941 as a production engineer, later, after serving at other District posts, to move up to the Edward G. Budd Company plant as Ordnance Inspector-in-Charge; and First Lieutenant William L. Stephens, Jr., some time in the future to appear as Major Stephens, Chief of the Property Branch.

Then there was Ben Ayres, vibrant as a bull fiddle, so runs one record, and so impatient with Washington because of delayed supplies that he went down in his own pocket for forms, binders and other items needed in his work. And not overlooking First Lieutenant, later Captain Eugene H. Uhler, one of the sparks to the Educational Order and Production Studies activities, who remained through the war years to head up Procurement Planning and associated activities including a Smaller War Plants Unit, Research and Development Unit, of which more is in another chapter.

Chapter XV

NEW HORIZONS

IT WAS in 1942 that the District organization began to "feel its oats." Administrational and functional procedures now had been fairly well integrated and both Ordnance and Industry knew where they were going. Signs of the times were of a long war, and with everyone settling down for the "pull," but not realizing that out of the hesitation, the confusion, and lack of ready "know-how," soon would develop a $3,000,000,000 business—a modern miracle if ever there was one—and this was it!

Labor Branch

Pirating of labor continued through 1942, a major problem. It was not uncommon for "procurers" of one company to carry on recruiting at the very gates of another. By November of that year, the Labor Section of the District, which had been set up in April 1942, with Major, then Captain, Joseph I. Wexlin, in charge, found itself dealing in large measure with such matters, in addition to labor piracy, as excessive absenteeism; poor labor needs—current and anticipated; need for additional women, and the likely demands of Selective Service.

Women in industry was a pressing problem. Meetings were held in plants for discussion of the various phases of this new development in industry. John Wunder and L. Gleeson of the Section capably handled these matters, delivering talks to large plant groups.

The first poll of women in war industry was not taken until February 1943. At this time, 382 plants reported 35,832 women employed; in May 1943, 406 plants reported 53,280 women at work; and in July 1943, 339 plants reported 60,026, with employment of women continuing on the up-side as the supply of available men reached for the "bottom of the barrel," and with increasing numbers of males of the draft age going into the Armed Services.

Losses to Selective Service of male employees of the District office reached a new high in September 1942. These losses were particularly serious among the ranks of Inspectors. In an effort to meet this situation, intensive training of women and the transfer to the contractor of increased inspection responsibility were being undertaken.

The earliest effort to establish in P. O. D. a going "Labor Unit" was in April 1942 when, following a brief period of "indoctrination," the irrepressible Captain Joe I. Wexlin was called into Colonel Hauseman's office and assigned to the labor activity. "What do you know about labor supply?" the Colonel snapped. Said Joe, "I hired a secretary once or twice." Characteristically, the Colonel replied, "Very well, you are in charge of Labor Supply. See Captain Carson in charge of personnel. He will tell you what the story is—and I want results—quick!"

Labor Supply was at that time in the hands of the Production Division of which Mr. Marion H. "Dusty" Miller was Chief. In turn, it had been turned over to Lieutenant Colonel, then Major, H. K. Kelley, and thence to Ray Farrington, who was sent to Washington to talk it over with the Under Secretary.

Effort had been made to bring into the District Office a Mr. Jones, an experienced labor man. For some forgotten reason the deal vaporized, and the search took other directions. Attention centered upon Lewis H. Van Dusen, Jr., member of a local law firm and of the law-famous Philadelphia family of Van Dusen who, caught in a cross-fire of P. O. D. logic of the day, was easy prey. Lew was a product of Episcopal Academy, St. Paul's School, Princeton, where he graduated in 1932 with an A.B., and New College, Oxford, England, where, with benefit of a Rhodes Scholarship, he completed his education in law. He was admitted to the Pennsylvania Bar in December 1935 and became associated about the same time with the law firm of Drinker, Biddle and Reath. Seven years later, in 1942, he was admitted to partnership.

Lew picked up momentum from the start. He was a keen lawyer and analyst with a decided flair for public relations work; just the right formula, as time was to demonstrate. Lew, now a

Major, departed the District 1 June 1943 for special duties overseas.

Major Van Dusen was succeeded, 7 June 1943 by Lieutenant Ross T. Henderson, of Perth Amboy, New Jersey. On 10 December 1942, Ross had been assigned to the Tank-Automotive Branch. On 11 January 1943 he was assigned Assistant to Officer-in-Charge, Small Arms Branch. In June 1943 he was assigned Assistant Ordnance Representative of the Industry Integration Committee on M1 Grenade Adapter Committee, with his station at J. J. Nesbitt Company, Philadelphia, Pa.

That Ross adequately met his responsibilities as the District's Labor Officer was borne out by a report 28 September 1943, from C. D. Briddell Company, Crisfield, Maryland, that stated: "The spirits of our men were sagging just a little because of the delay experienced prior to our contact with your organization. In the discussions ensuing, a morale visit was projected by the Lieutenant (Ross Henderson) and his sergeant, Charles Greenwood, visiting our plant to give our employees a bit of a description of what the real thing means. As a result of that visit our Ordnance Department 1 amed September "Greenwood Production Month." The result: Their August production record was beaten by more than 60 per cent in September."

On 12 February 1944, Captain Henderson was assigned the additional duty of Ordnance Representative on the Industry Integration Committee on Grenade Rifle A. T. M9A1, M11A2 and Grenade Rifle, Practice, M1 at J. J. Nesbitt Company. On October 1945, he moved on to Indiantown Gap, Pennsylvania, for separation from the Service he had so well served.

Followed First Lieutenant Bernard M. Zimmerman, lawyer and one time City Solicitor for the City of Lancaster, Pennsylvania, who came to P. O. D. 12 January 1943 as Assistant to the Chief of the Legal Branch, and shortly thereafter he received the additional and temporary assignment of Chief of the Labor Section, a post which he held until the assignment, 4 January 1945, of a permanent Chief, in this instance Lieutenant Jack Walsh, who had gained a share of his labor "know how" as assistant to the first incumbent, Lew Van Dusen.

Zim, who received his Captain's commission 19 June 1944, was a graduate of Franklin and Marshall College, from whence he moved on to three years of law at the University of Pennsylvania. Zim was "aces" on his P. O. D. assignments; for

note the following quoted from a letter written 8 February by Ralph Kelly, President, Baldwin Locomotive Works:

"I think that Baldwin, in taking the lead in the settlement of cost-plus-a-fixed-fee contracts on a negotiated basis, has made a real contribution to the contract settlement problem as a whole, and the settlements have been effected on a basis which I believe is fair to both the company and the Government. While our own people have done a good job, very little could have been accomplished in settlement if it had not been for the splendid efforts of the staff of the Philadelphia Ordnance District, not only as to the negotiation of the settlements themselves" . . . "In particular I should like to express appreciation for the efforts of Major Gilmer, Major Conger and Captain Zimmerman who, with our own representatives, carried the settlement program through to completion in the face of what appeared to be insurmountable difficulties . . ."

On 4 January 1945, Jack Walsh picked up the Labor Chief's baton. Jack came to P. O. D. 13 April 1943, a second lieutenant, straight from the coal business. His first assignment in the District was that of Life Insurance Officer and Assistant to the Adjutant. On 5 July 1943 he was named Surveying Officer; 11 August 1943, Assistant to the Chief of the Labor Section; 15 January 1944, Assistant to the Chief, Planning Section, where he distinguished himself, particularly in labor recruitment and in the adjustment of labor difficulties during the production drives of 1944–1945. His promotion to First Lieutenant bears the date of 8 April 1944.

Since compliments appear to be in order in the labor story, there would be no point in omitting Jack Walsh. Here is what the president of York-Shipley, Incorporated, York, Pennsylvania, had to say of him, in a letter dated 25 July 1945, addressed to the then District Chief, Colonel A. D. Kelso:

"I want you to know that the management of this company greatly appreciate the extremely fine cooperation received from the Philadelphia Ordnance District and particularly from Jack Walsh. You are to be highly complimented on having men of such a caliber in your organization."

With the support afforded him, there was noting in the L. T. O. (Labor Theatre of Operations) too hot for Jack to handle. There was, for instance, Second Lieutenant Harry N. Corbin, a Trenton, New Jersey lad with a lot of basic training in infantry in the Counter Intelligence Corps and O. C. S. His civilian wisdom had been acquired in the commercial refrigeration field, following several years of service with the New Jersey State Police as a criminal investigator. From P. O. D. on 26 June 1945 he moved on to the Ordnance School at Aberdeen Proving Ground.

Another stalwart of the Labor group was Robert D. Bernheim, who came to P. O. D. from Lehigh University by way of New York City where he had been engaged in the insurance business.

The third member of the Walsh Flying Labor Squadron, Second Lieutenant Ralph E. Curley, hailing from Worcester, Massachusetts, was assigned to the District 26 June 1945, following basic training and O. C. S. It was said that Ralph Curley could accomplish more with a quip and a smile than a mule-skinner could stir up with a rawhide whip and a hot iron. Down Worcester way, he had "white collared" for American Steel & Wire Company; again, handled Industrial Relations, as grievance representative for more than five thousand employees. Upon the demise of the Labor Section, in November 1945, when it appeared that the Section had served its program, Ralph was transferred out of the District and was heard of not again.

Chapter XVI

MIRACLE YEAR

The year of 1942 was a year of great and swift beginnings. Among other gains was the Machine Tool Panel. This marked an important advance in the handling of machine tool problems. The general procedures grew out of a meeting called 4 April 1942, in the office of the New York Ordnance Department, by Lt. General Levin H. Campbell, Jr., Chief of Ordnance. The meeting was attended by the Chiefs of the Districts east of and including Chicago, and the leading dealers of the machine tool industry in the corresponding Districts.

On 7 April 1942, a meeting attended by the District Chief; Major A. J. Seiler, Chief of Industrial Division; H. P. Gant, then Chief, Special Projects Section; and Mr. L. H. Swind and C. F. Pearson, respectively Chairman and Co-Chairman of the Machine Tool Panel, reached a mutual understanding as to conference facility, and the appointment as Liaison Officer and Secretary of the Panel, of Captain, then Lieutenant, M. H. Patterson. At the close of the meeting, H. Paul Gant presented the first case for the Panel's attention.

Upon subsequent organization, the Panel in this District comprised thirty-eight (38) members, each selected with respect to (1) his integrity; (2) years of specialized experience, and favorable regard of industrial firms in the District. All were trained engineers in the metal fields. They pledged their services, without compensation, to the District. The Panel came into official existence, 7 May 1942, at which time a meeting was called for the purpose of fully instructing its membership on:

a. Panel Procedure, with respect to (1) Approach of Ordnance contractors' personnel; (2) the necessary disregard in any decisions or discussions with contractors of all personal and business interests; (3) The reporting the state of

coordination of contractors' management and production officials; (4) Possible interference that might prevent progress of pilot line and the production requirements scheduled; (5) analysis of existing and needed jigs, fixtures and special tooling, and promised delivery dates; (6) obtaining a general picture of the machine tools available in contractors' plants, especially as a possible application and the critical tools involved to balance requirements; (7) information as to processing, maintenance of production, plant facilities, perishable tools, existing labor conditions and so on.

b. Procedure for Ordnance Contractors, with respect to their (1) certified drawings from the Ordnance Department; (2) executive personnel responsible for the completion of contract and shop organization; (3) efforts to meet contractors who have made the same items before; (4) study of processes and sources of fixture supply; (5) list of equipment usable to the fulfillment of contract; (6) possible sources of sub-contracting, and listing of such outside contracting; (7) preparation of pilot line; (8) source of raw materials and applicable delivery schedules; (9) situation as it concerned co-related equipment such as punch press needs, welding, heat treating, brazing, forging, plating, painting, cleaning, tumbling and woodworking; (10) continuing supply of perishable tools, etc.

Many visits to contractors' plants were made in an advisory capacity by Panel members, in relation to problems submitted by the Philadelphia Ordnance District.

More recently, the Machine Tool Panel had been instructed to render to the Industry Integrating Committee and the Conversion Engineering Section of the District in the attainment of their respective objectives as they related to approval of new equipment orders and suggestions of a conversion nature, all assistance that might be required.

Chapter XVII

INTEGRATION

SOMETHING had been added. A new word had been entered in the Ordnance lexicon. "Why Integrate—and what is it?" asked SPOGL, via an Ordnance Fiscal Circular, dated 22 August 1942, then attempts to answer his own query, thus:

> "Integration of an industry balances the production, with the result that the desired production is obtained with a minimum facility requirement. The skill and knowledge of the large manufacturer is made available to the newcomer or the small manufacturer, bringing him into full production in the shortest possible time. There is made available to the Ordnance Department on short notice complete information as to the productive capacity of the industry, its inventory of parts and material, and there is made possible rapid changes in production rates to meet the requirements of the using services."

Industry Integration was a phase of decentralization, comprising a system of Industrial Integration Committees originated by Lt. General Levin H. Campbell, Jr., then Chief of Ordnance. "The possibilities of the committee system," reported *Ordnance Magazine* (Page 72, Vol. XXIV, No. 136, January-February 1943) "first became generally realized as the result of remarkable accomplishments of the Mechanical Time Fuze Committee which General Campbell created before he became Chief of Ordnance. When the various committees struggling with the production of time fuzes started working together under the committee system they found that their various shortages or excesses of machine capacity, materials and other things balanced one another to a startling degree. By operating in co-operation under the Ordnance Committee System, they were able to attain a great increase in production."

In the tank department "tank manufacturers were encouraged to exchange information and services with one another. If one manufacturer is getting slow deliveries on tank tracks, the committee will find out immediately if some other manufacturer has an excess of tracks so that a balance may be reached. Formerly a manufacturer short on tracks would come to the Ordnance Department for information and guidance in finding a manufacturer who could help him out; now the manufacturer goes to his own committee headquarters, gets the centralized information, then makes his deal directly with the manufacturer who could help him out."

It was purely a committee system. The committee in each instance was made up of a chairman who was the Chief of the Ordnance Branch in which the committee was formed (the Ammunition Chief, for instance, was Chairman of all committees within the scope of his operations; a commissioned officer from the Branch, designated as Deputy Chairman; an Assistant Chairman appointed from Industry by the Branch Chief; one or more Ordnance officers experienced in military procedure; a production control clerk or such personnel as might be required; from each prime manufacturer, a member, preferably a production man.

Later there was noted a lack of uniformity in the interpretation of drawings and specifications—this among resident inspectors assigned to the inspection of the same Ordnance items. The variation was noted, not only between plants in the same District but, as well, between the Districts themselves.

To correct these discrepancies, misunderstandings and the occasional conflict and over-lappings of authority a key inspector was established within each Industry Integration Committee. It became this gentleman's duty to assist the Ordnance Department representative on the Committee in the co-ordination of inspection procedure and the solution of inspection problems.

The general operation now was for the Key Inspector and the Ordnance Department representative to call a council of chief inspectors from all the commercial facilities and arsenals producing the committee item, just as soon as the committee should be formed. When it appeared desirable, representatives also were invited from loading plants and proving grounds; and in all cases, each chief inspector brought to the meeting all inspection problems which had been encountered, including requests for interpretations or alterations of drawings and specifications.

At any rate, you get the idea. That was the way it was supposed to work.

On the Integration roster we find, among others, the following P. O. D'ers and their charges:

Dudley Cozad on the M110, B. N. Fuze.

Charles H. Kemper—60 mm. and 81 mm., Mortar Shell.

Harry Fritz—M1 Hand Grenade.

First Lieutenant Harry C. Troth, B. D. M66A1, M68, M72 Fuzes, M1 Grenade Adapter.

First Lieutenant John R. Graf—60 mm. and 81 mm. Shells, M1, A2 and A3 Adapter Clusters, t-1 Parachute.

First Lieutenant Ross T. Henderson—M1 Grenade Adapter.

Captain Corbit S. Hoffman, Jr.—M110 B. N. Fuze, M40, M41 Fragmentation Bomb, M41-A1, 20 lb. and 23 lb. Frag. Bomb.

Captain Donald A. Anderson—60 mm. and 81 mm. Shells.

Captain George Waterhouse—M4 Rocket Fuze, Bulova M6 and M22.

Captain John A. Zupez—Fuze B. D. M66A1, M68 and CPT 105.

First Lieutenant Julius Mehalek—100# Practice Bomb, M85.

First Lieutenant Bernhard G. Fortman, Jr.— 60 mm. and 81 mm. Trench Mortar.

First Lieutenant William O. Bruehl—Rifle Grenade, Adapter.

First Lieutenant Harry M. Gingrich—M40 Fragmentation Bombs, Parachute Assemblies.

There were others, but as we said before, you get the idea.

Chapter XVIII

CIVILIAN PERSONNEL GETS ITS MAN!

FROM one civilian employee to more than 4,100 in three short years was something of a record in building a highly specialized organization. In 1937 Miss Helen V. Meehan, who had been with P. O. D. since World War I, was the only civilian employee. Her paychecks were forwarded from Washington. Headquarters then were in the United States Custom House. That was in 1937, one of the years of sweet content when we were watching with amusement the performance of mid-Europa Opera Bouffe and the antics of its chief jesters—we thought. Two years later, in July 1939, the Philadelphia Ordnance District could point to a personnel of 72 employees. The procedure at that time with regard to civilian employment followed this pattern:

"Whenever it was desired to hire additional employees it was necessary to secure authority from the Office, Chief of Ordnance, at Washington. When such authority had been obtained it was necessary to requisition the Civil Service Commission for a list of eligibles. Upon receipt of such a list the eligibles would be requested to call at the District Office for interview by the Executive Officer, within whose jurisdiction was vested power of approval."

The first mention of a Personnel Division appears in the Mobilization Plan of 1939, of "The Philadelphia Ordnance District in Time of War."

Through the later part of 1939 and into 1940 a Civilian Personnel unit existed as a segment of the Personnel, Progress and Statistics Section of which Lieutenant William H. Crown, Jr., was Chief. The lieutenant reported to P. O. D. 5 July 1939, with a B.S. in Mechanical Engineering acquired at Penn State.

The Personnel unit of the Section immediately assumed the functions and processes outlined by Major Hamilton in his Mobilization Plan. The unit was thereby required to keep records, prepare payrolls, supervise training, provide inspection and other personnel, and, in general, look after the welfare of District personnel.

In April 1940, Lieutenant Crown was assigned to duty in Washington. His place in the Personnel Section was taken over by Captain Fred E. Smith. Two months later, with the assignment to P. O. D. as Executive Officer of Major D. N. Hauseman, Captain Smith was reassigned as Adjutant. Shortly following this shift, July 1940, the personnel activity was set up as an independent unit, with Lieutenant John F. Carson, a newcomer, in charge. The new unit was assigned to the General Office Division.

The first person assigned by Lieutenant Carson was Helen V. Meehan, whose duty it was to handle all paper work incident to personnel. At this time all applicants were sent to the United States Custom House at 2nd and Chestnut Streets for fingerprinting and for oath of office. Later, facilities for this work were provided in the District Office. In 1940, all appointments first had to be approved by the District Chief.

Lieutenant Carson arrived in Civilian Personnel at a time when, under impetus of the Defense program, the personnel total of the District was on the move. In his time—July 1940 to May 1944—he was responsible for the recruitment and indoctrination of more than 4,000 men and women—of all skills, from all walks of life.

Military duty was not new to Captain Jack Carson. Following high school and Chew Preparatory School, he entered West Point and, later, the Wharton School. He came to the District a Second Lieutenant. He received his commission of First Lieutenant, 2 December 1940; his captain's commission in February 1942. In January 1944 he was appointed a member of the Control Board of the District, and Member, Committee on Meritorious Civilian Awards. In May 1944, he was transferred to Aberdeen Proving Grounds for extended duty.

To 31 December 1940, the District had acquired 319 employees, and "overtime" was becoming an operating factor. There had been issued during the month, to meet this development, Office Memorandum No. 32, specifying compensation at the rate of time-and-half-time for all work in excess of 40 hours a week.

In January 1941 there were created two Salary Boards made necessary by District practice of making its own promotions. The first such Board, known as the Primary Board, was composed of an Inspection Section and a Clerical Section. The Inspection Section phase of the Board had for its members Lieutenant Colonel, then Captain Andrew W. Hamilton, Major, then Lieutenant John H. Beyer, Captain, then Lieutenant George L. Schiel, Fred S. Feldheim, Sam McClenahan and "Mr.", later Lieutenant, William A. Mortensen. The Clerical Section phase had for its members Major Fred E. Smith, Lt. Col., then Lt. Robert H. Andrews, Major, then Captain Eugene H. Uhler, and S. R. Shadel. The two Sections reported their findings and recommendations to the Secondary, or General Board, the members of which were Brigadier General, then Major Hauseman, Major E. S. Broberg, Lieutenant Carson and Major, then civilian John W. Ogden.

On 16 March 1941 the Wilmington Ordnance Office ceased to be a part of P. O. D. Personnel at this time of the combined offices was 536 persons, 25 of whom were assigned to Wilmington.

Effective 24 February the basic week for personnel was set at 39 hours—9 A. M. to 5 P. M., and on Saturdays, 9 A. M. to 1 P. M.

The pressure on in earnest, it was ordered 15 April 1941, by the Chief of Ordnance:

> "Effective immediately, District Offices are authorized to employ, in accordance with Civilian Personnel Regulation No. 1,294, such personnel as may be needed under the designation listed therein without prior authorization from this Office, with the exception of appointments to positions listed in Civilian Personnel Regulation No. 1294-2, etc., etc. Complete responsibility is placed upon the District Office for the maintaining of an adequate and balanced force as to numbers and grades, to meet its requirements."

All of which meant a faster tempo in personnel procurement, except in reference to the professional and scientific grades for which authorization still was lacking.

On 6 June 1941 had come Memorandum No. 71

directing that certain grades now would work 45 hours per week. On 11 June 1941, Memorandum No. 73 ordered that all officers and per annum employees put in 44 hours per week. However, and to make it equal all around, Memorandum No. 109, dated September, declared for a universal 44 hours.

The District came up to Pearl Harbor with a payroll of 1,561 persons—an increase within the year of 500 per cent. In January 1942 came another change in work orders. This time, the change was to a 48 hour week for all personnel, with overtime service essential. Then, in February 1942, Memorandum No. 22 ordered all divisions and Field Offices to maintain sufficient forces to carry on Sunday and holiday work. Employees were to work no more than six days a week. Those working on Sunday were not to work the following Saturday. In the course of time this order was changed, back to 40 hours a week and overtime.

Memorandum No. 124, which was issued 4 May 1942, charged the Civilian Personnel Branch with the duty of handling occupational deferments which, as more men were needed in war industries at the same time they were wanted for the Armed Services, imposed heavy burdens upon the Branch. However, even with personnel being so lost the District total had climbed by 30 June to 3,404 persons.

Early in the year the District Offices had moved from the Mitten Building to the old but more commodious Manufacturers Club Building, 150 South Broad Street. By September the rapidly expanding staff had outgrown these offices and, as a result, the Civilian Personnel Branch and several other of the Branches were moved to "overflow quarters" at 1420 Walnut Street.

The first of the Sections set up in the Branch to meet the onrush was the Personnel Records Section, with Helen V. Meehan designated as Chief, who had at one time, as secretary, Marie A. O'Donnell. That was in December 1940. An Interview Section, under James E. Tucker, with a B.S. from Ursinus College and fresh from a long siege with Hunter Pressed Steel Company, was established in January 1941. In November of that year the need developed for a Status Section to maintain complete records which would show at all times the status and station of all employees. This assignment went to Mrs. Pauline "Polly" McKinley with assistant Katherine A. Catafesta.

A Report and Records Section came into being in February 1942 with Margaret Mannion in charge, Lillian Phillips assisting. It was the function of this Section to maintain such reports as would provide a current index of the actual number of employees in the District organization and its various divisions and branches and their classifications.

Also in February 1942 there was established a Training Section with Ray P. Farrington, one time P. O. D. Chief Inspector, and Ferd J. Stackel sharing the responsibilities with, of course, the capable assistance of Lydia Walcott. Later, when the Branch had moved back to 150 South Broad Street and Ferd Stackel had "marched off to the wars," the training job passed to Berith S. Frommer.

Earlier, 15 December 1941, a class for inspectors was conducted in the District Office. This covered a period of three weeks and included such subjects as blueprint reading and theory, and use of gages. Ten of the eleven students taking this course completed their subjects.

Training courses at the six manufacturing arsenals were begun as far back as July 1940. Of 41 inspectors hired about that time by P. O. D., seven were sent to Rock Island, 13 to Picatinny, five to Watertown, five to Watervliet and 11 to Frankford. To the end of 1942 the Arsenals had provided training for 269 P. O. D.-S elected inspectors. Of this number 76 were returned for advanced and special training. And the totals grew as the need increased.

Later there were set up Junior Inspectors Training Courses; Vocational School Courses for Minor Engineering Aides and Minor Inspectors; Training Courses for Inspectors of Welding; Training Courses for Gage Checkers; Courses for Field Personnel; Supervisory Training Courses; Packaging and Carloading Courses; Arsenal Training Courses for Junior Clerks. And subsequently numerous special courses, among them, Payroll Machine Operation, Termination and Price Adjustment Accounting, and other accounting subjects; Production Follow-up and Expediting Course, Termination Negotiation, among others.

The Appointment Section was an April 1942 development, set up to handle all actions in reference to the Civilian 201 Folders—with attention to appointments, transfers and reinstatements. Among those who at one time or another ably served the Section were Mary Sutcliffe, Madeline

Biel, Dorothy M. Bauerle and Mary Tunny and Eunice M. Gallagher.

Also in April 1942 first appeared the Separations Section. Here we find Florence M. Long. Its main duties were concerned with paper work involving: resignations with or without prejudice; discharges with or without prejudice; furloughs for military duty; transfers to other Government agencies and leaves of absence without pay.

The Safety Section was another April innovation and the special charge of the "big man" himself, Captain Jack Carson, whose duties embraced:

1. Reference to medical facilities of employees injured in the course of duty
2. Submission to United States Employees Compensation Commission of reports on each injury resulting in a claim against the Commission
3. Submission to the Office of the Chief of Ordnance of reports on disabling injuries and a monthly summary of all injuries
4. The investigation of accidents to determine which safety measures were in effect at the time of injuries, and what measures were to be taken to prevent recurrence.

For first aid cases there was set up a Dispensary with Mary Lenny, Registered Nurse, in charge. Mary will long be well remembered for her skill, her patience and her friendliness in her relations with P. O. D. personnel.

The next following unit to dot the Civilian Personnel Branch organization chart was the File Section, established in August 1942. Here all mail for the Branch was received, stamped with the receiving date, sorted and distributed. Here too, Civilian 201 Folders came to rest, arranged for ready reference.

And in the Files Section at the time of this writing were such easily remembered personalities as Mary McCabe, Margaret "Peg" Dougherty, Lilian Bondi, Kay Staats, Mary Montgomery and Olga M. Cyza.

The Job Analysis Section of the Branch was launched in the Summer of 1942—in August. Its functions: The investigation, analysis, comparison and allocation of positions, i. e., appointments and reclassifications of P. O. D. civilian personnel, and the maintenance of classification records. Job descriptions and evaluations, as ordered by higher authority, were other responsibilities. Associated with the work of this Section were Mary McCabe, once of "files"; Sadie Ayer, Elsie M. De Camp, who later established her own fashion design studio in fashionable Red Bank, New Jersey; Anna O. Williams and Margaret S. Sheppard on Classifications; Andrea Farnese, and from time to time the special assistance of others.

In due course a War Bond Section found root in Civilian Personnel, where it thrived, as well it might under the driving force of two very energetic ladies, Mrs. Lela R. Friel and Dorothy Wall, who short months before had captured, hands down, a Delaware County Beauty Parade award.

Others pleasantly remembered who served the Branch are Roberta Hedrick, secretary to Captain Carson, a chief contributor to *Time Fuze Magazine* and quippist extraordinary; Helen B. McNally, the District songbird who served Captain Derickson, appointed in June 1942, assistant to Captain Carson, as secretary. Helen was always active in the Employees Association, in Welfare, as Secretary of the Civilian Suggestions and Awards Committee; and later, in addition, Secretary of the Board of Awards, and of meetings held by various of H. Paul Gant's P. O. D. enterprises. We recall, too, the always smiling Ann Kennelly, receptionist, who later was assigned to the Development Visualization Branch,* a P. O. D. attached unit.

A word about Captain John H. Derickson, Jr.: "Dutch" arrived in P. O. D. 7 June 1942, a First Lieutenant, and was immediately assigned to the Civilian Personnel Branch. His college was Randolph Macon, his year 1927. In April 1943 he was assigned as representative on the Employees District Committee of the District Chief. A further additional duty assigned 7 October 1943 was as assistant to the Chief of the Audit Section. His captaincy came along 17 December 1943. In July 1944 he moved up to Bethlehem as Assistant to the officer-in-charge of the Regional Office; was named officer-in-charge, 18 December 1945, and 5 February 1946, lost no time in checking in at Indiantown Gap.

"Induction into the Armed Forces" . . . was a problem of major dimensions back through 1942 and 1943. The District Office as well as industry was critically affected. The following brief table

gives one indication of what was happening at this time to P. O. D. personnel:

	Jan. 1943	Feb. 1943	Mar. 1943
1. Inducted into Armed Forces	80	84	60
2. Employed by private industry	72	26	20
3. Left because of insufficient pay	11	4	5
4. Discharged	25	14	11

The loss over the space of war to the Armed Forces of P. O. D. personnel was in excess of 1,000, among which were impressive enlistments in the WACS and the WAVES.

The number of inductions reflected the fact that all men in P. O. D. eligible for A1 classification were being drafted. To provide for an orderly withdrawal of manpower, the Branch, in conjunction with the Labor Section, asked permission for compiling manning tables.

The effect of the action of the Civil Service Commission and the War Manpower Commission in preventing "shifting" from one job to another, soon was reflected in the substantial curtailment in the number of employees leaving for work in private industry. And by employing a process of "sifting," and by assigning personnel to their highest skills the Branch was able over this period to maintain at low level the number of discharges, and the total of dissatisfied persons resigning for such reasons as insufficient pay.

In April 1943, the Civilian Personnel Branch ceased to be a unit of the General Office Division, and was made a staff function reporting through the Executive Office, Lt. Colonel Robert G. Allen, to the District Chief, Brigadier General, then Colonel David N. Hauseman. The purpose of this switch was to enable the Branch to work directly with other Branches and divisions.

There also were changes in the Branch itself: Placements, now the charge of Captain John H. Derickson, Jr., included such functions as: Recruitment, Appointments, Exit Interviews, Occupational Deferment and Sub-Office Relations.

Employee Forecasts and Analysis under the Branch Chief encompassed Job Analysis, Reclassifications, Merit Increases, Research and Statistics. Employee Records still were the re-

*This finally became known as the Editorial Unit, Research and Development Service, O. C. O.

sponsibility of Helen V. Meehan and included (for the Branch) jurisdiction of the typing and stenographic pool and the clerical pool.

Employees Services also still were Captain Carson's charge. They included War Bonds, Health and Safety, Employee Counselling, and Grievances. Captain Carson, now War Bond Officer, was assigned supervision of training activities.

The Job Analysis Unit was beginning to feel the pressure. In April 1943 there were processed 313 reclassifications; in May, 261, and in June, 271. War Bonds, too, were responding to the urge. In March 1943 the records indicated 84.5 per cent of personnel participating to seven per cent of payroll; April, 88.9 per cent, to seven per cent of payroll; May, 96.4 per cent to eight per cent of payroll, and, in June 1943, 93.5 per cent of personnel to nine per cent of payroll.

The Third War Loan Drive was initiated in September 1943, achieving a total, over-the-counter cash participation of $135,000, for a maturity value of $169,950, and in reach of its goal in P. O. D. of a participation of 90 per cent, for 10 per cent of gross pay.

It was in August of 1943 that machinery was put in motion in the District to encourage personnel to suggest ways and means of saving money, materials and time, expedite production, improve methods, machines and end items, and otherwise assist the war effort.

In his Office Memorandum No. 108, dated 5 August 1943, Colonel Hauseman pointed out that:

"It is the policy of the War Department to solicit actively, suggestions from all its employees as to practical ways and means for increasing the quantity and quality of performance, for eliminating unessential methods, records or procedures; for simplifying routine; for improving safety practices, and for new or improved devices for war materiel.

"In order to stimulate continued participation and to award appropriately those civilians whose suggestions are adopted, Congress has authorized payment of cash awards of not less than $5.00 and not more than $250.00, by the Act of 18 March 1943 (Public Law II, 78th Congress), and also meritorious within-grade salary increases for unusual

and outstanding performance under Public Law 20, 77th Congress.

In accordance with the policy indicated there was established a P. O. D. Committee on Civilian Awards, and serving on it, O. Howard Wolfe, Chief, General Office Division, C. Jared Ingersoll, Deputy District Chief, and Colonel, then Major A. Donald Kelso, Chief, Sub-Office Administration Division.

The first ceremony attending the award of service emblems for civilian service was held 8 December 1943 and was designated Civilian Awards Day in accordance with ASF Circular No. 131, dated 26 November 1943. The awards were for six months of satisfactory service. Those eligible for Exceptional and for Meritorious Civilian Service Awards would be scheduled for a later period.

The first WAC Detachment to reach P. O. D. reported 31 December 1943, following arrangements earlier made with Captain Elizabeth Roche for the assignment of 34 women to the Philadelphia Ammunition Supply Office. As of the end of the month, one officer, Lieutenant Rena Friedman, and sixteen enlisted women had reported.

January 17, 1944—The opening of the Fourth War Loan Drive. To prepare for this drive, and to develop means by which personnel might be encouraged to increase the total of their payroll deductions to 15 per cent of gross pay, there was held, 12 January 1944, a meeting of the principal Minute Men of the District. Various plans were devised. To the wind-up of the drive, 29 February 1944, participation had reached a high of 97 per cent, to 12.2 per cent of payroll.

"It pays to THINK," as fifteen P. O. D. personnel were to learn during January 1944 and March 1944 when the first large hauls of cash awards were brought in. The fortunate ones included: Merrill A. Conn, Fred T. Corleto, Ruth F. Milligan, Mary E. Mallon, Evelyn S. Duncan, Abraham Marcus, Karleen A. Nash, Turley Van Briggle, Clinton G. Reed, H. H. Plowfield, Gladys B. Kovesy, L. L. Hepburn, Alvin R. Almquist, Berith S. Frommer and Helen B. McNally.

Under the impetus of a sustained drive for suggestions in the Central Office, the Regional and Inspection Offices, into mid-1946, there came to the Committee many ideas which proved of value. There was received a total of close to 2,000 suggestions, of which 216 proved acceptable and were awarded to a total of $5,562.50. Savings to Government, provided all acceptable suggestions were put to work, would have been approximately of $800,000.00 per annum.

It was ordered in January 1944 by the Chief of the Civilian Personnel Branch that there be made a survey of all jobs in the District. The Control Board concurred. The groundwork for the survey was laid within the month. A member of the Classification Staff, William McCutcheon, Office, Chief of Ordnance, visited P. O. D. for a meeting with Lt. Colonel, then Major, Henry W. Gadsden, Executive Officer; Major Joseph C. Hoffman, Chief, Fiscal Branch; Captain Jack Carson, Civilian Branch Chief, and Sam McClenahan of the Regional Office Division, for the purpose of planning the survey. On 1 February all reclassifications were frozen and the survey got under way. During February, classification analysts of the Branch visited all P. O. D. Branches and field offices. On 29 February charts covering the survey were submitted to the District Chief via the Control Officer, Major W. L. Lafean, Jr. Representatives of the Classification Section, O. C. O., arrived in the District, 10 March, to review the charts, and to set up and allocate positions. One hundred and one classifications were processed within the month.

In preparation for the work of the O. C. O. reviewers, District analysts had developed functional charts for every unit, reviewed job description questionnaires and tentatively allocated positions. Mrs. Mary McCabe and Mrs. Anne Williams of the Branch were in charge of clerical and administrative positions. Miss Elsie De Camp and Mrs. Margaret Sheppard, also of the Branch, were in charge of inspection positions.

On 6 January 1944, the first of a series of Terminations Forum meetings was held; the purpose, to create an awareness in the thinking of P. O. D. personnel of the job which eventually would be on their doorstep and, as well, to open avenues of reliable data bearing upon the whole subject.

Motion pictures now were being employed to provide personnel with "close-ups" of the work of our Government and the progress of the war. Also as a means of stimulating war bond sales. During January, two hours of instruction in the operation of the R. C. A., 16 mm. sound projectors were given by J. A. Niland of the Public Relations Branch; to Patrick Viola of the Ordnance Design Sub-Office; Lieutenant F. W. Boege,

Military Personnel Branch; Daniel H. Bell, Conversion Engineering Section; Gordon Bitterlich, Gage Laboratory; Cy P. Cosgrove, Ammunition Branch; Joseph Deacon, Technical Data Section; Mrs. Berith Frommer, Civilian Personnel Branch; John J. Gillespie, Artillery Branch; Elizabeth W. Smeltzer, Technical Data Section; Alymar H. Stopes, photographer, Public Relations Section, and William F. Walsh of the Ammunition Branch.

Also in January 1944, the Employee District Committee made arrangements for a number of courses of instruction in a variety of subjects to be given under the auspices of the United States Office of Education. Of the Engineering-Service-Management-War Training (ESMWT) courses then being conducted at Temple University and in two local public schools, attendance was reported of 600 P. O. D. personnel, enrolled for typing, shorthand, chemistry, languages and contract termination courses.

Early in February 1944, there was requisitioned by P. O. D. from the Civil Service Commission, 103 inspectors, principally for assignment to the Philadelphia Regional Office. Because of the then critical shortage of manpower, difficulty was encountered in obtaining suitable personnel. On 17 February, at a mass meeting held in the District Office, C. Jared Ingersoll, District Chief, appealed to employees of P. O. D. to bring in relatives and friends to help out. Response to the appeal was gratifying, but not sufficient to meet the need. Frankford Arsenal helped out by lending the District 60 inspectors. These were assigned to the E. G. Budd Manufacturing Company, Proctor Electric Company and the Philco Corporation. The loan was for a period of 30 days.

Fifteen inspectors in addition were needed in the York Regional Office for duty at Lancaster; 19 inspectors were needed in the Baltimore Regional Office. Other critical personnel requirements in February 1944 were in the Terminations Branch, for which the following requisitions were filed with the Civil Service Commission: 20 accountants (CPA's, or with equivalent experience), eight material distributing men, two market analysts and price consultants, 30 redistribution and salvage supervisors, and 20 negotiators as well as a large number of typists and stenographers.

Further recruitment problems in February were the result of designation by the District Administration Division, O. C. O., of P. O. D. as a Recruiting Office for positions in Washington. Captain Carson was called to Washington with civilian personnel officers of other recruiting districts for the purpose of discussing and organizing the recruitment program. W. A. Sharpe of the Civilian Personnel Branch was sent to O. C. O. for instructions on recruiting. The District subsequently was divided into a Northern Section and a Southern Section—the former taking in Pennsylvania, New Jersey, Maryland and Delaware, the latter Virginia and North and South Carolina. However, on 15 March, the recruiting program was temporarily suspended on orders from O. C. O. but in view of pressing needs in P. O. D. interviewers were instructed to continue active recruiting.

As part of a health inspection drive, particularly in reference to tubercular symptoms, there was conducted 6–7–8 March 1944 under sponsorship of the Philadelphia Tuberculosis and Health Association in cooperation with the United States Health Service, X-ray examinations were made of 1,178 P. O. D. employees. Only eight of the total examined were discovered to have tuberculosis in some form, three of whom were noted to have been at one time "arrested" cases.

Effective 15 May 1944, Captain John H. Carson, Branch Chief since July 1940, was assigned to active field service. He had seen his charge grow from a personnel total when he took over of 115 persons, to a District high in October 1942 of 4,149 civilian employees. His most active month was August 1942 when 475 civilians were sworn in, of which 75 were sworn in during one eight hour day. Successor was Sam McClenahan, formerly in charge of Administration in the Industrial Division. On 8 May Captain John H. Derickson, Jr., was transferred to Bethlehem. He was succeeded by Captain, then Lieutenant, Philip J. Fields, formerly Chief, Communications Section (Mail and Records), Administration Branch. On 26 June, Captain Fields was transferred to the Baldwin Locomotive Works Inspection Office. His place was taken by John J. Wood, formerly Administrative Chief, Chester Tank Depot. His new duties embraced supervision of appointments, recruitment, transfer and separations. In May, '44 John Wood was named Assistant Chief of the Branch.

Allocations of jobs under the Classification Survey begun in March 1944 were printed and distributed 15 April 1944. At a meeting, called 18

April 1944, Lt. Col., then Major Henry W. Gadsden, Executive Officer, explained the background factors of the survey and the methods to be employed in presentation to employees of the results obtained. Chiefs and officers-in-charge were instructed to interview personally each employee, discussing with him his present and future possibilities under the survey. Recommendations then would be made of those Reclassifications actions to become effective as of 16 April. To the end of May, job descriptions were written of 2,408 positions reviewed during the survey. Two hundred and thirty-seven reclassifications were made effective during the survey period.

Personnel total at the end of May 1944, stood at 3,378.

Under the direction of J. J. Gordon there was initiated a Personnel Utilization Program; its purpose, the full and proper utilization of clerical and stenographic employes, it being District policy to use to full advantage the efforts of employes within the District before requisitioning additional personnel. At the then present time the type of personnel recruited through Civil Service was not of satisfactory grade and the Branch therefore had of necessity to rely on referrals of members of P. O. D.

As of 31 July the District had attained 153 per cent of its quota set for the Ffth War Loan Drive with a total in cash sales (cost value) of $128,058.50. At the time, 98.8 per cent of personnel total was participating to 13 per cent of payroll.

October 24, 1944 saw the initiation in P. O. D. of the 1944 United War Chest Drive. Rallies led by C. Jared Ingersoll, District Chief, were held in headquarters at 150 South Broad Street, and at 1420 Walnut Street. The quota for the Philadelphia Ordnance District was set at $11,000.00 Employes were asked to contribute one hour's pay per month for 10 months. Response was hearty— and the quota made.

The Sixth War Loan Drive was initiated 22 November 1944 in P. O. D. Quota was marked up at $122,000.00. The drive was opened with a series of rallies held in the District auditorium. A representative of the Treasury Department introduced to the gatherings Lieutenant James E. Oyer and Lieutenant William M. Middledorf of the Army Air Forces, presently back in U. S. following distinguished service as Flying Fortress pilots. The officers told of their harrowing experience and made earnest pleas for success of the drive. Local talent in the persons of Elizabeth Zerone of the Tank-Automotive Branch; Betty Dawson and Mary L. McGonigle of the Property Branch, and Margaret B. "Peggy" Dougherty of the Civilian Personnel Branch sang appropriate selections. By the end of the drive, 31 December 1944, the District had met and exceeded its quota. Sales were to a total of $126,098.50, or 103.4 per cent of the goal set.

A ceremony held in November 1944 in the "front office" was for the award to Helen V. Meehan of a service ribbon indicating 25 years of continuous service to the War Department, all of which time had been spent with the Philadelphia Ordnance District. The award of the ribbon and a special certificate, was made by C. Jared Ingersoll, District Chief.

Efficiency rating work in P. O. D. continued into 1945. The first quarterly rating was completed in February. A total of 2,995 civilians had been rated. Three hundred eighty-two rating officials (Branch and Section Chiefs) and 66 reviewing officials (topside) had participated in the rating work. The result was that, on a District basis, 15 per cent of the personnel total were rated "Excellent," 49 per cent were rated "Very Good," 30 per cent rated "Good," five per cent "Fair," and one per cent rated "Unsatisfactory." The rating served an excellent purpose in that it gave "raters" and "reviewers" opportunity to gain experience prior to the official rating which would take place as of 31 March 1945.

To assist personnel in solving personal problems, differences, and all the other happenstances that come to upset tranquility, or to impose hurdles of one kind and another, there was formulated in January 1945 in the Branch a counselling service, to be the special project of a senior counsellor.

And this was a time of "Give for Humanity and for Victory." The Red Cross Drive was gotten under way in February. While an official quota for P. O. D. had not been established, it was suggested that each employe give $5.00. The drive came to an end late in March with the District not doing badly with its contribution of $5,541.64. Followed, the Infantile Paralysis Fund Drive, sponsored by the Welfare Section. Collections were of $914.00.

Came another donation, this one to be felt throughout the District area in increased production. This donation was made in January; Sunday, January 21, when hundreds of P. O. D. personnel

came in without cost to Uncle Samuel to do a day's work. This noble gesture, and such it was, came following a suggestion made by Bill Dorsey of Ammunition who saw in it a challenge to industry and to other Government agencies. Even out in the Regional Offices the lads and ladies came trooping in. The "press" went all-out in laudations. Industry perked up and sent congratulations. It was great "public relations."

Considerable progress was made in January 1945 in the Civilian Personnel Branch in eliminating excess files and records. Too, there were combinations of files, a work which was to continue to and beyond the end of the war. Progress was made in the establishment of the utilization file which would make available for quick reference the skills of all employes of the District. Another file in the development stage was the Retention in Force File which later would be used for retrenchment purposes when reduction in force should be necessary.

In March 1945 came from the War Department new regulations in reference to occupational deferments which now could be requested only under conditions: Deferments would not now be granted to employes under 26 years of age who appeared acceptable for military service; employees of from 26 to 29 years of age could be approved for deferment only when all four of the following conditions should be met:

1. Replacement was not possible.
2. Employee's service necessary to the successful operation of his station.
3. His occupational classified as a critical activity as designated by the War Manpower Commission.
4. Employee's skill acquired only after a long period of training or experience and in substantial part prior to 7 December 1941.

Employees 30–33 years of age inclusive not known to be disqualified for general military service, deferment would be granted only if employee was necessary to and regularly employed in an activity in war production or in support of the national health, safety or other critical interest.

Employees 34–37 years of age inclusive not known to be disqualified for general military service; deferment would be on same basis as men in 30–33 years group.

On the basis of the foregoing outlined regulations 85 per cent of the physically qualified men in P. O. D. between the ages of 26 and 29 years of age were being classified 1-A and would, it was believed, be inducted by the Armed Services within the next following two months period.

Something new was added back in April 1945 to Branch activity. To satisfy personnel needs which might have developed as a result of the then initiated "no hiring" policy the Branch had been charged with the responsibility of establishing and maintaining an "In Service" placement program whose duty it became to ascertain the over-all personnel needs of the District; to locate employees in scarce-skill categories; to obtain maximum qualitative utilization of manpower through post-placement evaluation and follow-up; all of which data would be employed for purposes of reassignment, promotion, training and dismissal of employees.

A preliminary step involved individual interviews at which times brief "skills" questionnaires were completed, and evaluations subsequently made by each Branch or Section Chief of job performances of employees within his jurisdiction. Data thus obtained to be recorded on cards arranged in reference to skills.

The "In Service" Placement Section, organized for the "skills" census, was placed under the direction of John J. Wood, Assistant Chief of the Civilian Personnel Branch, assisted by Howard Biles, one time of the Eddystone Regional Office and Mrs. Elizabeth Farnum. Howard Biles was replaced as Administrative Chief by Catherine C. Conroy. The "no hiring" policy was continued through June 1945, with the one reservation that jobs which could not be filled from the "skills" file would necessarily be filled from outside sources.

The District received in May 1945 a visit by a survey team of the War Department Manpower Commission. The Branch was required during this visit to furnish to the operating Branches of P. O. D. a considerable volume of statistical data by way of assisting those Branches in preparing reports covering their respective activities. In addition the Civilian Personnel Branch was required to furnish the survey team with statistics covering District personnel activities over the then preceding years, or year and a half. No sooner had this Survey team departed than came another; this one from the Control Branch, Office of Director of Personnel, O. C. O. This team, consisting of two captains, spent 10 days in the District investigating the activities of the Branch and personnel administration policies of the District.

New files came into use. In May 1945 there was set up a position classification and assignment file which then presently was being maintained in the Classification Section. This file carried records of all civilian employees in the District and Regional offices. All promotions and reassignments were to be checked against this file.

The Official Regular Efficiency Rating was begun 1 April, and covered the period 1 April 1944 through 31 March 1945. A total of 3,138 graded employees and 103 ungraded employees were rated. Completion was 1 May, which was considerably earlier than in previous years. Several ratings were appealed.

Quota for the 7th War Loan Drive begun in April was set at $153,759.93. Although this figure at first appeared to be high, it actually was no more than $131,000.00 And as usual, P. O. D. made its quota. The application to the drive total of all payroll deductions for the period of the drive explains the latter figure. In May, there was set up in the lobby at 150 South Broad Street, a War Bond Sales Desk. To the end of the sales drive were to a total of $27,206.65.

A Salvation Army Annual Drive for funds, initiated in April 1945 accounted for $1,154.31, representing an increase over 1944 of $447.86.

Passage in July 1945 by the 79th Congress of the new Pay Bill resulted in the processing by the Classification Section of an extraordinary number of promotions. The change of regulations for the "time-in-grade" requirements and for "within grade" requirements from 18 months and 32 months to 12 and 18 months respectively resulted in an exceptionally large number of eligibles. Actions taken, including promotions, within grade promotions and reassignments were to a total of 1,045.

In July 1945 a new Chairman was appointed to the Committee on Suggestions and Awards— Major Joseph C. Hoffman, Chief, Control Branch, succeeding H. Paul Gant, who had left the District Office. Members were Captain Lewis A. Smith, Jr., Samuel McClenahan, and Helen B. McNally, Secretary.

A Job Instructor Institute to train instructors in JIT was held, 25 July, in the District Office. Attending were:
W. J. Cowan, Fiscal Branch
Lt. J. J. Law, Jr., Purchase Branch
R. W. Jones, Industrial Division

Berith Frommer, Civilian Personnel, Training Section

A. Q. Beaty, York Regional Office

Charles Albert, Bethlehem Regional Office

George Wallace, Philadelphia Regional Office

Merle G. James, Richmond Regional Office

Joseph L. Lee, Baltimore Regional Office

Then VJ Day, with a sudden burst of new activity in the Civilian Personnel Branch. The President declared 15–16 August a two day Victory holiday, not to be charged to annual leave. There were revised calculations of Retention of Staff records. There was a substantial upswing in the preparation of notices of separation for Reduction in Force in the Regional Offices. A total of 104 employees were separated effective 31 August 1945. At the same time 500 other personnel were being processed for separation within six weeks.

Victory also had its impact upon the operations of the "In Service" Placement Section, forcing certain changes in Section policy. For instance, it was deemed advisable to discontinue all field reviews until conditions in the District should become stabilized. The Section was principally engaged during this period in the reassignment of personnel declared excess by operating Branches.

Seven Meritorious Civilian Service Ribbons and Citations were awarded in August to P. O. D. personnel. The presentations were made by the District Chief, Colonel A. Donald Kelso. Citations by Lieutenant General Brehon S. Somervell, Commanding General of the Army Service Forces, and Lieutenant General Levin H. Campbell, Jr., Chief or Ordnance, were awarded the following:

William E. Gilbert—Expediting Production

Marie M. Jackson—Improved work methods in the Legal Branch

Mary R. Lenny—P. O. D. Nurse

Samuel McClenahan—Administration of Personnel

Sidney S. Press—Efficiency in Property Disposal Administration

William P. Schmid—Aid to Production

Eleanor Armstrong—Ace Receptionist

In October 1945 other P. O. D. personnel similarly were awarded. This time the citations bore the signatures of Lieutenant General Brehon H. Somerville and Major General Henry B. Sayler, Acting Chief of Ordnance. Presentations again were made by Colonel Kelso. This time, those honored were:

H. Paul Gant—Accomplishments in Procurement

John C. Swartley—Efficient Performance in Purchase

French E. Dennison—Inspection Administration

Harry V. Ayres—Outstanding work in the Philadelphia Regional Office

Thomas W. Beattie—Tank-Automotive Branch Activities

John W. Magoun—Performance at Chester Tank Depot

Robert T. Gebler—Historian

In December 1945, Meritorious Civilian Service Awards were presented by Colonel Kelso to Martin Sandler, long of the Purchase Branch and later of the Purchase-Terminations Division, and John O'Rourke, for outstanding service in the Artillery Branch. And in line with the wishes of Lieutenant General Levin H. Campbell, Jr., Colonel Kelso presented Certificates of Commendation to many personnel of the District who had given their best to the Ordnance effort. They included:

Property Disposal Branch

John McDowell	George Kazansky
Nicholas Mirras	Cecelia McNamara
Manuel Cole	

Price Adjustment Branch

W. M. McKee	T. G. Aspinwall
H. N. Rodenbaugh	H. G. Stewart
John H. Fassett	

Legal Branch

Agnes Stetson

Fiscal Branch

A. M. Fitzgerald	H. L. Wilson
R. C. Boreth	H. D. Magdelinskas
Mary E. Henrich	

Property Branch

S. S. Horner	Albert Donahue

Terminations Branch

B. J. Minnier	E. S. Duncan
P. W. Williams	C. W. Graves
Frederick D. Sarkis	

Ammunition Branch

C. P. Cosgrove	W. J. Dorsey
W. F. Walsh	C. F. Kemper
F. D. Mensing	Julius Gussman

Administration Branch

V. W. Strohlein   W. R. Johnson

Artillery-Small Arms Branch

D. P. McIntire   C. L. Goodrich

Production Service Branch

D. H. Bell   B. C. Bell
W. J. Jefferies   R. J. Bothwell
H. E. Snyder   Caleb F. Fox III
        H. R. Battersby, Jr.

Tank-Automotive Branch

H. B. LaRue   L. H. Seipp
        A. J. Volmer

Miscellaneous Branches

G. T. Francis, Jr.   H. V. Meehan
J. J. Wood   A. H. Ragni
R. E. Kuhn   E. R. Tucker
R. M. Keator   M. R. Gardiner
M. E. Quigley   L. C. Purdey
C. P. Webb   W. A. Martel
S. D. Bass   C. C. Moss

Richmond Regional Office

M. G. James   R. F. Jones

Baltimore Regional Office

R. E. Layton   J. S. Lee
        W. H. Hefgen

Bethlehem Regional Office

C. V. Peterson   J. S. Rodgers
R. W. Kolb   G. A. Baumer

Philadelphia Regional Office

H. D. Goldberg   C. L. Phillipi
Harry Allison   E. B. Hatch
        R. F. Meyers

York Regional Office

W. W. Henry, Jr.   A. Q. Beaty
W. T. Metzger   P. E. More
        M. C. Stapleford

Military Personnel

Major Rutledge Slattery
Major Charles W. Sørber
Major William L. Stephens, Jr.
Major W. Fred Feustel
Major Oliver C. Conger
Major Wilbur L. Lafean, Jr.
Major Joseph I. Wexlin
Major Welles H. Denney
Major Joseph M. Baxter
Major Eugene H. Uhler
Major E. W. Lafferty
Major John H. Beyer
Major Roland C. Disney
Major Paul H. Carlson
Major Homes C. Case
Major Joseph L. Wilmsen
Major Arthur B. Allison
Captain Bernard M. Zimmerman
Captain R. Gerard Palmer
Captain William F. Rathgeber, Jr.
Captain Lewis A. Smith, Jr.
Captain Oliver K. Hearte, Jr.
Captain Neal W. Slack
Captain James H. Nisbet
Captain Walter T. Young
Captain Walter E. English
Captain William S. Canning
Captain William A. Dilks
Captain Maynard H. Patterson
Captain James L. Mingle
Captain Edwin G. Chambers
Captain Cecil Bentley
Captain Robert D. Scarlett
Captain Lawrence B. Redmond
Captain Richard A. Furniss
Captain Norman L. Cavedo
Lieutenant Robert O. Watson

Following separations and resignations, the result of VJ Day cessations, the P. O. D. personnel total, as of 30 September, had dropped to 1,635 employees. As of 31 October, the decline had been to 1,580; 31 November, to 1,369, and to 31 December, to 1,057 employees. A particularly acute problem during the Reduction in Force Program was that of maintaining high employee morale. The Welfare Section stepped into the emergency, enlarging its recreational facilities and activities, including a Victory Party and Dance, 14 September 1945 at Town Hall. And although enthusiasm for the job had waned here and there, War Bond Sales participation remained at a high level. Civilians were participating at a level of 96.5 per cent, to 13.0 per cent of payroll; enlisted men, at 8 per cent to a total of $506.25; and officers at 62.5 per cent, to a total of $4,837.50 for the month. In October, civilian participation was at 98.0 of payroll; enlisted men still at 87 per cent, to a total of $480.00, and officers at 80 per cent, to a total of $3,375.00. In November, civilians were participating at the 97.6 per cent level, to 11.2 per cent of payroll; enlisted men at 87 per cent, to a total of $480.00; and officers at 81.0 per cent to a total of $2,837.00. Closing the year, in December, approximately the same percentages obtained. Payroll deductions in December 1945 were $72,748.75; cash purchases, $24,128.75.

In October 1945, the Training Section came to the end of the road. Hereafter, all training would be on the job.

October was a busy month for the Classification Analysts, four of whom were assigned temporarily to work through a period of three weeks with an analyst of O. C. O. in establishing and allocating positions following the conversions to a Field Service Depot of the Pottstown Ordnance Plant. The remaining week was given to a similar task at the American Car & Foundry Company, Berwick, Inspection Office.

It became necessary in October and through November 1945 to "monitor" a number of employees with "Veteran Preference," those with permanent status, and veterans returning from World War II seeking their former positions. Many of those then presently employed soon would be reached on separation lists. It was necessary to contact other War Department installations so that as many as possible of these persons might be placed. Approximately 120 employees were "monitored" during the two months. When positions were not available for veterans holding a permanent appointment, the completed file was forwarded to the Secretary of War for action. Those employees holding a War Service Indefinite Appointment were referred to the Civil Service Commission for possible vacancies.

Practically all Civilian Personnel Branch activity during the year-end period bore upon two major problems, (1) reduction in force, and (2) the returning veteran. Fortunately for one phase of the general problem the District had early in 1945 recognized the fact that the end of the war would call for drastic reductions in staff and had prepared itself accordingly. For this reason it was possible, at the proper time, to cut back the civilian strength without serious hindrance to the job yet to be done.

The problems arising in connection with the employment of veterans were somewhat more serious. There had been more than 1,000 P. O. D. employees on military furlough from the District. Approximately 400 had exercised their reemployment rights or had made known the fact that they would not exercise them. The District, however, was unable to re-employ during the period any of its veterans for the reason that all positions for which men appeared to be qualified either had been or were about to be eliminated, hence the necessity for monitoring these men to other War Department agencies.

In November 1945, all employees at the Cressona Ordnance Plant assigned at that time accepted transfer to the Cressona Ordnance Depot, of the Field Service which, on 18 November became successor to the Cressona operation.

We now are into 1946 with the personnel barometer dropping lower and lower. For instance, in January, there were 365 separations against a low of 18 appointments; February, 207 against 16; March, 120 against 15; April, 111 against 7; May, 92 against 1; and in June 1946, 92 separations as compared to one appointment.

In January 1946 came again the Infantile Paralysis Campaign Fund with personnel contributing $243.10; blood tests, as a phase of Philadelphia's drive against VD, with 273 persons taking advantage of the free tests offered P. O. D. personnel and, finally, in January, the Annual Victory Clothing drive to provide wearing apparel for people in the destitution areas of Europe. In February, the Red Cross Drive, with P. O. Ders turning in $461.68; and a mid-winter dance at the Stephen Girard Hotel attended by 800 persons; and to wind up the month, the Salvation Army Drive which netted $207.25.

At the beginning of the year, the activities of the Classification Section of the Civilian Personnel Branch were largely confined to the task of obtaining classification information from Branches and other divisions throughout the District; and arranging this date for a report requested by the then District Chief, Colonel J. P. Harris. The final report was prepared by the Records Section. Data obtained were to be used with regard to the establishment of positions are required by the proposed plan of organization of the District for peace-time service.

Though the war now was far behind us, and P. O. Ders moving out by the dozens, the District Employee Association was holding on tightly. A meeting was held, 27 May, with top-man William F. Walsh appointing a nomination committee whose duty it would be to report good timber for consideration at the semi-annual meeting to be held 7 June. Cy Cosgrove was appointed Chairman; Anna Ragni and Agnes Stetson, members. The following subsequently were nominated and elected:

Anna M. Almeida—Administration Branch
Charlotte Burkhardt—Fiscal Branch
Katherine Byrnes—Price Adjustment Branch
Cyril Cosgrove—Industrial Division
Anna H. Ragni—Administration Branch

Agnes C. Stetson—Legal Branch
Joseph W. Stone—Administration Branch
Harold Turtle—Property Branch

At the first meeting, held 17 June 1946, the following were elected:

Cyril Cosgrove—President
Joseph W. Stone—Vice President
Agnes C. Stetson—Recording Secretary

Anna Ragni was appointed by the District Chief, Colonel Gordon B. Welch, to serve as Executive Secretary and Treasurer.

A swimming party at Somerton Springs Pool followed by a few days the election of officers.

And so, at this point we say a reluctant farewell to the Civilian Personnel Branch, at least until the next war which . . . well, you know the usual hope. To Catherine Conroy, who has carried on since 23 March 1946 in the sturdy boots of Sam McClenahan, we make a pretty bow.

P. O. D. population? Exactly 166. It seems only yesterday that there were more than 4,100 of us.

Group of civilian personnel receives "Suggestion" Awards from District Chief, C. Jared Ingersoll. Others, L. to R: Executive Officer, Major Henry W. Gadsen, H. Paul Gant, Captain Lewis A Smith and French De Ennison.

Chapter XIX

MORE HORIZONS

A SUCCESSION of "good men and true" contributed to the history of gages in P. O. D.: Edward H. Cahill, James N. Kuntz, Clinton Vernon, Lew L. Rittenhouse, W. H. Vogelsberg, Robert O. Watson and not overlooking Charles O. Guernsey and William H. Stephens, Jr.

The Gage Laboratory had its beginning in the Philadelphia Ordnance District, 26 August 1940, when two civilians were hired to check gages. They soon were sent to Watervliet Arsenal for a six weeks' training course in Ordnance gage system and procedure which embraced gage checking and Ordnance inspection. The two civilians were assigned during this period to the Sub-Office Administration Division of the District. These were Harry L. Landauer and William Benat.

The Gage Section, including the Gage Laboratory, was established in January 1941, with Major, then Captain, Edward H. Cahill as Chief, with the two civilians as assistants. Captain Clinton M. Vernon was assigned 2 February 1942, relieving Captain Cahill.

Successor to Captain Cahill was Captain Clinton M. Vernon, whose natal residence in U. S. A. was Middletown, New York. His first contact with Army Service, following Ordnance School during December 1940, was that of Adjutant, then Company Commander, First Battalion, Ordnance Replacement Center. On 8 May 1941 he was assigned Company Commander, 82nd Ordnance Company, Fourth Army, Fort Ord, California. The Captain got under way in P. O. D. 11 November 1941 for one year of extended active duty following a request earlier made by Colonel Hauseman that he be assigned to the District for duty at the Reading Sub-Office. Upon reassignment 29 November 1941 of the then Captain Victor W. Smith, as Chief, Executive Division, and his appointment as Chief of the newly formed Philadelphia Sub-Office, Captain Vernon was assigned to the vacated Executive Division post. On 1 January 1942, he was ordered to the York Sub-Office for temporary duty in reference to procurement, and on 29 January 1942 he was transferred, now as Surveying Officer, to the Baldwin Locomotive Works, for inspection of the wooden model of the Medium M3 Tank, thence to the Birdsboro Steel Foundry & Machine Company—and on 2 February 1942 to his eventual post of Gage Chief. As of 30 September 1942 the Captain was relieved of his duties as Chief of the Gage Section and assigned to the Military Personnel Section. On 25 November 1942 he was relieved of all duties in P. O. D.

When appeared, in October 1942, in the Gage Laboratory, crying need for a property officer, choice logically was of Walter H. Vogelsberg, who only a few months before had emerged from Lehigh University with a lot of ROTC "know how," a B.S., diploma under his arm and a lot of first rate determination under his hat. Walt, commissioned 5 November 1941, a Second Lieutenant, was assigned 22 February 1942 as assistant in the Laboratory. On 11 October 1942 he stepped up to the Property Post which he held until 5 November 1946 and his reassignment as officer-in-charge of the Philadelphia Regional Office.

Need developed in May 1942 in the Gage Section for another officer. Selection this time was of James N. Kuntz, a product of Beaver, Pennsylvania, who came to P. O. D. a first lieutenant, 1 May 1942, on the heels of his relief as chief engineer in charge of maintenance and operation for the Department of Justice, U. S. Marshall's Office, of a one thousand ton refrigeration and air conditioning plant. Earlier, following his graduation in 1931, from Pennsylvania Military College, with his B.S., he entered the employ of Heintz Manufacturing Company, Philadelphia, Pennsylvania. It was during this period that he was commissioned a Second Lieutenant in the Officers Reserve Corps, and assigned to 316th Infantry, 79th Division, receiving his discharge 6 June 1936.

Came in due course 1 October 1942, and the

assignment as Chief of the Gage Laboratory, Lewis L. Rittenhouse, succeeding Captain Vernon. Little is known at this time of this rare personality except that he was one of the most versatile of those men who had deserted industry to serve Ordnance. Marjorie Rittenhouse, Lou's daughter, who was employed in the Packaging Section of the Office of the Chief of Inspection, was one time asked to snoop around a bit and get the lowdown on her father. It didn't work. All that she brought back, written by her father, was:

"Lew Rittenhouse lives in Merion, Pennsylvania; came to P. O. D. in June 1942, and eventually became Chief of the Gage Laboratory."

He might have added, but did not, that he came at the behest of Charles O. Guernsey, Technical Director.

At any rate Lou did right well by Gages, leaving the stage set for the next incumbent, Robert O. Watson.

With the issuance 9 September 1942 of Office Memorandum 244, gage procurement became the responsibility of the Miscellaneous Materials Branch under Major, then Captain, Welles H. Denney. The Gage Section, with Lieutenant Kuntz as Chief, was then added to the Branch.

There was no relationship between the functions of the Gage Section and those of the Gage Laboratory other than as parts of the District organization. Various attempts subsequently were made to combine in one Section a Gage Laboratory and the Administration of gage contracts, and contracts for plant expansion of gage facilities. However, separation of the two functions proved to be the more practicable. It was not until 30 December 1943 that this hurdle was got over, and the Gage Laboratory combined with the Gage Section of the Miscellaneous Materials Branch as the Gage Section, with Second Lieutenant Watson moved from his post as Chief of Raw Materials Section of the Miscellaneous Branch and placed in charge.

Gage business on the down side from VJ Day on, and Section personnel declining from its "high," in March 1945, of seventy-five persons to a grand total of two, the Gage Section was terminated as an independent unit of the Production Service Branch and assigned to the Inspection Branch of the Industrial Division. Lieutenant Bob Watson, following his release from Gage, was reassigned Survey Officer for the District, relieving Major William Eadie and Captain David H. McIlvaine, both released from Service.

It was in Cristobal that the doctor chuckled to Chief Quartermaster for the Panama Canal Zone, "Watson, it's a boy! Very likely he will grow up here through his high school years, then head for Indiana and Purdue University where he will sign up for mechanical engineering and easily straddle his B.S." And that is exactly what he did!

It was in 1940 when Bob Watson heard and responded to the P. O. D. call for experienced engineers. To supplement his ROTC training, Bob was shuffled off to Aberdeen Proving Ground for his OQ degree (Ordnance Qualifications), commissioned second lieutenant and in August 1942 shipped to the District Office.

In the midst of his duties as Chief of the Raw Materials Section of the Miscellaneous Materials Branch there came in December 1942 from Pentagon a "dead-line" order for transfer from Raritan Arsenal to Philadelphia of all Mobile Shop activities. Major Denney and Lieutenant Watson were sent to Raritan to supervise the work of transfer—a job that kept these men on the jump for up to twenty hours a day, more or less, for three full weeks.

When later arose the problems of crating the vehicles assembled in the new, Philadelphia Mobile Shop Depot (Thornton-Fuller Company) Lieutenant Watson was sent to Barclay White Company (Tioga Packing Plant) for survey work and to assume responsibility for crating at that facility.

The assignment at Barclay White Company completed, Bob was assigned coordinator on the heavy shell casings program at the Kennedy-Van Saun Manufacturing & Engineering Company, Danville, Pennsylvania. In November 1943 he was promoted to the rank of first lieutenant and assigned, in January 1944, as Chief of the Gage Section, where his duties embraced the procurement, maintenance and accountability, engineering and inspection of gages; a large order when it is considered that the requirements for one type of shell might be of thirty different gages; a fuze might require three hundred and fifty gages, and a primer percussion, thirty or more; and the record indicates a job magnificently consummated.

The story of the Gage Section would fall short of complete did we not retell here some of the tales often told of that early Chief of the Section who so ably discharged that responsibility—Major Edward H. Cahill, who, like Paul Gant and Citizen Stokes, hied himself to the solace (?) of the farm.

Before we have moved out of Gages, there is a story told of the Gage Lab's early Chief that is worthy of record: While on a tour of OD duty, Ed, so the story goes, clad only in shorts, left the OD room in the Mitten Building to investigate a noise—probably mice—when a draft blew the door closed, locking it. Ed had of necessity to walk down fourteen flights of stairs to the lobby where he found the night watchman.

"The Major had a penchant," Paul Gant recounted one day, "for so often unwittingly meeting with trouble, according to his own report. For instance, going out to lunch one day he stepped off the curb in the path of a taxicab which was backing up. He was bumped, but not enough to cause serious injury. 'I told you I was always getting into some kind of trouble,' he said. A few minutes later, during luncheon, the waiter accidentally poured water down Ed's back."

"Colonel Hauseman once told another story about Ed. It was customary, it seemed, that officers, upon leaving the building, would sign a book, indicating their destinations. One day Ed went up to Frankford Arsenal but forgot to register. He remained at the Arsenal until long past eight o'clock and never did get around to telephoning Mrs. Ed. With dinner going cold and nerves on edge, Mrs. Ed called the office only to learn that from the OD that the Major had left no record. He had completely vanished! Then she called Colonel Hauseman, demanding to know what had been done with her Major. Colonel Hauseman, thoroughly alarmed, said he would be right over. He arrived at the Cahill's just as Ed walked in as large as life; but not feeling so large next day as he left the Colonel's office."

"I can tell you another," said W. J. "Bill" Jefferies, who came to the District in 1940 to take over the responsibility of Inspection and Engineering aspects of the work under way at that time.

"I remember," he said, "the time when Major Cahill was attached to my office. He was a stickler for thoroughness in everything he touched. Once, when required to sign an important document, he put his pen down for a moment and started talking with me. While still talking, he picked up a pencil, dipped it in the ink and continued to sign his name with the pencil. He was not at all pleased with the very splotchy result.

"He was a great fellow, had a great mind, knew his business from A to Z, and made important contributions during his several important responsibilities."

Wilhelmina
Hecksher

Alfred Testa

Dorothy Stewart

Fred Sarkis

Betty Dickerman

Richard M. Keator

Chapter XX

PURCHASE

URING the early days of the Defense Aid days in P. O. D., the purchase activity was lodged in the Planning Section, and purchasing was confined to miscellaneous office supplies and incidentals apart from military requirements. Back in the late 1930's, one Ben Ayres had a hand in this, and one persistent rumor is that Ben, unable to obtain record forms through Government channels, bought his own, out of pocket.

On 19 June 1940, a memorandum outlining a concrete plan for munitions procurement and dealing with the apportioning among the various Ordnance Districts of artillery, ammunition and bomb requirements, was addressed by the Office of the Chief of Ordnance to the Assistant Secretary of War.

The Plan required the reporting within a specified time to the Office of the Chief of Ordnance of all bids obtained on the various quantities of material apportioned to the District. The actual awards were to be made in Washington and reported through the Districts to the successful bidders.

Proposals under the plan were to be obtained as the result of competitive bidding and sent to Washington within a stipulated period where they would be compared with proposals from other Districts and the most interesting selected by the Office of the Chief of Ordnance for awards.

It is important to note that the actual preliminary negotiations or the obtaining of proposals was solely the function of the District Office. The preparation of the ultimate contract also was its responsibility, but Washington actually made the award.

The new procedure continued practically unchanged until 4 April 1941, when the Purchase Section was established as a separate department in the Philadelphia Ordnance District. Before this time the Procurement Planning Section did the negotiating, and upon receipt of notification of award from the Office of the Chief of Ordnance, the Legal Division of the District executed a formal contract. Notification of award was in the form of a letter of intent, and during the period under discussion about eighteen awards, amounting to approximately $24,000,000, were made from this District Office.

The various Arsenals (Watertown, Watervliet, Rock Island, Frankford and others) were, during this period, purchasing directly most of their own requirements of Ordnance material. A directive from the Office of the Chief of Ordnance, 22 August 1940, indicated that the Arsenals were free to call upon the District offices for assistance in negotiating all contracts for their special requirements. The Arsenals soon found this policy operating to their advantage, thereafter leaning more heavily on the Districts. There was, as a result, less of misunderstanding, prices and deliveries also were better. District officers were closer to and in more frequent contact with sources of supply.

Pretty well into 1940 the Purchase activity was a responsibility of the Executive Division of P. O. D. under the administration of then Captain John W. Ogden, who doubled as Chief of the Administration Section of the Division. At that time, the Priorities Section of the Division was the charge of Captain Edward H. Cahill; the Procurement Plans Section had been assigned to First Lieutenant Eugene H. Uhler, who, in turn, supervised the activities of Thomas S. Potts on Surveys, and William A. Eadie, Jr. Lieutenant Marvin C. Jilbert was in charge of the Technical Data, Gage Check and Proving Grounds Administration Section. Major Uhler completes the set-up, as Chief, Industrial Information Section.

Caution begins to take its place in purchase procedure. On 12 May 1941 the District Central Division teletyped instructions that the contracting officer should check the financial stability of all firms whose bids were relayed to the Office of the Chief of Ordnance. It was also directed that the machine tool situation and the probable performance of each facility be carefully investigated when obtaining bids.

Some time during March 1941, the responsibility for procurement was shifted from the District Control Division of Office of the Chief of Ordnance to the various Materiel Divisions which then were the Small Arms, Ammunition, Artillery and Tank and Combat Vehicle Divisions (later the Tank-Automotive Division). Considerable confusion resulted from this change because each of these Divisions adopted a different method of procurement, and conflicting instructions were issued to the District Offices. Most of the resulting problems were referred back to the old District Control Division for solution. This condition persisted for some time, in fact almost to December 7, 1941.

On 4 April 1941 there was established an independent Purchase Section. No longer before than 1940, as noted, Purchase had been a Property Branch Activity, of the Executive Division. In 1941 we find Property Chief, Lt. Colonel, then First Lieutenant, William L. Stephens, Jr., concerned with such matters as the purchase of a typist's chair for the Wilmington office, two watercoolers for Henry Disston & Sons, and four typewriters for use at Baldwin's by the Ordnance Inspector. In addition to these "odds and ends" we note an item of 2,200 of 155 mm. shell forgings received from Taylor-Wharton Iron & Steel Company, Easton, Pennsylvania, and shipped to the Minneapolis-Moline Power Implement Company, Minneapolis, Minnesota.

On 16 April 1941, Martin Sandler, who was destined to serve the war's length as Purchase Director, joined up with P. O. D. His original berth was that of Chief of the Purchase Information Section of the Executive Division where Jack Ogden held the reins. Associated activities of this period within the division still were a Procurement Plans Section, under Lieutenant Uhler; Surveys, with Tom Potts, and Educational Orders and Production Orders under William A. Eadie, Jr.

To this time personnel of the Purchase Section (formerly Purchase Information Section) had grown from eight to fifty-four, twenty-eight of whom were girls.

That Martin Sandler was the man for the job is borne out by the following paragraphs borrowed from the recommendation which earned for him the Exceptional Civilian Service Award, Medal and

Citation, presented 17 September 1946, by the then District Chief, Colonel Gordon B. Welch:

"He originally was assigned as Chief of the Purchase Section of the District Office, the responsibility of which under his direction was the initiation of bids and the negotiation for procurement of required materials and supplies. He was directly responsible for the organization of this rapidly expanding unit and for the selection, training and supervision of its personnel, which, at one time, October 1943, reached an emergency total of eighty (80) persons. The average of personnel was sixty (60) persons, a strikingly low total when it is recalled that under Martin Sandler's direction and supervision the District was responsible to the time of his release, 19 October 1945, for the allocation of contracts to a dollar value in excess of three billion ($3,000,000,000) dollars.

"In addition to his responsibilities as Purchase Section Chief, Martin Sandler was early assigned the added duty of Assistant to the Executive Officer in reference to general administration and procurement of Ordnance materiel. Shortly thereafter, likewise as an added duty, he was assigned as a special assistant to the District Chief, in which capacity he exercised final authority in coordinating the overall activities of the District, with special emphasis on all critical and complex purchasing problems and developments. Again, he later was given full power and authority to make final decisions for the District Chief on all involved matters affecting purchase policy.

"A succession of added responsibilities, beginning with his appointment, 28 February 1942, as a member of the Coordinator's Committee of the Philadelphia Ordnance District, brought Martin Sandler more and more into the all-over affairs of the District and made increasingly available his now indispensable services.

"On 14 March 1942 he was named Purchasing Coordinator.

"At its inception, 17 January 1942, he was made a member of the Board of Awards.

"Director of Purchase—30 September 1942.

"Member of Board of Sales, from 14 December 1943. Member Control Board, from same date.

"Also, 14 December 1943, he was named Chief, Purchase-Termination Division, which combined the responsibilities of the Purchase Branch, Termination Branch and the Property Disposal Branch. Personnel under his direction in the combined operations reached at one time, February

1945, a total of two hundred and forty (240) persons.

"Member of Board of Terminations, from its inception, 5 February 1944.

"Forward Pricing Coordinator, from 1 July 1944.

"Chairman, Board of Terminations, from 12 July 1945.

"Chairman, Board of Sales, from 16 July 1945.

"Chairman, Board of Awards, from 16 July 1945."

May 27, 1941 marked an important development in the matter of awards. The Office of the Chief of Ordnance instructed the Districts at this time that it was now within their authority to make awards on their own responsibility, on contracts up to $50,000.

It was also decided that contracts could be negotiated on a cost-plus-fixed-fee basis only when that form was absolutely necessary and from this date cost-plus-fixed-fee contracts were definitely discouraged. Also, the Districts were given authority to negotiate for Ordnance materiel without advertising, as authorized by Act of Congress, approved July 2, 1940.

This District's purchasing authority was increased from time to time until, under General Levin H. Campbell, Jr., the Districts received authority to award contracts, without consulting the Office of the Chief of Ordnance, for sums up to $5,000,000. There were certain restrictions, of course, but the authority existed to the end of hostilities.

Growth in Production

On May 30, 1941, word was received that the Secretary of War had issued a directive ordering prompt action in obtaining maximum production. Contractors had to be impressed with the necessity for increasing production to the maximum extent possible in order to assure early deliveries. Idle equipment had to be regarded as intolerable and facilities were urged to run three shifts per day seven days per week, in order to avoid bottlenecks in production. Increased costs due to such action were to be paid to the contractors and all contracts were to be amended accordingly.

It is significant that shortly thereafter, U. S. war industry soon was producing various Ordnance items on so accelerated a scale that the availability of raw materials quickly became a serious problem, and brought a halt, except in a few isolated cases, to three-shift operation.

Sub-Contractors

During this period, a liaison office was established in the Philadelphia Ordnance District to work closely with the Regional Office of the War Production Board. The late Harry E. "Dick" Snyder was selected for the liaison work. The purpose of this new office was to insure that all qualified prime contractors and sub-contractors had equal opportunity to quote on Ordnance requirements. War Production Board recommendations were accepted without question, and the names of various facilities were added occasionally to Procurement Planning prime contractor bid lists. However, this office felt that the efforts of the W. P. B. might be more profitable if greater attention were given to the creation of lists of qualified subcontractors rather than to depend upon occasional discoveries made by prime contractors. When a prime contractor required outside help, the need was brought to the attention of the War Production Board through the Philadelphia Ordnance District Liaison Office. Assistance, usually, was promptly forthcoming. Considerable importance was placed on the extent of subcontracting in bids received; and awards frequently were established at somewhat higher prices in those instances in which the prospective contractors offered to spread the work over a larger number of subcontractors than shown in other bids received.

Every effort was made to spread the work, and bidders were required to list the names of all subcontractors. There was a clause requiring that the sub-contractor do the subcontracting indicated in his original proposal. In short, the contractor was not given an opportunity to change his mind regarding the percentage of ultimate sub-contracting.

Defense Aid Tools

Early in June 1941, Lend Lease procurement was instituted and a directive was received with instructions bearing upon Defense Aid purchasing procedure. Procurement was confined to machine tools, although the variety and quantity of materials purchased for foreign governments were shortly enlarged. Separate funds were allotted for such procurement although during the early period it was necessary to keep track of the cost of telephone calls, teletypes, etc., relating to Defense Aid purchasing, a practice subsequently discontinued.

In August 1941, a special form for reporting all negotiations for procurement of Defense Aid machine tools was developed by the Office of the Chief of Ordnance, who made it clear that bid mistakes were the responsibility of the contractor. The Directive was particularly interesting in that it reflected the attitude of the Office of the Chief of Ordnance toward negligence on the part of the contractor. P. O. D., however, did not take advantage of obviously typographic errors in bids. For strategic reasons, every effort was made to assure to the contractors a fair profit.

Another milestone in procurement procedure was passed when, on August 19, 1941, the Army Contract Distribution Division was established. Its purpose was to advise and assist the Supplies Arms & Services in spreading the defense effort, by splitting awards between a number of bidders, subcontracting or otherwise. It was the responsibility of this Division to formulate policy for the distribution of defense work to companies which were distressed by the impact of priorities. A complete and covering directive was received from the Office of the Chief of Ordnance on September 23, 1941, entitled "Administration of Defense Orders," which instructed the District Office to give distressed areas every consideration in placing awards.

Local Pools

The Philadelphia Ordnance District Office was likewise directed to work with certain recognized war production associations then being formed. For example, at York, Pennsylvania, local manufacturers had grouped themselves into what was known as the York Plan for mutual cooperation in handling defense work. The work of this group was covered in a Saturday Evening Post feature story. At Trenton, New Jersey, was also established the Central New Jersey Pool. Important contracts were awarded to facilities in both groups.

All bids aggregating $50,000. or more were required to include a properly executed "Statement Required from Prospective Contractors."

Early in November the authority of the District with regard to procurement was raised from $50,000. per contract to $500,000. Six weeks later, December 29, 1941, the authority again was increased to $1,000,000.

Problems

In connection with the procurement of tanks which had been of a partial nature to this time, the Office, Chief of Ordnance directed that we obtain proposals on the complete light tank from the American Car and Foundry Company, Berwick, Pennsylvania. This was a radical departure from earlier procedure, and results were obtained only after considerable pressure had been applied to the facility. The Philadelphia Ordnance District had been purchasing various important components and spare parts, also organizational equipment, etc., and the Office of the Chief of Ordnance decided that it was easier to schedule production by placing complete responsibility for the entire tank in one place.

It must again be mentioned that all small manufacturers were encouraged by the Philadelphia Ordnance District to consult the Defense Contract Service of the War Production Board. It was P. O. D. policy to deal with prime contractors only, and every effort was made, therefore, to shunt the small sub-contractors to the War Production Board for servicing.

And on Sunday, 7 December 1941—Pearl Harbor!

A week later came from the Office, Chief of Ordnance, from the Industrial Service, District Control Division, a letter, Subject: "Expansion of District Office Activities," signed C. T. Harris, Jr., Major General, Assistant to Chief of Ordnance, Chief of Industrial Service. Because of its historic significance, we quote from this letter the following paragraphs:

"1. *General.* With the declarations of war there comes the necessity for forecasting, insofar as practicable, the increased volume of District work, change in the procedure of operation and organizational changes incident thereto.

"2. *Increased Volume.* In addition to the purchasing under the Second Defense Aid Program which has just been initiated and the Third Supplemental Program to be released in the very near future it is anticipated that tremendously large appropriations will be made for Ordnance Materiel in the not distant future. It is estimated that the dollar value of business in your District will be doubled or possibly tripled before June 1, 1942.

"3. *Change in Purchasing Procedure.* As an indication of what is expected in stepping up the work and as a clue to changes in procedure which will be effectuated through the removal of restrictions under which the Ordnance Department is now operating, there is quoted in full below, the memorandum of December 8, from the Under Secretary of War to the Chiefs of Supply Arms and Services:

"1. It is essential that our procurement be put into highest gear at once. All steps must be taken to increase the speed-up of maximum production of munitions.

"2. All officers and civilian employees should be required to work as many additional hours each day as it is necessary to get the day's work done. It is suggested that you address a communication to all officers and civilian employees in your branch of service exhorting them to make their maximum effort regardless of the long hours or hardship which may be involved.

"3. You are directed to take all necessary steps to boost munitions manufacture to the highest possible level. To do this you are authorized, wherever it will accelerate production, to reimburse contractors under cost-plus-fixed-fee contracts for all productive overtime work and for work on additional shifts. Furthermore, wherever it will accelerate production, you are authorized to negotiate supplemental contracts in proper cases for the payment of additional amounts to contractors having lump sum contracts to cover added costs for increased overtime work and for second and third shift operations. Our production must be quickly put on a 24-hour basis. You are directed to take such steps as will achieve this as soon as possible.

"4. You are requested to report promptly to me any delays outside of your control in the procurement procedure."

"Although not yet obtained it is expected that approval will be given to the Chief of Ordnance to make contracts greatly in excess of $500,000 without the necessity of obtaining approvals from the Under Secretary of War and the Office of Production Management. Within the approved limitations given to the Chief of Ordnance it is intended to modify the scheme of procurement to the extent that production orders for selected articles of Ordnance Materiel will be placed with District Offices, under which contracts may be negotiated and executed fully without requiring approvals outside of the District.

It is probable that the Districts will be required to communicate negotiated prices to the Ordnance Department for checking purposes.

"4. *Organization.* Even with the limited background outlined above both as to increased volume of work and the assignment of the great responsibility of contracting, it is nevertheless requested that you plan immediately for the expansion and strengthening of your organization. The responsibility for developing your organization rests with your office but it is desired that you take note of the following factors:

a. The type of organization suitable to one volume of business is not necessarily correct when the business is doubled or tripled.

b. Individuals, military and civilian, who until this time have performed their duties in an excellent manner might have reached their full capacity already.

c. The employment of a much greater number of highly qualified, mature businessmen for use in both advisory and operating capacities is indicated. The maintenance of morale cannot be disregarded but paradoxically this is no time for sentiment and it may be found necessary to supersede some of your present personnel with new, broader-minded and more experienced individuals. The difficulty in securing high grade personnel is real, but the problem may now be less difficult with our country actually at war as indicated by the receipt of applications of qualified people for employment and of the requests for active duty assignment of some Reserve officers now in the War Department pool.

"5. *Report.* It is requested that the problems confronting your office be fully studied and that a report thereon be made to this office, to be received on or before December 23, 1941, Attention: District Control Division. The report should include, but not be limited to, the following:

a. Total additional personnel requirements with identification only of the number with rank or classification of key officers and civilians.

b. A program for training of materiel inspectors.

c. Office space requirements with a

statement of contemplated difficulty, if any, in securing adequate accommodations.

    d. Submit a skeleton organization chart if any change in present organization is contemplated.

    e. The suitability of present provisions for obtaining prompt payment of vouchers.

By order of the Chief of Ordnance."

There was the crux of all purchasing procedure, and it was the authority which the Districts had been fighting for and which the Office of the Chief of Ordnance now had decided it was willing to relinquish. Unfortunately, later events proved that it was only a partial surrender for some of the individuals, and a few of the Branches in the Office of the Chief of Ordnance continued, by various means, to hold on to their power. This naturally resulted in occasional disagreements. Relief came with the appointment to the Office of the Chief of Ordnance, of Major General, later Lieutenant General, Levin H. Campbell, Jr., as Chief. General Campbell advocated decentralization from the start.

The principal problem in connection with procurement was the continual stream of changes ordered by Washington after the initiation of procurement. In one instance, a certain item was cancelled and re-established no less than four times in the short period of three months, and during this same period there were also a large number of mandatory changes in design and manufacture. It became increasingly difficult through this period to effect procurement, under such conditions.

With decentralization of procurement came the establishment 17 January 1942, by P. O. D. Special Order No. 55, of a Board of Awards, consisting of three members: Lt. Colonel, then Maj., Joseph A. Whelan, Legal Branch; H. Paul Gant, Planning Director, and Martin Sandler, now Director of Purchase. These worthy gentlemen were appointed to study all bids and to assume responsibility for recommendation to the District Chief, for his approval, of the most interesting bids received. The first meeting was held on the same day the Board was ordered into being. It continued to function practically without change throughout the war, holding daily meetings. Certain new forms, such as the breakdown sheet, designed to enable the Board to obtain a clear statistical and factual record of each transaction and to allow for their easy perusal and comparison, were early developments.

The Board of Awards also insisted, before making an award, on written clearances by the various Divisions in the District office, covering procurement planning, financial responsibility of facility, manufacturing ability, labor supply, G-2 intelligence and plant protection. The Board arranged for the immediate photostating of these breakdown sheets as soon as the Board's recommendation had received the District Chief's approval.

The Chief of the Purchase Section now realigned the purchasing staff along commodity lines. Certain negotiators were appointed to handle specific items. Each authorization, depending upon its character, was routed to a particular individual. The designated negotiator was responsible for "carrying through" until definite proposals had been secured. These proposals were subsequently studied and a summary prepared for submission to the Board of Awards. The summary is the breakdown sheet referred to above. In the negotiations the representative of the Purchase Section was supported by a representative of the District Legal Division; also by a representative of the Commodity Division concerned. The assistant representatives sat in on all conferences and helped to clarify the drawings and specifications or points of law as they might develop.

Early in February 1942, Martin "fortified-folders" Sandler was named Purchase Coordinator, and took his place in the councils of the Coordinators. The story of the Board of Awards, and the later associated groups, the Board of Terminations and the Board of Sales, is another story, appearing elsewhere in this narration.

The organization chart of the period shows the Purchase Section, with Director Sandler and William A. Eadie, Jr., in charge of the Purchase Information Section, attached to the Procurement Service Branch, under Major Walter C. Pew.

The chart of 20 August 1942 indicates a Special Assistants Group (an evolutionary development of the Coordinator Group) with H. Paul Gant, Planning Director, and in charge, W. P. B.-Conservation and Surveys; and Martin Sandler in charge of purchase policy. Purchase units had been set up in the Commodity Branches, as follows:
Small Arms:

Ammunition Section—Charles L. Dostal

Gun and Mount Section—Charles L. Dostal
Artillery:
   Cannon Section—C. W. Weiler
   Carriage Section—C. W. Weiler
   Anti-Aircraft and Fire Control Section—C. W.
      Weiler
Ammunition:
   Fuze Section—Charles L. Dostal
   Bomb Section—Martin B. Beline
   Projectile Section—Martin B. Beline
   Cartridge Case Section—Charles L. Dostal
   Powder, Explosives and Propellants Section
   Textile Section—William J. O'Brien
Tank-Automotive:
   Light Tank—Edward Chalikian
   Medium and Heavy Tank—Edward Chalikian
   Miscellaneous Vehicles—Edward Chalikian
   Armor—Edward Chalikian
   Depot Section—Edward Chalikian
Miscellaneous Materials:
   Raw Materials—William J. O'Brien
   Machine Tool and Equipment—William J.
      O'Brien
   Gage Section (Procurement)—William J. O'
      Brien

Eight days later, 28 August 1942, the Purchase Units of the Commodity Branches had vanished from the District Chart—but purchasing went on just the same, and in increasing volume.

On September 1, 1942, the Motor Transport Service of the Quartermaster Department of the Army was disbanded and the Purchasing Section of the District office was assigned a number of incomplete folders covering unfinished transactions for the procurement of automotive vehicles. This change necessitated much additional work, which was made particularly difficult by the manner in which the vehicles originally had been placed in production. It would appear that the policy had been to get a job started with a letter contract, and then bicker for a year or more about the price—as a result of which no contracts were ever finalized. (The complete story of this transfer appears under Philadelphia Mobile Shop Depot, with special mention in the Fiscal Branch history chapter.)

As of 17 April 1943 the charts reveal Martin Sandler, Purchase Director; Major, then Captain, Theodore C. Sheaffer, Assistant; Major, then 1st Lt., J. Albury Fleitas, Chief, Purchase Section; and Major, then Captain, Joseph M. Baxter, Chief, Price Analysis Section.

In December 1943, with the conbination of the

Purchase Branch and the Terminations Branch as the Purchase Termination Division, the Purchase phase takes the label of Negotiation Branch, with Major Fleitas as Chief, Captain Sheaffer taking over the Purchase Control Section. H. C. Middleton is assigned to the Ammunition Section of the Negotiation Branch; Meridith I. Gardiner, World War I Air Corps Lieutenant, to Artillery; Harold Dripps to Small Arms; Edward M. Chalikian, former instructor at the Bok Vocational School, to Miscellaneous Materials; and John Swartley to the Tank-Automotive Section. A few days later, Purchase Sections again appear in the Commodity Branches, except the Miscellaneous Materials Branch, which drew its last breath about this time.

Coming into 1944, March, we find practically the same line-up as appeared in December 1943, except that a Purchase representative, W. S. Stokes, appears assigned to the Gage Section. Small Arms having wedded Artillery, an Artillery-Arms Section is revealed with Meridith Gardiner handling the double duty. Joe Baxter, all the while, is directing Price Analysis.

The foregoing arrangement holds pretty well through 1944. As of 7 June 1945, Major Sheaffer is heading the Purchase Branch of the Purchase Termination Division. Major Fleitas is Assistant; Captain Louis F. Unger, Stevens, 1933, is in charge of the Control Section; F. A. Dubbs has replaced W. S. Stokes in the Gage Section. Captain William T. Young has some time since been moved from the Legal Branch to the Price Analysis pilot-house. In October 1945, Captain Young is named Chief of the Purchase Branch, Major Sheaffer, Major Fleitas and Martin Sandler having meanwhile gone "to the showers." Captain Young turned Kentuckyward, midway of December 1945, when H. L. Wilson took over.

The Purchase story is a long and exciting one. As a major activity of P. O. D., it rates more searching treatment than can be given here. It is suggested that the reader peruse it in its relationship with other activities of the District, and in the light of its accomplishments.

At this point we must pay our respects to those many others, not named herein, who gave so much, and so well, to Purchase and related efforts. There were many, and if there are omissions, it is not because some served less. "Fats" Waller once was asked to describe a jive band. Said he, "That kind of band is one in which every musician tries to keep two notes ahead of everyone else." That's the way we worked in Ordnance—seems as if.

Well, here are a few named from among the many:

Among the men: G. H. English, George T. Francis, Jr., Frank M. Knight, Jr., T. Liversidge, C. R. Marsh, F. T. Corleto, Wm. T. Newbold, Louis C. Purdy, Kenneth C. Trauger, Max Dunning, Lt. James J. Law, Jr., J. A. Shearer, Lt. John I. Spiegelhalter, C. E. Colgan (Tank), Captain R. Paul Fugate, Thomas B. Irwin (Artillery), G. C. Jaco, Fred C. Graham (Tank), J. T. Mohr (Tank), Allen McK. Beecroft, Martin W. Reed, Samuel Bass, Abraham Beavers, G. W. Hogue, the late Thomas Lunny, Lt. Edward J. Lynch, W. A. Martel, WOJG Harry Succop, and Staff Sgt. Arnold Wolpin.

Among the women: First mention must go to Mrs. Elsie V. Mugnier, long Secretary to Martin Sandler, and those other capable ladies who later served the "big man" in that capacity—Suzanne D. Sedlock, and Marie T. Ruf. Some others on the fair side were: Mary Spack, Margaret McCarron, Rita Kavanaugh, Ruth Benner, Geraldine Garbeil, Jane Jones, Maragret Lynch, Sylvia Nagrem, Helen Newbold, Margaret O'Hagan, Elizabeth D. Robinson, Thelma Morrow, Winifred Park, Adele Wilder, Anne Bright, Regina Corrsin, Florence Diffenderfer, Margaret Held, Kathleen Kenna, Anna Miller, Katherine Rhone, Yolanda Rubini, Florence Stewart, Katherine Ambrose, Beatrice Avrach, Edna Brown, Anna Durkin, Catherine Glackin, Jeane Griffith, Dorothy Lewis, Susan Maloney, Catherine Mannion, Caroline Moore, Margaret Murray, Mary Powell, Catherine Seeber, Helen Sherrick, Anna Straghan, Mable Thomas, Marian Vance, Mabel Will, Rose Barsh, Jane Daniels, Helen Diskin, Veronica Fenningham, Ruth Gillian, Agnes Haslam, Agnes Keenan, Helen Kelly, Anne Kerns, Edith Mignogna, Frances Ritter, Regina Rose, Mary Sinoroff, Mary Soprano, Alene Sphohrer, Elizabeth G. Toomey, Caroline Trauger, Frances Walsh, Frances Wells and Mary Bealmear.

Gathered about Dorothy Wall, one-time Atlantic City beauty contestant, are, L. to R.: Clare Tietz, Mrs. Anne Swartz, Kay Cattafesta, Kay Scully, Mary Montgomery, Mrs. Lee Friel, Lois Peck, and at the desk, Dorothy herself

Top, L to R: Captain Dan H. Pletta, Captain Morton H. Fetterolf, Captain Howard P. Klair, Captain John W. Ogden. Second row: Lt. Alvah H. Thomas, Lt. James C. Hassett, O. Howard Wolfe, Major Oliver C. Conger. Third row: Major Robert G. Allen, Lt. E. H. Young, Lt. Norman L. Cavedo, Lt. Howard A. Cressman. Bottom: Captain Arthur J. Boyer, Lt. Guy E. Hancock, Jr., Lt. George L. Schiel, Captain Lewis, H. Van Dusen Jr, (Rank indicated is at time of picture)

Chapter XXI

SMALLER WAR PLANTS—NOT SO SMALL

SPEAKING at the "Production for Total Victory" Dinner held 5 February 1945, by the Philadelphia Post of the Army Ordnance Association, Joseph E. Colen, President, Machined Metals Company, Norristown, Pennsylvania, recalled:

"In 1941, the President, sensing the need of smaller war plants in our war effort, laid foundations for the Smaller War Plants Corporation as an integral part of the O. P. M. (later supplanted to smaller business enterprises). Beginning with the time when the President designated the United States as the 'Arsenal for Democracy,' and for some time thereafter, production did not 'measure up' to expectations. Possibly we were confused by the shouting and the tumult that followed. However, after that brief period of confusion we began to realize the seriousness of the challenge that was upon us and so small business rolled up its sleeves and went to work."

Quoting further from Mr. Colen's talk:

"It is an undisputed fact that early in our war effort, small business looked askance at the larger plants then being awarded substantial war contracts to the absolute elimination of the smaller plants. It was noted, however, that there was a great loss of time in what was known as the "gap".— the time elapsing from the development stage of an item to the time of its reaching a point of mass production in one of the large plants. This lapse of time was most critical, and something had to be done or our cause was in jeopardy. Small plants with their great flexibility was the solution. Naturally, re-tooling, readjustment and tooling-over could not be expeditiously carried out in the larger plants. The smaller plants, however, could quickly enter into the program and more speedily adjust themselves. In fact, in many cases, it was demonstrated that small industry had the finished product on the firing line while the big plants still were making over."

It is a matter of record that in a number of instances time was saved by having development work and production studies carried out in the smaller plants as an assistance to the mass production facilities in making quicker starts.

What small business did not fully appreciate "way back when" was that during early 1942 we needed vast quantities of everything and in a hurry. It was a logical procedure to tackle the big producers first. Small business, now suffering and greatly alarmed, bombarded Congress with appeals, and certain elements seized upon the whole matter as a political opportunity—but that is another story.

S. W. P. "took off" in P. O. D. in the early Summer of 1942 when Vrest Orton, fresh out of Weston, Vermont, and with a string of accomplishments to his credit, to say nothing of a Harvard education, was assigned by H. Paul Gant, the then Director of Planning, to study the aspects of the Small Business Act as it might apply to the District. A copy of the Act was all the S. W. P. Administrator had for a guide, and to this time there did not exist in W. P. B. an S. W. P. group with whom he might have held discussion.

With the increasing emphasis now being placed on S. W. P. the Procurement Planning Section of P. O. D., of which the S. W. P. Unit was a part, began working more closely with S. W. P. Corporation, attempting through the use of "Distress Reports" to suggest deserving facilities for awards. The "District Reports" recommended to S. W. P. Corporation those facilities that had lost employees, or much of their business, through lack of either civilian or war orders, or facilities for which there were prospects of such losses.

On 7 October 1942, the District Administration Division, Office of the Chief of Ordnance, directed the appointment in each of the Districts of a Smaller War Plants Administrator, and on 23 November 1942, Warren Webster, Jr., President of the Warren Webster Company, Camden, New

Jersey, a smaller war plant that already had shown its mettle (no pun), received the appointment.

It was only two months following his S. W. P. appointment in P. O. D. that Warren Webster, Jr., turned Pentagonward. Lt. General L. H. Campbell, Jr., Chief of Ordnance, had been watching W. W. Jr. in action—and as liberal doses of that brand of action were just then needed in S. W. P. on the other side of the Potomac, there was nothing else to do but pack this young man off to the big house to assume the S. W. P. functions in the Office of the Chief of Ordnance—all of which brought Caleb F. Fox III, who had been reporting to Chief E. H. Uhler of the Planning Section, to the fore.

The "third" of the Calebs turned in a good job; but what else from one brimming of Episcopal Academy, St. Pauls School and Princeton. "A waste of time," hinted Control Branch's George Francis, Jr., "when a couple of semesters under John Harvard would have given him the same result."

Safely out of Princeton, and with a flair for sales work, he accepted a berth with B. Wilmsen Company, Philadelphia, where he soon was signing himself Caleb F. Fox III, Sales Manager, resigning this responsibility mid-way of 1942 for a baptism of paper work in the Procurement Planning Section which, by the way, was down-to-earth preparation for the S. W. P. assignment later on.

In December 1944, the "third" Caleb was named Chief, Procurement Planning Section, to succeed Major E. H. Uhler, who had been assigned Chief of the Production Service Branch. On 10 August 1945, having passed the peak of his responsibilities, and with the old urge getting in its licks, Caleb

"punched the clock" for the last time, Harvey R. Battersby taking over the Fox command.

Harvey, a Philadelphian by birth, came to P. O. D. a graduate of Penn State College, where he received his B.S. in mechanical engineering.

And make no mistake about it, S. W. P. in P. O. D. was something in the nature of "big business." Nor can it be overlooked that at no time were there in the Smaller War Plants Unit of the District more than three persons—the unit chief, his assistant and one secretary. "Now," as the late Al Smith might have said, "let us look at the record."

From February 1943, when S. W. P. in the District began to roll, to the close of business, 31 October 1945, just a little while after VJ Day, the Smaller War Plants Unit placed three thousand four hundred and twelve awards, to a total dollar value of approximately $1,623,900,000.—and that was about half the District's total of awards—of all awards, in all categories. Broken down, the report revealed that six hundred thirty-four awards, worth in good American dollars $81,549,000, went to contractors who boasted no more than one hundred employees; nine hundred and sixteen awards to a total dollar face value of $225,068,-000. went to contractors employing from one hundred to five hundred personnel, and to contractors whose payrolls indicated employment of more than five hundred persons went one thousand eight hundred sixty-eight awards to the magnificent total of $1,211,646,000.

That just about winds up the S. W. P. story, and the S. W. P. Unit as well, for with the advent of VJ Day began an about-face in the direction of its eventual oblivion.

Left to right: Martin Sandler, H. Paul Gant, Lt. Col. Joseph A. Whelan, Mrs. Helen W. MacFarland, Secretary

Chapter XXII

THE BOARD OF AWARDS OR
TINKER TO EVERS TO CHANCE

VITAL adjunct to the Procurement Planning Section and the Purchase Director was the Board of Awards, for it was at this point that it was determined who merited the order; and it was around the table of the Board that the major activity of the District, procurement, was spearheaded.

In its issue of May 1943 the editors of *Time Fuse* tell the story of this important activity. As we recall it at this late date it went something like this:

"Your baseball lore may not carry back to that old, classic game-winning play of "Tinker to Evers to Chance"; but if you've spent much time around 150 South Broad Street, you have at least an eavesdropper's acquaintance with that infinitely greater, infinitely more vital winning combination of "Gant to Whelan to Sandler.""

"It's the Board of Awards—and they're slapping down aces on everything Adolph, Mussi or Hirohito can pull out of the deck.

"The Board of Awards was set up in January 1942 in the District when it became clear that the District Chief could not scrutinize, analyze and otherwise search every allocation coming to him for placement in the District. The first Gant to Whelan to Sandler play made the headlines, January 17, 1942, and has been repeated every business day since.

"The general procedure leading up to the 'play' is something like this: When the Office, Chief of Ordnance makes an allocation to the District, the Directive goes immediately to the Procurement Planning Section (Mr. H. P. Gant, Chief) and the interested Commodity Branch.

"Procurement Planning studies the allocation, and usually, within twenty-four hours calls a meeting of a planning board, together, with representatives of the Commodity Branch and the Purchase Section.

"The Procurement Planning representative is concerned with such matters, among various others, as availability of suitable facilities, the outcome aspects, public relations and general policy involved in the preparation of a "bidders list." The Commodity Branch is concerned only with the facilities' ability to produce the item—"Enough and on Time"—and of specified quality. The Purchase Section representative is there to inform himself on background matters of each procurement.

"The Planning Board, in its meeting, prepares a list of qualified bidders, copies going to the Commodity Branch, Plant Protection, Fiscal, and Labor sections for final clearances—and then out for bids.

"When bids are all in, they are entered on 'breakdown sheets,' which, with pertinent folders, are passed along to the Board of Awards for selection.

"This very 'cagey' team—the Board of Awards—knows at all times what goes on in the plants of facilities, what is being made, and how; facilities, fire, labor and saboteur records; ability to meet delivery schedules, to maintain uniform, required quality. If there is any situation, condition or lack that might interfere with the demand of 'Enough and On Time,' this group knows it.

"When finally, the 'All Clear' is sounded on an allocation, when the green light is flashed, the contract is prepared, checked in the Legal Branch, and passed on to the contracting officer for final action, and from then on things happened".

Much has already been recorded of two of the members of the Gant to Whelan to Sandler team. Of the middle member, Lt. Colonel, then Captain, Joseph A. Whelan, there still is much to be told and for that task we again call upon the editors of the oft-remembered *Time Fuze*, where, in the same issue wherein is revealed the workings of the Board itself, we find such interesting fragments as the following:

"Joseph A. Whelan, the genial Chief of the Legal Branch (as of that period) enjoys the distinction of having lived in France at the dawn of two world wars. With his two brothers, he was a student at the Ecole de Mentone, near Monte Carlo. By the summer of 1914 Europe was at war and what had been a quiet school in a sleepy village was soon converted into a hospital. Colonel Whelan will

be forgiven for not joining the army in 1914, for he was scarcely eight years of age at the time.

"Twenty-two long years were to elapse before his next domicile in France. This too was a critical period in the world's history. In June 1936 Hitler moved into the Rhineland. In October Joe Whelan followed him, crossing into Belgium and arriving in Antwerp on the day riots broke out between the Facists and anti-Facists. War was in the air. But war was farthest from Colonel Whelan's mind—he had just been married—he was on his honeymoon trip.

"Joe Whelan graduated from Yale Law School. He set up later, a practicing lawyer, in Philadelphia. He was a reserve officer in the Engineer Corps to the time he joined up with P. O. D. Outside of law Colonel Whelan's major interest has always been engineering, and while at Princeton, in addition to pre-law, he also qualified for an engineering degree. Engineering also comes naturally to him. Born in June 1906, in Philadelphia, he was five when his family moved to Atlantic City where his father was in the construction business. Whelan senior encouraged his sons' interest in construction—so much so that when Joe was 14 years of age, the elder Whelan and his three sons built a house in Ocean City, just to provide the boys with practical experience. And they sold the house! One brother subsequently became an architect; another an engineer, while Joe Whelan became a lawyer, specializing in the legal phases of construction."

In 1940, when Colonel Whelan assumed charge of the Legal Branch in P. O. D. he and Legal were new to Ordnance. There were then a few Educational Orders totalling perhaps $5,000,000. By February 1943, when he received his commission as Lieutenant Colonel, he had helped to develop a gigantic legal mill which had ground out contracts aggregating $2,000,000,000—an increase of 40,000 per cent—in less than 2½ years. Meanwhile the Legal staff had grown from one lawyer and Mrs. Jackson, secretary, to 10 lawyers and 53 girls (and was to grow very much more).

The District, as it happened, was soon to lose the services of this legal brilliant. There was need elsewhere for his skills. Shortly following Colonel Hauseman's appointment as Chief, Redistribution Branch, Office Chief of Ordnance, in Pentagon, Joe also moved along to the Capitol to take his place on the Hauseman team, where he again made history.

Chapter XXIII

NOW YOU HAVE IT AND NOW YOU DON'T—
OR PRICE ADJUSTMENT

BACK in late 1945 there was circulated in the District Office copies of a cartoon epitomizing, crudely but eloquently, the purpose of renegotiation. The cartoon revealed two colored gentlemen who had just consummated the sale and purchase of a hen. The consideration was one dollar. The purchaser, with the hen dangling from one hand, and gripping appropriate cutlery with the other, was saying to the seller: "You got mah dollar; now let's renegotiate!"

Primarily the real purpose of price adjustment and renegotiation was not to reveal dishonesty, although there were instances in which dishonesty was evident, but rather to recover to Government excessive profits, the natural result of increasing economies growing out of better integrated production techniques, increasing "know how," conservation of materials and other improvements in production by contractors of war's needs.

Just to give you an idea: Within the first six months from the signing by the President of Section 403 of Public Law 528, the legal basis for renegotiation of contracts, there was recovered to Government, through voluntary reductions of P. O. D. contractors alone, a sum comfortably in excess of $20,800,000. Not bad. As of January 1946, renegotiations including voluntary reductions by District Contractors "ran the bases" for a score of over $200,000,000. Recovery was practically in balance. Kudos came from Pentagon, indicating that there are situations in which one can have his chicken and his money, too—or some of it.

The Price Adjustment Branch of the Philadelphia Ordnance District was set up 28 August 1942, four months to the day following the effective date of the law. The Section was charged under the law with the responsibility for statutory price renegotiation and voluntary reductions of contracts. Major Brendan D. Walsh was designated as Chief of the Section, which included a Section Board of three men, an Administrative Unit and a Cost Analysis Unit.

The law required the Secretaries of the Army, Navy and the Maritime Commission to insert in Government contracts and in subcontracts in excess of $100,000. renegotiation clauses; actually to renegotiate Government contracts and to recover to the Government, when found, all excessive profits. The law also provided for the prevention or recapture of excessive profits, thus supplementing and re-inforcing the objectives of the excess profits tax; all of which represented something new in Government-business relationship. The proper negotiation and renegotiation of contracts, it was pointed out, must attempt to reconcile the avoidance of excessive profits with the maintenance of incentives to economical management.

Amendment and change in detail came with experience, but for the length of the war, the principle was kept intact—and with little resentment from industry. The law was sound from every industrial point of view, and Uncle Sugar was more than fair in its application.

The Price Adjustment Branch as originally constituted was as follows: Major Walsh at the Head; Major, then Captain, W. F. (Fred) Feustel as Chief, Administrative Unit, and associated with him, J. J. Walliser and S. M. Jemison, C. P. A. As Chairman of the Price Adjustment Board, John M. Fassitt, who resigned 15 September 1943; and serving on the Board, W. M. McKee, H. Cary and J. M. Taylor, the latter "joining" up two days following the resignation of "Jack" Fassitt.

On 18 December 1942, Charles P. Stokes, he of the "vintage hats," was assigned as Chief of the Price Adjustment Branch, in addition to his other duties, succeeding Major Walsh, resigned.

On the District Chart of 17 April 1943, we find a Reports Unit established with T. H. Roth in charge, and the name of S. G. McNees replacing that of H. Cary of the Price Adjustment Board. On subsequent charts we find the names of T. G. Aspinwall, H. G. Stewart, H. N. Rodenbaugh, and Chief Charles P. Stokes while those of S. G. McNees, and J. M. Taylor now are missing. By 2 January 1946, the whole burden of price adjustment had fallen upon the able shoulders of Major W. F. Feustel, now Chief of the Branch, succeeding Charles P. Stokes, also taking his place on the Board, and H. N. Rodenbaugh and W. M. McKee.

The total of P. O. D. personnel was moving swiftly toward its all time high when Major Brendan D. Walsh, Philadelphia insurance broker, first signed into the District Office, in May 1942, and was temporarily assigned as assistant to the Chief of the Plant Protection Section, and, as an additional duty, officer-in-charge, Internal Security, posts which he held until his assignment in August 1942 as Chief, Price Adjustment Branch. B. D. was "all Philadelphian and a yard wide"; born here, grew up here, attended William Penn Charter School and the University of Pennsylvania, set himself up in business here, and long since has returned to the Quaker City's marts. Due to illness, and following a sojourn at Walter Reed, Major Walsh reluctantly parted company with P. O. D., 18 March 1943.

The second Ordnance officer to occupy the top post of the Price Adjustment Branch, Captain William Frederick Feustel, made his debut in P. O. D., 24 August 1942, and immediately was assigned to the Branch, as Head Renegotiator and Assistant to the Branch Chief. "Fred" was born in Springfield, Massachusetts, attended Penn State College and Georgetown University—excellent preparation for his career in insurance, with such noteworthies as Traveler's General Accident Corporation and Employer's Liability Corporation.

On 21 August 1944, just four hundred and thirty-two years, short of two months, after the discovery of America, Fred received his commission of Major. The earlier date is, to use a well-known Sandlerian word, "interjected" here in respect to Fred's repertory of not-so-tall tales. Beyond this, Fred, the Van Johnson of Ordnance, vied with Captain "Dutch" Derickson, Captain Bob Merz, Captain John Spiegelhalter and Lt. Colonel Bob Allen for nomination as the District's number one dramatic artist and holder of the P. O. D. Oscar.

Incidentally, but not too much so, this was Major Feustel's second World War.

Not to take one whit of glory from a great officer and a capable executive, Major Fred could thank his lucky star for the fate that brought him the assistance of Lieutenant Maurice P. Felton of Philadelphia's Feltonville Feltons. "Maury," a product of Syracuse University, University of Pennsylvania and the Benson School of Welding and Wrought Iron, from which founts of wisdom he apparently attempted, according to the archives, to absorb about everything these institutions had to offer, came to P. O. D. 25 June 1942. There had been a full session at Aberdeen Proving Ground OCS, and before that, a turn at Camp Shelby, Mississippi, with Battery C, 116 Field Artillery.

Nor did this young man hesitate to take his honors at Shelby—and fast. He entered in January 1941, a private. Two or three weeks later he was promoted to corporal, and a little later on was again promoted, to the rank of sergeant— first instrument sergeant, then ammunition sergeant and, finally, motor sergeant.

On 18 July 1942, following shortly his arrival in P. O. D., Maury was temporarily assigned to the Miscellaneous Materials Branch, remaining here until his reassignment, 14 September 1942, as assistant in the Military Personnel Section and Custodian of the Production Display Section. On 20 October 1942, he was named Assistant Adjutant, on 31 December 1942 he was assigned the added responsibility of Chief, Training Section, Civilian Personnel Branch. Came 7 June 1943, and Second Lieutenant Felton was sent to the Administration Section of the Price Adjustment Branch. Three days later he was commissioned a First Lieutenant. Maury continued at his P. A. post to his separation from the Army, 28 October 1945—living up to and beyond expectations all of the way.

Chapter XXIV

THE COMMODITY BRANCHES

TO JULY 1939 all P. O. D. contracts and purchase orders for Ordnance materiel, machinery and productive capital equipment were handled as a group without regard to classification. Under this system the organization of the Philadelphia Ordnance District was very simple, consisting of the District Chief, an Executive Officer, the Chief Inspector and staff of inspectors, clerks, stenographers and typists.

Late in 1939, an attempt was made to classify contracts and requisitions in four groups, each of which was to be supervised by an Executive Assistant, as follows: Ammunition Section; Artillery Section; Miscellaneous Machinery Section; Automotive Section.

On 10 August 1940, the organizational set-up further was simplified by the addition of two sections. These were Powder and Explosives, and Miscellaneous Machinery. Administration of contracts for machine tools, productive capital equipment, jigs, fixtures, gages, some small arms, small arms accessories and metallic belt links were assigned to the Miscellaneous Machinery Section. Administration of P. O. D. and Arsenal prime contracts from other Districts for steels and other raw materials, ammunition containers and miscellaneous items which were not components of commodities handled by other Sections were assigned to the Raw Materials Section. Assistance to other Districts on raw material contracts was a particularly important function of this Section.

By December 1940 the administrative duties of the various Commodity Sections had increased to a point where additional assistance was required. Therefore the Sections were set-up as Commodity Divisions, each headed by a Division Chief, and each composed of three units, thus: Contract Section; Engineering Section; Inspection.

Because Powder and Explosives were so definitely related to the whole group of Ammunition items, the Sections devoted to powders and explosives were merged with the Ammunition Division. At the same time, the internal organization of the Commodity Divisions was modified by replacing the Contract Section with a Production Section, in view of the fact that the functions of the Contract Section was fast becoming one of production.

As time rolled on other Sections were added; for instance, Priorities Section, Procurement Liaison Sections, Technical Sections, C. M. P. Sections, Packaging Sections and so on.

Then, of course, each Division developed its particular specialty groups. These included, in the Ammunition Division: an Ammunition Section, a Gun and Mount Section, a Hand Arms and Equipment Section; and still later, a Production Section and a Purchase Section. And these changes were typical of changes taking place all through Commodity groups.

To this time (still December 1940), inspection, engineering and production functions were handled through the various sub-offices and inspection offices, with the exception of the immediate Philadelphia area, where the Commodity Divisions were in direct contact with the manufacturers. This direct contact became in time something of a burden, interfering with the general work of the Commodity Divisions. Therefore, late in 1941, as narrated elsewhere, the Philadelphia Sub-Office was established to take over local duties in those categories.

Definite steps were taken, following the declaration of war, to increase the scope of the production sections. From this point on, it was seen that the functions of the Commodity Divisions definitely would be production and inspection.

It was decided in April 1942 that since the functions of the Miscellaneous Machinery Division and the Raw Materials Division were similar and in no way related to particular commodities, the two should be set up as a single Division. Accordingly there was established the Miscellaneous Division, composed of two Sections, Inspection and Production; each further divided into a Raw Materials Section and a Machinery Section.

Gages: Until July 1942 procurement of government inspection gages was an Arsenal function, and fast becoming a bottleneck in production, due to the limited number of gage facilities. Steps which previously had been taken by the Office of the Chief of Ordnance to expand small shops in an effort to take the load off the regular gage facilities were not producing the desired results. The reason for the failure was the lack of a direct placement of orders from the various Arsenals with the particular gage facilities which had available capacity. Since the Ordnance Districts were set up to handle both the jobs of gage procurement and facility expansion these functions were turned over to the District. Because of the technical nature and precision with which gages must be made, inspection was left with the Arsenals. In the Philadelphia Ordnance District, ten small shops had been expanded through additions of Government-owned equipment. Others were developed with private funds.

The Districts, it will be recalled, were required to shape their Commodity Divisions on the pattern of those in the Office of the Chief of Ordnance. Accordingly, to round out the Philadelphia Commodity organization, in line with the directive, it was necessary to establish a Small Arms Division. There was assigned to the new division all those small arms contracts previously administered in the Miscellaneous Division. All Divisions now were labeled Branches. The Miscellaneous Materials Branch as it now was named, was made up of four Sections: Machinery Section, Raw Materials Section, Contractors Assistance Section, Gage Procurement Section.

The old Miscellaneous Machinery Division had for its Chief Frederick S. Feldheim. In charge of the Production Section was Alfred S. Testa. Born in Philadelphia, he was removed by his parents, before the age of vehement protestation, to Vineland, New Jersey. He completed his high school studies there, dabbling with electricity as a sideline. The sideline won and he came back to Philadelphia to enter Drexel, where he wound up with a B.S. in electrical engineering. His was a co-op course which found him dividing his time between an industry job (Kimball Glass Works, Vineland, N. J.) and Drexel. He worked for Drexel for a time as maintenance engineer in the Institute Laboratory. Following graduation he found employment

with the Radio Corporation. Two years later he accepted a berth with the Pennsylvania Railroad where he was assigned to the job of inspecting and testing equipment used on the electrification project then in process on the Harrisburg run.

In July 1940, Al Testa came into P. O. D. to do his "stint." His first assignment was that of inspector. Six months later he was in production work in the Branch. This included the handling of Lend-Lease contracts which then were beginning to bloom in earnest.

In 1943, when the Miscellaneous Materials Branch was shelved, all Machine Tool contracts were signed over to the Production Equipment Section. Because of his familiarity with all machine tool matters, Al Testa was promptly assigned to production equipment. His final P. O. D. assignment was that of use analyst, assistant to the Chief of the Section.

Serving with Frederick Feldheim was Henry E. Marcus, in charge of the Inspection Section. Henry is a product of Central High School, Philadelphia, the Alma Mater of Alexander Woolcott and other notables, including Henry. And in the Alger tradition he went to work for Philco Corporation to obtain enough money to pay for a course in journalism at Temple University. Later, his thirst for knowledge far from satiated, he enrolled for electrical engineering at Drexel, thence to Pennsylvania for two years of vocational training, and received upon graduation a Pennsylvania State Teacher certificate.

Upon his arrival in October 1940 in P. O. D., he was sent to Rock Island Arsenal for special training, thence to the Miscellaneous Machinery Division. When Lieutenant Robert O. Watson became Chief of the Gage Section, he requested the services of Henry Marcus, got him, and Henry stuck.

In the Raw Material Division we find Lieutenant Robert C. Wager in charge. The Lieutenant, Columbus, Ohio born, graduated in 1935 from Ohio State with an I.E. Degree, and by way of Ralston Steel Car Company, Surface Combustion Corporation where he had the assignment of production engineer; Glenn L. Martin Company, where he acted as budget clerk; and the Bendix Radio Corporation, as time study engineer, he arrived, 23 January 1941, in P. O. D. Following his work in the Raw Materials Division, he was assigned, 7 November 1941, to the York Sub-Office, and on

23 January 1943, was assigned to the Jefferson Proving Ground.

The Production Section of the Division had for its Chief Walter J. Mullin, of whom it was said he could get more out of a pipe than any other man living. Walter later came under the Command of Major Victor Smith and was rated a "top-flighter" in the Philadelphia Regional Office.

The Engineering Section was assigned to Fred Purella, Penn State Engineering School. Realizing that he would be gathered up in the draft, he enlisted in the Navy, but not without difficulty. Immediately it became known that he was seeking enlistment, his draft board cancelled a deferment which it previously had granted. It now became necessary for him to obtain a special deferment to keep himself intact until the Navy should give him the green light, which it did in due course. The last we heard of Fred, he had been promoted up through the grades to lieutenant commander, and later, out of the Service, was working on the Navy's guided missile program.

The Inspection Section of the Division bore the mark of W. A. Mortensen, from Jack Bennyville, otherwise Waukegan, Illinois. Bill headed into the big time as chief gage maker for Nash Motors. Later he went to Rock Island Arsenal as a toolmaker, entered Ordnance in the Pittsburgh Ordnance District and was assigned to Philadelphia, 26 November 1941, and in July 1942, was assigned to the Miscellaneous Division. On the 16 June 1942 he was promoted to first lieutenant, went to Aberdeen in May 1945, and shortly thereafter was back in P. O. D. Bill Mortensen was just about all there was of the Raw Materials Division during the setting up period. He was Chief of the Division and all of its Sections to boot.

A bit later we discover Maynard L. Hodgson at the head of Inspection in the Raw Materials Division, and Joseph P. Bell in charge, Engineering Section, Miscellaneous Machinery Division.

Casting caution to the wind, and with one long leap, we are into April 1942. This is the month during which the Miscellaneous Machinery Division and the Raw Materials Division threw their arms about each other and became one—the Miscellaneous Division, with Captain Welles H. Denney, headmaster. This was also the first of a sequence of months that saw a heavy influx of officers. Notable among the April arrivals were: Major Walter C. Pew, Captains Arthur J. Boyer, Robert H. Merz and Joseph I. Wexlin; first lieutenants

John R. Armstrong, Henry W. Gadsden, Frank W. Kron, Lawrence R. Redmond, David B. Robb, and John Stevens; second lieutenants Melvin Gingrich, James C. Hassett, Jesse C. Jessen, James L. Mingle and Maynard H. Patterson.

In June 1942, the Division organization appears set up about like this: Lieutenant Robert I. Felch, Assistant. Major Denny was acting as chief of production, with Camille J. Gulli as assistant. Constituting the Production Section is a Raw Materials and Components unit, with William Quinn, ably looking after emergency steels and substitutes; Al Testa has jurisdiction over Shop Equipment, Small Tools and Plant Expansion, and under him, Harold G. Hall, Jr., assigned to Production Details and Expediting.

On the inspection side, Bill Mortensen still was sitting in the driver's seat. Under him, were Paul W. Williams, in charge of Metals, Components and Containers; Henry Marcus on Machinery; Joseph P. Beel on Plant Expansion and Eddie Goliaszewski doubling on Inspection and Engineering.

In July 1942 when Gage Procurement was transferred from the Arsenals to the Districts, it became necessary to set up, in the Miscellaneous Division, a Gage Section. No sooner said than done, and Lieutenant James N. Kuntz, Penn Military College, 1931, and a former chief engineer, Department of Justice, was named Chief. His became the responsibility for administration of gage procurement and repair contracts in conjunction with the Procurement Planning and Purchase Sections of the District Office.

In August there was set up a Steel Expediting Group with B. C. Bell and P. J. Corriston sharing the honors. Also at this time, we find Lieutenant Maurice P. Felton in charge, Administration, Chester P. Elliott heading Production and Bill Mortensen on Inspection; a Raw Materials Section with Lieutenant Felton, Chief; Chester Elliott, attending Production, and William J. O'Brien on Purchase matters. In the Machine Tool and Equipment Section, the omnipresent Mortensen again throws his shadow, with Al Testa on Production, Henry Marcus on Inspection, and Bill O'Brien again doing the Purchase chore. And the Gage Section grows apace; Chester Elliott has the Production post, B. C. Bell appears on Contractor Assistance, and O'Brien, again—on Purchase. Late in the month F. S. Harshbarger was assigned the Gage Section.

Came September 1942, and Paul Williams was replaced in the Gage Section by J. O. Briscoe. Too, there were organizational readjustments in September. Now, a Production and Administration Section with Chester Elliott, and a Procurement Liaison Section under F. S. Harshbarger. Other divisions are: Raw Materials, Machinery and Gages. Heading Raw Materials is Lieutenant Robert Watson, with Camille J. Gulli, his production chief; J. O. Briscoe handling inspection, and, as before, P. J. McCorriston and B. C. Bell on Special (Steel) Expediting. Under Machinery it is now Lieutenant Mortensen with Albert Testa and J. I. Schwabe assisting, on Production, Henry E. Marcus on Inspection. Under Gages: L. H. Yeazel on Contract Assistance; F. S. Harshbarger on Procurement, assisted by B. M. Long, Eddie J. Goliaszewski on Expediting.

In October came the Thornton-Fuller Company contract W-670-Ord-3286 (Philadelphia Mobile Shop Depot, of which the complete story in another chapter) involving, at this time, more than $1,000,000, and the assembly of 2,500 mobile shop trucks of 14 types. Administration of this contract was placed with the Miscellaneous Branch, now the Miscellaneous Materials Branch. In December, Branch Chief Major Denny and Lieutenant Watson betook themselves to Raritan, New Jersey, to supervise the shipment from the Quartermasters to Philadelphia of various trucks and equipment. These officers completed their task in 22 days, moving to Philadelphia 98 freight car and 1400 truck loads of material and equipment. Organization during this period at Convention Hall, then being made ready to receive the incoming activity, was under the supervision of Lt. Colonel Arthur J. Seiler, Industrial Chief, and M. E. "Dusty" Miller, Director of Production. In addition to 108 Production Orders placed by P. O. D. in behalf of the contract, the District inherited 16 pertaining contracts and 144 Production Orders.

The fact that military and civilian personnel had been transferred from Washington and Raritan to set up in Convention Hall a Sub-Office of the Office of the Chief of Ordnance, was one indication of the extreme importance with which the contract was regarded in Pentagon circles.

February activity in the Miscellaneous Materials Branch was directed in large measure to the set-up within the Branch of a functioning group, and of routines bearing upon the mobile shop project. Major Denney was given complete personal charge of all shop matters. Collier A. Elliott was assigned as Administrative head to correlate efforts of Branch personnel and their specific duties. Lieutenant Bill Mortensen was assigned as administrative head to correlate efforts of Branch personnel and their specific duties: Lieutenant Bill Mortensen was assigned in charge of inspection and engineering; Al Testa, production, and Lieutenant Bob Watson, supervision of all matters in reference to crating at Barclay White Company. A. F. Haise, Jr., took over scheduling and traffic, while to Neal Armstrong was assigned the responsibility for the production of bodies at the four selected body facilities (Hicks Body Company, Perley A. Thomas Car Works, Hackney Brothers Body Company and Phillips & Buttorff). Barclay White Company had set up the crating enterprise in the old Ordnance Warehouse No. 2, in Tacony. J. O. Briscoe was made packaging chief.

Principal changes in 1943 in the Miscellaneous Materials Branch were the additions to the Mobile Shop Section of Captain Homes T. Case, Jr., as Chief, W. H. Lownsbury on packaging and on inspection, A. F. Haise to Production Planning.

In October 1943, all Mobile Shop Depot contracts were transferred to the Tank-Automotive Branch of the District, crating contracts going to Barclay White Company, generators and compressor units to Schramm, Inc., and ST-6 bodies to Hackney Brothers Body Company and Perley A. Thomas Car Works.

Two months later, in December, the Miscellaneous Materials Branch, having served its purpose, was liquidated. Major Denny moved over to the Production Service Branch under Major Paul H. Carlson; Albert Testa, to Production Equipment, and Chester A. Elliott, to the Conversion Engineering group.

☙❧

Chapter XXV

LABOR ROLLS ALONG

NAPOLEON was at least half right when he proclaimed that an Army proceeds on its stomach. Had he lived during World War II he would have without doubt placed emphasis upon transportation as well. The best trained Army, the most efficiently planned and directed supply program would have been well nigh useless without adequate means for the transport of soldiers, of material, of labor itself.

At the moment of entry by the United States in World War II, 85 per cent of this country's transportation was by automobile; 15 per cent by mass transportation units including buses. All automobile, truck and bus travel and a measurable portion of street car travel was on rubber. To the beginning of the war and to a moment shortly thereafter, 90 per cent of the world's rubber supply had fallen into enemy hands and imports—till then the market for 72 per cent of that production suddenly had ceased—and the military demand for rubber had risen to hitherto unheard of heights. Stock piles were negligible and the synthetic rubber supply was yet practically at zero.

Mass conveyances could not possibly reach all industrial areas. Many workers still depended upon automobiles to move them to their jobs.

Alarmed, the Office of the Chief of Ordnance ordered a survey of the personnel transportation problems of all Ordnance manufacturers, to the end that each plant would have a practical plan which would assure proper transportation for all workers.

Meetings were called by the then District Chief, C. Jared Ingersoll, with Army, Navy, War Production Board and Transit Company officials. Questionnaires were prepared and circulated throughout industry. Special studies were made of particular situations and, throughout, cooperation sought. Other agencies, in duplicating these activities, caused much confusion and, no doubt, occasioned delay in making plans effective.

In a report dated 15 September 1942, Colonel Hauseman wrote:

"The situation is becoming critical. By this Fall (1942) mass transportation units will have reached the saturation point. Action is needed now! Staggered hours, car sharing and other devices to increase the efficiency of both the private auto and public conveyance must be put into effect on a far wider basis than the present feeble attempts. Even if such expedients are applied immediately, their effects will only postpone trouble. Next Spring will probably see thousands of autos forced off the roads by lack of tires.

"It is not enough to leave planning to the Office of Defense Transportation and their local volunteer administration who suffer from lack of punitive authority. Plans proposed by that Office are for the maximum use of public conveyances and the minimum of private autos. They propose to change business and office hours, school hours, and stagger plant shifts. They would rearrange transit schedules and "hope" to carry the general public at peak hours. For private autos, the plans contemplate group riding, 'discourage' needless driving, and call for more care of tires and vehicles. . . . In due course all of these, and other expedients had of necessity to be adopted."

And out of it all developed the need for a regularly employed, full time transportation engineer, which brought to that task the assignment of big, genial, hard working William S. Canning, a Sharon Hill, Pennsylvania, "bundle from Heaven." Bill got under way in P. O. D. 1 June 1942, a few days following receipt of his commission as major in the Army Specialty Corps of the United States. It was during this period that the Transportation Unit was set up in the Conservation Section under the Planning Director. Later, as the problem of housing labor grew to critical dimensions, it became necessary to extend the functions of the Transportation Unit to include a housing program, the latter under Joseph M. Fronefield, III. The Unit then took the designation of Transportation and Housing Unit. In early 1944, the Unit assumed responsibility for fuel rationing, a task earlier discharged by the late Harry E. "Dick" Snyder, Thomas S. Potts and Lieutenant Paul E. Nieman. "Dick" Snyder, who even earlier had been in charge of scrap salvage, moved on to the Philadelphia Regional Office then under Major Victor W. Smith; Tom Potts to the Miscellaneous Sales Unit, Redistribution and Salvage Section, Production Service Branch of the Industrial Division; Lieutenant Nieman was named assistant to the officer-in-charge, Philadelphia Regional Office.

The Unit now was labeled the Transportation and Fuels Unit, Canning directing—continuing at the top post until August 1944 when the Unit, past the peak of its greatest usefulness and upon the release of its Chief, was added to the responsibilities of the Labor Liaison Unit under Lieutenant Jack Walsh.

The Unit, from its inception, and through its periods of increased responsibilities, to its eventful assignment to the Labor Officer, and for some time following, had been a vitally important activity in the District. Often there had been serious breakdowns of transportation that easily might have caused serious labor shortages and unwilling absenteeism. Tires on private cars and buses had a habit of wearing out in the face of rubber shortages. Gasoline soon was on the way to becoming a collection item. Vehicles broke down.

As to mass transportation, increased mileage was advocated in many instances, extra trips urged, skip-stops recommended, work hours staggered. Bad roads, snow clearance and weather generally had to be treated as tools of war production. Housing was an increasing problem. This lead to no end of surveys and programs set up by the National Housing Agency, HOLC, Chamber of Commerce, real estate brokers, War Housing Centers, War Manpower Commission and other pertaining agencies. There were meetings with and reports to the Petroleum Administration of War. Fuels as well as tires and gasoline had been rationed. During coal shortages many contractors turned to oil with consequent problems of plant facilities, safety factors and advisability generally of such changes.

The Unit was a busy one. At its head, W. S. did a conspicuously efficient bit of work. For a time he had the assistance of Joseph M. Fronefield; but for the longer route he handled the responsibility pretty much on his own.

Major Canning came to P. O. D. from the Keystone Automobile Club, Philadelphia, Pennsylvania, where, from 1927, he had been employed as Engineering Director, rendering counsel to the officers and directors of the Club in reference to all matters pertaining to highway construction, a service which also was available to the membership, and to municipalities and political subdivisions in alleviating traffic congestions or dangerous highway conditions.

During World War I Major Canning held the post of Construction Engineer and Area Engineer for the E. I. du Pont DeNemours Company, Inc., supervising the work of some three thousand men in the Pulping area of the Old Hickory Smokeless Powder Plant, Nashville, Tennessee.

All of which adds up to this: that the Keystone Automobile Club knew exactly what it was doing when it threw a net over Bill at the moment of his release by P. O. D.

Chapter XXVI

WE DID PRODUCE

AND P. O. D. actually was under way, in acquiring its production ABC's, quite some time prior to Pearl Harbor. The Production Studies and the Educational Orders of an earlier period, starting back in 1938, had taught personnel of the day much that proved helpful in later planning and had given contractors of the area a good foretaste of things to come.

Procedure and policy, as they developed through 1941, were based on lessons learned and experiences gained from World War I. Policy was almost wholly concerned with inspection activities. Production thinking was almost wholly confined to means and methods bearing on procurement activities. These activities, administered by Major, then Lieutenant, John W. Ogden, were concerned with the expediting of machine tools and the interpretation of the not-too-frequent O. C. O. directives on production procedures.

The Commodity Branches at this time were self-contained units, each with its own reporting procedure, and its own multiplicity of forms.

The few production men then in the Philadelphia Ordnance District circulated in the Field, largely to obtain information for the Monthly Control Report to O. C. O. These reports provided a concise production picture in reference to the contracts then in operation, and provided information regarding any unfavorable aspects relative to production. The production men helped only when specifically called in by the contractor.

Well, that was all changed. Increasing pressure from our allies-to-be and expanding operations under the National Defense Act made it necessary to organize groups in P. O. D. which would be in line with the need. For instance, Office Memorandum No. 85, dated 8 August 1941, clearly defined the duties of the Office of Production Director to be in reference to the supervision and coordination of all production activities in the District. Too, the Production Director now would be responsible to the District Chief, via the Chief of the Industrial Service (later, the Industrial Division). The Office Memorandum brought to the hitherto chaotic production set-up the first flush of order, which it achieved by establishing in each of the then five Commodity Branches, Production Units and Production Chiefs whose responsibility it became to review and coordinate the production activities of the Sub-Offices. These Production men were charged with the task of sound scheduling, anticipation of work stoppages, and general assistance to the contractors toward an increasingly efficient production. Reporting to the Officers-in-Charge of the Sub-Offices, they also were responsible for the preparation of Production Follow-Up-Reports and the other data required by the District Office.

All of which necessarily lead to an increase in Production Division personnel, although pressure had been somewhat relieved by transfers from among the Inspectors.

Still, there existed no very definite production policy. Sub-Office and Commodity Branch personnel were scattered over seven states. Materials were growing increasingly scarce and the War Production Board was running into critical shortages. Warnings were being broadcast of growing manpower shortages, and industry generally was beginning to feel the pinch.

There also was an obvious need for Ordnance decentralization from Washington. Inspection and Procurement already were decentralized, the latter to some extent, but Production remained no more than a liaison between the contractor and the Office of the Chief of Ordnance. For some time following 7 December 1941, many committees came from Washington, mainly to consider whether procurement and production activities should be assigned the Districts or given over to the War Production Board or other agencies. These committees included such "prominents" of the time as Bernard Baruch, Lt. General William Knudsen, Lt. General Levin H. Campbell, Jr., Brigadier General John K.

Christmas and others. Apparently satisfied with the thinking and the direction in which the Districts then were moving, these "prominents" decided that the Districts would have to stand on their own feet, and evolve some method or centrally controlled means within each District for planning and controlling production, in order to properly fulfill their functions.

The Production Chief during this period was Captain Hayward K. "Ken" Kelley, who had taken over the Production post a few months earlier, in August 1941. Shortly after Pearl Harbor it became necessary to initiate some temporary basic control as a stop-gap until a more complete Production Control System could be devised. This was one of Captain Kelley's early problems.

Analysis by Lt. Colonel, then Captain, Arthur J. Seiler, Chief of the Industrial Division, and Captain Kelley, of production facilities up and down the District, revealed a situation as startling as it was disastrous to production progress: Many facilities in the District still were clinging to pre-war philosophies; and some still were trying to operate with the old-fashioned type of inventories which had been efficient when materials were plentiful. Production men of P.O.D. soon came to the realization that they must step in and show these facilities how to control production lines by controlling and assuring a steady flow from suppliers of material and component parts. This was the essence of the whole production problem; and in the face of a continued resistance from a number of facilities to what they considered interference.

It was during December 1941 that Short List forms were installed. These listed the component and major items most urgently needed to balance assembly lines and thus hasten supplies to overseas points. When an item was shown on the Short List, the following actions were taken:

1. Efforts to increase work hours to three 8-hour shifts, seven days a week.
2. Closer touch with machine tool and material requirements.
3. Labor problems, actual or impending, were given every consideration, and recommendations made for remedial action.
4. Higher priority ratings secured when necessary.
5. Personnel gradually to be expanded to include production engineers to be assigned to specific projects at individual plants.

At the same time it was apparent that hurried employment of Ordnance Production personnel had resulted in procurement of the basically wrong type; men who were of Civil Service clerical level and, while capable of making reports, did not exhibit the analytical and aggressive qualities needed. It therefore became necessary to look outside Ordnance for persons with industrial experience capable of grasping and tearing apart the multiplicity of problems beginning to stack up, and of initiating individual action within the then limited Ordnance framework. It was realized that, although beginning with some measure of technical "know-how," these men would have to think as Ordnance men before they should be able to influence the thinking of industry. Further, only a few manufacturers were familiar with Ordnance procedure and P.O.D. production assistance was being requested to an ever-increasing degree.

In developing properly qualified personnel it was also realized that capable production engineers with college training or comprehensive industrial experience should be given a prominent place. In January 1942, two machine tool and processing specialists were employed, men capable of analyzing the complete processing of any item, and of appraising the requirements, the proper machine tool set-up on individual operations, grinding, heat treating and other processes.

Many changes in reference to personnel of the Production Director's office were made during the early months of 1942; many new personnel were acquired. Organization charts were drawn in accordance with basic thinking; job analyses were worked out with the Civilian Personnel Branch, and Civil Service Ratings obtained for the entire framework. Hiring of personnel gained momentum, and Production Sections in the Commodity Branches were greatly expanded to keep up with demands imposed by the steady conversion to war production of contractors in the area.

It was during the early part of 1942 that Lt. Colonel, then Captain, Seiler, Major, then Captain, W. L. Lafean, Jr., Chief, Statistics and Reports Section, and Marion E. "Dusty" Miller collaborated in setting up the District's first Production Control System. It was realized as more and more experience was gained that any such system would have of necessity to provide a complete picture of all phases of production on each contract.

A pioneer chart system was initiated, in January 1942, in one plant, in reference to 90 mm. Anti-Aircraft Guns. The company had been several months in production, but to 1 January, not one gun had been completed. Contractor personnel believed that several more months must pass before results could be achieved. A Detail Control Chart therefore was prepared to meet the particular requirements of this contract. When completed, the chart was set up in the plant. When all the production factors had been entered thereon, it became clear to "Dusty" Miller, who engineered this assignment, what were the bottlenecking factors. "Dusty" spent 48 hours in the plant "on one stretch," sparking the operatives, supervising their procedures, getting them into the spirit of the task. He rubbed his hands, yawned, rustled a cup of coffee and headed for home—but not for long. He soon was back in the plant. The miracle had fouled! So, 36 more long hours, headaches and what not; but this time the idea struck fire. One gun was produced in January; three in February. The contractor considered this an excellent result, inasmuch as the company previously had been unable to offer a definite schedule, and had not expected to deliver the first gun before late in March.

The same basic control plan was applied to a contract at "X" Company for adapter clusters. Colonel Kelley and Thomas W. Beattie took on this assignment 1 February 1942. It was immediately apparent to these "sharp eyes of Ordnance" that the problem here was largely one of obtaining materials and that, on the basis of delivery schedules obtained by the contractor from some of the suppliers, it would be approximately 1 May before production could be got under way. The Ordnance schedule had called for deliveries to start 15 February. The item then was broken down into twenty component parts and each part charted. Then the expediting; a la Kelley and Beattie, the latter sweating it out at the plant from 7 A.M. to eleven and twelve o'clock at night, answering innumerable telephone calls, keeping in touch with Colonel Kelley, who was handling the P.O.D. end. Thus were the bottlenecked components and materials expedited to the plant and in time to begin production 1 March, two months ahead of the contractor's schedule. And that will give the reader a general idea of this Production Control procedure.

Following many sessions of "knock-down-and-drag-out" discussion, a more or less final form of Detail Control Chart was evolved—one adapted to practically every type of materiel produced in the District. Thinking in reference to a Production Control Program had matured by 26 March 1942, and on this date all Officers-in-Charge and Chiefs of Production in both Commodity Branches and the Sub-Offices were called into a meeting. Colonel Hauseman outlined the need for the Program. The first day of the meeting was given to talks covering the various pertaining phases. On the following day the Chiefs of Production were given concrete problems to work out. The results became subjects for discussion.

Preparation of a Production Control Manual was a logical development of the meetings and the earlier experiments. This manual, the production bible, traced in detail every step of the production job from the Notification of Award to the completion of the end product, assembled, and shipped. Duties and responsibilities of the Sub-Office Production Sections; matters bearing upon Production records, Production Reports, requests for assistance and all other related matters and contingencies were covered at length. And publication of this critical manual came at a time when mass conversion of industry was reaching for its peak.

A most pressing problem at this time was that of procurement of materials. Emphasis consequently was placed on this phase of production control, and the District was made conscious of the obstacles involved. Following this, the matter of sub-contracting moved into the bottleneck area—which made it necessary that P.O.D. redouble its efforts to provide assistance to contractors. In succession, deliveries of Government and Manufacturers' Gages came to "trouble and vex." Emphasis subsequently was placed on procurement of these items through other than the then established sources.

In March 1942 Lt. Colonel, then Captain, H. K. Kelley was relieved of the Production assignment and reassigned as Chief of the Ammunition Branch, succeeding Captain A. W. Hamilton, later Lt. Colonel. The assistant Chief of Production, "Dusty" Miller, moved into the berth relinquished by Lt. Colonel Kelly, his former chief.

There had developed to this time a pressing need for a means of keeping the Production Director more intimately informed of production progress in the Sub-Offices. To meet this need, the Director added to his staff, in March 1942, five Zone Supervisors whose main duties were to co-ordinate the activities of the Sub-Office Production Sections with those of the Commodity Divisions and the Office of the Production Director. There had also developed at this time the need for further instructing new personnel in their duties as Production representatives. This lead to the introduction, in June 1942, of a Production Control Training Course. Using the Production Manual as a basis, a program for the training, grading and intelligent assignment of the various types of production personnel was worked out. N. M. Dunning and Albert P. Cormier, former instructors at General Electric Company, and Sears, Roebuck Company, respectively, were called in as instructors, and a course of study covering the history of the Ordnance Department, the organizational set-up of P.O.D., and duties and responsibilities of production personnel was put to work and, as the record reveals, with telling effects.

Now, with industry pretty much in stride as regarded conversion to war production, the problem became one of balancing and scheduling. The District now was being frequently reminded by Washington of the critical need for accurate predictions—for bringing production to a high level and in line with contract schedules—to the end that the General Staff might know at all times which items, and in what quantities, would be available, and at the right time. To accomplish this, Monthly Plans for Production were required on every prime contract and on important sub-contracts bearing production order numbers. These plans contained predictions of the number of items which would be produced over the life of the contract, but were subject to revision in accordance with changing conditions. They did not necessarily follow contract schedules.

Later, when it became apparent that the Plans for Production could not be used as a basis for predicting production one month in advance, due to repeated revisions during the month of production, there was developed a system known as semi-monthly production estimates. Nor was this the final development in keeping check on production progress. As new situations developed during the changing tides of war, new procedures, each with its complement of forms and formalities, were quickly integrated. Enough has been covered in this chapter to introduce the reader to the problems involved in starting off an Ordnance production division. There were developed Daily Progress Reports, and Summary Progress Reports prepared at the end of the month on the basis of the Daily Progress Reports. There was a Schedules and Production Book, providing schedules and estimates. This was the bright idea of Robert Rimsky, further developed by Captain W. L. Lafean, Jr., both of the Statistics and Reports Section of

P. O. D. There were Production Follow-up Reports; Spare Parts Progress Reports, Work Plan Sheets and so on, and so on, with the usual revisions, obsoletions and innovations to be expected in connection with any fast expanding organization.

Production graphs were initiated in April 1942—providing quick pictures of production trends. These graphs were employed as bases for the Production Review meetings initiated in May 1942. Red List contracts officially were initiated mid-way of 1942. These were a development of the semi-monthly Production Review meetings.

As of the early 1942 period, production and allied topside stood as follows:

Production Co-ordinator . . . . MALCOLM WHITE
Production Chief . . . . MARION E. "DUSTY" MILLER
Production Expediting . . . . C. J. SEYFFERT
Labor Supply . . . . . . LT. LEWIS H. VAN DUSEN, JR.
Machine Tools . . . . ROY R. JOHNSON
Priorities . . . . CAPTAIN LEWIS A. SMITH, JR.
Statistics and Reports . . . CAPTAIN W. L. LAFEAN, JR.
Technical Data . . . . LT. MARVIN C. JILBERT
Clerical Section . . . . SAMUEL R. SHADEL

And so, through 1942 and into 1943 and the registration, 15 February, as Production Director, of Marion E. Miller, who departed the District Office for the post of Director of Production for Thornton-Fuller Company, operating contractors of the Philadelphia Mobile Shop, where production at the moment was being stepped up to what then seemed an impossible 1,200 units per month.

On 1 March 1943, Charles O. Guernsey was assigned "Dusty" Miller's former post, in addition to his duties as Technical Director and Industry Integration Committees Liaison. One of the first steps to be taken as a result of this change was the elimination of the Zone Supervisors, based upon the conclusion that the prior requirements for Sub-Office (now Regional Office) integration of production procedures had been accomplished, and that now these offices were equipped to "pull their own weight."

Personnel changes, to the end of March 1943, in the Production Section, were as follows:

1. The remaining three Zone Supervisors were reassigned thus—A. O. Tepper was made Chief of Production at the Mobile Shop Depot; Carl J. Morash was assigned to the P. O. D.,

Special Assistance Section, and Murry Kester was assigned to the same section, temporarily. He resigned, 31 March.

2. Major Ed. W. Lafferty, was appointed Chief, Production Equipment Section, which comprised the former Machine Tool Section, and the Production Engineering Group.

3. Roy R. Johnson, 'till then Chief of the Machine Tool Section, reassigned as Chief of Production, Ammunition Branch.

4. Jack Miller, Chief of Production in the Ammunition Branch, was made assistant to Ammunition Chief, Lt. Colonel "Ken" Kelley.

5. Robert F. Rundle was named Chief of the Special Assistance Section and was assigned to Major, then Captain, Paul H. Carlson, Chief of the Production Service Branch, as assistant.

6. Robert L. Kirk was appointed head of the C. M. P. Section and Priorities Section.

7. Captain Lewis A. Smith, Jr., Chief of the Priorities Section was reassigned to the Tank-Automotive Branch.

8. Blythe J. Minnier, Administration Assistant to M. E. Miller was assigned as a member of Chief Guernsey's staff.

9. John Green and L. L. Hepburn, were assigned to the Production Engineering Section as assistants to Major E. W. Lafferty.

The production responsibility no longer weighed heavily upon the Production Director. Procedures now had been well integrated, production men trained in their respective responsibilities, points of difference and of conflict satisfactorily adjusted. The District had grown up. In December 1943, the Production Chief resigned—and was not frequently seen in these parts thereafter.

From here on through the balance of the war production program, the historian is hearing and seeing more and more of one William E. Gilbert, who first landed in P. O. D. in June 1942, turning up as a Production specialist. In June 1943, he appeared in the Philadelphia Regional Office as a Contract Supervisor, an easy step to his transfer two months later to the Industrial Division, Production Service Branch, as Industrial Specialist. In this latter capacity "Bill" inherited all the Production headaches of the District together with the job of keeping the production house in order; all contracts running according to schedule—and better, as might be required by the exigencies of battle. His, the job of routing out all the production bugs, sprinkling O. C. O. salt on their tails and smearing their obnoxious carcasses with his particular brand of D. D. T. He was all over the place like an epidemic, pointing a production short-cut here, expanding a bottleneck somewhere else and speeding up a procedure in between. "Bill" Gilbert knew production, and what was even better, he knew human nature. It is not in the archives that he was often fooled—and then, not for long.

Production, like other P. O. D. activities, was always in good hands.

Chapter XXVII

"METAL" AND SOME OTHER "URGENCIES"

THIS is the story of the Conversion Engineering Section of P.O.D. and how it grew. Also, why.

Soon after Pearl Harbor the District Chief and the Chief of Ordnance unleashed a flood of requests for investigations—infinite in their variety; investigations of contractors' plants, of contractors' equipment, ability and know-how; and of items of material. At the same time, topside was requesting in rising volume and increasing tempo, means of utilizing idle industry in the area.

There was in existence in P.O.D. during those early days a particular group which immediately could be charged with the responsibility of integrating and expediting the rush of requests. So, under orders of Brigadier General, the then Major Hauseman, there was organized by H. Paul Gant, Planning Director, a Special Projects Section which "hung out its shingle" early in July of 1942 with H. P. at the head, assisted by four capable engineers—Thomas S. Potts, Ed. Rubincame, George D. Mateer, Charles J. Tehle. The names of Joe Anglada and Blythe J. Minnier also appear.

It was the responsibility of the newly formed group to handle anything of a special nature coming into the District, conduct investigations, interview visitors having ideas, and to study the feasibility of conversions of products to non-critical materials, and use of unskilled labor.

A special investigation in reference to "The Ecomonic Distress, and the Expansion of the War Industry in the Anthracite Area of Pennsylvania." made during the spring-summer of 1942, by George D. Mateer was an outstanding report—comprehensive, and immeasurably helpful to procurement personnel.

It was the Special Projects Section group which in 1942 expedited the Emergency Urgent assignment of locating and developing a facility for the manufacture of Mobile Shops. Under Paul Gant's direction each member of the section was assigned a definite part of the task. Several days were spent in establishing contacts. Raritan Arsenal, Raritan, New Jersey, was visited and a report made of the manufacturing procedures followed at that installation. It was following that visit that a cost-plus-a-fixed fee contract (mentioned in an earlier chapter), was entered into with the Thornton-Fuller Company, for the assembly of Mobile Shops and other Service units.

As had often happened under the swift changes incident to this war of movement, change also came to the Special Projects Section—change and, in a way, oblivion. The Section as such had outgrown itself. The several activities had developed to a point where decentralization had become an imperative. In the break up, there was established a separate and independent Conversion Engineering Section.

Hence Dan Bell.

Daniel H. Bell, Pittsburgh born, and engineer extraordinary, was an inductee of Charles O. Guernsey. Dan Bell brought with him a B.S. in mechanical engineering earned at the University of Pittsburgh, and a rich experience gained as Research Director for Electric Service Supplies Company, Philadelphia, and as Design Engineer for the Pittsburgh Railways Company. Dan was the man for the job, as events were to prove.

The new section was not long in making its presence felt. By 31 December of the same year, Dan Bell and his boys had passed along to Pentagonia a total of 127 suggestions. Of these, 37 were approved; 13 were hanging fire as the month ended. By 31 January 1943, there had been submitted to the Fire Control Section, Frankford Arsenal, more than 200 suggestions in reference to Directors M5 and M6, and Telescope Mount, M16. During the life of the Conversion Engineering Section, there were submitted to Washington more than 600 suggestions of which more than 300 had been approved, the remainder about equally divided between "rejects" and those held for further consideration. Among the many and varied suggestions comprising the grand total will be found such as the following:

Fuze, Dummy, 72–5–9, M69, M69B1, 40mm.—Plastic to Zinc Die Casting

Tube, A398397, Multiple Gun Motor Carriage, M54—Seamless to Electric Welded Tubing

Commander's Tripod—Canvas and Leather to Plywood

Torpedo, Bangalore, M1, 82–15–10—Steel, Terne Plate and Copper to Aluminum

Target, Rocket Projector, M1—Redesign

Adjusting Stem, B201309, 37 mm., A Gun Carriage M54—Down-grading of Bronze

Follower, B136720 Fuze Setter, M10—Brass to Secondary Aluminum

Terminal Box, C54724, 6 in. Barbette Carriage—Bronze to Malleable Iron

Powder Box, M2, 74–6–53—Metal to Plywood

Seal, A231472, 105 mm. Howitzer Mount, M4—Crude Rubber to Synthetic

Head, C85228, 240 mm. Gun Carriage—Machined Part to Steel Casting

Trap Assembly, 82–5–26L, Rockets M6 and M7—Method of Manufacture

Axle, Front, D58264, M3A3 Small Tank—Method of Fabrication

Panel, C87268, 6 in. Barbette Carriage—Simplification of Design

Drill Cartridge, 27–3–76, 90 mm. Gun, M1—Malleable Iron to Meehanite

Hub, C85322, 240 mm. Gun Carriage—Machined Part to Stamping

Brace, B154327, 37 mm. Gun Carriage—Elimination of Machined Part

Major Victor W. Smith when Chief, Philadelphia Regional Office, and part of his hard hitting team. *Left to right:* Lieutenant Frank W. Kron, Lieutenant Phil Welch, the late Harry "Dick" Snyder, William Patterson, the Major, William Holloway, Lieutenant Hugh Troth, Harold D. Goldberg and Lieutenant William H. Nichols

Turret Platform, M4 Tank—Elimination of Bolts

Grip, B141536, Medium Tank—Rubber to Plastic

Disc, Flash Hider, B24351 Cal. .50 M1 Machine Gun—Saving of Metal

Motor Trucks 73RTA410—Omit Useless Sheet Metal Parts and Running Boards

Fin, 82–1–78D and 79D, M9A1 and M11A1 Grenade—Spot Welded to Crimped Design

And so it went, day after day, week on week, month following month, with incalculable savings in critical materials, in manufacturing time and in speeding up production when speed was of the essence. Early in 1944 when it appeared that the Conversion Engineering Section had served its larger purpose it was made a part of the Planning Engineering Section where it continued on a reduced basis until it finally departed the District Office to become a function of the Philadelphia Ammunition Supply Office at 906 Chestnut Street.

The work in the Conversion Engineering Section, according to Tom Potts, had its humorous interludes, sessions with crack-pot inventors and embryo Rube Goldbergs coming with a sincere desire to expedite victory but whose engineering thinking was definitely "off the beam." One "inventor," for example, proposed the use of bolas as defensive weapons against tanks. The idea was that anti-tank groups would be supplied with these bolas which they would throw in the path of approaching tanks; the weight-balls on the three ends of the connecting cords would, it was promised, entangle with the sprockets and throw off the treads, or jam the tracks so that the tank could not move. When told that the enemy might very soon discover so ingenious a device and use it against U. S. tanks, the "inventor" calmly stated that Ordnance being as smart as it was would devise some means of quickly removing the bolas wrapped around the tracks so that they could continue in action. "But suppose," added Tom Potts, "the enemy developed a means of preventing our unsnarling the preventive device?"

Followed, from another amateur Kettering, a device which, it was claimed, would allow an airplane time to get away after dropping a bomb load. The contraption consisted of a large ring suspended from the aircraft, said ring carrying about twenty "holders" each of which would hold an 81 mm. Shell or some type of small bomb. The plane was to fly in its course over its target and cut loose the series of projectiles. As the ring of bombs fell, a parachute which was attached would open, easing the descent. Due to this abrupt change of speed, the latch holding No. 1 bomb would release, and as No. 1 left its holder it would release the latch for No. 2 bomb, and so on until all twenty bombs had been released.

To conserve steel on another project, an inventor suggested that bombs be made of plywood.

These suggestions were not in all cases the product of minds on vacation. Very likely many grew out of desperate desires to have the war quickly over and loved ones back home; well-intentioned persons driven by anxiety to do something, anything, or to feel that they were doing something. These persons, all of them, whatever their mechanical "concoctions" were welcome at 150 South Broad where they were assured of courteous, interested attention; and good reason, for no one could know from whence would come the next big idea in Ordnance.

Happily, Dan Bell was blessed with capable assistants. For instance, Tom Potts, of whom more earlier in this narrative; Charley Tehle, out of Cornell with his mechanical engineering sheepskin, picking up on his way to P. O. D., a World War I assignment as a Director of Construction for the Emergency Fleet Corporation, and almost 20 years with Westinghouse Electric Corporation, on Navy contracts. And, of course, George Mateer, Drexel Institute of Technology star pupil in electrical engineering.

"And whither hath flown these pretty birds?" Dan Bell, so goes the record, found himself upon completion of his P. O. D. assignment, with the Philadelphia Transportation Company, as Superintendent of Rolling Stock and Shops—Surface and Bus Lines; Charley Tehle unearthed new opportunities with the Aviation Gas and Turbine Division of the Defense Plant Corporation; George Mateer elected to return to private engineering practice; Tom Potts found escape in a busy niche of Reconstruction Finance Corporation—these and all the other good men of the old Section, no doubt toughened for the reconstruction era ahead.

Mr. John A. Anglada, a senior mechanical engineer in the Conversion Engineering Section, died on 14 December 1942. Anglada, who had previously served in Technical Division in Washington on development of tanks and automotive vehicles, gave valuable support to work of this section to which he reported 16 November 1942.

Chapter XXVIII

SMALL ARMS, BIG BUSINESS

IN JULY 1942, the Miscellaneous, Artillery and Ammunition Branches of P. O. D. went out of the small arms business. From now on the District was to have an independent Small Arms Branch as per requirements then recently received from "down under."

Functionally, the new Branch followed generally the lines established in the older Commodity Branches—a Branch Chief, in this case Captain Joseph I. (Perpetual Motion) Wexlin who actually put the Branch together and made it tick.

Set up and ready to operate, the Small Arms Branch was about like this:

Chief—Captain Joseph I. Wexlin
Administration—P. W. Sutro
Production—W. B. Richards
Inspection—Paul W. Williams
Technical Unit—P. W. Sutor

The activities of these men were further distributed over the Ammunition Section, the Gun and Mount Section and the Hand Arms and Equipment Sections of the Branch. Personnel changes were frequent and in line with the changing phases of war's requirements. In mid-1943, Lieutenant R. T. Henderson appears as successor to P. W. Sutro in the Administration position; a CMP Section added with A. Koch in charge, and a Packaging Unit added, headed by P. H. Guthrie—all of whose duties still embraced the Sections of the Branch.

Among the contracts taken over by the new Branch were those covering:

Ammunition Belts, Cal. .30

Packing Cartons for 5 Round Clips

Packing Cartons for 8 Round Clips

Core, Armor Piercing, Cal. .303

Metallic Belt Links, Cal. .30, M1

Metallic Belt Links, Cal. .50, M1

Mount Tripod, M2, for Cal. .50 Machine Gun, Anti-Aircraft

Before the end of the year the following had been added to the responsibilities of the rapidly accelerating Joe and his lads:

Bandolier, M1, Cal. .30

Belt, Ammunition, Cal. .30, M1917

Box, Ammunition, Cal. .30, M1, 250 Rounds

Box, Ammunition, Cal. .50, M2

Carton, Aircraft, Ammunition, Cal. .30, M1

Carton, Bandolier, Cal. .30

Carton, Packing, 8 Rounds, Clips

4 Ball, Cal. .50

Core, A. P., Cal. .303

Cup, Cal. .30

Holster, Pistol, Cal. .45, M1916

Metallic Belt Links, Cal. .50, M1 and M2

Machine, Belt, Filling, Cal. .50

Linking Machine, Cal. .50, Ammunition

Mount, Machine Gun, Cal. .50, M3

Mount, Tripod, Anti-Aircraft Gun, Cal. .50, M2A1

Assembly, Rifle, U. S. Cal. .30, M1917

Strip, Gilding, for Cal. .50, A. P. Bullet Jacket

Later the Small Arms Branch received from the Rifle Section, Office of the Chief of Ordnance, an allocation of 9,500,000 of a requirement of 300,-000,000 clay pigeons. Four million of P. O. D.'s share was to be procured from hardware and sporting goods stores. Of the larger quantity there isn't much to say, because neither P. O. D. nor the clay pigeon facilities ever reached first base; and only 2,675,000 of the silica columbidae to be obtained through the retail stores ever reached Army destinations via this District.

However, what prestige the District may have lost in connection with the "birds" it regained by a wide margin in a procurement of fliers' armor. The Wexlin star was again in the ascendency.

The fliers' armor allocation landed in the District in the Fall of 1943. It called for 74,891 suits of Body Armor, T-2 and 87,139 Suits, T-3. This was a new item for both P. O. D. and the facilities—and it brought all the headaches of procurement, expediting and administration during a period when just about every item was critical and P. O. D. brain-power driving on all cylinders, but the District made good with a vengeance.

In January 1944 the Small Arms Branch was merged with the Artillery Branch of P. O. D. to form the Artillery-Small Arms Branch, the Major continuing in charge of small arms matters. Later, with the increasing pressure being put upon contract terminations, Joe switched to the top assignment of the Terminations Section, Artillery-Small Arms Branch, a post which he held to the moment of his separation in December 1945.

Among others who served under the Wexlin banner were Lieutenant Bernhard D. Fortmann and Second Lieutenant Guy E. Hancock, Jr. Lieutenant Fortmann, then Second Lieutenant, Lehigh University 1934, senior ROTC, was transferred 17 June 1943 from the New York Ordnance District to P. O. D. and on 15 July 1943 was assigned to the Small Arms Branch. In the New York Ordnance District his critical responsibility was the supervision of production engineers assigned to production of Ordnance material at forty or more facilities. On the basis of his performance he was assigned to the Office of the Chief, Industrial Division of that District.

On 8 April 1944, Second Lieutenant Fortmann was promoted to First Lieutenant, and on 1 October 1944, he began his assignment as Ordnance representative on the 60 mm. and 81 mm. Trench Mortar Integrating Committee, succeeding Captain L. B. Redmond, Officer-in-Charge, York Regional Office. The Committee was placed on an inactive status, 24 August 1945, and Lieutenant Fortmann was reassigned to the Property Disposal Branch—and by 12 October he was on his way to his separation point.

Guy Hancock was born in Newark, Delaware. He was a graduate of Beacom College, Wilmington, Delaware, and of Iowa State College where he graduated in 1941 in general engineering and acquired his B.S. degree. In his pre-Ordnance days he had been associated with the Phillips Packing Company, as supervisor of shipping and, later, with Ingersoll-Rand Company as office engineer. He reported 22 May 1942 to the District Office,

when he was assigned to the Small Arms Branch, where he remained until his assignment, 29 September 1942 to the Berwick Regional Office. On 22 January 1943, he received his commission as a first lieutenant. Four days later he was reassigned Office, Chief of Ordnance, Field Service Division, with station at Zone 2, Baltimore Ordnance Zone.

All of which brings the narrative cheek to jowl with Small Arms royalty himself, Joseph Irwin Wexlin, who entered active duty in P. O. D. 15 April 1942. Joe was a born and bred New Yorker, and a graduate of Cooper Union and Columbia University where he majored in chemistry and physics. He later enrolled at George Washington University for special studies. As a result of the chemistry and physics studies, Joe was able to obtain a position in the laboratory of the Bethlehem Steel Company, Sparrows Point, Maryland. He entered the Navy early in World War I and saw service on one of those ships that touched practically every principal port around the world. Fire control was his chief interest during this period. In 1922 he went to Washington for research work in the Biological Laboratory of the Veterans' Bureau. An officer of that installation, interested in Joe's zeal, recommended him to Bausch & Lomb Optical Company. That company saw in our future Major the makings of a real salesman, supplementing his already demonstrative ability in scientific research. The result? When, in 1928, they opened a Philadelphia office, Joe was elected to take over, which he did.

The sea was back in Joe's blood in 1939 and he enlisted in the Naval Reserve. However, he was not able to devote any time to sea duty and had therefore to resign. During this period, and via his work with the optical firm, he had many contacts with Frankford Arsenal, for the greater part in reference to range finders. Here, Lieutenant General, then Major, R. L. Maxwell, Deputy District Chief, Philadelphia Ordnance District was attracted to Bausch & Lomb's young man, interested him in Army Ordnance with the result that in March 1936 he was commissioned a Second Lieutenant in the Army of the United States.

Came May 1940, and Joe was appointed a First Lieutenant, and in April 1942, a Captain. His Majority was validated 27 January 1944. He was assigned on the heels of his First Lieutenant's commission to the Massachusetts Institute of Technology, and, subsequently to the University of Michigan for special metallurgical work. There was a plan on foot about this time for the District to take over Frankford Arsenal optical procurement, and the Captain's services were held in reserve for that work. However, the plan did not come to fruition, and the Captain, now on the loose, was assigned to the now forming Labor Section, following which he was assigned, in May 1942, as Officer-in-Charge, Bethlehem Regional Office, arriving at Bethlehem in the wake of a flood that had threatened to wreck the then critical 75 mm. Shell Program. In one shop at Bethlehem Steel Company he found it necessary to use a rowboat when making an inspection. Fortunately for the war effort, the salvage work was quickly accomplished and a new program initiated. At the time of his release to other duties shells were being produced at the rate of 120,000 monthly. On 18 July 1942 he took over command of the new Small Arms Branch.

Joe also was one of the organizers of the Officers' Mess in P. O. D. retaining his interest to the final, or "Victory Mess," at which he was master of ceremonies, which was held on 7 December 1945, in Kenny's Cafe, Camden, New Jersey. It was at this "blowout" that the military of P. O. D. were given an opportunity to say farewell to the departing District Chief, Colonel A. D. Kelso, and to present that fine officer with a token of their admiration and respect.

Many a humorous situation developed in P. O. D. over the spread of Major Joe's association with the District. One of which he liked to recount the gruesome details, was of Major Charley Michener's bivouac. "This first was discussed during a little get-together at the Racquet Club," Joe told your historian. "Colonel Hauseman said he had been thinking of having a shindig of some kind for the officers, and he suggested the bivouac. Lt. Colonel, then Major, Robert G. Allen picked up the idea and things started to move.

"I'll never forget what happened when I tried to make a picture of the outfit, which, incidentally, was making camp at the York Proof Range. The whole gang lined up for the picture and I was supposed to be the official photographer. The funny part of it was that the boys were about half frozen and couldn't stand still. That night it was even colder. Everybody was shivering around the big fire that the fellows had built at the bottom of a hill, and eating beef that had been obtained from the Q. M.

"It was fairly early during the evening when Major Nichols of the Quartermasters, the officer from whom the P. O. Ders procured the beef, pulled out a fur lined jacket, and after I had fixed up his pup tent, crawled, thoroughly chilled, into bed. Oh, I forgot to add that the Major before retiring gathered up some brush to make a pillow for me, which, I hope to Hannah! was all of an inch thick. I later made the discovery that half of the brush was poison ivy. Such is war!

"Furthermore, the Major and some others of the wags built a fire at the bottom of the hill but had arranged my tent to face up the hill. As a result I was in a constant draft all night and by morning I was frozen to death. They buried me in a little patch adjacent to a nearby 'pub'."

The Major liked to tell the story of a procurement from H. W. Butterworth Sons Company of Philadelphia. "Remember," he said, "they were required to produce M2A Gun Mounts. We got all set and all of a sudden the report came through: We didn't have any racks, and we didn't know where, at this late date, we could get them! Consequently we couldn't put the thing together. The end item was critical. We had to save face. Industrial Division Chief, Lt. Colonel, then Major, Seiler, called me in and told me I was to get the racks. We called Washington but got very poor consolation from that direction. Finally, I went out to John O'Rourke and told him, 'We have got to get those racks as we have topside authority for asking for them. We need three hundred and fifty of them. What do you suggest we do, John?' The only suggestion he could offer was to get them through a washing machine company.

"So John, who always got what he went out for, went to Cleveland and came back with three hundred racks. He worked from eight-thirty in the morning until sundown and then did some hard-fisted 'horse trading'! Until the last minute he feared he might have to come back without them.

"Immediately the blanks arrived we stuck them into the heat-treating machine, running out all the racks then in existence.

"Later, when we asked John what were his instructions he replied, 'Well, all I remember was I had a "message for Garcia." ' "

When this story was first told to a group in P. O. D., Major A. W. Gilmer recalled, "I think an interesting story is of the time one of our inspectors went up to Butterworth's and told Harry Butterworth's people to get out in a hurry five thousand of a particular sub-assembly they were working on at the time. If they accomplished this, the inspector told them, they would be doing a beautiful job. Inspired by this sort of talk they got out the five thousand units as requested. The inspector then started fireworks by telling the men, 'Let's get out five thousand more!' Those men were already on the verge of exhaustion."

Now a word about John O'Rourke, long in P. O. D. John was born in Chester, Pennsylvania. He received his education in the schools of that city, Washington, D. C., and over on the Jersey side. During World War I he served in the 78th Division, 311th Infantry, spending one year overseas. He was honorably discharged in May 1919. Before entering the Service he had been employed by Taylor-Wharton Iron & Steel Company, High Bridge, New Jersey. Upon his return to civilian life he was placed with a subsidiary of that company, the Tioga Steel & Iron Company of Philadelphia, manufacturers of forges, shafts, cylinders and shells. The two companies later merged their operations, and moved to Easton, Pennsylvania.

In 1940, when war became imminent and it appeared that the United States eventually would be drawn in, John offered his services to P. O. D. and was employed in July of that year. His first assignment was to Watertown Arsenal for basic inspection training. This was the first such assignment made to that Arsenal. Upon completion of his instructions at that point, he was assigned to join the first advanced group at Rock Island Arsenal for a special ten weeks' course. Returning to the District he was sent by Major, then Captain, William H. Stephens, Jr., Chief of the Property Branch, to American Car & Foundry Company, Berwick, Pennsylvania, for supervision of shipping the first order of tanks got out for the British. Back again in Philadelphia, he was asked to assist Major, then Lieutenant, John H. Beyer for a period of two weeks on Artillery items. The two weeks

stretched out into more than two years, during which John O'Rourke made plenty of production history, right to the eve of his departure in mid 1945.

Earlier in this chapter, mention was made of Paul W. Williams, Assistant Chief, and in charge of Inspection in the Small Arms Branch. His first employment out of Gettysburg College was by the Midvale Company of Philadelphia. While with that Company he matriculated for an evening course in metallurgy which Penn State College was conducting at Temple University. Practical knowledge of fabrication of steel together with his studies of metallurgy made of him valuable timber for P. O. D. in 1940 when there was critical need of "men who knew and knew that they knew."

One of Paul Williams' first assignments was to Picatinny Arsenal for training in inspection techniques. Upon his return to P. O. D. he was made assistant to the Chief of the Raw Materials Branch, W. A. Mortensen. It was decided in July 1942 to place with the several Commodity Branches all responsibility for pertaining raw materials. With this liquidation of the Raw Materials Branch, Metallurgist Williams was assigned to Small Arms Branch where he remained until the merger in January 1944 of the Artillery and Small Arms Branches from which he shared with Major Wexlin the termination responsibility of the newly formed Branch.

To Paul goes particular credit for his work in reference to production, according to specifications, of Metallic Belt Links. Quality control on this item had not clicked. Difficulty had been experienced with tolerances. The item was critical. It was up to Paul. The result: The District was soon out in front, and long held the distinction of maintaining the highest quality level on this item.

So, an orchid to Joe Wexlin and his tribe. May they increase in Ordnance.

Chapter XXIX

PASS THE AMMUNITION!

THE Ammunition Branch provided the historian with an outstanding example of the flexibility, of the quick adjustment of a large organization to new and exacting situations, under critical conditions. Changes and shifts made overnight in Ammunition would have required in private industry much longer periods, and then only after deliberation and much "knocking on wood" around the directors' board. And most remarkable, the Ammunition Branch was so equipped in quality of manpower that there never was any doubt of the outcome of any change. An orchid to the Ammunition group!

The Branch really got under way in December of 1940, with Captain Andrew W. Hamilton, Jr., Commanding Officer. Serving with him were John J. Target, succeeding Robert G. Kerr, on Contract and Administration, and on Inspection; Ben F. Ayres on Engineering. A few months later, John Target transfers to Inspection; Julius Gussman is assigned to Chief of Production, and W. R. Hilliary, who later was assigned to Priorities under Captain Lewis A. Smith, Jr., was made Production Chief. There were approximately 85 contracts in effect at this time, in the hands of some 30 contractors.

Growth was rapid. By the end of 1941 the number of contracts in effect had increased to 246, The number of contractors, to 106. Captain, then Lieutenant John R. Graf had been designated Assistant to Captain Hamilton. The Inspection Section now boasted its first officer, Lieutenant William J. Feigley. There now were five inspectors. Julius Gussman has taken over the Engineering Section, vacating his Production post to Lieutenant William J. Bright, Penn State, 1936, who began his life in P. O. D., in 1938, a civilian inspector.

Under Big Chief Target of Inspection appear the names of Howard H. Stock on Shell and Shot; Cy Cosgrove on Fuzes and Textiles; Raymond E. Best on Explosives; Lieutenant Feigley on Loading and Bertram C. Winward on Reports. Assisting

Engineering Chief Julius Gussman are James J. Doherty on Drawings and Specifications; Raymond A. Baker, on Gage Control, Bill Bright's Production Section shows Harry P. Mellor heading Production Control; Harvey R. Battersby of later day Small War Plants fame in charge of Metal Components Unit; S. B. Hulse on Textiles; William H. Tifft on Explosives and Loading; Wilbur F. Haight, Production Clerk, and Helen M. Conway on Records.

Late in 1942 there was accomplished a complete change in the structure of the Branch. Replacing the former Production-Inspection division of activities, there were set up commodity groups—Projectiles, Bombs, Fuzes, Cartridge Cases, Powder-Explosives, and Textiles. Within each of these units were Production, Inspection and Clerical Sections. In addition, a Technical Service Section was created, a development of what formerly had been known as the Engineering Section of the Branch, and within the Technical Service there was established a Price Change Unit, an Allocations Unit and a Packaging Unit.

On 15 April 1942, Captain Hamilton was transferred to the York Sub-Office, and Lt. Colonel, then Captain, Hayward K. Kelley, golfer, figure skater, devotee of the arts (very military appearing, and good-looking, too), Cleveland born, and bearing the colorations of Cornell and Harvard, was named Ammunition Chief. Assistants were Jack C. Miller on Administration; ditto on Production; John J. Target, on Inspection; and Julius Gussman as Technical Assistant.

The Fuze Section was headed at that time by Captain Corbitt S. Hoffman who doubled on Procurement Liaison. His Production assistant was Bill Young; Inspection Chief, M. Dudley Cozad. The Bomb Section bore the imprint of Jack C. Miller; Production was his immediate assignment. Cy Cosgrove was in charge of Inspection; George D. Keller on Procurement Liaison. Projectile Section was headed by John J. Target who also held the Inspection assignment. Charles P. Egolf, a marine of World War I, was in charge of Production. George Keller, again, Procurement Liaison. Charley Egolf was responsible for the District Chief Mr. C. Jared Ingersoll going on the air to tell industry to sit tight. Charley thought that current fears and misgivings in reference to possible wholesale cancellations and consequent sudden end of jobs must in one way or another slow up the production effort. In recognition of his keenness of perception, and the resulting suggestion, Charley Egolf was suitably rewarded by Ordnance.

A word about George Keller: This highly rated engineer received his B.S. at Harvard. He brought to his job in P. O. D., in 1941, and particularly in his Ammunition assignment, a wealth of operating experience. George was a trouble-shooter extraordinary.

About here, Dudley Cozad rates particular mention. Out of Syracuse University with his B.S. in mechanical engineering, he returned to the family farm for a spell to help his brother. Deciding soon thereafter to be "on his own" he found for himself a position as Rolling Mill Inspector for the Syracuse Plant of the Crucible Steel Company. In 1937 he went to the Otis Steel Company, Cleveland, to make a study of open-hearth furnaces. That assignment completed, he accepted a position in the Inspection and Engineering Department of the Seneca Falls Machine Company where engine lathes were assembled. In 1939, believing he could be of use to Ordnance, he took a Civil Service exam, with the result that shortly thereafter, 25 April 1940, he found himself an Inspector in P. O. D.

Gloria Stuart, movie star, drops in to assist Lieutenant Phillip J. Fields of Mail and Records Section in War Bond Sales Drive

Cartridge Case Section: It is Captain Corb Hoffman once more. Once again we run into Charley Egolf, and again on Production. And, also again, Cy Cosgrove, on Inspection. Captain Hoffman once more on Procurement Liaison.

Powder Explosives and Pyrotechnics Section. It's Captain Bill J. Feigley, Chief, holding down all the assignments with the exception of Production which was the charge of Walter E. Ross. The remaining Section, Textile, was the assignment of Lieutenant H. M. Gingrich, Philadelphia, with a brace of years at Duke, handling both Inspection and Procurement Liaison. Walter Ross again in the Production column.

The number of contracts under administration meanwhile had climbed to 418; representing 180 different contractors, 26 per cent of the total number of those serving the District.

Early in 1943, an early P. O. Der back in the District for a visit would have noted many changes in and additions to the Ammunition Branch organization. For instance, Jack Miller is now Administration Chief; Roy R. Johnson, later to head up the Machine Tool Section of P. O. D. is in charge of Production; John J. Target, Inspection; Julius Gussman, Technical Chief; John E. Ryan on C. M. P. and C. J. Pfaff, Packaging Chief.

Fuze Section: Cyril P. Cosgrove, the boy wonder at Villanova, Chief of the Section; Arthur Louis on Production; Harry L. Fritz, Inspection and "the Cosgrove" himself on Procurement Liaison. In the Bomb Section, Wilmer J. Dorsey appears at the top post, also handling Procurement Liaison; Ed C. Moore on Production and Lee C. Matter on Inspection. The Projectile Section: Dan H. Murphy Chief, and as usual for chiefs at this time, taking on Procurement Liaison; Charley Egolf, Production Chief, Howard H. Stock, Chief of Inspection. Powder Section, still Lieutenant Bill Feigley; William F. Walsh, Production Chief; Lieutenant Paul J. Nieman, Inspection. Lieutenant Feigley on the Liaison job.

In the Textile Section, Moss and Ross have it all their own way. Charles C. Moss is Chief, and appears also as Procurement Liaison while Walter Ross directs Production and Inspection. The Cartridge Case Section is purely the affair of Harvey P. Mellor.

The year approached its end with the Branch organizations structurally about the same. Lt. Colonel H. Ken Kelley and Jack C. Miller still at the controls. John C. Target carries the title of Chief Inspector; Martin W. Reed, Production Chief, and P. D. DeWitt on Procurement Liaison.

The three principal divisions of the Branch— Operating Section, Engineering Section and the Technical Service Section lined up in this fashion: Operating Sections, John C. Miller, Chief, and John Target and Martin Reed, Assistants; Engineering, Julius Gussman, and Technical Service, Captain Frederick C. Wedler. In the Operating Sections column Charley Egolf appears as Chief, with Howard H. Stock and Theodore A. McCracken as Assistants; Bill Dorsey heads up Bombs, with the help of Lee C. Matter and Ed C. Moore. In Fuzes, Cy P. Cosgrove, with the help of Dudley Cozad, Harold L. Fritz and Arthur C. Louis. In Powder it's Lieutenant Feigley, Walter Mullin and Nicholas C. Mirras. In Cartridge Cases, it's Martin V. Reed; and under Containers, write Charles J. Pfaff.

Take the Engineering Section. Yes, it's Julius Gussman. On his staff, George D. Keller in charge Engineering and Research and Development contracts. Technical Data has S. S. Preston for Chief, and Eugene V. Barthmaier, J. J. Hoar and C. W. Lytle for Assistants.

Nearby in the Technical Data Section, it is Captain Fred C. Wedler who also heads up his own Salvage Section with the assistance of A. B. Clark. In charge of Price Changes and C. M. P. Allocations Units, John E. Ryan. Packaging is a Charley Pfaff activity.

Digression, please: We must properly introduce Fred Wedler who carried on his sojourn through Ordnance infinitely more than his belted raincoat and his bulldog pipe. Fred spent five of his pre-Ordnance years with the American Viscose Company where he was engaged in chemical and mechanical development work, and for which he received plaudits and the Samuel Agar Salvage Gold Medal. Sir Samuel Salvage for whom the medal is named was an earlier President of the Company. The medal specifically was in recognition of two outstanding developments in the field of rayon; one, a process for rayon drying and finishing; the other, a contribution to development and establishment of color test methods. His researches carried him to Europe, from whence he returned to the U. S. on the very day in September 1939 that our Allies declared war on the Axis. The Captain, among his other accomplishments was a

mean man with a shot-gun and an excellent horseman.

In early January 1944, with Lt. Colonel H. "Ken" Kelley still in command, we discover Captain Wedler listed as Assistant. The principal divisions of the Branch stood thus: A Purchase Section with J. Albury Fleitas and H. C. Middleton; Termination Section, Major Harold L. Vennell; Contract Section, Captain John R. Armstrong and Captain Howard L. Burns; Production Section, Jack C. Miller; Inspection Section, the inevitable John Target, and the Technical Section, ditto, Julius Gussman.

Quick change, again: Late February 1944, a new branch is born in P. O. D.— the Property Disposal Branch. Lt. Colonel Kelley was assigned as Chief, with Major Paul H. Carlson as Assistant; and into the high post in Ammunition Branch came Captain Fred Wedler, as Acting Chief; and continuing with the Captain those three musketeers of Ammunition: Jack Miller on Production, John J. Target on Inspection, and Julius Gussman heading the Technical Section. Captain Wedler subsequently was named Chief, at the same time Wilmer J. Dorsey takes over Jack Miller's assignment on Production.

Came early in December 1944, the German "bulge" into Belgium, and a consequent tremendous demand from the E. T. O. Command for more and more, and yet more ammunition. The situation was critical beyond measure. To meet this development there was needed at the head of the Ammunition Branch and its several Sections, men who had grown up in Ordnance through cheek to jowl association with industrial factors in the field, in industry; men who knew what P. O. D. contractors had done, could do.

To fill the top assignment, then Major Ernest J. Langham was brought up from his station as Assistant Industrial Division Chief to the Ammunition post, yet not relinquishing his Industrial responsibilities. For his assistants in the emergency, Major Langham was assigned as hard a hitting team as a leader could have: Major Ed W. Lafferty, as Chief, Heavy Shell Section; Major Eugene H. Uhler, as Chief, Fuze Section; Captain Frederick C. Wedler, Chief, Medium Shell Section and Lieutenant Paul E. Neiman, Chief, Bomb, Cloth, and Powder, Explosives, Propellant Section.

It was a wallop-packed contingent all through the Branch back during those high pressure days of 1944 and 1945. Just take a look around. Under

Major Ed Lafferty, there was Charley Kemper and Howard H. Stock on Inspection; Captain Albert E. Lee, Jr., who had been working around explosives since his advent October 1941, in P. O. D., in charge of Production, and Lieutenant Guy Beaumont on Machine Tools. Under Captain Wedler, it again is Charley Kemper and Howard Stock in Inspection; Wilmer Dorsey as Chief, Production with Charley Egolf and Edward Peace; Lieutenant James R. Aydelotte, on Machine Tools, with Major Gene Uhler on Fuzes, Dudley Cozad with Harry Biddle head up Inspection; Cy Cosgrove, and his crew of Arthur C. Louis and Jane McDevitt on Production. Machine Tools was the chore of Lieutenant Charles E. Wood, up from Wilmington following two years with DuPont, expediting construction of TNT plants.

The P. E. P. Unit of Lieutenant Paul Neiman's Section, had Lieutenant Feigley for its mainspring, with Bill Walsh supporting. Bill also directed Production; John McLean handling Inspection. The Bomb Unit had been assigned Henry Backall with the assistance of P. Pfender. Inspection was a Lee Matter affair, with Anthony Calabrese backing up. Textile Production was assigned Walter Ross; and Textile Inspection to W. Lafferty.

The Engineering Section carried Julius Gussman, with George D. Keller and Seymour "S.S." Preston assisting. The Procurement Unit carried the Keller insignia.

In the Price Analysis Unit, it was Lucian C. Sneed and Eugene V. Barthmaier. In Use Analysis, Leonard L. Eyster. Technical Change Order Analysis was another Keller activity; while Seymour Preston had charge of Technical Change Orders.

The overall Production assignment was shared by Wilmer Dorsey and Cy Cosgrove; the Inspection task going to John J. Target and his able secretary, Louise Evenson.

History will record, we are sure, that it was the precise planning, and the intensity of drive which the Ammunition Branch, under Major Langham, brought to bear during June 1944 and the December 1944 and early 1945 expanded Ammunition programs ordered by the Chief of Ordnance, that the District was able to make the tough schedules imposed upon it. And all of this was accomplished during periods of critical machine tool shortages and when it appeared that ammunition plants in the Philadelphia area already were extended to physical limits.

To implement the programs, Major Langham's "flying squadron" conducted a series of production meetings which were held separately with prime contractors, sub-contractors and District personnel, and at which he emphasized the urgency of the programs and what of necessity had to be done if vital overseas needs were to be met. However, the extra capacity developed as a result of these meetings was far from adequate. It was clear that new production facilities would have to be found; plants manufacturing other types of Ordnance items pressed into production of unfamiliar Ammunition items and for which tools and equipment would have to be found, and workers trained in new skills.

Just to give the reader an idea, the American Viscose Company, new to the production of the M21A4 Booster, and not equipped for its manufacture, was prevailed upon by the Major to accept contracts for the item in the quantities of 1,055,000, 750,000 and 300,000 units; General Machine & Manufacturing Company which never before had manufactured Ammunition items, and who were sub-contracting to the Mack Manufacturing Company, vehicle manufacturers, was drawn into the booster program, and the E. G. Budd Manufacturing Company, a press and die shop, was assisted by the Major and his boys to manufacture 8 in. and 240 mm. Shells, delivering 228,519 units of a contracted 401,500 units before VE Day cancellations.

It was a further result of the drive that the Philco Corporation was able to acquire an additional plant at Belvedere, N. J., implement the plant and train workers, and begin, as it seemed then, almost overnight, a greatly increased production of the M51 Fuze, and at the time of VJ Day cancellations, was prepared to manufacture at the rate of 1,000,000 units per month. The Kaiser Industries, already concerned with critical and capacity production in the Middle West, were brought to Scranton, Pennsylvania, set up in a National Guard Armory for production of M21A4 Boosters. Equipment was expedited for production of 4,205,000 units: All "in jigtime," as they then were saying around P. O. D.

It is also in the book, that the Major and his boys, every man picked for particular qualifications, were responsible for assisting Harrisburg Steel Corporation into mass production of Heavy Shells—the 8 in., the M106 and the 155 mm. T26, thus establishing a "first" for the District. This particular accomplishment well rated the designation of "miraculous." The Company already was up to its neck with war orders. It appeared an impossibility that this company, or any company could do more.

And it is worthy of note that 40 per cent of the total increased requirements in reference to the Heavy Shell and Fuze schedules were produced in the Philadelphia Ordnance District.

For his performance during the "drives" the Legion of Merit award was requested for Major Ernie.

At least one phase of the Ammunition programs of 1944 and 1945 will be long remembered by the Executive Officer at that time, Lt. Colonel Henry W. Gadsden, and by Sam McClenahan, Civilian Personnel Chief: That was the little matter of personnel needed to implement those problems. Where to get it? And how? This was a tight labor market. All kinds of assistance was at a premium, and the premium was high.

Demand was not alone from P. O. D. and its contractors. It was descending from all directions upon Civil Service and the United States Employment Service; and these agencies were "hard put" to stir up interest. The "drive" within the District having banged into a stone wall of resistance, Lt. Colonel Gadsden took over, with Sam McClenahan sharing the burden. It was a shirt-sleeve job from start to finish.

By means of meetings in the District and Regional Offices and in the field generally at which employees were encouraged to canvas friends, relations and acquaintances; by enlisting the assistance of contractors; by encouraging contractors to turn over to P. O. D. their personnel files of applicants who had been checked as "in line" but could not be currently employed because of lack of "openings," and by open recruitment where there appeared to be any prospects at all, the drive "clicked." In September 1944, for instance, Civilian personnel in P. O. D. stood at 2,722. In October the total checked at 2,804. By January 1945 it had spiralled to 2,986. By March, to 3,298. Only a leadership of a high order, supplemented by the gritting of teeth and an utter disregard of headaches could have accomplished so amazing a result under the heart-breaking conditions that prevailed.

Once over the hurdle, the next tough assignment was that of bringing about an orderly retreat of personnel, in substantial numbers, without disturbing work in hand throughout the District Offices; without alarming the personnel which was retained and, of course, causing no resentment on the part of those selected for separation. It is worthy of note that the retreat was accomplished, in an orderly manner, without excitement, and with the net result of only one complaint. The scaling down was about like this: By June 1945, the total of civilian personnel had been reduced to 2,778. At the end of July it stood at 2,508. As of 31 August, 2,313. And from then on out, the Pacific war having been brought to a full stop, the "reduction in force" in P. O. D. was rapid.

In June 1945, Major Langham was relieved of his duties as Ammunition Chief and reassigned as Chief, Industrial Division. Major Ed Lafferty, who had been moved up as Assistant Chief during the heat of the drive, was named Chief of the Ammunition Branch, a post which he held until September and the appointment of Captain William A. Dilks, Assistant Chief under Major Lafferty.

And that was Ammunition in World War II.

Chapter XXX

HERE COME THE ARTILLERY!

IT WAS just exactly one year to the day before Pearl Harbor that the Artillery Branch of P. O. D. was set up as a separate and distinct unit. Prior to December 1940, Artillery, as were the other Commodity Branches, was simply a mental reservation in the mind of the Inspection Division Chief.

The Ordnance items for which the Artillery Branch as first organized was responsible, were:

Cannon—including finished machine guns, or gun tubes, and trench mortars.
Artillery Carriages—including mobile field, anti-aircraft and Barbette carriages.
Sighting Equipment—including sights and sight mounts.
Fire Control Equipment—including aiming posts, range finders, fuze setters and related items.
Gun Forgings—including forgings for gun tubes, liners, hoops, breech rings and breech blocks.
Recoil Mechanisms—including recoil mechanisms for tank gun mounts, as well as for mobile and fixed artillery carriages.
Small Arms—among these: machine gun mounts, rifles, bayonets and all other small Ordnance items except small arms ammunition and ammunition belts.

That, generally was the way it appeared on paper back in 1940. Very simple: and quickly told. But, deep in the war years the list would have gone something like this:

Cannon:
  37 mm. Guns, M3, M3A1
  37 mm. Guns, T-32
  37 mm. Gun Tube, M1A2
  37 mm. Gun, Sub caliber, M13, M14
  60 mm. Mortar, M2, T18E6
  75 mm. Gun, M2, M3
  81 mm. Mortar M1 and Mount
  81 mm. Mortar T27 and Mount T21

  3.7 mm. Gun Tubes, British
  90 mm. Gun Tubes, M1
  Rocket Launcher, 4.5in., M12E2 (T35E1)
  Rocket Launcher, Multiple Tube, 4.5 in., T66
  Rocket Launcher, Multiple Tube, 7.2 in., M64
  Rocket Launcher, T53

Artillery Carriages:
  20 mm. Mount (AA)
  37 mm. Carriage M3 and M3A1 (AA)
  37 mm. Carriage M4 and M4A1 (AA)
  40 mm. Carriage, M2 (AA)
  57 mm. Carriage, M1, M1A1 and M1A2 (AT)
  57 mm. Carriage, M1 (Pack Howitzer)
  75 mm. Carriage, M2A3 (AT)
  57 mm. Carriage, M2A3 (AT)
  75 mm. Mount, M3 (AT)
  240 mm. Carriage, M1 Howitzer
  3 in. Mount, M2A2 (AA)
  90 mm. Mount, M1A1 (AA)
  105 mm. Mount, Howitzer, M4
  6 in. Carriage M1 (Barbette)
  7 in. Carriage (Barbette)
  8 in. Carriage M1A1 (Railway)
  8 in. Carriage M1 (Barbette)

Sighting Equipment:
  Mount, Telescope, M16
  Mount, Telescope, M39
  Mount, Telescope, M56
  Mount, Telescope, M57
  Mount, Telescope, M61A1
  Mount, Telescope, M65
  Mount, Telescope, M70
  Mount, Telescope, T89
  Mount, Telescope, (T92) M64, with Headrest
  Mount, Telescope, T-95
  Projector, Target, Rocket, M1
  Quadrant, Elevation, M9 (T10)

Fire Control Equipment:
  Fuze Setter, M8

Aiming Post, M1
Aiming Post, T4
Aiming Post, M6
Aiming post, M10
Director, M5
Optical Elements for Binoculars

Gun Forgings:
All calibers of tubes from 37 mm. to 240 mm.
Howitzer, Hoops, Jackets, Liners for guns up
to 8 in., Breech Rings for guns from 37 mm.
to 240 mm.

Recoil Mechanisms:
74 mm. Mount, M1 and M34 (for Medium Tank.
A Tank-Automotive Project from early 1942)
Co-Axial Mounts (for British Tanks. Also in
Tank-Automotive Branch from 1942)

Small Arms:
(All handled by Small Arms Branch from its
inauguration, July 1942)
Cal. .50 Mount, A.A. M2 and M2A1
Cal. .30 Rifles
Machine Gun Parts
Shot Guns
Scout Car Cradles

". . . and other things too numerous to mention,"
as the old song goes.

The young man selected as "one most likely to
succeed" as Artillery Chief, was Major, then
Lieutenant John H. Beyer, Michigan 1936, just
landed in P. O. D., 12 November 1940, following
a bit of toil with the Read Machinery Company,
York, Pennsylvania. The Contract Section of the
Branch was an immediate responsibility for him.
The Engineering Section was assigned to Michael
C. Marcin; and Inspection, to Joseph W. Yunger.
By April 1941, the Contract Section had given
way on the chart to an Engineering Section under
Charles B. Weiler.

Inspection activity in the Branch in April 1941
involved: Prime Contracts, 54; Sub-Contracts, 347;
number of items, 741, and number of plants, 109.
By September, the totals have moved along the
high route to: Prime Contracts 87; Sub-Contracts,
209; number of items under manufacture, 1,136.
The number of plants, however, shows a drop—
now 94. For some time to come these figures would
be on the up side. War for us was not far off and
from then on the statistics would spiral.

January 1942: It was during this, the first full
war month, that the 240 mm. Howitzer rolled
through Philadelphia, bound for Aberdeen on its
way from Elizabeth, New Jersey, where it was met
by an escort from P. O. D. (Readers will find the
full account elsewhere in this volume.) Also,
during the month, York Safe & Lock Company
delivered its first 90 mm. A. A. Mount.

Early in February 1942, Parish Pressed Steel
Company completed its first 57 mm. Gun Carriage,
M1, and again, its first 75 mm. Gun Mount, M3.
"Firsts" now were popping all over the District
map, and soon, and for some months, they would
cease to excite comment. The number of "firsts"
produced after Pearl Harbor indicate to this historian something of the extent of our country's
unpreparedness. On the other hand, the number
and variety of these "firsts," and the speed at
which they were forthcoming, bear witness to the
ability and well developed skills which were available to Ordnance during those early critical days:
and not least among the possessions of these qualities—Major Johnny Beyer and squad.

April 1942 found the Artillery Branch pretty
well set for the long haul ahead. Major, then Lieutenant, Beyer surrounded himself with a group
that held together pretty well for duration.

There was Captain, then Second Lieutenant,
Josef H. Buerger, Jr., laden with the old Nassau
tradition and a round of practical training with
Carnegie-Illinois Steel, who joined up with Ar-
tillery, 9 February 1942, as Chief of Production in
the Cannon Section. Captain Buerger was the
chap who turned cast steel pipes into gun barrels.
The story appears forward in this narrative. In
charge of Inspection for the young Branch, was
M. L. Hodgson; on Production, John L. O'Rourke.
The early records also reveal the names of Frank A.
Bowles, Nelson M. Buck, Charles B. Weiler,
Lieutenant E. C. Peterson, Lieutenant E. L. Young,
Marie T. Callahan, subsequently Mrs. Silk, and
Stella Ludak.

Few shifts during the Summer of 1942; but in
August, appears for the first time in Artillery, the
name of Captain Joseph Wilmsen, of Chester Tank
Depot fame. Captain Joe came to Artillery to
head Procurement Liaison in the Cannon, Car-
riage, and Anti-Aircraft and Fire Control Sections.
Lieutenant Peterson is listed as Technical Director;
Lieutenant Young, Clemson, 1940, is running the
Inspection Unit in the three sections; Frank Bowles
in charge of Production in the A. A. and Fire Con-

trol Section; Nelson Buck doing the honors on Production in the Carriage Section, and Captain Buerger, on Production in the Cannon Section.

Good business: The Artillery Branch now is pointing with pride to its 256 Prime Contracts; but blushing a bit because of its Single Sub-Contract. And as of this period there are a total of 282 Artillery items in production in 105 plants. Of course, the number of Sub-Contracts climbed to a higher level. However, with some slight variation one way or the other, the number of Prime Contracts, items and plants held a fairly even keel throughout.

It is something of a jump to April 1943, but we must proceed with the story. The rush for production is on—and the trend in everything in the Branch is up. Captain Buerger, the Administration Chief, is handling Procurement Liaison through all the Section. John O'Rourke, one of the gallant lads of the World War I, 311th Infantry, 78th Division, and the "big iron and steel man," was Production Chief for the Branch, and for the Production Unit of the Anti-Aircraft and Fire Control Section. The Inspection activity of the Branch now was the responsibility of David P. McIntire, through all three Sections.

David McIntire was born in Hong Kong, China, the son of missionary parents. David, safely landed on our well-known earth, the family returned to its work on Negros Island of the Philippine group, remaining there for five years. Back in the U. S., they settled in Cambridge, Massachusetts, where David McIntire received his early education. He later attended Huntington Preparatory School in Boston, and upon graduation entered the Massachusetts Institute of Technology where he received his B.S. in electrical engineering. The "depression" going strong about this time, and jobs practically unknown, Dave, rather than settle down to easy chairs, tea and crumpets in Commonwealth Avenue lounges, betook himself to a temporary assignment as a maintenance laborer. Followed, a Civil Service exam for junior physicist. He took it, passed, and went to Watertown Arsenal —that was in 1935. Later, was transferred to York for Ordnance inspection, from whence it was an easy step to P. O. D.; Elias Vander Horst doing Production in the Cannon Section—gun tubes and mortars his specialty. Harry E. Hyde, down from his post at Textile Machine Works for production in the Carriage Section. Lieutenant Peterson hanging up an excellent performance as Technical

Chief, and Lieutenant Young on the Packaging circuit.

A well remembered personality of Artillery is Mrs. G. S. David who had been assigned in charge of C. M. P. for the Branch. No idler, this lovely lady. As if C. M. P. were not enough to keep her nose to the grindstone there was that farm down Maryland way with its full complement of farm animals and its acres of tomatoes and corn, and succotash and such. Came Saturdays and Mrs. David was heading South with her husband for an exhausting week-end. And further, it was rumored, the Davids had developed a considerable business as shippers of tomatoes for other farmers thereabouts. Once, we heard the late Cyrus Curtis say, "If you want a job well done, get a busy man to do it." All of which may have something to do with Mrs. David's success in Artillery.

Running the editorial eye down the scroll, we find Frank Bougher, assisting Lieutenant Peterson, and Arthur F. Le Bon who came to P. O. D. with J. G. Brill Company Engineering Vice President, Charles O. Guernsey. Art assisted Chief Guernsey for a time, went to Conversion Engineering, eventuating in Artillery on his way west to follow his first chief into new fields.

By the end of September 1943, the Branch was achieving new peaks of activity: Now, 213 Prime Contracts, adding up to 257 items in 101 plants. At Christmas time the scores stood 228, 267, and 103, respectively; and that's the way things were progressing. Personnel now stood at 35, including four officers. As to performance, Major Beyer and his loyal men were either within 10 per cent of schedules, or turning in Accuracy of Prediction records at par, throughout the year, and the years following, as a matter of fact.

January 1944: Colonel Fred A. McMahon has departed the District. Mr. C. Jared Ingersoll again is named Chief. New faces appear about Artillery. Charles W. Graves and the late Maximillian McSweeney are seen in the Inspection Sector; comes J. W. Wernett to Spare Parts; Harry J. Costello is signing himself Salvage Representative, and Richard Dressler and John Gillespie, in Contract Change Section.

But March 1944; there was a month! That's the month the Wexlin interests were taken over by the Beyer clique to form the Artillery-Small Arms Branch, Major Wexlin going into Terminations work, soon to appear as Chief, Terminations Section of Artillery-Small Arms. The merger was made effective 10 March, following instructions issued 3 March 1944, by the then Industrial Chief, Lt. Colonel A. D. Kelso. The merger brought Lieutenant Bernard Fortmann over from the old Small Arms group to the C. O. post of the Cannon Section. The Small Arms Section of Artillery went to Ward T. Perry. In the Inspection Section, the roster reads: David McIntire, Chief, with Charles W. Graves, P. A. Guthrie and Maximillian McSweeney, Assistants. Arthur Le Bon is heading Contract Change, with the aid of John Gillespie.

Through 1944, with few changes, few additions to show for it; but it was a year in which integrated procedures in Artillery-Small Arms were paying off overseas. The Branch had achieved a measure of fame in 1944, and into 1945, by drawing a "true bow" on Predictions. During one period, Major Beyer scored a succession of seven hits for his command.

And into 1945, and Victory. Major Beyer was well beyond his long illness—an illness which came very close to costing Johnny his life, and the Philadelphia Ordnance District, a fine, young officer.

On 18 September 1945, Major Johnny Beyer, with two wars out of the way, told a reluctant goodbye to friends he had known in P. O. D. since back in 1938. And in his place as Chief of the Artillery-Small Arms Branch came Captain Josef H. Buerger, Jr., who also had long and ably served the District. Captain Joe in his turn departed P. O. D. 18 December 1945 when the assignment fell to Paul W. Williams, whose record is written across many phases of P. O. D. operations.

General Office Division head, O. Howard Wolfe, congratulates Captain Robert H. Andrews, Fiscal Chief, upon his promotion, 7 November 1942, to Major. *Left to right:* Lieutenant W. B. Wellborn, Lieutenant Howard Gallaher, Chief Wolfe; Helen Conlon, Secretary to Major Andrews, Betty Tucker of the Executive Branch; Dorothy Stewart, Secretary to a succession of three Fiscal Chiefs; Lieutenant Alvin Cressman, Assistant Chief of the Fiscal Division; Lieutenant Otto Kritter, Fiscal Division Auditor-in-Charge at Baldwin Locomotive Works; Lieutenant "Jerry Palmer"; Lieutenant Henry Sekerak, Assistant Chief of Audit Section, and Lieutenant William F. Rathgeber, long time of Fiscal. All officers subsequently moved to higher echelons.

Rehearsal at Baldwins — with Lieutenant Colonel Arthur J. Seiler "at the controls"

Chapter XXXI

THE TANKS ROLL OUT

WE WERE heading for Washington on the 5.43 out of 30th Street. "What are they making in there?" queried the portly character, addressing the bright young man with whom he had just shared a match.

"Lawn-mowers," replied the b. y. m. with a generous hee-haw.

The portly character was annoyed, but said nothing. The porter frowned. Turning to the p. c., evidently a stranger in these parts, he said:

"Dey makes tanks in dat place—millions of 'em, and dey puts cannons on 'em a block long, I hears. I guess dey is lawn-mowers all right, de way I hears dey mow down them Germans . . ."

And more of the same.

They certainly did turn out "mowers" at Baldwin's and also at American Car & Foundry, with contributions of components and parts and supplies from firms scattered the length and breadth of the land. Yes, we were turning out "lawn-mowers;" and in the Eddystone Sub-Office, and back in the Mitten Building, and later at 150 South Broad Street, P. O. D. was signing up and developing the executive personnel that rolled 'em out, and on time.

The Tank-Automotive Branch of the District stemmed from an almost shy beginning as did the others of the Commodity Branches. Back in 1940, in August, there was established an Automotive Section under the direction of Hugh B. La Rue who bore the title of Inspector, a post which he held for duration.

Hugh B. La Rue, Missouri born, cleared the University of Missouri in stride, emerging with full honors in electrical engineering, entered the Army and was commissioned first lieutenant,

110

Ordnance Department, in August 1917, and shortly thereafter landed in Europe. His initial station was with the first Advance Ordnance Depot established in France. Due to changes in military strategy this station was closed, and his subsequent assignment, a temporary one, Puteaux Arsenal, Paris, where secret recoil mechanisms of the famous French 75's were manufactured and repaired. His success at this point and at the French Artillery School of Fire at Fort Vincennes brought him his captaincy. He participated in three major offensives—Aisne Marne, Oise Aisne and the Somme, and was one of 25 officers selected by General Pershing to do special liaison work with the 10th French Army. His success in this work resulted in an assignment by the Chief Ordnance officer, AEF, as Inspector of Ordnance at Saint Chammond in the French Alps.

Upon his return to the U. S., Hugh La Rue was assigned to Rock Island Arsenal, as assistant to the Officer-in-Charge of manufacture of artillery items. He was discharged from the Service, October 1919, but continued at the Arsenal as Civilian-in-Charge of hydro-pneumatic mechanism, Mobile Artillery, development program of Caliber-bored Units. When finis was written to this program H. L. sallied forth into industry and in due course, July 1940, landed in P. O. D.—top tank man.

The Automotive Section, dating from the La Rue invasion, survived many changes of designation. In December of 1940, the Section was elevated to the rank of Division. In July of 1942, it was renamed Tank and Combat Vehicle Branch. In September following, we were hailing it the Tank and Motor Transport Branch, and, finally, the name which stuck for duration—Tank-Automotive Branch. These changes were not inspired by whimsy or by an increasing dignity. This was a mobile war and here was mobility headquarters. Maybe that is a side-explanation of title changes. Actually these shifts in designation were inspired by the increase in the types and number of vehicles coming into battle-front demand.

During the very early days of the Branch there were only two prime contracts for automotive vehicles assigned for inspection to the Philadelphia Ordnance District: One, with the Corbitt Company, was for two wrecking trucks, and was assigned to P. O. D. for inspection under a Rock Island contract; the other, also of Rock Island origin, was with American Car & Foundry Company, specifying 329 Light Tanks, M2A4, 13 tons. Lt. Colonel H. W. Rehm, Army Inspector of Ordnance, was detailed as Chief Inspector of this program. His office was at the York Safe & Lock Company.

It is worthy of note that American Car & Foundry Company was recipient of the first substantial contract to be awarded by the United States Army. Experienced personnel of Rock Island Arsenal were called in by the contractor to assist in coordination of the initial processes of manufacture and to give first aid in locating suppliers of raw materials, jigs and fixtures.

The Automotive Section of P. O. D. shared none of the responsibility for production. Its function at the time exclusively was one of test and check against specifications and terms of the Arsenal contract.

On 1 September 1940, Colonel Rehm relinquished responsibility for the M2A4's, and P. O. D. was bequeathed the job—a pretty complex affair, so it turned out. The gyrations of responsibilities in reference to inspection, production, expediting, and design changes reached such proportions that decentralization became a practical necessity, with the result that a Sub-Office was set up at Berwick, right in the ACF plant, with Lieutenant James E. Maloney, the only P. O. Der to battle his way through three full courses (9 years in all) in one institute of technology—Drexel—in charge. It was at about the same time that an Educational Order for 10 Light Tanks of the same type was given Baldwin Locomotive Works, but this development faded out in its infancy. Baldwin subsequently and ever after turned attention to the medium and heavy tanks, mainly.

It was also in September 1940, that the Automotive Section, rechristened the Automotive Division, was reorganized with three basic sections: Contract, Engineering and Inspection, and was now responsible for the following Ordnance items:

> Tanks: Light, Medium, Heavy
> Wrecking Trucks
> Half-Track Vehicles
> Half-Track Cars
> Half-Track Personnel Carriers
> Armor Plate
> Miscellaneous Items

Business in the Automotive Division now was definitely on the upswing. In September and October, American Car & Foundry Company was awarded two large Rock Island contracts for Half-Track Vehicles—2,439 of them. Total value, $9,480,000.00. P. O. D. had no part in the design of these vehicles. That detail had been taken care of by an Engineering Committee composed of the chief engineers of the Autocar Company, White Motor Company, Diamond T Motor Company and Major J. E. McInery and Charles Miller of the Office, Chief of Ordnance.

Late in October 1940, Baldwin's was awarded a contract for 685 Medium Tanks, M3, weight approximately 28 tons. This was the first large cost-plus-fixed-fee contract awarded by the Ordnance Department. Shortly following this award, Baldwin received from the British Purchasing Commission an identical order for the M3's. The two contracts had a combined dollar value of something over $100,000,000. Contracts of this magnitude did not lack their quota of problems. Before tank production could move, for instance, the American Car & Foundry Company had to build an armor plate plant, supplementing capacity at Henry Disston & Sons who, to this time had been producing the greater volume of armor plate for combat vehicles in this District. Another problem was lack of boring-mill capacity of a size to accommodate turret rings and other sub-assemblies.

Baldwin's also had their problems. Once in the program, the facility found itself head on with the problem of mass production, and the need for integration on a production line basis—and the further necessity of delivery in quantity, in short order. The ingenuity of Baldwin and P. O. D. engineers was taxed to the nerve-cracking point. At the beginning it was necessary to sub-contract a large part of the machining operations. This made necessary survey over a large area of machining facilities—in some cases as far away as the Pacific Coast. The task, on the whole, was an arduous one.

Although assigning major attention during the early days to the manufacture of light tanks, Baldwin was beginning to reach out into other items, notably heavy tanks. It is a matter of record that the company designed and built the only heavy tank made in the U. S. This tank, the M6, weighed approximately 60 tons and was armed with a 75 MM Long Range Gun. The contract for the Pilot Heavy Tank was awarded to Baldwin, 12 August 1940, by the Chief of Ordnance. The contract provided for design and production of drawings, fabrication of a wood model and pro-

duction of a pilot vehicle. These phases were completed, and the pilot delivered 8 December 1941.

The heavy tank was to be of such dimensions that it could be transported on a flat car, by rail. The design incorporated a cast steel hull, weighing 22,540 pounds. The original order was for 50 units. This order subsequently underwent various changes both as to quantity and design. Eventually 40 heavy tanks were built; 20 with mechanical drive, eight of these having a cast hull and 12 a welded hull, and 20 with electric drive and cast hull. The order finally was completed in March 1944.

During this period, contracts were executed in the District, but were not actually administered by P. O. D. personnel. For example, a large order for armor plate for tanks was in process at Disston's. During the summer and through the balance of the year, instructions from Rock Island were that inspection should not be made at the source. Faced by lack of control, the District had bravely to look on at the assembly point. Had there been specific instructions and adequate templates, the production of plate, and specifications could have been controlled at source with a consequent saving of time. Ultimately, all contracts pertaining to tanks and automotive equipment processed in the District were referred to the Automotive Division for administration.

All of which will give you an idea.

From October to mid-December, Hugh B. La Rue served the Division as Chief. W. J. Jeffries, many years with the Navy, came in as Chief Inspector. Ben F. Ayers held sway over the Engineering and Contract Sections. There were more shifts in December: Lieutenant George L. Schiel was assigned as Chief of the Division; W. J. Magoun, metallurgist, former associate of Modjeski, world famous architect and bridge builder, took over Ben Ayers' post as Chief, Contract and Engineering Sections.

We're moving now—into April of 1942, and more shifts. Lieutenant Schiel still tops the Division, but now has Major, then Lieutenant Welles, H. Denney, and Captain, then Lieutenant, Alvah H. Thomas, as assistants. Hugh B. La Rue still was heading Inspection, with Fred Van Sant, Jr., and John W. McDonald as Inspection Assistants. Also in the La Rue column were Emil Mathias, in charge Technical Data; and, heading Contract Control, no less than Fred D. Sarkis. Serving under

John Magoun, over on the Production side, who but Richard S. Lee and Edward L. Kengla sharing the Light Tank Section; George Kazansky bearing up under Medium-Heavy Tanks and an Armor Plate Section, and F. W. Adams handling Miscellaneous Vehicles.

In July 1942, it was different, again. Lt. Colonel, then Major Robert G. Allen hove in sight as Chief, Automotive Division, now the Tank-Automotive Branch of the Industrial Division. Lieutenant Schiel was continued in the Branch as Assistant Chief.

Lt. Colonel Robert G. Allen was one of the District's four-letter men: He knew his way around, industrially; good looking, could conjure up a smooth speech before an audience, and was a downright forthright, all right person to know. As president of the Duff-Norton Manufacturing Company, Pittsburgh, he had made a name for himself in Pennsylvania industry and incidentally collected a lot of lore that stood him well in P. O. D. Colonel Bob Allen once served the Pittsburgh District (not Ordnance) in Congress, and he long has operated his own cheese factory in Vermont. Late dispatches reveal him going "great guns" in the plastics industry.

It was during the Allen regime that the name of Captain, then Lieutenant, Jesse C. Jessen first appears. He had been assigned as Chief, Light Tank Section, and the Medium-Heavy Tank Section. Jess brought with him a Drexel B.S. in mechanical engineering and some other special achievements via Temple University and Villanova College. He remained with the Tank-Automotive Branch until September 1945, when he was assigned to Terminations, remaining with that Branch until his separation, 28 January 1946, at Indiantown Gap.

Also shaping up the Allen team we find Lieutenant Alvah H. Thomas, as Chief, Miscellaneous Vehicle Section; Lieutenant George L. Schiel, directing the Armor Section, and John W. Magoun, heading the Depot Section.

Effective 29 July 1942 the Branch had annexed to its rapidly expanding responsibilities, administration of the Chester Tank Depot, in the Ford plant at Chester, Pennsylvania. But that is another story.

A few days ahead of the Chester annexation, other Branch personnel moves were effected. There were no changes made in the line-up of Section Chiefs, but a few shifts appear to alter the former

pattern. Hugh B. La Rue still is master mind in Inspection, heading that unit in both the Light Tank and Medium-Heavy Tank Sections. Richard S. Lee, on Production in Light Tanks; George Kazansky on the heavier vehicles; Procurement Liaison in both categories assigned to Captain Jessen. In the Miscellaneous Vehicle Section, the arrangement now is, Fred Van Sant on Inspection, Lieutenant Adams on Production, and Captain Thomas, the Section Chief, taking care of Procurement Liaison. In the Armor Section, Lieutenant Schiel, handling Procurement Liaison for his Section, Fred Van Sant, bringing up the Inspection Unit, and George Kazansky, pitching for Production. In the Depot Section it is John Magoun by an overwhelming majority; heading the Section and all its Units save one, Inspection, which is in the lap of the ever-present Hugh.

In October 1942 Ordnance astronomers begin to sight new stars in the Tank-Automotive sky while the Branch, at the same time, is slithering its tentacles in new directions. A Staff Section appears with Hugh La Rue assigned to Inspection, Thomas W. Beattie to Production, Fred Sarkis to the Contract Unit and Lieutenant Schiel to Administration.

Thomas Beattie was well equipped for his work in the Branch. Following completion of his school work there were nine months of service in World War I in heavy artillery overseas. Thence to the Ford Motor Company and twelve years in assembly machine and sales work. The Edward G. Budd Manufacturing Company was in need about this time for someone to head a group of men then being organized to go to Paris for a special assignment with the Citroen Automobile Body Building Plant. Tom Beattie took the job. The plant was in the hands of receivers when the group arrived to take over production and financial problems. A tough assignment, but at the end of thirty-two months the Company had been rescued from bankruptcy with $2,000,000.00 free and clear in the cash register. Tom came back, and glad of it, to Ford, where he remained until January 1942 when, moved by a desire to be useful to his Government, he offered his services, was accepted and, quite logically, dropped into a critical niche in Tank-Automotive.

All right, now for the rest of the team: Because of the terrific tempo of expansion, Captain Jesse Jessen is giving his full time to the Light Tank Section—also handling Procurement Liaison; Hugh

La Rue is his Inspection Chief, and Richard S. Lee dominating the Production area. The Medium-Heavy Tank Section goes to a newcomer, Captain, then Lieutenant Maynard H. Patterson, who arrived in P. O. D., 7 April 1942, from his birthplace in Gaspe, Province of Quebec, via Lehigh University, bringing along a B.S. in metallurgical engineering. The case of Captain "Pat" Patterson wiggles the nasalated digit at the bewhiskered theory that young men fresh out of college are not ready for heavy responsibility. "Pat" pulled a heavy load from his first days in P. O. D.—and little more than two years after his first appearance he was heading the Branch and was deep in the councils of his superiors.

As appeared to be the custom of the times—we are speaking of October 1942—Captain Patterson directed Procurement Liaison for his Section. The Inspection Section went to Hugh La Rue; Production to George Kazansky. The Miscellaneous Materials Section, under Lieutenant Fred W. Adams, had Fred Van Sant on Inspection, Chester M. Loveland on Production, and the Lieutenant himself on Procurement Liaison. In Armor, the now Captain George Schiel, in charge, again brings up Fred Van Sant on Inspection, George Kazansky on Production—and on Procurement Liaison, the usual arrangement. The Depot Section? As you were. The Motor Transport Section under Lieutenant Thomas, reveals Frank C. Graham, who went into World War I with a heap of automotive "know how" to his credit, and came out with something new in that field of activity, in charge of Inspection. Tom Beattie going "all out" on Production, and the Section Chief taking Procurement Liaison under his wing. Remains now, only the Tool and Equipment Section—assigned to David R. Clark, who incidentally ran all the other units except Inspection. That went to Hugh La Rue who stuck to the Inspection posts with the grit he displayed in hanging on to the mustangs in the wide open spaces—where men are men and the women wouldn't have it otherwise.

Incidentally, Dave Clark was not least among the winners of the larger cash awards made during the District's drive for suggestions. On 12 May 1944, there was presented to Dave a cool $250. The suggestion? It had to do with the manufacture of spare, or repair links then being shipped with all tow chains. These links to be used in the field in the event of breakdowns. They permitted "on

the spot" repair with a minimum of hazard to personnel and equipment. It was believed in Washington that adoption of the suggestion would make possible a saving of from $400,000.00 to $500,000.00 annually by cutting down by 25 per cent requirements for replacement chains.

December 1942 marked the departure from Tank-Automotive of Lt. Colonel Bob Allen, who had been named Executive Officer, succeeding Captain John Ogden, and the ascendency to the Tank peak of Captain Roland C. Disney, from 2 June 1941, Officer-in-Charge, Eddystone Sub-Office, where he first signed up, as Assistant a few months before.

Shortly before "Diz" docked at 150 South Broad, Charles E. Brinley, president of Baldwin Locomotive Works, took time out to tell the new Chief, in a letter dated 10 July:

"I have been an industrialist in one capacity or another for forty-two years and I am supposed to know something of the qualities which are required to make a successful and useful man in an industrial capacity. Your position here, as Officer-in-Charge for the Ordnance Department, combines the necessity for a full understanding of Baldwin's problems as a manufacturer, with the obligation to represent and protect the interests of the United States Army, of which you are the chosen representative. This dual responsibility is a heavy one, but there can be no question as to your successful accomplishment.

"I can say with assurance that Baldwin men consider that you are doing a constructive job and that you are contributing everything within your power to the furtherance of our production program."

Looking back over the Disney reign in the Tank-Automotive Branch, we can clearly see that we should have taken a hint from the Brinley letter and tagged the young officer, "Everything-in-my-power" Disney. That's the way the man worked, and it was nip and tuck with his hard-riding staff.

And that staff: Major, then Captain, Disney (he received his majority 11 November 1943) had for his assistant, Thomas W. Beattie. The Staff Section remained in status quo. Only change made in the Light Tank Section was, E. P. Quinn for Richard S. Lee, in Production. In the Medium-Heavy Tank Section, Captain James R. Stewart succeeds Hugh B. La Rue on Inspection. In the Miscellaneous Vehicles Section, Charles B. Weiler takes over the Lieutenant Adams assignments, and

Frank C. Graham succeeds Fred Van Sant on Inspection.

In Captain Patterson's Armor Section, Hugh La Rue succeeds Fred Van Sant on Inspection. In the Depot Section it still is 75 per cent Magoun vs. 25 per cent La Rue. (Historian's Note: If the District ever runs out of La Rues we're going to have the devil's own time keeping chart panels filled.) The Motor Transport Section has Arthur C. Long at the key spot, vice; Captain Thomas, and Louis H. Seip on Production replacing Tom Beattie. The Tool-Equipment and Spare Parts Section goes to Captain Lewis A. Smith, Jr., with H. B. La Rue continuing on Inspection, and Dave Clark on Production. Captain, then Lieutenant, James L. Mingle came in to head up a Packaging Section.

It was in December 1942 that the first M6 Heavy Tank having a cast hull and mechanical drive was completed at Baldwin's. The tank was accepted and shipped to Fort Knox, 31 December. Also, in December, Baldwin's made delivery of the first among the converted Tank Recovery Vehicles, T-2. Again, in December, 196 M3 Medium Tanks came in from the field for complete reconditioning. This contract had preference over all other contracts at the Baldwin plant.

At the end of Major Disney's first month at the top of Tank-Automotive, the Branch reported inspection control of: 1,053 Prime Contracts; 2,599 Sub-Contracts; 459 Requisitions from other Districts.

It had become apparent in January 1943 that the Ford Motor Company, at Chester, could no longer box the overflow of Mack Manufacturing Company vehicles. The Mack Company therefore notified its intention to sub-contract to the Barclay White Company who would set up facilities in the old Northern Metal Products Company, in Philadelphia. We mention this as one of the many problems with which the Branch had to deal.

Early in the year, in April, Arthur C. Long was appointed Chief, Motor Transport Section, replacing Lieutenant Alvah H. Thomas, transferred from Ordnance to Air Corps. Abram Beavers joined the Section in a technical capacity. Arthur C. Long had resigned in August 1943. Sid Press was assigned to the Branch as Chief, Salvage Section, coming from the Philadelphia Mobile Shop Depot to take over this important assignment.

We bound along through the balance of 1943,

into 1944, over pretty rough terrain. Good men and true come and gone. Records made, only to be broken. Programs. Problems. Bottlenecks. If we have missed anyone in this narrative, or anywhere in this history, that has not been our intention. According to the personnel records almost 8,000 persons have gone through the District Office, its Regional Offices and Inspection Offices since 1938—and to give everyone the credit that is his due—well, you, mild-mannered reader, figure it out for yourself.

At any rate, came in due course, 15 November 1944, and those vociferous bubbles rising in Tank (no pun intended) is the upcoming of Captain Maynard H. Patterson, as everyone predicted. So, as of this date, the title is, Chief, Tank-Automotive Branch.

The organization as it stood at the time Captain "Pat" took over command was as follows: Tom Beattie remaining as Assistant; Captain Jessen was out on the left wing as Chief Contract Section with Lieutenant John H. Schumacker, from the Production Service Branch, as Assistant, and in Charge Procurement Liaison. The two group chiefs under Captain Jessen were Lieutenant Irving V. A. Augur, supervising two Contract Change Supervisors: Mrs. Banister and Miss Murphy; and Lieutenant James I. Kelley, from the Property Disposal Branch, and under his command, E. L. Biddle, Contract Change Supervisor, T. A. Nyland, Assistant, and Miss Paul, Obsolete Material Clerk.

Over on the right wing of the organization there is the Engineering-Inspection Section, with Lieutenant Charles R. Downie, Texas A. & M., in charge. The Engineering Section was a "Man Mountain" Mathias project. The Inspection Section, a La Rue enterprise. On the Mathias side, we find, A. F. Popouschek on Engineering Cost Analysis, W. J. Walker on Engineering Change Analysis, and H. Gay and R. F. Hartz, the same. For his associates Hugh La Rue had Margaret H. McNamara and Genevieve V. Janulis.

Down the center we meet up with Lou Seipp, as Chief, Production Section, with four Production Assistants, thus: W. L. H. Bunker, Hoosier born P. O. D. Dramatics Director, Production Assistant in Charge, Tools and Equipment; Chester M. Loveland carrying the ball for Miscellaneous Vehicles; A. J. Volmer, on O. S. C. and Spare Parts; and on Combat Vehicles, George Kazansky.

Bill Bunker was a man of many parts. Tank-Automotive found plenty to keep him busy, yet he could find time to head up P. O. D. theatricals and to write a column on neighborhood and amateur dramatics for the Philadelphia Record. Bill, as many another P. O. Der, saw Service in World War I. His job was that of an assistant to the Chief Engineer of Construction at Hog Island. Upon the wind-up of the war, and consequent obsoletion of the shipyard, Bill went to sea as a representative of the U. S. Shipping Board. Early in 1920 he was assigned as Assistant Director of the Board at Copenhagen. He spent 18 months

there in organizing Shipping Board activities in the Scandinavian District. For the two years following he was in London as assistant to the Shipping Board Director. That work reaching completion, he returned to Copenhagen as District Shipping Board Director. By 1926 he had had enough; he high-tailed it for home and into the automobile business, life insurance, "Little Theatres," and in 1942—P. O. D.

It is January 1946. The pressure days are well behind us and gradually we are working our way back to the old status—older, perhaps wiser, and with new conceptions of our individual responsibilities.

On 16 January 1946, Captain Patterson was separated from the Service—ready for whatever assignment should come his way—and the Tank-Automotive Branch was right back where it started in 1940, and under the old management, Hugh B. La Rue.

But let's glimpse the job that was done here during the war years. The record shows that within that space the lads of the T-A Branch administered the production and delivery of:

> 16,898 Tanks—all types
> 1,150 Recovery Vehicles
> 1,247 Remanufactured Motor Carriages
> 4,841 Gun Motor Carriages
> 47,923 Trucks and Trailers
> 1,255 Bus Bodies
> 7,305 Wood Cargo Bodies

and that gives not so much as a hint of the thousand and one items and their attendant problems which kept the Branch on its toes all the way—commander's vision cupolas, batteries, winterization kits, periscope kits, tools—and so on.

Left: 60 Tube, Multiple Rocket Launcher by Heintz Manufacturing Company. Tubes could be jettisoned as a unit following discharge

Chapter XXXII

THE PROOF IS IN THE RANGES

CURIOUS to learn something of the beginnings of the Proof Ranges we sent out a detachment to search the records and to round up a certain Lieutenant Edward S. Tinley and a Captain Giles Wetherill. Frustrated in this effort we were about to forget the whole thing when we picked up a little black book which long had been buried in the debris stored in Fibber McGee's closet, and there was our story, sketchily put together; but our story.

The early entries in the precious book ran somewhat in this fashion:

September 1940:

"The installation at American Car & Foundry Company, Berwick, Pennsylvania, of an Armor Plate Range, is contemplated. The company supplying the land, buildings and general equipment; and the Government supplying the special proof equipment. Advice has been received from Office, Chief of Ordnance, to proceed with this project."

October 1940:

"Approval was received for the installation at ACF of Proof Facilities for the testing of armor plate. According to the arrangements, suitable military and civilian personnel for conducting the tests will be supplied by the Philadelphia Ordnance District; the Company supplying the labor for handling the plate. Personnel is being secured and sent to Aberdeen for training. Negotiations have been under way for the installation at York Safe & Lock Company, York, Pennsylvania. Approval is awaited."

November 1940:

"A number of conferences were held during the month relative to the installation of proof firing facilities at Berwick and York. Facilities at Berwick are under construction and the necessary proof equipment is on order. A letter of intent has been issued to York Safe & Lock Company; and the District Office is preparing the contract."

December 1940:

"In planning the Armor Plate Proof Range to be established at ACF, considerable difficulty was experienced in obtaining 37 mm. equipment. It is understood that a 37 mm. Field Piece will be provided in lieu of Mann equipment."

Page after page of this, and as subsequent events were to prove, furnishing an excellent example of the benefits to be gained by providing bolts, bars and locks for the stable while you still are in full possession of the horses.

The York Proof Range was established on the basis of an agreement between Colonel Hauseman and S. Forry Laucks, then president of the York Safe & Lock Company, for the purpose of proof testing the 37 mm. Guns and 37 mm. Carriages manufactured by Mr. Laucks' company. With the increase in procurement of Ordnance materiel, the Office of the Chief of Ordnance decided it advisable to proof-test other items in addition at York.

In December 1940, several months before operations got under way, Major, then Lieutenant Howard P. Klair, bristling with erudition gained at the Bliss Electrical School and Johns Hopkins; William J. Zimmer and seven proof technicians were sent to Aberdeen for extensive training in proof testing ordnance materiel.

Lieutenant Klair and his squad reported at York early in March 1941 for the purpose of designing, supervising the construction of, and installing the various types of equipment and adaptations indicated in the plans. As this was a closed range, equipment had of necessity to be so designed that mounts and carriages could be elevated and depressed and yet maintain horizontal fire. A tilting table was designed to proof fire carriages. This table operated electrically and could be raised or lowered to take account of any elevation or depression of the gun.

The first firings at the York Proof Range, 29 April 1941, consisted of the M22 Mount for the Light Tank, the M4 Carriage and the M5 and M3 Guns.

Considerable difficulty was encountered during the critical period at York in obtaining ammunition shipments. There was much travel and no end of telephone calls between York and Aberdeen Proving Ground and Picatinny Arsenal, by way of expediting delivery of 37 mm. Proof Ammunition. This irksome detail was brought under control with the establishment, 15 April 1941, in P. O. D. of the Proof Facilities Section, with Lieutenant Edward S. Tinley, staggering under a B.S., an M.S., and a Ph.D., all in electrical engineering, garnered at Lehigh.

As production was upped at York, various sections were established to meet the increasing needs. There was a Receiving Section and Cleaning Section; a Star-Gaging-Before-Firing Section whose duty it was to inspect and gage guns and tubes prior to proof-firing; a Proof-Firing Section to do the "show-down" job; a Star-Gaging-After-Firing Section, which gaged, accepted or rejected proof-fired materiel. And, of course, a Shipping Section and a Records Section. Because of this flurry in organization-building, technical personnel quickly jumped from eight to forty persons.

As the Range grew, more and more new materiel items came along "to be given the business." The Aircraft Tube, M4, for instance, and the Anti-Aircraft Tube M1A2. All of which called for new fixtures. An adapter was designed to fire the M1A2 Tube on the M22 Recoil Mechanism, while an automatic mechanism was used to fire the M4 Tube. The latter device, however, proved impractical. By way of correction, an adapter therefore was designed that would permit manual firing.

Also in April 1941, the Range was requested by O. C. O. to run extensive tests on high pressure firing on 37 mm. materiel. York said, "Yes sir." On the basis of the data turned in, the standard service round pressure was changed from 36,000 to 50,000 pounds per square inch.

In July 1941 the effervescent Klair was spirited over to Berwick to take command spot in the Berwick Regional Office. Captain, then Lieutenant Louis F. Unger, Stevens Institute, 1933, moved into York. He was relieved of that post several weeks later and transferred to P. O. D. Procurement Plans Section; and later still going

down to the Richmond Regional Office as Assistant to the Officer-in-Charge. Lieutenant Unger was succeeded at York Proof Range by Captain, then Lieutenant, Harper E. Adams, of Drexel and Temple. His assistants were Lieutenant David S. Plewes, Lehigh 1937, and Lieutenant Robert C. Wager, Ohio State 1935. On 3 May 1942, Lieutenant Plewes was assigned to the San Francisco Port of Embarkation; Lieutenant Wager, on 22 January 1943, shipped out to Jefferson Proving Ground, Madison, Indiana.

In February 1942 came Captain, then Lieutenant, Giles P. Wetherill, Antioch College, and the United States School of Foreign Service, to relieve Captain Adams as Officer-in-Charge. Civilian personnel now had reached a total of 60 persons. Production had climbed to a new high, stimulated by the very substantial increase in proof-firing of 37 mm. materiel—the major part of such materiel manufactured in the United States.

The first official order of the "dashing" Captain Giles was the installation of reinforced safety walls. This proved its value shortly thereafter when several tubes were fractured during proof-firing. No casualties.

And so to Berwick!

That installation, in the manner of York's founding, was established on the basis of conversations and an agreement between then Colonel David N. Hauseman and a company official; in this instance, Mr. Guy C. Beishline, District Manager for the American Car & Foundry Company. The objective was the effectuating of a close tie-in on the production line at A. C. F., of the armor plate and the application to tank bodies of suitable plate.

It was here at Berwick where he reported, 28 February 1942, that Captain Giles P. Wetherill was introduced to the business of proof-firing, and it developed that he had the "nose" for it; meaning no reflection upon his physiognomy which, we were quick to observe, was quite in the classic tradition. Coming along with the Captain were Harold J. Herbein, Chief Civilian, Harry Crain, and Harold F. Sigmund, laboratory mechanic, and Rembert C. Bussard, gunner.

The first shot was fired at Berwick Proof Range, 12 March 1942, a month earlier than York's first bid for the official nod. The personnel at Berwick, military as well as civilian, previously had completed six months of special training at Aberdeen under Major E. H. Harrison of that installation.

While at Aberdeen the P. O. Ders prepared a 1941 edition of the "Manual for Testing Thin Armor Plate," wherein was committed to paper the then best known armor plate proof-firing procedure.

As at York, difficulty during the early stages, of obtaining ammunition shipments seriously bottle-necked proof-firing of the unexpectedly heavy shipments. Local hardware stores as far as 150 miles away were scoured for standard service rounds of Caliber .30 to meet insistent demands. Also, by using "borrowed" ammunition of service load and velocity, sufficient ammunition was obtained to take the edge off the pressure. Aberdeen went "all out" to assist.

The production schedules at A. C. F. increased by leaps and bounds. The ammunition problem finally was worked out in the Proof Facilities Section.

The Berwick Proof Range was regarded as the earliest attempt during World War II to set up the ballistic test of armor plate on a production basis. To the end of January 1943, at least, the production record at Berwick, in man hours, was without equal. And, as far as was then known, the 37 mm. Mount developed at Berwick was the only one in existence which did not employ the principle of placing the 37 mm. Gun Tube as an adapter inside the bore of such of the large caliber guns as the 5 in., 6 in., 7 in., and the 8 in. Howitzers. This mount was fully adjustable for verticle and horizontal traverse.

Production at the Ranges kept pace with the increasing demands imposed by an accelerated output of materiel. For instance, within the period 20 December 1941 through 19 January 1942, there was proof-fired at the York Range, for the U. S. Program:

    34—37 mm., M4 Carriages
    327—M2 Combination Mounts
    11—M24 Combination Mounts
    135—37 mm. M3, M5 and M6 Guns
    256—37 mm. M3, M5 and M6 Spare Tubes

and for the British Program:

    50—37 mm. M4 Carriages
    223—M24 Combination Mounts
    413—37 mm. M3, M5 and M6

At the Berwick Proof Range, for the same period, 12 development plates were proof-tested. As a means of conserving armor-piercing ammunition proving grounds generally discontinued the use of these plates.

Not much of a news value coming out of Berwick and York Ranges from now to December 1942 except more and more sweat and elbowneering and, for good measure, more of the same. The one very important event in December was the consolidation of the York Regional Office and the York Proof Range. This was one economy resulting from the survey and study of detached office processes and routines undertaken by Colonel, then Mr. A. Donald Kelso, at the request of Colonel Hauseman who was out for more production in less time with less paper work and less cost. At the same time the Exempted Inspection Office at York was really exempted, extinguished, dismissed, according to Office Memorandum No. 308, dated 19 December.

In January 1943 the Proof Facilities Section was transferred from Philadelphia to York; Captain Wetherill succeeding Lieutenant Tinley as Officer-in-Charge. The Lieutenant, as elsewhere noted, had departed for Jefferson Proving Ground. Orders under AXS-711 were received at about this time for the firing at Berwick of 20 mm. and 57 mm. Ammunition.

We do not recall what Army did to Navy, or vice versa, in 1943 but we do seem to remember that we of Army Ordnance received on 18 November, from Captain D. F. Ducey, Naval Inspector of Ordnance at York Safe & Lock Company, a letter which officially turned over to the Philadelphia Ordnance District authority for the operation of the former Navy Range, assigning this installation to the charge of Captain Wetherill. However, schedules for the Navy Ranges remained practically unchanged—55 Twin All-Purpose, 40 mm. Gun Mounts for Battleships and PT Boats, and approximately 700 units 40 mm. Navy Water-Cooled Gun Tubes. No changes were made as a result of the "turn over," of York Safe & Lock Company or of Government personnel at the ranges.

In April 1943 Captain, then Lieutenant, John P. Grimwade was assigned as Assistant to the Officer-in-Charge, York Proof Range, a post which he held to February 1944 and his assignment to the York Regional Office.

Moving along quickly through a maze of hard work we land heads up in 1944, in April, when Captain Wetherill was designated for special duties overseas—for observation of German V2 Bomb performance. Upon his return, some months later, he was invited by District Chief C. Jared

Ingersoll to tell P. O. D. topside of his observations and experiences. This he did, in the Auditorium of 150 South Broad Street, with chalk talks. In August 1945, the Captain visited Indiantown Gap, for the usual purpose.

October 31, 1944 saw the last of the proof ranges and proof facilities Administration. The main job had been accomplished to the satisfaction of everyone except some obstreperous chaps over the Rhine and here and there in the Pacific Ocean. "Delete York Proof Range," said the fateful memorandum, and delete we did, not only at York, but all along the battle lines.

Lieutenant General William E. Knudsen stops off at the Budd Company plant during tour of District in July 1943 to study ways and means and bottlenecks. Scene is in office of the late Edw G. Budd, Sr., then President of the Budd Company. *Left to right:* Deputy Chief, C. Jared Ingersoll, Lt. Colonel William M. Collins, Aide to General Knudsen, Lt. Colonel Arthur J. Seiler, Chief of P. O. D. Industrial Service, Colonel Alfred H. Johnson, of the Air Force, Mr. Budd, Sr., Lt. Colonel H. "Ken" Kelley, Edward G. Budd, Jr., Lt. General Knudsen, Captain D. H. MacIlvaine, Public Relations Officer, and Captain, then Lieutenant Jules Mehalek, Officer-in-Charge, Army Ordnance at the Budd Company

Chapter XXXIII

THE MOBILE SHOP DEPOT

EARLY in October of 1942 P. O. D. found itself suddenly in the vehicle business in the only shop of its kind in the United States—a converted museum which only a short time before had housed a world famous collection of industrial, anthropological and other educational exhibits.

Writing of this development in an issue of *Time Fuze*, Sam Marx of the Administration Branch, and a *Time Fuze* editor, said:

"If the mummies who inhabit various American museums were to stage a convention in Philadelphia, the logical meeting place would be the Municipal Auditorium, known as Convention Hall. In ordinary times the mummy-delegates here in Philadelphia would have very little distance to travel because their home in the Commercial Museum adjoins Convention Hall. Visiting mummies from Chicago, Minneapolis and Kansas City would find strange goings-on in both the Commercial Museum and Convention Hall.

"They would find some of their Philadelphia colleagues at the Commercial Museum moved from their accustomed places to a new location upstairs; others boarded up and prevented from attending the convention. And especially would they find strange creatures wandering about the once quiet museum halls—creatures who live, laugh, run, talk and work—1,261 creatures who make up the staff of the Philadelphia Mobile Shop Depot . . . As recently as December of 1942 there was nothing at the Commercial Museum but dank corridors and musty exhibits, and the huge Convention Hall was like a deserted village. Within two months a new, animated world had come into being."

The "miracle" started innocently enough. A cost-plus-a-fixed-fee contract (W-670-Ord-3286) had been made with the Thornton-Fuller Company, a local, long-established automobile firm, for the assembly of 2,500 Mobile Shop Trucks of 14 types. The amount of money involved at the time was roughly $1,000,000. The Thornton-Fuller operation, it was assumed, would augment the plant at Raritan Arsenal where the Mobile Shops were being assembled under supervision of the Quartermaster's. Speed was the primary consideration in getting things under way in Philadelphia. By 5 December 1942 the Commercial Museum, the largest strategically located building available, had been leased; and it was believed that during the ensuing six months the engineers would have laid out the building for production with the required equipment, storage bins, and all other facilities in place.

That would have been something of an accomplishment, but Washington had other ideas. On 5 December, a Saturday, a telephone call, like a bolt out of the well-known "blue," directed that the *entire* Raritan operation be immediately moved to Philadelphia and without one day's loss of production between the two communities! Accordingly, Colonel David N. Hauseman, District Chief, relieved Major Arthur J. Seiler of the duties as Chief, Industrial Section, and assigned him to this seemingly impossible job. Major Seiler assigned Captain Welles H. Denney to handle the Raritan end of the move, and M. E. "Dusty" Miller, Production Chief, the Philadelphia end.

Captain Denny immediately betook himself and Lieutenant Bob Watson to Raritan to supervise the shipment from the Quartermaster's of various trucks and equipment. These energetic lads of P. O. D. by dint of everything they could give the job completed their task in 22 days—moving to Philadelphia, 1,400 truck loads and 98 freight car loads of material and equipment. The task was not only to move all of this stuff but, as well, to set up a complete, fully manned functioning plant at the same time that the equipment was rolling in from Raritan. "To complicate matters," Sam Marx reported, "there was a complete lack of handling equipment. An old pole-setter abandoned by the Bell Telephone Company and two army wrecking trucks similar to ordinary garage tow-trucks, were pressed into service." In recalling the "great move," G. H. "Pat" Thornton said, "That cavalcade swarmed down upon us like a cloud of seventeen-year locusts. The streets in every direction were lined with trucks and no place to concentrate them. Worse, they were filled with an assortment of more than 2,700 different items. What to do with them; how to quickly get them into their right places for immediate production use were problems of the first magnitude for all of us."

In addition to 108 Production Orders placed by P. O. D. in behalf of the contract the District inherited from the Quartermaster's 16 pertaining contracts and 144 Production Orders.

To go back a little bit, confirmation of transfer to Philadelphia was contained in a teletype dated 8 December 1942, signed by Brigadier General Harry R. Kutz, forwarded to the Commanding Officer, Raritan Arsenal, in which it was stated, ". . . personnel and equipment pertaining to the Engineering Division will be transferred to the Ordnance Shops and Equipment Field Office at the Philadelphia Mobile Shop Depot, cite SPOFM."

A complete plan of inspection to cover the operations in the assembly of Mobile Shops was drawn up following a meeting, in January, between personnel of the District and personnel of the Thornton-Fuller Company who, in Office Memorandum No. 272, dated 27 October 1942, had been designated to operate the Depot with the instruction that: "The policies and practices now covering the operation of the Chester Tank Depot will be followed in the operation of the Philadelphia Mobile Shop Depot."

The plan of inspection adopted called for 29 contractor inspectors and seven Ordnance inspectors under full scale operation.

There were only three other such plants as the Philadelphia Mobile Shop Depot in the United States. War had dictated its necessity.

P. M. S. D., as it was designated in the memos, received complete G. M. C. and Studebaker 2½ ton trucks with the same type body. Its function was to equip these trucks with the necessary tools or materials for operation in the field. Of the 14, and later, 16 types of shops assembled, some contained milling machines; others motor-driven generators, and others, motor-driven compressors. All trucks were heated, and ventilated, and so arranged that mechanics could work during blackouts.

The contractor early was under pressure to pro-

vide competent labor. Some workers were available from the force that had grown up with the company. Others were necessarily recruited wherever they could be obtained and, interesting to relate, did surprisingly well. As a typical example, Margaret Lee, assigned to electrical assembly work, was 26 years of age and had been a waitress before coming to the Depot. One worker recently had been paroled from jail; another had been a "human pincushion" with a circus; another, evidently a man of some means, was driven to work in a Cadillac. He had two boys in the Army and wasn't content to let them do all the fighting. Another worker was a well known consulting engineer in peacetime. When asked what salary he wanted, he replied: "That doesn't matter." Many negroes were employed and "all were doing excellent work," "Pat" Thornton said.

One woman, well past middle age working on the night shift attracted "Pat's" attention. "How is it," he asked, "I find a woman of your age working nights?" "Well," she said, "I can do this work, and I need the money. I make more at night. You see, my boys are overseas and I have their wives and babies with me. They can't work and care for babies, too; so here I am, enjoying it, and knowing I am doing my bit."

Next to the Tank Program, the Mobile Shop Depot received more visits from generals and colonels and energetic majors than any other Army manufacturing installation. The importance of the War Program of the Depot was early recognized by Lieutenant General Levin H. Campbell, Jr., who visited the Shop. On 7 January 1943, he wrote to Lt. Colonel Art Seiler, thus:

"You are doing an excellent job and I wish to thank you and the officers working with you for the effective efforts put forth."

The fact that military and civilian personnel had been transferred from Washington and Raritan to set up in Convention Hall a Sub-Office of the Office of the Chief of Ordnance was one indication of the extreme importance with which the contract was regarded in Pentagon circles.

Administration of the Thornton-Fuller contract had been placed with the Miscellaneous Materials Branch for which a special group was established. This work was completed in February 1943. Major Welles H. Denney was given full charge of all Shop matters; Collier A. Elliott was assigned as administrative head to correlate efforts of Branch personnel and their specific duties; Lieutenant Bill Mortensen with Henry Marcus, were assigned in charge of Inspection and Engineering; Al Testa, Production, and Lieutenant Bob Watson, supervision of all matters in reference to crating at Barclay White Company. A. F. Haise, Jr., took over Scheduling and Traffic, while Neal Armstrong was assigned the responsibility for the production at the four selected body facilities, (Hicks Body Company, Perley A. Thomas Car Works, Hackney Brothers Body Company and Phillips & Buttroff). Barclay White Company had set up the crating enterprise in the old Ordnance Warehouse No. 2 in Tacony.

The first assembled vehicle was completed at the Depot in December 1942 when 40 Ordnance Maintenance "C" Trucks were accepted. This was a Spare Parts Truck and was included in the Mobile Shop Depot program for the reason that, in this case, cabinets and benches were assembled on chassis for shipment on Lend Lease.

The first Mobile Shop was completed in January 1943. This was one of a group of 226 Shops completed during the month. On 2 February 1943, the Barclay White Company undertook a sub-contract for crating Mobile Shop Units for Thornton-Fuller Company. The old Ordnance Warehouse had to be reconditioned for this purpose. This meant substantial repairs to the building, electrification for both light and power, repairs to a long-unused 20-ton crane, resurfacing floors, and general cleaning up. By 6 February, templates had been made and the first crating accomplished. An initial deadline for packaging by 10 February 1943, of 53 units for Soviet shipment also was accomplished. By Wednesday, 17 February, the first complete U. S. order, involving 155 units, was packaged and heading seaward; and all this was accomplished by Barclay White Company in the face of various shortages of material and the lack of fully adequate organization. As the month ended, the packaging facility was searching for additional space.

During the period of its existence, four commanding officers had written their names in the archives of the Philadelphia Mobile Shop Depot. First of these was Captain George L. Schiel, Officers Reserve, transferred from the Tank-Automotive Branch where, as second in command under Lt. Colonel, then Major Robert G. Allen, he had been Chief of the Administration Section, doubling at the production post and heading the Armor Section. Earlier, preceding organization of

the Branch he had been Chief of what then had been known as the Automotive Division.

George Schiel, Pittsburgh born, came up from the Baltimore Ordnance District which, then, early in 1941, was attached to the Philadelphia Ordnance District. He was commissioned First Lieutenant, 17 June 1941, and Captain, 1 September 1942. He was an Ordnance ROTC graduate of Lehigh University where, in 1938, he received his B.S. in Metallurgy. Subsequently he was named a Student Associate, American Institute of Mining and Metallurgical Engineers; a member of the American Society for Metals; member of the American Electrochemical Society and of the American Relay Radio League.

When the first Officer to wear the PMSD colors took over his command in November 1942 he had one assistant, Ralph A. Fisher, Allentown lad who had come to P. O. D. 1 July 1941 as an inspector. The two men held down a small temporary office at one end of the building. Captain Schiel continued at his post until 23 January 1943 when he was succeeded by Major, then Captain, Homes T. Case who was brought down from Raritan Arsenal for this assignment. On 3 February 1943, Captain Schiel was released for duty at Office, Chief of Ordnance, Detroit.

Major Case hailed from Syracuse, New York. He brought with him to P. O. D., a comprehensive experience of mechanical engineering and executive ability which were to serve him well in these parts.

The now Lt. Colonel Arthur J. Seiler was to tell "Dusty" Miller, 1 May 1943, via teletype:

"Your accomplishment in April 1943, of 1,200 Mobile Shop Trucks is one of the most outstanding achievements in the history of P. O. D."

On 1 June 1943, Major Case was brought back to the District Office and assigned to special duties in the Miscellaneous Materials Branch, under Major Welles H. Denney, holding this post to his assignment, 5 October 1943, to the Tank-Automotive Branch, under Major Roland C. Disney. A further move was his transfer, 1 December 1943, to the Bethlehem Regional Office, with station at the Mack Manufacturing Company, Allentown, Pennsylvania. He received his Majority 22 August 1945 and on leaving P. O. D. 17 December for Indiantown Gap he left behind him a record he could review with satisfaction and pride.

Assigned as Contracting Officer, 5 January 1942, was Lieutenant Augustine D. Edwards, who some time earlier had been transferred at his own request from the Infantry Reserve to Ordnance Reserve. He was born in Birmingham, Alabama, graduated from the Citadel in 1939 from whence he returned to his native heath to gather in his arms, at the University of Alabama, his M.A. Next move was to the Calhoun, Alabama, High School, where he had been named instructor in history and general science and director of athletics. He continued at his Mobile Shop Depot to December 1943 when he was relieved of his duties and reassigned to the Philadelphia Regional Office, for special duty at Autocar Company as Transportation Officer on Inspection and Testing. On 15 January 1944 Lieutenant Edwards was appointed assistant to the Officer-in-Charge, Captain, then Lieutenant, William H. Nicholls. Captain, then Lieutenant, James L. Mingle also was assigned at this time as assistant.

Came 29 February 1944, and Lieutenant Edwards was reassigned to the Philadelphia Regional Office for duty at Barclay White Company; and on 26 June 1944, a further transfer took him to the Richmond Regional Office where he held forth to the time of his transfer, 25 July 1945, to O. R. P., Ordnance School, Aberdeen Proving Ground.

Upon the reassignment, 1 June 1943, of Major Homes T. Case, Captain Henry W. Gadsden, assistant to the Executive Officer, Lt. Colonel Robert G. Allen, was assigned the No. 1 job at the Depot where he continued to 30 August 1943 when he was called back to the District Office to receive his Majority and to succeed Lt. Colonel Bob Allen who had been called for overseas duty. It had been a pretty safe bet that Henry Gadsden would chalk up a good job at the Depot. A keen analyst, steady, an organizer of unusual ability, he did exactly what was expected of him. Things had a habit of running smoothly under the Gadsden touch and personnel knew always that his sense of fairness meant quick death to "friction" in the organization wherever and whenever frictions might occur. However, there was little of disturbance during the Gadsden regime—and there was a great deal of everyone getting a lot done—according to specifications and on time.

With the recall to the main office of Major Gadsden, the command post at the Mobile Shop Depot was assigned to Captain Joseph B. Anderson, York, Pennsylvania hardware merchant. Captain Joe had joined the Mobile Shop Depot forces early following a service to P. O. D. beginning back in

June 1941. His first tour of duty in the District was as Chief, Sub-Office Administration Division and when that responsibility was passed along to Colonel, then Major, A. Donald Kelso, Joe moved upstairs to the Production Section. Still further back, the Captain had done a turn in World War I, emerging a Second Lieutenant of Infantry. His World War I training had been well earned at Central Machine Gun Officer Training School, Camp Hancock, Georgia. On 2 October 1944, Captain Anderson moved on to Fort Dix, New Jersey, for his adieus to P. O. D. and World War II, but not to his many friends in the District Office and in the field.

Operations came to an end at the Depot in August 1944 with the completion of Thornton-Fuller contract, W-670-Ord-3286—and Captain John B. Jones, of Kincrae, Minnesota, stepping into a post previously occupied by Lieutenant Stanley B. Honour who had been shifted to the Redistribution and Salvage Section of P. O. D.; and later, to the Cressona Ordnance Plant, at Cressona, Pennsylvania. Captain Jones had with him at the Depot as assistants, Ralph Fisher and John Grenhart.

Captain Jones brought with him to P. O. D. an experience of accountancy, management and distribution involving General Motors Corporation and Chevrolet distributors. His first war-time assignment was effective 14 September 1942, to the Lowell, Massachusetts Ordnance Plant. Special Orders No. 141 brought him in June 1943 to P. O. D., to be assigned 5 July, as Assistant Property Officer at the Depot. On 22 July 1944 he was assigned additional duty as Chairman of the Thornton-Fuller Special Salvage Board; and on 4 October, with the completion of his work, he was assigned to Ordnance Warehouse No. 2, along with Ralph Fisher.

On the basis that, as it was then reported, ". . . present plans are to turn over to Reconstruction Finance Corporation, all except 50,000 square feet of Warehouse No. 2, at Pencoyd, Pennsylvania, which, when accomplished, will considerably curtail the activity at this location . . . ," Captain Jones requested, 13 July 1945, in a letter to Colonel Kelso, then District chief, that he be released from active duty; and by Special Orders No. 231, dated 28 September 1945, he was; and with hearty thanks for a good job.

But, back to the Depot story:

Early in 1943 the production line was re-planned

to meet its maximum output of 1,000 units per month, representing an increase over the original schedule, of 600 units—all of which schedules were made, incidentally. All except a Soviet schedule, in February 1943, when 140 units, 10 less than the goal set, were produced. Failure in this instance was due to delayed approval by the Russians, of soft top cabs.

By April 1943, production at the Depot had been upped to 1,200 completed units; and during each June and July, production was of 1,000 units.

Of course there were production hurdles to be got over. Delays were caused by damage in transit to chassis; lumber for crates was not always sufficiently strong; bodies were sometimes needed faster than the builders could get them through, and a considerable amount of expediting, particularly through June 1943, was required to supply body builders with heaters and screens, both critical items. Again, it was necessary, at Schramm, Inc., West Chester, Pennsylvania, to expedite Purchase Orders on which schedules had been stepped up to meet the increased demand for generators. A strike at the Willys-Overland Company plant, bottlenecked the delivery to Schramm, Inc., of "Jeep" motors. There was also needed at this time 5,000 feet of copper or brass tubing, another critical item. Berlin C. Bell of the Miscellaneous Materials Branch handily took care of the latter need.

In October 1943 all contracts dealing with Mobile Repair Shops were transferred to the Tank-Automotive Branch of the District, with Thornton Fuller Company on assembly. Barclay White Company on crating, Schramm, Inc., on generator and compressor units, and Hackney Brothers Body Company and Perley A. Thomas on ST-6 bodies. In addition, the following personnel were transferred to the Tank-Automotive Branch, to continue their Mobile Shop activities:

Major Homes T. Case, Jr., Chief of Section
Mrs. Olive M. Sprows, Secretary
William H. Lownsbury, Inspection
A. F. Haise, Jr., Production.

In December 1943, the Miscellaneous Materials Branch of P. O. D., having served its purpose, was dissolved. Personnel, including Major Welles H. Denney and his assistant, Collier Elliott were transferred to the Production Service Section.

On 3 March 1944, with suitable ceremony, much singing and speechmaking, P. M. S. D. celebrated the completion of the 10,000th vehicle.

The August schedule definitely brought the Thornton-Fuller contract to a close, and saw all Government owned equipment at the Depot turned over to the Navy Department, with the contractor designated to process landing equipment on a Navy contract. The greater part of excess materials already had been shipped to Lordstown Ordnance Depot.

And that about rings down the curtain on a great enterprise, except that we do want to give a nod to those others not already mentioned in this narrative who rendered an invaluable assistance; among them: Anthony Papouschek, Cost Analyst; U. F. X. McGlinn, Auditor; Roy S. Latimer, Administration Officer; Daniel K. Betts, of whom the reader already had heard much; William A. McCracken, Inspector and Administration Assistant; Craig Biddle, Jr., Industrial Specialist; Salvatore J. Feleccia, Auditor; Howard Abraham, Jr., Auditor; A. C. Tepper, Chief of Production, and Charles H. Axe, Inspector—and, by all means, kudos to the ladies, the guards, the gentlemen from Washington and Office, Chief of Ordnance, Detroit.

Interior view of a Mobile Shop assembled at the Philadelphia Mobile Shop Depot, an operation of the Thornton-Fuller Company

Chapter XXXIV

CHESTER TANK DEPOT

THE story of the Chester Tank Depot is one of the most fantastic to come out of the war. It is a story of industrial magic; of the length to which men sometimes willingly go to accomplish the impossible; a story of sacrifice; of unattainable deadlines attained—a magnificent epic, long to be remembered. Should history fail to record the impact upon the tides of war of what was accomplished here, those who fought in North Africa, with the odds against them, will not fail to recall that in one instance at least, the men at Chester not only saved their skins, but, as well, very definitely turned the course of the war.

The operation at the Chester Tank Depot, a converted Ford Motor Company assembling unit, was one of four such Tank Depots in the United States.

It was in March 1942, that contract W-670-Ord-2033, for the Receiving, Storing, Preparing, Modifying and Packaging for domestic and export shipment, within a period of 18 months, a total of 10,000 vehicles, including Tank Killers, Heavy Tanks, Medium Tanks, Light Tanks, Wrecker Trucks, Half-Tracks and others was awarded the Company.

Ten thousand vehicles processed and on their way appeared at the time a sizeable assignment. Actually, the Depot completed in that eighteen-month period, not 10,000 vehicles, but, actually, 50,000 vehicles, which fully justified a celebration, 18 August 1943, which concluded with the presentation to the Chief of Ordnance, Lt. General Levin H. Campbell, Jr., of the final unit making up that total. Before the war would come to an end, the Chester Tank Depot was to deliver to Uncle Sam more than 185,000 vehicles packed and headed for victory. While this amazing job was in process, the Depot saw almost 900 of its trained workers march off to the Armed Forces.

Characteristic Ford speed and efficiency marked even the first month of the contractual operation. Without prior experience in handling and process-

ing mobile fighting equipment, the Depot gave a "good going over," packaged for export and reshipped, 329 of the 514 Light and Medium Tanks it had received during that period. Medium Tanks then were arriving from the Detroit and Cleveland Ordnance Districts. Light Tanks were coming down from the American Car & Foundry Company at Berwick. Light tanks then were being received in unserviceable condition, insofar as the Field Service was concerned. These Tanks, M3's, were stored at Chester to await receipt from Rock Island Ordnance Depot, Schenectady General Depot and Watervliet Arsenal of armament, armament spare parts and accessories.

Policy and details in reference to the execution of contract W-670-Ord-2033, were the responsibility of the Philadelphia Ordnance District. Shipments into the Depot were on orders of the Depot Unit in Tank-Automotive Center later named Office, Chief of Ordnance—Detroit. Preparation for shipment of tanks and parts, for both domestic and export shipment, and all shipping details were carried out on orders from the Field Service.

During the first three months of operations at Chester, administration of the Depot was handled solely in the Field Service Section of the P. O. D. Property Branch, under Lt. Colonel, then Captain, William L. Stephens, Jr., with his good man, Captain, then Lieutenant, Robert W. Vogelsberg. Subsequently inspection, engineering and production functions were assigned to the several branches of the District ordinarily charged with these functions, leaving the P. O. D. Field Service Section with the proper control in and out of the District of all pertaining motorized equipment.

The Depot at Chester boasted six miles of railroad track and a 500 foot long, 150 foot wide berthing for ships to as much as 30 foot draft; a box shop with facilities for fabricating approximately 600 boxes every 24 hours, the largest of which were used for boxing scout cars and half-track units consuming 2,000 board feet of lumber, and required 40 man hours in the making. There was an infra-red ray drying oven of tunnel-like construction, lined with 1,900 bulbs, each of 240 watts in goldalated reflectors. Vehicles driven wet-painted through the oven emerged a few minutes later with paint dried hard.

At one time there was on hand in the yard at the Depot a total of 4,000 motorized units comprising 26 different types, built by 18 different facilities. These units carried armament varying in size from 6 in. Guns to .45 Cal. Sub-Machine Guns. There were 155 mm., 75 mm., 37 mm. Guns, 75 mm. Howitzers, 105 mm. Howitzers, 81 mm. Mortars, .50 Cal. and .45 Cal. Machine Guns, and 76 mm. and 90 mm. Guns—and spare parts.

Commenting on the work at Ford Motor Company, Lt. Colonel, then Captain Stephens, Property Chief, once said:

> "I was interested in the forging developments for the processing of tanks at the Ford Motor Company (Chester Tank Depot). They did all their research work on their own. I remember one instance: I was the first P. O. D. officer to contact the Ford people on the development of tanks. We went down to see Mr. Charles R. Beacham and Mr. N. S. Brown to talk the matter over. They agreed to allow us no more than 5,000 square feet of space because they were fearful lest that once Ordnance got in it would take over the plant, which was exactly what we did. When I went down there they had a jeep line running full swing and we actually pushed them right out."

Modifications operations varied. The most common was the application to medium tanks of sand guards, the counter-balance on the M10 and the sealing of pistol ports on the light tanks. Too, much work was done inside every vehicle in reference to cartridge holders, spare radio tube box, spare parts box, water can holders, map holders, etc., and welding flare holders. Half-track vehicles were modified for spring idler and such motor modifications as fans and surge tanks.

The On-Vehicle-Material Department at Chester stocked numerous items, many of which were pioneer equipment including shovels, picks, saws, axes and various other tools which had of neces-

sity to be kept on hand in sufficient quantities to meet any possible excess need.

Maintenance spare parts were shipped from Chester in one-quarter sets comprised of hull parts and engine parts. There were approximately 2,800 items to a one-quarter set of medium tank spare parts, required for packing a total of 350 cases, to a total weight of 248,400 pounds, or three carloads.

The Depot received at the gun room and prepared for shipment, .30 Cal. Fixed, .30 Cal. Flex., .50 Cal. and .45 Cal. Sub-Machine Guns. These Guns were removed from their boxes and serial numbers compared for verification. They then were dipped in oil for rust proofing, and wrapped in waxed paper, replaced in the original boxes, the boxes wrapped in Triplex paper, the paper stapled to the box and all seams sealed with pitch. The .45 Cal. Tommy Guns were received, ten to the box, stocks removed and the entire gun submerged in oil, then treated as above. The .50 Cal. Guns sometimes were packed in two boxes, by removing the barrels. This, to enable packing in the smaller vehicles.

It was necessary in preparing tanks for export to first mount each tank on a set of blocks. This enabled the treads to run free. The treads then were sprayed with an anti-rust solution. During this operation, a crew of men were cleaning and painting inside the tank. The motors were each run fifteen minutes with rust-ban solution as a protection for all internal motor parts. Following, the entire exterior of the Tank was sprayed with the rust-ban. Before closing the doors, fifteen one pound bags of silica-jell were placed inside the motor compartment to absorb moisture. Twenty-five bags of the absorbent were placed inside the tank proper. Doors then were closed and all vents sealed with Utilitape. As an extra precaution all external points were sprayed with a body sealer.

Scout cars were boxed at the rate of five per hour, or 120 every twenty-four hours. These boxes each contained 2,800 nails. Boxes were covered on top with Triplex paper, then the regular lid and a one-eighth thick compressed cardboard covering which in turn was covered with a coating of pitch.

There was much more—many routines and many devices—all directed to the end that battle lines be properly implemented—adequately fortified as far as Chester was concerned—for final victory; and the sooner the better.

More than once the fortunes of battle were turned for the Allies because Chester adequately had met schedules, and on time. An example: Late one afternoon the Depot received an urgent order to ship tanks by special train. At 5 P. M., J. C. Davidson, Ford superintendent, posted a notice to the Depot's 4,800 workers requesting all who could "to work two hours overtime tonight." Tanks had to be washed, rolled into the plant, modifications installed—equipment for a particular type of warfare installed, radios to be tested, a set of on-vehicle-material (327 items) to be assembled for each tank, and the tanks waterproofed and loaded. The men and women worked, and the entire shipment was on the special train at 2:30 A. M. next morning!

On an even more spectacular performance, who does not remember how Chester went all out in the Summer of 1942 in performing what Don Eddy, writing in a September 1944 issue of Liberty magazine, described as a "nine day miracle . . . the secret high-speed production drive that delivered the tanks and guns which turned the tide in Africa . . ." Here are fragments of the story as Don Eddy told it:

"When Churchill visited the White House in May 1942, he confided to the President that the British 75 mm. Cannon was no match for the German 88's, and that disaster threatened the 8th Army in North Africa unless it could be supplied with bigger and better guns and tanks . . .

"There appeared to be no immediate danger. Churchill thought the 8th Army could hold its own until the new weapons were supplied in normal time. So the problem was referred to Major General L. H. Campbell, Jr., chief of Ordnance, and to engineers of the War Department's Tank-Automotive Center. Secretly they evolved a new gun, a tank killer known as the M-7, which was a 105 mm. Howitzer installed on an M3 tank chassis. (Could travel 35 miles an hour; smash targets seven miles away.)

"By mid-June production had begun and a few were being tried in secret maneuvers when all at once calamity struck in Libya. In a brilliantly executed "offensive-defensive" Rommel lured the tank squadrons of the 8th Army into an artillery ambush and slaughtered them. Three hundred British and American tanks lumbered into that trap. Three-fourths of them were wiped out. The fate of the Allies hung in the balance!

"That was the situation on the last Friday of

June. That night the air over the Atlantic crackled with cipher messages between London and Washington . . . Only a miracle could save Egypt . . . [A miracle of mechanical production, assembly and transportation.] In the last hours before dawn a plan was born. The British called it, 'Emergency Order ZZ.' General Somervell's Service of Supplies called it R-7. The Army Transport Division called it 8643.

"It called for the greatest burst of speed in war time industry. Back-breaking speed. Within nine days a monumental quantity of mechanized equipment had to be constructed, assembled and laid on the docks at an Eastern port. Ships had to be waiting, and naval escorts assigned. They had to get the shipment to Cairo before Rommel realized the plight of the British Army and had moved in for the kill.

"American industry, which means management and labor, had to be persuaded to forget about wages and hours, about holidays and overtime. They had to forget their wives and children and miss a few meals; and they had to do it blindly, not knowing what it was all about, for the whole scheme must be blanketed in the utmost secrecy . . .

"On Saturday morning, code messages flashed out of Washington to hundreds of key factories, Ordnance depots, army posts, tank plants, arsenals, military airports. Almost every state in the Union was given a specific job to do . . .

"Men worked through July 4, July 5 and Monday the 6th . . .

"Items rushed by train and plane . . .

"Orders to get railroads clear. 'High ball' all empties! Nothing could get in the way . . .

"Foreman of a nearby plant yanked into a police car to scout for boxes of bolts; cops helping. Twelve thousand dollars worth of small items commandeered from factories in adjoining areas . . .

"President of United Automobile, Aircraft and Agricultural Implement Workers of America, CIO was asked if his men would play along. [When he learned what it was all about, he agreed.] He didn't go home for the next two nights and three days, and neither did some of his men. One group worked 22 hours at a stretch . . .

"One of the complicated sets of instructions that reached the desk of Major Andres, Ordnance Officer at an Army Tank Depot [all names were fictitious; a military necessity at time story was written] which meant that each shift would overlap . . .

"Sixth day: Rate of loading, 80 tons an hour . . .

"On seventh night, plant hospital filled, men stretched in corridors; mostly fatigue cases. Ten per cent of men had been injured. The doctor in charge, formerly a musician with Victor Herbert, had four assistants; five nurses worked non-stop around the clock . . .

"Eighth day: Rate of loading, 258 tons an hour . . .

"Last of six ships loaded at dawn; had pulled out of port on Atlantic seaboard, hand-picked for speed and capacity . . .

"The ships went out to sea some time in the night. One of them had the largest and most precious load of tanks and big howitzers, so they put her in the center of the convoy, but they could not protect her from spies ashore. Three days out she was torpedoed . . .

"Once more, the log of 'Emergency ZZ' was opened. Once more men worked like demons to replace the lost cargo. Once more proud passenger trains took to sidetracks . . . Another ship was rushed to the port. In addition to the tanks and howitzers she carried steam locomotives and tenders.

"Substitute vessel had to travel without escort . . .

"The rendezvous was kept, the cargoes transferred to the big planes; and 51 hours after the take-off the mighty ships roared down on the British army field at Cairo. On the log books, the flight was described as 'routine,' yet, some of the pilots who made the trip had never before flown the Atlantic.

"There were pleasant aftermaths, of course. British Field Marshal Sir John G. Dill wrote a fine letter to General Somervell, and General Somervell wrote a fine letter to Sir John. Colonels wrote letters to Majors and Majors wrote fine letters to Captains. It was all quite scrumptious!"

No less spectacular was the 1942 Christmas Shipment, so named. This time, workmen looking forward to a plant party and the annual holiday with their families were doomed to disappointment but, as the record reveals, took it all in stride. At 4:30 P. M., 24 December, thoughts were of the fun ahead, when at that precise moment came a call from Tank-Automotive Center, Detroit, for a deadline shipment, New Year's Eve, of one hundred completely modified tanks—to a 3 in. Gun Motor Carriage for use as an Artillery weapon—self-propelled Artillery being a need of the hour.

There was all the procedure of tearing down and reconstruction—adding to each tank 3800 pounds of counter-weight to balance the turret—pigs of lead had to be hand-melted; troughs made at rear of turrets; Rush! Rush! everywhere and everything in order. Men worked through the holiday, uncomplaining—and they beat the deadline by one full hour.

The Ford men at Chester Tank Depot turned in a worthy job. Visiting "brass" always was loud in praise of everything from plant housekeeping to the meticulous observance of production techniques and schedules. On 24 November 1944, the Philadelphia Ordnance District presented the contractor with an especially prepared scroll commemorating the completion at Chester of the 125,000th vehicle. Presentation was made by Mr. C. Jared Ingersoll, District Chief, to Mr. C. R. Beacham, for the company.

Spearheading for Ordnance the chain of accomplishments at Chester, we find topping the lists the names of Major Willard L. Curtis, Commanding Officer; Lieutenant Norman L. Cavedo, Executive Officer and Chief of Operations; Lieutenant John A. McKinney, Transportation Officer; Henry H. Ruttinger, chief inspector and Joseph Lehecka in Charge Sighting of Guns, and turning an able hand to inspection. On 17 November 1943, Major Curtis was reassigned to Tank-Automotive Center–Detroit, for temporary duty. Major Joseph L. Wilmsen, late Officer-in-Charge, Eddystone Inspection Office succeeded him.

Then there was James R. Stewart, of whom more later, who was commissioned a Captain and "put to the wheel" in the Tank Automotive Branch, thence to the Technical Data Section, as Chief.

Few men came better equipped to P. O. D., for outstanding service than Major, then Captain Willard L. Curtis. An Ordnance Lieutenant in World War I, and the recipient from the French Government of the Medaille Commerative, he brought to his assignment at Chester Tank Depot, 21 March 1942, an education embracing attendance at University of Wisconsin, Northwestern, Harvard Summer School and Johns-Hopkins University; and an experience of business and industry gained in brokerage work, statistical method, mechanical design, testing of railway equipment; and drilling, testing and oil exploration work, and Chester, during the critical days, gave him opportunity for full play of his exceptional ability.

From Richmond, Virginia, came Norman L. Cavedo to do his stint. Mopping up in 1936 at Virginia Military Institute with a B.S. in chemical engineering he moved over to the firm of A. L. Cavedo & Son, Inc., where he donned the mantle of vice president, and for the next six years prior to his advent, 17 June 1942, in P. O. D., were spent in absorbing about everything anyone knew about forging facings and supplies, grades of sand, etc. That he learned well is borne out by the records he was able to hang up at the Depot.

When John A. McKinney came to P. O. D., 14 March 1942, he could not have guessed that his entire Ordnance life would be spent on a single District assignment, that of Transportation Officer, Chester Tank Depot. There was a brief warming up period spent from 24 April to 10 July 1942, in the Fiscal Branch. Other initiates assigned on the same Office Order were Captain Arthur J. Boyer, to Plant Protection Service, along with Captain Robert H. Merz; Lieutenant James C. Hassett, to the Property Branch; Captain, then Lieutenant, Richard S. Edmonds, to the Artillery Division; and Captain, then Second Lieutenant, James L. Mingle, as Assistant to the Chief Inspector.

With the cessation late in 1945 of Property activities at Chester, Captain McKinney, was recommended, 6 December 1945, for release from active duty, and on the 18th of the month he was headed for Indiantown Gap.

Philadelphia-born-and-reared, Joseph L. Wilmsen first saw duty at P. O. D., 24 July 1942, coming to the District following twelve years as General Manager of B. Wilmsen, Philadelphia manufacturer. His first assignment as Officer-in-Charge, Eddystone Sub-Office. On 11 September 1943 he received his commission of Major. Two months later, 17 November 1943, he was assigned as Commanding Officer of the Chester Tank Depot. He was succeeded in the Eddystone berth by Captain, then Lieutenant, William A. Dilks. On 18 August 1944, in addition to his regular duties, he was assigned as Chairman, Chester Special Salvage Branch. Joe continued at Chester, making good and making friends, an old Wilmsen custom, until his separation 25 May 1945.

From Haverford, Pennsylvania, where he first saw the light of day, came Captain David R. Shelmire, joining up 14 July 1942, in time to miss having a hand at Chester Tank Depot where he was assigned 30 September 1942, in the famous Red Cross shipment of tanks to Libya. His promotion

to the rank of Major came through 18 May 1943. On 16 September 1943, Major Shelmire was relieved from duty in P. O. D. and reassigned to the New York Ordnance District for duty with the Field Service Division. The Major's War Department service dated from 26 May 1917. For the five months following, as a Sergeant, he served with a Q. M. Detachment at Newport News, Virginia. From 1 October 1917 to 8 April 1919, first as Sergeant, then as Sergeant 1st Class, he was attached to Motor Truck Companies also at Newport News. Then, to 17 February 1929, during which time he was promoted to Second Lieutenant, he served with the Q. M. Section, Officers Reserve Corps.

That World War I hero to come out of commercial life to lend Uncle Sam a hand was James R. Stewart. Jim was an Arts man at Gettysburg, leaving there late in his third year, 1917, to tote a gun overseas. Also attended Officer's Material School U. S. N. R. F. University of Pennsylvania. Thence into the wholesale and retail automobile business—from whence, 14 December 1942, he set himself up in the Tank-Automotive Branch of P. O. D. On 17 May 1943 he moved into the Technical Data Section, holding forth at that point until his assignment, 14 December 1943, to the Chester Tank Depot where, 15 January 1944, he was appointed Chief Inspector at that installation, an activity at which he continued until his separation, 10 December 1945, and his return to the oil business.

In the civilian department were names and experiences to conjure with—among them, John W. Magoun, Sparrows Point, Maryland boy, who took the big towns by storm. A graduate of City College, Baltimore, Maryland, he betook himself to Cornell University for further punishment, emerging four years later with his degree in mechanical engineering. First employment was with Pennsylvania Steel Company which later was merged with Bethlehem Steel. Remained there twenty years.

Late in his association with Bethlehem he became a member of the vice president's staff, shortly after finding himself with Major Masters, former Chief Inspector for the District, and Major Modjeski, world famed architect. Came to the District Office in December 1940. He was assigned as Chief of the Depot Liaison Unit of the Tank-Automotive Branch, rubbing elbows with Hugh B. La Rue, Edward M. Chalikian and Edward L.

Kengla. When the Tank Depot took its bow in March 1942, John went to Chester, it having been whispered about the District Office that no one else was better qualified to supervise modification of tanks on their way to destination—and destiny. No need to ask if he turned in a good job; the Meritorious Civilian Service Award made to him in October 1945 is the answer to that query. The end of the Chester contract brought John Magoun back to the Central office, and a later special P. O. D. assignment, to American Car & Foundry Company, Berwick, Pennsylvania.

Another graduate of Chester Tank Depot rating better than honorable mention is Joseph R. Lehecka who broke the spell by staging his birth in Easton, Pennsylvania. Joe picked up some knowledge of engineering on his way through Lafayette College. Principal employment during pre-P. O. D. years was of twelve years with Lockwood-Green Company, Boston engineering and architectural firm, and four years with Bethlehem Steel Company. Came to P. O. D. early 1940, assigned to Inspection in the Gun Shop, Baldwin Locomotive Works. There until his assignment, March 1942, to the Tank Depot where he was appointed Fire Control Liaison between Ford Motor Company and Frankford Arsenal. Other duties were in reference to the installation of sighting equipment and synchronization of telescopes with gun bores, also instructed Ford personnel regarding procedures and, for good measure, took a turn with inspection. Joe rolled along with Chester to the termination in November 1945 of that contract, returned to 150 South Broad Street to the Property Branch and then, 1 February 1946, was out of the District forever and into the maws of the Reconstruction Finance Corporation.

Sharing the honors with Joe Lehecka, was Henry H. Ruttinger. In World War I, he served overseas, in France. Following his discharge in 1922 from Walter Reed Hospital, and the Army, he became associated with The Baltimore Tube Company, Baltimore, Maryland. He later accepted appointment in the Transportation Section. Western Maryland-Fairfield Farms Dairy. He held this berth until early in 1942, when he resigned to help in the war effort, via the Q. M. C. Contracts Section, as Production Pilot Model Inspector. When the Ordnance Department took over this operation in September 1942, Henry hitch-hiked, Pullman first class, to Philadelphia, and directly to Chester Tank Depot.

So, these were the men who with others of P. O. D. nomination, made brilliant history at Chester (German and Japanese generals to the contrary notwithstanding).

And there were many others to write their names in the archives of Chester. We recall Mary M. Manning, secretary to Joseph R. Lehecka. In the Communications Unit under the great Lehecka were Helen M. Guidetti and Joy V. Ward. In the Fiscal Section, under George W. Smith, Field Auditor, appear the names of Frank C. Malatesta, Harry T. Leedom, Adolph E. Buccieri, William Jaffe and Catherine A. McNicholas, secretary.

While heading the Property Section, Captain, then Lieutenant, J. A. McKinney, had for his assistants, Andrew J. Sabonis, Erwin K. Horn, Abraham Brown, Mary Gorenflo and Margaret H. Guydes. Later, when Captain McKinney had moved to the executive post, and his old assignment, combined with the Transportation Section to form the Property and Transportation Section under Andrew J. Sabonis, we find the assistants to include Erwin K. Horn, Margaret H. Guydes, Abraham Brown and Catherine Szczepanski, secretary.

Captain McKinney, doubling as Chief, Salvage Section, during the Wilmsen regime had for his staff in that unit, Andrew J. Sabonis, Elmer Mount and Frank P. Gallagher. William H. Milligan, directing the Order Department, was assisted by Ramona D. Burgos, Jane L. Ward and Barbara M. Jasinski. The Records Unit was the charge of Ethel P. Dickson. Under Captain Cavedo's incumbency, we find Elmer Mount switched to the Property Disposal Unit, and Margaret N. Blythe added to the Order Department.

Inspection under Captain James R. Stewart has Walter C. Lytle as assistant, and for inspectors, Luch M. Widdecombe, John T. Hanley, Evelyn F. Bullard, Erma A. Street, Joseph W. Anderson, George M. Arnst, Harry D. Burnett, George R. Garrison, William H. Hoffecker, Ralph E. Johnson, Peter Jumper, Philip D. Peschi and William J. McFadden.

Too, we note, Roy N. Pierce, Milton H. Heidelbaugh, Wesley McG. Roberts, John E. Hennessey, Donald I. Sellers, James B. Tabor, Joseph E. Tschopp, Sherwood S. Underhill, George R. Warner, John H. Hutchinson and Peter A. Schwartzbauer.

Later, the names of J. McCumisky, Robert E. Hincken, Helen C. Dringil and Dorothea M. Persinger signed up with Captain Stewart's squad.

In the Field Service Section we first find Captain W. R. Burlingame in charge with Joseph Lehecka as assistant and Ethel Dickson on Records. Later, Joy V. Ward is added to the Section, replacing Joseph Lehecka who is assigned to three or four other jobs. The Modifications Section is spear-headed by John A. Magoun who is also serving in the Salvage Committee with Major Wilmsen and Captain Stewart. For assistants, Chief Magoun had Edmond L. Frank, Benjamin S. Buck and Dorothy J. Sickman. Ethel Dickson has the Records assignment.

The Industrial Service Section, established early in 1945, has Captain McKinny as its Chief, with Mildred L. Dougherty and, again, Ethel Dickson, for assistants.

Scanning the more remote archives we tumble upon the names of Hugh F. X. McGlinn, Field Auditor; Walter C. Saunders, John R. Bushel and Herman J. Daniels, Inspectors. Donald Yealy, Joseph Stover, also Inspectors. Then there was John J. Wood, Administrative Officer, way back, transferred to Sam McClenahan's staff at 150 South Broad Street. More Inspectors: Peter Picconi, Charles Mann, Arthur R. Roderick, E. J. Kearney, Charles W. Mervine and George R. Garrison. Joseph E. Hatch, who moved up to Cressona to take over the Fiscal activity where he

later was joined by Peter Picconi. Carolyn L. Warner who left to join her husband who had been assigned to the Adjutant General's staff in Pentagon. Again, Inspectors, in the persons of Albert S. Connelly, Sr., and John T. Donnelly. And not overlooking Lieutenant Julius Mehalek, one time assistant to the Officer-in-Charge, and Major Lorin E. Warlow who went down in February 1944 for one month of special duty. All good soldiers on the Ordnance front.

And that was that, except that early in September 1945 there came down from Detroit an order signed, "Joseph M. Colby, Colonel, Ordnance Department, Assistant," which read, in part:

"1. Due to the cessation of hostilities with Japan, the necessity to retain the Industrial Service Tank Depot at Chester, Pennsylvania, no longer exists.

"2. It is the desire of this office that contracting negotiations be continued with Ford Motor Company (Contract W-670-Ord-2033) in order that Ordnance materiel now located in the Chester Tank Depot may be removed to other destinations at a rate which will permit the Philadelphia Ordnance District to terminate the operations not later than 24 October 1945."

Top, L. to R.: Lt. Robert W. Vogelsberg, Lt. Wilbur L. Lafean, Jr., Lt. William A. Mortensen.
Second row: Lt. Maurice P. Felton, Captain N. Fred Feustel, Lt. H. M. Gingrich, Captain Joseph L. Wilmsen.
Third row: Lt. Jesse C. Jessen, Lt. James M. Kuntz, Captain Brendan D. Walsh, Lt. Andrew W. Hamilton, Jr.
Bottom: Lt. John R. Armstrong, Captain Bernard V. Lentz, Lt. Philip J. Welch, Captain Joseph M. Baxter.

(Rank indicated is at time of picture)

Chapter XXXV

PROPERTY—WHOSE, WHERE, WHAT AND WHY

THAT Property was the largest operation in the P. O. D. Central Office, at least, in point of numbers of persons, was a pretty well accepted fact. At one time the Branch could claim 287 employees scattered through a maze of Sections and Units and Sections within Units. Someone once said that a sudden victim of amnesia might wander for days around Property where even an Ellery Queen or a Nick Carter easily could lose all trace of him.

The Property Branch which, in its beginnings, was a segment of the old Fiscal Branch, sharing honors with Property Records, Purchase, Payroll and Travel, was born in P. O. D. 1 September 1940—and fathered from the start, through the war, by First Lieutenant, later Lt. Colonel, William L. Stephens, Jr., formerly a freight traffic manager for the Pennsylvania Railroad. Bill held the rank of lieutenant at the time of his Property assignment, and at that time, he had only three staff members. One of these was Samuel, popularly known as Sid, Horner who held the rank of Civilian Chief, Assistant to the Chief of the Branch. His earlier assignments included responsibility for a segment of Travel, accounting for the direction of shipment of all Government property and, of all things, typing.

Bill was a Philadelphian from the moment the call went out for the doctor. He grew up through the railroad business, which made him an excellent selection for the Property job. A crack pistol shot, he wrote one of the best books extant on the subject. He designed the crossed-guns insignia of P. O. D., and was editor of the *Bulletin* published back in the time of Major Hamilton. It was during his Reserve Officer days—November 1935—he was assigned to the P. O. D. Transportation Division. In November 1939 he was assigned as Chief, Traffic Section of the District; Property Chief, in September 1940, as noted; Acting Quartermaster in October 1940. Transportation Officer in May 1942—and other added assignments as time went on. Came June 1946, and it was an assignment in the Canal Zone for the Lt. Colonel.

The functions of transportation and accounting of Ordnance property were carried on as early as 1 July 1939, but were largely confined to the preparation of Travel Vouchers, purchase of office equipment and supplies and payment of bills.

Back to the Branch: Increasing responsibilities for procurement assigned through the Summer of 1940 to the District were reflected in the Property Branch, and from there on growth was rapid. On 1 August, Fiscal activities were separated, leaving Property Branch an independent unit. The Branch as then set up was charged with two main duties: accountability for all Ordnance Materiel and property, and prompt, efficient, transportation of materiel from its various sources to final acceptance by the Field Service.

Another activity of those dim days was that of Purchase, and no longer ago than January 1941, we find the Branch concerned with such matters as the purchase of a typist chair for the Wilmington Office, two water-coolers for Henry Disston & Sons, and four typewriters for use by the Ordnance Inspector at Baldwin's. Against this trivia, more or less, we note an item of 2,200 of 155 mm. Shell Forgings received from Taylor-Wharton Iron & Steel Company, Easton, Pennsylvania, and shipped to the Minneapolis-Moline Power Implement Company, Minneapolis, Minnesota. It was a period of transportation: little business fading out· big business looming—and very soon, booming.

Specialization and decentralization in the Property Branch dates from the establishment in January 1941 of a Traffic Section. Daniel K. Betts, up from the Adjutant General's Office in Washington was given the post. It became his responsibility to secure shipping instructions and issue bills of lading. To this time bills of lading had been prepared by Frankford Arsenal. A large number of existing contracts were being changed to "f.o.b." manufacturers' plants, permitting the

Government to assign all finished material to arsenals and the loading plants then being established throughout the country. Growth was rapid from the start. For instance: during the first half of 1941, the Traffic Section prepared and issued 6.103 Government Bills of Lading; for the first seven months 1942, there were issued 21,464 Bills of Lading. From 21 shipments in January 1941 the volume of traffic rose in November 1941 to 1,357, and in July 1942, a total for the month of 4,091 shipments weighing 77,611 tons, equal to 3,000 carloads.

As work increased there was set up in the Traffic Section, in April 1941, a Freight Traffic Unit, whose job it was to obtain shipping instructions from Washington and to forward these to various facilities; and as well, to expedite shipments. Came shortly after a Transportation Unit to keep necessary records in reference to bills of lading, the movement of household goods, and to issue Transportation Requests, this latter work was soon after discontinued and the work of the Traffic Section spread over a number of small units. It was just about this time when John F. Bacon, World War I, Infantry Captain came to Traffic. Prior to his arrival he had been Credit Manager and Purchasing Agent for the Richfield Oil Company. Sensing in early 1941 that motor fuel would become increasingly short under European demands and that the U. S. might become involved he decided to do what he could to help the cause, and bethought himself of Ordnance.

Lend Lease was having its growing pains just about now. That problem was promptly dropped in John Bacon's lap. Things were pretty well snarled at the time and that old quality of patience was pretty well strained throughout the Section. But it was not long before J. F. B. had the whole thing by the tail with all procedures so smoothly operating that items manufactured in Philadelphia plants soon were being delivered, via land and water, to a European destination within seven days.

Some time in December 1941 Albert J. Donohue, an expediter, was added to the Freight Unit to speed up shipments, to take care that shippers were supplied with freight cars and trace critical shipments to destination. A. J. D. brought to his responsibility 20 years of experience in transportation acquired during his association with International Mercantile Marine Company and T. W. A. A bit later, W. F. Neil, with a transportation and traffic background of 17 years, joined up.

Port congestion had for some time been something of a difficulty. The Ordnance Department contributed a substantial measure of relief along the Atlantic Coast through the establishment in the Ford Motor Company plant, at Chester, of the Chester Tank Depot. This was in March 1942. The Traffic Section supervised shipment of tanks and other rolling-devices from this point where these items were prepared for export shipment and stored until cargo space should be available.

Let us double-track for a moment back to January. That month meant much to the now Captain, growing busier with each succeeding tick of the clock. It was the phase of the moon that brought Mrs. Anna M. McCabe to the Property Branch, from her job as reporter and a departmental editor of the late lamented *Evening Public Ledger* which fizzled into limbo the month before.

Mrs. A. had survived a hard session or two at the University of Pennsylvania, in dramatics, public speaking and accounting. Found herself a position as accountant with a small firm, subsequently becoming a partner. Motherhood claimed her for a time. Later, back to the daily grind.

When she applied to P. O. D. for employment she came directly to the Major, who was impressed. He needed another Sid Horner. Whether a male or a female, it didn't matter. There was a job to be done. She came in as Civilian Chief of the Administration, Property Section of the Branch. There were eight girls then in the Branch. Before the year was out she had a staff of 120 persons.

In its turn, came April, and the assignment of Lieutenant James C. Hassett, a combination of Purdue and Northwestern, as Traffic Chief. In February 1944, Lieutenant Hassett was reassigned as Chief of the Storage Section, holding fast until September. There was set up in the Section, almost at the moment of Lieutenant Hassett's arrival, a Freight Rate Bureau, with a freight-rate specialist, John Durney. In October 1942, the Traffic Section took over the transportation of motor transport vehicles and spare parts manufactured in the District.

Traffic totals were hitting the ceiling. In September 1942, saw figures such as the following, among others, highlighting the record:

Hand Grenades, MK11................300,000
Fibre Containers, M-41................500,000
Rifle Grenades, M9A1-HE.............149,000
Projectile Ball for 20 mm. Hispano Gun...289,000

and at the same time many car loads of ammunition, arms, bombs, projectiles, parachute assemblies and countless other incidentia of war were passing through in the general direction of points East.

Sooner or later someone was sure to rear up on his hind legs and roar, "Quit!" at the paper work. It happened in February 1943 when some perturbed gentlemen from Mack Manufacturing Company came tearing into P. O. D. to discuss ways and means by which the quantity of paper required for packing lists could be whittled down. It is a matter of record that Traffic really did itself proud, following that set-to. Carload shipments at this time had broken 4,500. Total shipments for the month, 6,513. In March, carloads had reached 5,736; total shipments, 9,115. We really were on the move.

And in May 1943, we arch our eyebrows when the Captain passes along the news that his carload business had crossed 6,000, and total shipments, 10,293. Now, hold your breath: In December 1943 the District shipped 175,915 tons, an increase over November of 35,000 tons! We've wandered a bit from the Traffic Section—but the figures intrigued us; hence the digression.

The year 1944 began in Property with seven officers and 146 civilians; Traffic had one of the officers and 40 of the civilians. Rocket launchers by Heintz Manufacturing Company, now were making production history. In February, the Traffic Section, with the assistance of Captain J. A. Fleitas, Chief, Purchase Branch, was able to expedite an unusual order for stacks, adapters, metal hose and miscellaneous waterproofing equipment, from Carrier Corporation, York Safe & Lock Company, destined for American and British concurrent front line action.

Shipments demanding special handling were being taken in stride. One in particular is worthy of note. It concerned a shipment from Heintz to Fort Pierce, Florida. Shipment originally had been planned for Railway Express. Due to dimensions it was necessary instead to arrange a special movement by motor truck. The carrier provided two drivers in order that the truck might be driven around the clock. As a consequence, delivery was made in approximately 60 hours.

Strong team now in the Property Branch. Major Stephens of Property still out front. Samuel "Sid" Horner, number two man. Property Section, formerly known as the Industrial Service Section (more of this later on) in charge of Captain David B. Robb who first dropped in upon P. O. D. 7 April 1942, bringing to his job an experience of two years gained with R. F. C. in the Administration of Loans to Defense Industries.

The Field Service, of which also more elsewhere, in the safe hands of Captain Bob W. Vogelsberg, of the Vogelsberg brothers, who romped through wartime P. O. D. to the credit of the family and P. O. D. Captain Vogelsberg made his earthly debut in Newark, New Jersey, home of Prudential Life Insurance Company, Hoffman's Pale Dry Ginger Ale and Frelingheusen Brew. Like many another P. O. Der, he captured a B.S. in mechanical engineering at Lehigh. Through R. O. T. C. he was commissioned a Second Lieutenant. Dropped down to U. of P. for evening study of industrial engineering and law.

Captain Vogelsberg's first paying job was with De Laval Steam Company, erecting and testing heavy machinery, steam turbines and blast furnace blowers. Some years later he switched to the Moffatt Bearings Company as Sales Engineer. With just about everybody turning attention in 1941 to war industry Bob took the hint and on 25 June marched right into P. O. D.—first in the Plant Survey Section then, in July, to the Field Service Branch.

It is April 1944, shipments to Ports of Embarkation of Fording Equipment and Rocket Launchers are on the upswing. The Heavy Ammunition program is bearing down on the Traffic Section, stressing the need for stepped up procedures for handling shipping instructions. Shipment of 2,668 tons of material on Terminated Contracts marks a new high. Also in April there were issued 4,480 bills of lading. Back in 1941 we thought 226 bills spelled big business.

There was a flurry of increased activity in April, the result of the new Vendors' Shipping Document. There were spots in industry that did not quickly catch on. That meant many meetings and, of course, sudden increases in the consumption of paper.

Then that little affair at Cressona—the Cressona Ordnance Plant. Negotiations were begun about this time with Day & Zimmermann, Inc., Philadelphia, for the establishment at Cressona of a reclamation plant, to act as a receiving center for shipments from overseas and from camps throughout the U. S., of materiel for classification, inspection, re-use, standby or scrap. It was required by O. C. O. that the now Major Stephens' boys in the Branch maintain the property account. Captain J. M. Harding was appointed Assistant Property Officer.

The District was fortunate in that the comptroller for Day & Zimmermann, Inc., was a former employee of the Ordnance Department, and had been District Property Supervisor representing O. C. O. in the Midwest.

Orders were out in November 1944 to round up storage space. The District area was combed and the combing continued for some months thereafter. Pencoyd Warehouse, the newly established Redistribution Center for the Property Disposal Branch, goes to work this month. The Traffic Section adds two new Sub-Sections—a Domestic Sub-Section assigned to William Neil with responsibility for all shipping instructions, with the exception of War Air; and an Export Sub-Section, under John F. Bacon with responsibility for Export shipping instructions.

By February 1945 civilian personnel of the Branch had checked off 266. Also, there were eight officers, eight enlisted men. In the Traffic Section, there were 44 civilians, no officers or other military.

Storms and freight embargos were crippling shipping. In a number of instances critically needed supplies were lost in transit, and in other instances materiel in open cars could not easily be removed because frozen in. Critical heavy ammunition was kept moving by the shipment of entire production totals at various facilities by Railway Express.

The embargo finally was lifted 31 January 1945, but the snow and ice lingered on.

In May 1945, Lieutenant J. A. McKinney was relieved of his duties as Property Officer at Chester Tank Depot. A. J. Sabonis was named Assistant Property Officer under Major Stephens, Jr., head man of the Branch.

In the Traffic Section—bills of lading in July were down to a new low, 1,012. The largest decrease was at Chester Tank Depot, indicating that automotive equipment had been drastically cut back. Came August, and victory in the Pacific. Traffic Section activities were reorganized to provide the best service to the Property Disposal Branch. Large quantities of pre-inventory material still was being shipped against current shipping orders. A number of Raritan Arsenal contracts for cleaning and preserving materiel still were in effect.

During the period of World War II the Traffic Section (a) Secured and issued Shipping Instructions on 290,241 shipments· (b) Issued 273,273 Bills of Lading· (c) Routed and shipped 5,928,512 tons.

The total tonnage shipped by P. O. D. during World War II, was equivalent to 264,000 freight car loads or, in other words, an unbroken string of loaded freight cars reaching from Philadelphia to Albuquerque, New Mexico, a distance of 2,000 miles.

Ordnance tonnage was multiplied 7-fold in 21 months, from a low in December 1941 of 31,000 tons to a peak in September 1943 of 210,000 tons.

During the peak year of 1943, a total of 2,085,655 tons of materiel was shipped.

One of the first effects of the good news from Tokyo was the drop in August of tonnage, to 89,721 tons. In July 1945, 105,546 tons had been shipped.

And now into 1946 and . . .

Chapter XXXVI

THE INDUSTRIAL SERVICE SECTION

THE Industrial Service Section of the Property Branch, once known as the Property Section of the Branch, came into existence in February 1941, drawing its motive power from James G. Price, Chief, and his assistant, Harold T. Turtle. On 21 April 1942, Captain, then Lieutenant, David B. Robb was assigned as Chief.

The large increase of paperwork in the Property Section of the Property Branch is shown by the fact that during the last five months of fiscal year 1941 approximately 3,000 vouchers were used, while during the same period in 1942, 17,000 vouchers were accounted for.

The procedure for handling shipments directly in the field was different from that governing shipments on contracts for materiel in process of manufacture. With the increase in both categories it was decided (July 1942) to split the Section into a Field Service Section and an Industrial Service Section. As personnel and duties increased it became necessary to divide the Industrial Section into Units, and being unable to sub-divide the Units into atoms, or iotas, or electrons, they had to stop.

At any rate, under this scheme of division, that was in October 1942, the units stood as follows:

ADMINISTRATION UNIT

Survey Unit—Handling O. S. D. (Over, Short and Damaged) Reports sent by Inspectors to the Branch for approval or disapproval, and those Reports which originated in P. O. D. and disapproved by other Districts and Arsenals. The Unit also had responsibility of Reports of Survey, Inspection and Inventory Reports.

Receiving Report Unit—Responsible for Receiving Reports (QMC, Form No. 431) covering Industrial Service items received by the Property Branch, and for checking these against Receiving Report Register maintained within the Unit.

While we are in the mood for units, let's go on: Now, there was also in the Industrial Service Sec-tion, a Shipping Ticket Unit which routed shipping tickets for the accountability of materiel to other Ordnance Districts, Arsenals or Field Units, to which materiel purchased from contractors had been shipped. Weight, cost of transportation, actual destination, date of shipment and procurement authority, was indicated on the Shipping Ticket of which seven copies were made forwarded to destination office.

And there was a Gage Unit responsible for Shipping Tickets and posting of Receiving Reports covering gages for which the District was accountable or responsible. At that time approximately 35,000 gages were in use in the District.

There was a Machine Tool Unit in the Section: Back in October 1941, the Property Officer had been instructed to tag with Government numbers all tools, fixtures, dies, and other incidentia (that word again) acquired for Government account by facilities in the District. The Unit, however, was not in operation until February 1942. At this time, orders were placed for 53,000 brass tags, but due to priorities, the tags did not materialize until June.

September 1942 saw the advent of a Machine Tool Advisory Unit, set in motion with two expert machine tool men, John Baizley and Harry J. Voltz, to advise the Machine Tool Unit as to correct manner of tagging and caring for machine tools.

There was a Memorandum Receipt Unit, later tied up with a Shipping Ticket Unit; a Posting Unit, under P. McDonough; an Audit Unit, auditing property voucher files for audit by the Service Command; and a Filing Unit to file the vouchers. A Purchasing Receiving Report Unit—and so on into infinity.

The Industrial Service Section, as of 1 October 1942, had at its head, Captain Dave B. Robb. Assistant to the Officer-in-Charge was James G. Price. The Administration Unit of the Section was headed by James F. Doyle whose assistants included John J. Dugan, Arthur H. Skall, Anna Mc-Cabe, John Baizley, J. B. Parsons and Madeline Heckscher who also directed the Survey Unit, under M. Rose; Machine Tool Section, under A. George; Auditing and Filing, with John J. Dugan, and the Machine Tool Advisory Unit, as already noted, with the Baizley-Voltz team.

By September 1942, War Aid Shipments were barging out in rising volume. For instance, in September, the British Ministry of War Transport were accounting for supplies from the District including, among many other items, 70,000 pounds of blasting gelatine, 450,000 pounds of gelignite, 12,800,000 Cal. .303 A.P. Bullet Cores, 200,000 pounds of TNT, 2–7 in. Railway Mounts, 36,720 Cannon Powder Boxes and no end of machine tools.

To the Soviets went toggle presses, anvils, 253 tons of amodyn, 335 tons dynamite. And how the volume and variety of these shipments, to the Soviets and Britain and all the rest, stuck to the high road through the war period.

During the Fall of 1942 James G. Price of the Section was doing a bang-up job at the York Proof Range, establishing an independent Property Office at that point; from whence this nimble young man "volplaned" down to Chester Tank Depot to work with Lieutenant James A. McKinney of that installation in "putting the bite" on property records. At the same time, P. McDonough was sparring with property records at the Philadelphia Mobile Shop Depot.

Early in 1943, the administration of the Warehouse became an Industrial Service Section responsibility. Captain, then Lieutenant, Phil Andress had been calling the turns at that spot.

In July 1943, "Mr. Price Goes to Washington," where, with a group of military and civilian personnel of higher eschelon he settled down to the job of developing a standard shipping document to facilitate the movement overseas of Ordnance materiel. The group subsequently visited the new port of Embarkation, the Boston Port and the Schenectady Ordnance Depot. Upon his return, Jim Price began working out a standard form; then back to Washington for more conferences.

With the wind-up of August there went to O.C.O. a report on all Government-owned production equipment in industrial establishments throughout the District. The report indicated an aggregate value of $27,250,295.03.

In October 1943, the Machine Tool Unit of the Industrial Service Section was transferred to the Production Equipment Section of the Industrial Division where W. L. Weintz was holding down the main job.

Spare Parts Reports now were looking up. The number processed in December 1943, topped the first Section tabulations, October 1943, by 14,062 items.

The District was informed in October by O. C. O. that there would be conducted in P. O. D., by O. C. O., for the benefit of this and other Districts, a school in reference to the War Department Shipping Document. During the month a complete installation of the Document was made at York Proof Range. To the end of the month 75 facilities in the area had initiated use of the system. In February 1944, Regional Offices came in for introduction to the Document.

Earlier in the year, the Industrial Service Section was renamed the Property Section of the Property Branch. This step was taken in recognition of an increasing confusion of designation. To know whether, when it was mentioned, the Industrial Service Section of Property or the Industrial Service Division of P. O. D. was meant, one had to stop and count ten, knock wood, flip a coin, dial a long distance number, and if Mail and Records answered, hang up.

It was decided mid-summer of 1944 to assign a Property Officer to the Gage Laboratory. Lieutenant Bob Watson was elected to assume accountability for gages and precision instruments. Shortly after, the wheel turns and reveals Lieutenant Theodore L. Hayes administering the Machine Tool Unit of the Section with its personnel of 34 burden-bearers. Cap'n Ted was born practically in the shadow of the Military Academy; the family later taking a long jump to Falls Church, Virginia. He majored in journalism at Columbia. Soon found himself in the real estate business. In June 1942 he signed up with Army Ordnance. Came to P. O. D. in February 1944 and thence into Property Branch. In the fading hours of P. O. D. he held the post of Adjutant, succeeding Captain R. Paul Fugate, who had been assigned overseas. Early in November 1946 Ted betook his great personal charm to new fields.

We have paid little attention as we have rambled along, to the comings and goings, and the consolidation of Units; but no doubt by this time you have a pretty good idea of what the Branch and its offspring sections and units did, and why, and what happened to them. There now were, and for some time had been, a Scrap and Salvage Unit, a Plant Clearance Unit, Record Unit, General Records Sub-Section, a Vendors' Shipping Document Unit, Transfer Unit and Machine Tool Record Sub-Section scattered through the Branch.

And so, through 1945, through the gruelling period of terminations, plant clearances, gage discrepancies, reconstruction of cost-plus-a-fixed-fee contracts, audits, and audits of audits, straightening out of property accounts—and an interesting item in the final report submitted by W. A. McCracken of the Audit Section—"There remains in the Property safe, cash in the amount of $18.10. This cash was received from various Philadelphia Ordnance District Guards who lost or misplaced articles of clothing and have paid the full price of the loss." And so, as we started to say—into 1946, starting off that year with a Branch personnel low of 94 which, by June 1946, would be down to 21.

Storage Section

The Storage Section of the Property Branch first topped the horizon with the morning sun of March 1941, with Captain, Philip M. Andress and ten assistants. The origin of each warehouse was linked with an unexpected need for storage space. Physical limitations of the buildings which were early and hurriedly leased and the distances between them resulted in inefficiencies and high costs. The first lease drawn up had been for the most quickly available building, (suitable or otherwise) and it became a collective "lay down space" for millions of dollars worth of Ordnance items in their inadequate "temporary" packaged or unpacked state.

There were three warehouses in operation and another on the way at the time Captain Andress assumed command. Warehouse No. 1, a six-story fireproof building with storage space of 55,000 feet; Warehouse No. 2, in the Tacony section, with 36,000 feet of ground space, a patchwork of concrete and soft sand housed in an unheated and unheatable foundry-type building. To operate this building, the Government was spending $500 a month for lack of two $5 pieces of equipment. Material moving in and out of No. 2 was costing our Uncle from $40,000 to $250,000 per car. To improve this sore spot, the new C. O.

borrowed equipment, indicating that the new equipment required would pay for itself within two to four months. But the answer from Washington (April 1942) was to the effect that these warehouses were temporary installations; that the Government would buy no such equipment, as there would be no use for it after the war.

Warehouse No. 3, a slightly better building, although of all-wood construction, presenting a definite fire-hazard which threatened the stored materials even if the antiquated sprinkler system didn't. Warehouse No. 4, later to come along, brought the total of storage space to 200,000 feet. The Plant Protection Section of P. O. D. wasn't too pleased, either, particularly with No. 3.

There were skid platforms all over the place. Some 1,500 were discards purchased from a printing firm at forty cents each—delivered. The staff on hand built a number of skids in addition—better, of course—at a cost of about one dollar each. The stevedores then employed cost the taxpayer a dollar an hour. They were difficult to supervise, ten miles away. But they worked! The guards, $1,200 a year men, were good. They were from all walks of life. Many had retired before the war began. All agreed early in 1942 to buy their own blue uniforms and hope for the best. However, the guards later were reimbursed for the pretty clothes, and in good time the average pay for the guards was upped to $2,400.

Personnel of the Storage Section was not long in climbing to a total of 58 individuals, and No. 4 Warehouse no longer dotted the Section map; but in its stead appeared Warehouses 3A and 3B.

The guard force had increased by 31 March 1942, to 24 men, five were assigned to each warehouse except 3B, which temporarily was being handled by four men. Five guards were assigned to the Mitten Building, P. O. D. headquarters. The new uniforms first appeared in March, consisting of one 12 ounce Navy blue serge blouse with brass buttons, one pair 12 ounce Navy blue serge trousers, one Navy blue eight point police cap, one black garrison belt, one Navy blue poplin shirt, and one black four-in-hand tie. Black shoes, of course. Lieutenant Augustine D. Edwards, Jr., then Assistant Officer-in-Charge, wrote in his report: "Particular pride in the uniform has been evidenced by the guards, and morale of the entire force has been greatly improved."

Captain Andress was exulting a few "exults"

as the result of the cooperation of Kahn's Furniture, Inc., in providing offices, plumbing and lighting necessary for proper administration of the offices. At this time movement of materiel in and out of the warehouses was on an average of 66 cars in and 49 out per month.

In February 1943, the Warehouse Administration, the Storage Section, was absorbed by the Industrial Service Section, and finally lost all its separate identity when the Industrial Service Section was re-tagged, the Property Section. However, the business of warehousing continued through the war, and after, as a considerable activity. For instance, in March 1943, the Warehouse Administration Unit was making a physical inventory of machine tools and equipment throughout the District, which, upon completion registered a value of $27,250,295.03.

Early in 1944 there was much activity in the direction of the procurement of storage space. Sites were being explored everywhere "from John O'Groat's to Land's End" and back again. It was reported in January 1944 by Major Bill Stephens that the Pennsylvania Ordnance Works in Williamsport would be turned over to P. O. D. and, in addition, that the District would have space in the Lehigh Valley Railroad Yards, at Easton. During the same period, negotiations were in process for the leasing of a warehouse for the storage of machine tools.

Sites subsequently acquired were the Halethorpe Yards, near Baltimore, of the Baltimore & Ohio Railroad, capable of handling 500 cars, and the Pencoyd Iron Works of Lower Merion Township. In order to expedite the handling of material consigned to and at storage points, there was set up in April 1944, a separate Storage Section, under James C. Hassett, formerly Chief of the Traffic Section.

In April 1944, Pencoyd definitely was in the District Warehouse picture. It was estimated that storage space would be available by 1 June. On 5 May, Lieutenant Hassett and his staff moved to Pencoyd. The first shipment received there was of three-boring lathes from the Pennsylvania Forge Company. The cost of converting Pencoyd was placed at $76,000.

To the end of June 1944 there had been taken in at Pencoyd a total of nine carloads to a net weight of 310,322 pounds, the greater part consisting of machine tools procured by Heintz Manu-

facturing Company, Pennsylvania Forge Company, John R. Wald Company and Henry Disston & Sons, Inc.

During September 1944 the total of shipments received at all warehouses were to a total of 2,730,270 pounds. Total shipments issued were of 1,784,238 pounds. In November 1944 Harry Steele came down from the York Proof Range to head into the Storage Section. He had been Traffic Supervisor at the Range.

January 1945 receipts at Warehouses were to a total of 2,868,333. Down from December's total by 3,667,696 pounds. In February 1945, shipments were up a bit, to 4,233,573 pounds. That's the way it was. Up a little, down a little. Shipments out, in February, were of 3,461,599 pounds. The greater part of the stored material at Warehouse No. 2 now consisted of terminated inventories from contractors' plants, plus surplus materials which had been declared available to the various disposal agencies, including the Treasury Department and the R. F. C.

What goes up must come down. In April 1945 the Section was told to get the Work Simplification Program under way. Major Joseph C. Hoffman, Fiscal Chief, had been assigned to head up the work for the District organization. In the Property Section, it became Mrs. Anna McCabe's job. The purpose of the Program was to find ways of reducing total man hours. Mrs. McCabe turned in her report, 24 May 1945. Survey had been made of 22,672 man hours. Her recommendation was of savings aggregating 4,618 man hours.

We were into the Summer of 1945, and before the leaves turned, the Japs had caved in, and Property Branch and all its kith and kin were up to their bifocals in bristling activity. The Third Service Command completed by mid-December all audits at Cressona, and at the Firestone Tire and Rubber Company, Pottstown Ordnance Plant; a new Gage record set up; the Machine Records Unit completed the punching of 200,000 cards.

Liquidation of warehouses was well under way by late September 1945.

Material inbound during September and October 1945 was chiefly surplus from contractors. This was consigned for future disposal to the Redistribution Center at Pencoyd. Other October shipments were divided between School Board donations and the Allegheny Iron & Metal Company, for scrap iron and steel.

By 31 May 1946 the Warehouses were no more: Leases had expired; personnel, disbanded.

January 1946, and the war five months into history. Gage discrepancies now take the spotlight, but not too unfavorably. Of 200,000 gages handled during the war, discrepancies affected only 7,000, with a loss of approximately 800 gages, which required a Report of Survey. The cost-plus-a-fixed-fee contract at Baldwin Locomotive Works had been completed, and a "Finding of Facts" had been passed along to Lt. Colonel Albert W. Gilmer and Fred Sarkis of the Contract-Settlement Division; the contracts at Barclay White Company, Cressona Ordnance Plant, Thornton-Fuller Company and Chester Tank Depot, and the Firestone Tire and Rubber Company now were completed and all audits in.

The temperature in downtown Philadelphia, at noon, 31 January 1946 was 54 degrees; cottage cheese was substituting for butter, black markets in everything from tea to crumpets were active, and the familiar cherry in the bottom of the glass was missing. Peace, of a sort, had settled over the Property Section of the Property Branch of P. O. D.

FIELD SERVICE SECTION

The Field Service Section of the Property Branch was established in June 1941 in accordance with Ordnance Department Order No. 169. Lieutenant Robert A. Scott, Johns Hopkins 1939, with a B.E. in chemical engineering and metallurgy, was nominated Chief, and assigned two assistants, William M. McKee and Lieutenant Robert W. Vogelsberg who took a bow earlier in this narrative. Lieutenant Scott arrived in P. O. D., via Beacon Steel Products, Bethlehem Steel Company and the Baltimore Regional Office where, 27 December 1940, he was assigned as assistant officer-in-charge. Lieutenant Scott served only a short while in Field Service. He was succeeded in the main tent by Lieutenant Vogelsberg who remained with Field Service to the time of his separation, 10 December 1945.

In the operation of the original mobilization plan, the Arsenals were able to receive, and deliver to the troops, all designated Ordnance Materiel. However, because of the unexpected swiftness of the war and the corresponding swift increase in the volume of materiel flowing overseas, there was early set up a procedure by which materiel would be shipped directly to the point of use, or to Lend Lease countries, without passing through the Arsenals. The Field Service Sections of the Districts were charged with the responsibility for maintaining records of such materiel and of shipments thereof. In addition, these Sections were required by orders of the Chief of Ordnance with the proper distribution of materiel.

Spare Parts, too, were a Field Section headache. This logically was a Traffic Section function. However, because of the involved clearances required for War Aid Materiel, and because of the complexities then characteristic of Spare Parts procedures, it was decided in August of 1940, by agreement with the Traffic Section, that all War Aid Materiel and Spare Parts distribution activities would first be cleared by the Field Service Section where, after processing, they could be routed to the Traffic Section for issue of bills of lading.

The rapid, and very often wide changes in design of Tank-Automotive and Artillery items imposed many problems during the early days—and some continued through duration. A single list of parts, "back when," for some automotive units, for instance, called for more than 3,000 items. A set of parts sufficient to maintain 100 light tanks in service for one year would require the loading capacity of 10 freight cars. Standard nomenclature lists in the hands of troops were never up to date because of design changes. Parts were reaching operations lacking sufficient data to enable identification as to their use. There was a lack of information needed to enable troops to identify parts common to more than one vehicle, or to identify standard hardware items which could have been procured through local sources.

Code systems were developed. Tags fastened to parts did tend to relieve the difficulty; but these in turn developed other difficulties: As a case in point, such standard hardware items as rivets, screws, nuts and bolts often were given the same code numbers regardless of the material of which they were composed. Duplications were in large number and there were numerous instances of items with more than one code number. It was somewhat the same with an interchangeability which did not always interchange, and with the weekly receipt from Washington of changes and revisions. Inaccurate and long-delayed shipping instructions brought other "situations." Then someone invented a device called a "Deficiency Requisition" and in due time someone else invented something else, and as the Section gained in "know how," and prevision and clairvoyancy, troubles grew less and less acute. There are those who will question this. They will tell you that war being a problem everything connected with it is of necessity a problem—and no end.

The natives of the Field Service also recalled for us that the Chester Tank Depot was one of their responsibilities immediately subsequent to the establishment in February 1942 of that operation. For three months, they informed us, Depot administration was solely theirs. In May 1942, the various functions of inspection, engineering and production were spread over the pertaining Branches and Sections of the District Office.

Lend Lease had been an early arrival in the Field Service Section—June 1941, to be reasonably accurate—and there was set up a Lend Lease Unit in which John F. Bacon played an important part along with Lawson H. Gotwols. Functions of the Unit were (1) to report the availability of material and materiel, to the War Aid Section of the Chief of Ordnance, by means of a standard data report which provided contract numbers, descriptions, quantities, delivery schedules, rail facilities available, valuation of material, and weights and measures; (2) to act as liaison point between O. C. O. and foreign government agents; (3) to issue letters of instructions, deadline delivery dates, and quantities to be shipped, and (4) to coordinate these instructions with the Traffic Branch, in order that bills of lading would be properly forwarded to accomplish shipments, and (5) to maintain a consolidated record, by contract, of material being shipped to War Aid countries, including with this record, the actual money value of the material transferred. In the beginning each Lend-Lease transfer was accompanied by 35 copies of the shipping papers. This later was reduced to twenty-three.

In April 1942, P. O. D. was sending overseas such items as light tanks, M3, Smokeless Powder, diphenylamine, debuyte pthalate, wrecking trucks, personnel carriers, medium tanks, Gun Motor Carriages, M3, polar blasting gelatine, 3.7 in. A.A. Loose Gun Barrels, Shells BL, H.E. s/1 7.2 in. Howitzer, reamers, compressors and many, many others, on a list as long as a woman's "few minutes."

Then, in October 1942, came transfer to the District, for administration, a number of contracts from the Quartermaster's, in reference to Mobile Shops.

In December 1942, the War Aid Unit was transferred intact to the Traffic Section which, from the dawn of Lend Lease in P. O. D. had been performing control functions.

Loyal to its Spare Parts Progress Reports, the Field Service Section bent over backwards to keep current. The tabulations per month made in compiling these reports often were of 30,000 and more items.

The Machine Records Unit was not doing badly, either: Processing 100,000 and more cards per month was easy going for this group. Analysis of Active Contracts, another Unit function, for Fiscal Branch, frequently reached 1,600 per month. Listing for Tank-Automotive Branch, of unshipped balances of replenishment spare parts; data on Machine Tools in the District; preparation of Master Cards, covering as many as 340,000 items; punching data cards on Heavy Truck Concurrent Contracts and other chores were all in the day's work.

Tabulation reports for the Terminations Branch was added in November 1944, by way of keeping the Unit on its toes. The Office of the Chief of Ordnance—Detroit had requested cancellation of a large number of items on contract with the American Car & Foundry Company. A four-part report was prepared for each item, listing (1), drawing number; (2) stock number; (3) description, and contractor's number and (4) undelivered balance on order.

There was set up during this period a Supply Control Procedure under which the Field Service Section assumed responsibility for the preparation of Forecast and Progress Reports for all Parts and Supplies items on order in the District.

A special project was under way in December 1944 in the District; initiated at the request of the Use Analyst of the Artillery Branch. It had been the practice of the Field Service Depots to forward to P. O. D. lists of excess material on hand. The Use Analyst of the Commodity Branch concerned screened these lists and wherever excess material could be used in the District for the manufacture of major items, the Use Analyst made arrangements to supply such material as Free Issue to the manufacturer.

Coming up to March 1945, there is noted a considerable let-down from the first of the year, of shipments to ports of Embarkation. Such shipments steadily had been sliding off, and material formerly shipped to Ports now was being designated for storage. This was true not only of U. S. export, but in reference to Lend Lease as well.

The Machine Records Unit took up in May 1945 the task of preparing for the Administration Branch of P. O. D. a punched card inventory covering office equipment in the District Office. Listing required of 8,000 cards which listed both the item and its location. The total of cards processed in April, for all purposes, was in excess of 200,000. In July 1945, the Unit listed for the Tank-Automotive Branch, a list of all tank-automotive spare parts on order in the District. The list covered more than 100,000 items. In August, Unit attention was turned to gages and special tools on Property Records.

The end of 1945 is leering down upon us. All the Units now are shooting at totals of one kind and another. One Status Report upon another appears in the records. Over in the Contract-Settlement Division they were burning the oil to have the job done by New Year's Eve. Legion of Merit recommendations were being hustled "down-under," and on Chestnut Street and tributaries can be seen the Executive Officer, Lt. Colonel Gadsden dashing hither and yon in search of a colorfully appropriate civilian cravat to drape about the neck of the departing District Chief, Colonel A. Donald Kelso.

So let's call it a day for Field Service Section. There was more—but the main job had been completed.

Smiles that reveal a hurdle just got over. *Left to right:* Then Deputy Chief, C. Jared Ingersoll, Price Adjustments and Advance Payments Chief Charles P. Stokes and the District Chief, Colonel D. N. Hauseman

Chapter XXXVII

PURCHASE AND SUPPLY BECOMES ADMINISTRATION

THE Purchase and Supply Section, once known as the Purchase Section of Property, was in existence back in 1939. Until July 1940 the Section boasted but one employee. There were four in March 1941.

As personnel increased there appeared to be an increase in activities and the number of forms required to keep up with the "goings on." There was, for instance, Purchase Ledger Records, keeping accounts showing items ordered, with descriptions, Purchase Order number, date prepared, and cost; and, of course, this all tied in with a Receiving Report. Then there was an "Arch-File," to show Purchase Orders awaiting completion—and all relevant data. Too, an "Outside Requisitions" File for the purpose requisitions from the Chief of Ordnance, Third Service Command, Arsenals and other installations. Also a file for Invitations to Bid.

Matters of priorities soon were engaging the Section. In August 1942, the Fiscal Division turned over to the Purchase and Supply Section all of its records in reference to purchases of gas and oil, and lubrication service. Vehicle Maintenance records became a responsibility and thus the work grew.

The first chief of the Section was "Sid" Horner. He gave way to Major Stephens when that officer arrived. The Major relinquished to Dan Betts, and shortly after Dan was transferred to Traffic, Lieutenant John I. Spiegelhalter was named chief. And "little did he reek," this Spiegelhalter, that he had inherited an all-girl aggregation—but he found out. It was one lone man against ten girls—count them: Mrs. Libby R. Rudnick, Assistant; Rita O'Brien for the Motor Transport Unit; Netta Davis and Helen K. Martin on the Purchase Order Unit; Mrs. Mary W. Bealman and Mrs. Ruth Beach on Invitation to Bid Unit, and Motor Vehicle and Office Machinery Maintenance Unit; Mary Magee and Anna M. Moran on Receiving Report and Ledger Record Unit; Helen Martin, again,

heading the Requisition Unit; Mary Magee doubling as Chieftess, Motor Vehicle Speedometer Unit; and engineering the Postage Stamp Unit, Helen Diskin.

In late 1943, O. Howard Wolfe, Chief of the General Office Division departed P.O.D. for an assignment with the Treasury Department. The General Office Division ceased as of that date. All of its functions were transferred to a newly formed Administration Branch under Captain Lewis A. Smith, Jr. The Purchase and Supply Section of the Property Branch was transferred to the Administration Branch in the reorganization. Lieutenant Spiegelhalter went along as assistant to the new Chief.

The duties of the Administration Branch were outlined about like this—"responsibility for providing and maintaining office facilities; procuring, stocking and controlling issue of all office equipment and supplies; administering communication services; supervising maintenance of official District records; controlling operation of reproduction equipment; administering clerical center; providing and controlling military and civilian travel service; administering motor pool, and handling all related matters. There were set up at the time of reorganization an Office Service Section, a Communication Section, a Travel Section and a Clerical Section—with a combined personnel group of 127 individuals.

In April 1944, Captain, then Lieutenant, Philip J. Fields who long had been on Communications was transferred to the Civilian Personnel Branch. He was succeeded by Lieutenant Stanley M. Levenson, Colby College lad, from the regular Army.

Units grew at good speed in Administration. There was a Stock Control Unit which later was renamed the Forms Design and Standardization Unit. This was the special responsibility of Sam Marx, once of Civilian Personnel (writing an excellent history of the Branch while he was there) the Public Relations Section, and other special assignments in line with his signal ability. The main part of Sam's assignment in Administration was the consolidation and obsoletion of forms, and the development of more practical forms. By way of illustration, in one month alone, November 1944, he handled 416 requisitions, approved 852 forms; ten new forms were accepted, 11 forms eliminated.

The Administration was set in a dither in April 1945 by a request (with all the earmarks of a command) from the District Chief, C. Jared Ingersoll, that something be done pronto about excessive telephone calls. In response, Captain Smith set up a test period of 10 days during which topside and their associates would keep the "stop-watch" on their outgoing calls—and crack down on the number. It worked. The daily average fell to 796 calls, or 68% under preceding 10 days when 2,518 calls were recorded. That we slipped a little "when the heat was off" goes without saying—but it was not intentional. We had war on our minds, and getting over with it.

All through 1944 and 1945 the Branch was doing a very excellent job in consolidating completed contracts and getting them out of the way— to the Contract Record Branch in St. Louis. Other files were being boxed and shipped to Curtis Bay.

In August 1945 Captain Smith, with assistant Joseph W. Stone, and Major J. C. Hoffman, Control Officer, began planning for the orderly liquidation of P.O.D. equipment and office space. In the process, some units were moved from 1420 Walnut Street to 150 South Broad Street, where consolidation and reduction in staff had created space.

Into 1946—and down to a low of 28 employees scattered over the Communication Section with its File, Teletype, Mail and Records Consolidation Unit, still the charge of Lieutenant Levenson; the Office Service Section under Joseph W. Stone with the Forms Design and Standardization Unit in the capable hands of Concetta C. D'Ettore; the Stock Control Unit under William B. Hart; the Service

Unit and Property Disposal Unit under Joe Stone himself; Supply and Reproduction Unit with Thomas Carey; Clerical Unit under Anna Almeida; Purchase Unit, Florence Mayr. The Travel Section, the charge of Lieutenant Howard D. Ginsburg who succeeded Lieutenant Spiegelhalter back in September 1944. The Units of the Travel Section now were—Order and Voucher Unit with Mary Falls; Travel Unit with Mary Brady, and Motor Unit with Anna Merle Jones.

The Travel Section first was a Fiscal Branch activity; known as the Payroll and Travel Section, with Citizen, later Lieutenant, Rathgeber running the show. As the work expanded, Citizen R. took to other duties; Lieutenant David H. McIlvaine, took over, continuing at this post until his appointment, 25 November 1941, as Public Relations Officer. On 5 April 1943, he was returned to the Fiscal Branch, relinquishing to Vrest Orton his duties as Public Relations Officer.

With the reorganization in November 1943 of the General Office Division and its re-establishment as the Administration Branch, Travel moved down from Fiscal and became the responsibility of Thomas P. Lowry, Jr., the automobile mogul from Jenkintown—and "the glass of fashion and the mould of form," as the saying goes. Tom Lowry came into P.O.D. in August 1942, joined the Anderson-McClenahan team in the then sub-office Administration Division. Served there until Travel reached out for him, and gathered him in. A few months later, feeling the old automotive urge, he was up and away—to Jenkintown of course. And then Lieutenant Spiegelhalter again sweeps into prominence, donning the Lowry colors on the day of that gentleman's farewell. Came September 1944 and Spiegelhalter stepped aside for Lieutenant Howard "Murphy" Ginsburg, and in time—even "Murphy"—stepped—after which Travel became just an additional duty for Captain R. Paul Fugate —and gradually thereafter disappeared altogether.

Chapter XXXVIII

REPRODUCTION SECTION

THE Reproduction Section, so named late in 1942, formerly had been listed on the P.O.D. map as the Supply and Reproduction Section, under the guidance of William Casella from the inception of the Section, 1 January 1941. At that time there were three persons employed. Their job—to expedite office supplies and reproduce various types of work. No records were kept and all District employees had access to needed supplies. There was then a hand-operated mimeograph machine and a multilith unit. In January 1941, four thousand forms were printed. To the end of March the Section had ground out 114,650 forms.

The Section early assumed responsibility for allocation and delivery of office furniture and equipment, and for keeping a record of assignments, removals and transfers (duties later assumed by the Office Service Section where first appear the names of J. Harry Fernan, Fred W. Harvey and William B. Hart—but not all together). By September monthly production on the mimeograph machine had increased to 133,000 copies; on the multilith, to 500,000 copies. Business was coming with a rush. During the following month more than 4,000 jobs were processed with an output of 2,000,000 impressions.

In November 1943, with the transfer to the newly formed Administration Branch, successor to a number of General Office Division functions, there was set up in the Administration Branch an Office Service Section, which in turn took over the Property Branch, Purchase and Supply and Reproduction Sections, and the responsibilities which these units had administered. Also, the Office Service Section was given control of requisitions on the issuance of old or new forms, transferred from the Control officer.

The Office Service Section under Fred W. Harvey, Chief, continued the activities of the office manager, covering the filling of requisitions, assignment of new office space due to consolidations and changes in functions of branches and sections, changes in telephone locations, corrections of property records, issuance of memorandum receipts and delivery of equipment, among other matters.

It was during the Harvey regime that dictaphones first were introduced in the District office. It was in June 1944 when stenographic assistance was at a premium.

Procedures proceeded through 1944 and 1945—and as well as could be expected, in a swift-moving, though highly efficient organization. There were the usual quick shifts of furniture and equipment, frequent and rapid changes in telephone locations, sharp-shooting at the cost of supplies, an almost surgical attention to stock control, and the integration of economics, generally. In May 1945, Joseph W. Stone, and Cettina D'Ettore of the Forms Design and Standardization Unit were whirled down to the Pentagon to attend a conference in reference to the elimination and standardization of forms for field installation use: Came back bristling with ideas plus that one new thing one is supposed to learn each day.

The District was not far into 1946 before personnel could be counted on the fingers of two hands, with a few toes thrown in for good measure; and by mid-Summer—well there still was Joe Stone and a few, a very few of the faithful—

L. to R.: Lt. Ross T. Henderson, 2nd Lt. J. Rowan Murphy
(Rank indicated is at time of picture)

Chapter XXXIX

MORE ECHOES OF PROPERTY

THE Guards! These well-remembered men, as noted elsewhere, came, during the early days, from retirement. They did the job that was expected, acquitting themselves with honor. They were a credit to the District, always.

The Guard Patrol originally was established in P.O.D., 13 February 1942, with 2nd Lieutenant, John R. Murphey, as guard officer. The District Office then occupied the mezzanine, and second floor, the twelfth, thirteenth, fourteenth, fifteenth and part of the sixteenth floor of the Mitten Building. Four guards chosen from the guards at the warehouse kept constant patrol of the Mitten Building twenty-four hours a day in eight-hour shifts. Constant watch later also was kept at 150 Broad Street.

Among those who nobly served, we recall Frederick A. Yeggle, Harry P. O'Connell, Arthur M. Rea, Edward B. Paul, Jr., James P. McCue, Francis E. Fleming, Michael G. Boback, Joseph L. Chapman, Matthew Andrews, John F. Aiken, John Hill, William L. Stahl, Stanley F. Letcavage, William E. Jones and Allmond M. Gray. Wherever they are today—"Thanks a million!"

The story of the Property Branch would not be complete did it neglect to give a nod to one of the most interesting personalities to come to the District. Reference is made to Ellis Mather, born in Manchester, England in 1870. His early trade was that of a buggy-trimmer. He traveled about the country with a kit of tools, ready for work wherever he should find it. Business, however, was changing. He soon realized that one pair of hands could not compete with the machinery of a growing industry. So, he studied bookkeeping; got a job with a bakery. In due course he found himself in the United States and, in 1943, in search of a connection.

Well, one day, the now Major Stephens looked up from his property records and there was Ellis Mather, erect and eyes sparkling in spite of his years—seventy-three of them. "I suppose they won't let me carry a gun," he said, "but isn't there something I can do to help get this ugly war over? I know a lot about figures and I'm pretty steady."

Almost any modern personnel director would have turned him down on the basis of age without bothering to learn what he had stored up in his good-looking head. But Ordnance needed STEADY men, particularly men who knew figures. Major Stephens saw something in this man, and got him.

Ellis Mather tackled the job with a vim. Card records were new to him but he soon caught on, and when he did—it was "heigh ho, and devil take the hindmost." "He was a pace-maker," Major Bill Stephens once told your narrator. "I'll take all the Ellis Mathers I can get."

Helen J. McCabe

John Ryan

Jane Rich

Top row, L to R: Captain Harold L. Vennell, Lt. Hamilton Page, Captain Rutledge Slattery, Lt. Maynard H. Patterson. Second row: Lt. John I. Spiegelhalter, Lt. W. H. Nicholls, Captain J. Albury Fleitas, Major Edw. H. Cahill. Third row: Lt. Albert E. Lee, Jr., Captain Albert W. Gilmer, Captain Paul H. Carlson, Lt. James L. Mingle. Bottom: Captain Wm. S. Canning, French E. Dennison, Lew Rittenhouse, Lt. Josef H. Buerger.

(Rank indicated is at time of picture.)

Chapter XL

JUNK GOES BACK TO WAR

" JUNK Goes Back to War." That was the theme A. D. Rathbone, IV, a well known writer of the time, selected for his story of the Cressona Ordnance Plant operation, Cressona, Pennsylvania, appearing in the 10 February 1945 issue of *Liberty* magazine.

Your historian cannot say that he particularly likes that title: The tons upon tons of war-wearied materiel and supplies rolling daily into the plant may have been junk when it arrived, but when it rolled out—it was "not by no means" junk. And what happened in the interim tells the amazing story of Cressona.

The huge plant at Cressona, two miles from Pottsville and one mile from Schuykill Haven, Pennsylvania, which later, in 1944, was to become the P.O.D. administered Cressona Ordnance Plant was built in the summer of 1943 by the Defense Plant Corporation for the Aluminum Corporation of America. Its function was to be the processing of aluminum extrusions which involved the handling of original "pig," and also to melt scrap from airplane plants. The plant also was designed for making extruded shapes and tubes. Among the equipment in the plant at the time it fell into the lap of Ordnance was one 4,500 ton extruding press, one of the only two such presses in the United States.

Cressona was the last of the aluminum plants to come into production and, to its own distress, at a time when other plants adequately were meeting all needs. Equipment installed by the Aluminum Corporation of America had been tested; but the plant was never operated at even near capacity. By mid-1944 production had dropped to approximately 20% of capacity. The plant was estimated to have cost $15,000,000, or thereabouts; its equipment, $10,000,000.

Ordnance first became interested in the project when it was made known that the plant contained idle hydraulic equipment; a basic requirement for heavy shell forgings. The heavy shell program had

been so hastily placed that the building did not receive proper consideration, nor was it properly cleared with all the interests involved.

Subsequent to the heavy shell program, there came the problem of establishing reclamation centers. It was at this time that the Cressona Plant was recommended by the Philadelphia Ordnance District.

On 6 September 1944, the Defense Plant Corporation issued a letter of intent authorizing Day & Zimmermann, Inc., to "enter into possession of certain land and facilities, undertake such engineering and construction work, to acquire any necessary machinery and equipment, and to complete such re-arrangement and reconversion of said plant facilities as may be necessary to establish the same as an Army Repair Depot—conducted in such a manner as not to interfere with the gradual termination of operations of the Aluminum Corporation of America."

As a result of an engineering survey by the Day & Zimmermann group which did indicate the possibilities of the plant in reference to the reclamation program, cost-plus-a-fixed-fee contract— (W-36-034-Ord-3364) was awarded, 18 October 1944, to the contracting firm which was authorized by the contract to—"do all things necessary, convenient or incidental to and/or deal with, handle or dispose of such items of Ordnance materiel and/or parts therefor as sent you for that purpose."

The contracting engineers appointed as plant manager, George Vesselago, of their own organization. P.O.D. appointed Major Howard P. Klair to serve as Commanding Officer. As of 21 January 1945, the P.O.D. staff at Cressona consisted of six officers and 28 civilians.

Officers and civilian chiefs at Cressona as of 21 January 1945, were—Commanding Officer, as already indicated, Major Howard P. Klair, Executive officer, Captain E. P. Waite. In charge of Inspection, Lieutenant Frank F. Hagenbuch, who joined up with P.O.D. 9 October 1944. In charge of the

Reclamation Coordination Section, the dashing Captain Giles P. Wetherill. Directing the Traffic, Property, Reports and Production Liaison Section, Captain J. M. Harding. The Fiscal Audit Section was the charge of Joseph E. Hatch, with assistants John O. Glover and Stanley J. Ward. Under Inspection there is a General Inspection Section with John O. Dixon as chief; and as assistants, Leonard A. West, Bynum W. Jones, Leon F. Heckman, Ammon T. Stahl, George E. Clinton. A Packaging Unit under Gerald B. Jacobs, listed James O. Harrison as assistant. Under Captain Wetherill there were assistants Ammon T. Stahl, in charge of On-Vehicle-Material, and George E. Clinton, on Small-Arms-Artillery. Under Captain Harding—Bert Krause heads up the Material Expediting Unit, with Charles H. Reese, Roy D. Miller and Mary T. Varano as assistants; Lieutenant Stanley B. Honour, in charge of the Traffic and Property Unit had for assistants Earl L. Fennelly, Morgan O. Edwards, Marion A. Donovan and Anna E. Wommer; the Procurement Unit under Wilmer Alam, listed assistants Virginia R. Eifert, Eura B. Schnerring and Margaret M. Kelley.

And a word for the secretaries who carried a good share of the load in P.O.D. headquarters: Mildred A. Bonin, Mary A. Tomes, Lillian Cain. Then there was Helen B. Bergen on files and reports, and Virginia V. Rowan, commandress of the teletypes.

The working force at Cressona grew from approximately 1,200 in October 1944 to a high in August 1945 of 4,010 employees, from which point it tapered off by a series of weekly reductions to 25 November 1945, when the total was reported as of 2,587 persons. Contractor's weekly payroll climbed to a high for the week of 4th of August 1945, of $157,000, scaling off from this total to a low, 25 November 1945, of $86,052.

The total area occupied by the Cressona operation was of 116.61 acres. The main buildings covered an area of 1,400,000 square feet. The main mill building, a typically modern one story manufacturing building of steel and concrete, wide column spacing and served by overhead traveling cranes, was 380 feet wide by 2,445 feet in length.

Other buildings were a heating plant, a producer—gas plant, delivering 400,000,000 feet per month, machine shop, warehouse, cafeteria, wash-rooms, laboratory, wood box shop and general office building. Parking spaces would accommodate as many as 1,900 cars. Paved concrete roads provided access to all buildings. The cost of converting all

this to Ordnance needs was placed, roughly at $1,400,000.

The work of the Cressona Ordnance Plant: Under Ordnance supervision in the various war theatres, all collected materiel which either was not clearly identified and known to have had an existing demand in the same theatre in which it was collected, or which appeared to be usable but not serviceable, was assembled and boxed and returned to ports of embarkation where, theoretically at least, Ordnance materiel was sorted and sent to Cressona. This materiel was received at Cressona in all conditions from excellent to scrap, and might consist of anything among the more than 200,000 items of Ordnance.

Procedure at the plant was as follows:
1. Rough classification according to types
2. Uncrating
3. Immediate rejection of obvious scrap
4. Clearing
5. Identification
6. Parts inspection

Good materiel was repackaged and sent to depots and other Ordnance organizations; among them, Aberdeen, Anniston, Benicia, Blue Grass, Butler, Columbus, Fort Wayne, Frankford, Letterkenny, Lincoln, Lordstown, Palmer Woods, Red River, Rock Island, St. Louis, Terre Haute, Watervliet and others.

And of what did this incoming materiel mainly consist? For the greater part, it was unpredictable, both as to type of item, or condition. Nor was there any set pattern for outgoing shipments. Either way, whatever happened was determined by conditions far and beyond control of Cressona. A roving eye might pick from the weekly lists items such as axle-assemblies, tank parts, wheel and disc assemblies, decontaminating apparatus, ammunition chests, tools and equipment, half-track parts, auto engine assemblies, batteries, full tanks, trailer parts, grommets, automotive parts, cleaning and preserving materials, transfer cases, 90 mm. Guns (one week, 26 of these), shoe tracks, gun carriages, hydraulic jacks, tire chains, periscopes, telescopes, carburetors, jacks, springs, modification vacuum booster kits, canvas covers, winches, crank-shafts and many others.

When repairs were beyond the scope of the plant, material was shipped to designated Ordnance Repair Depots. Material which was designated surplus, with no then present or expected future need by Ordnance, it was turned over for disposal to the

Treasury Department. Such materiel was stored on behalf of the Treasury which maintained a display room in the plant.

In addition to its normal reclamation assignments, the Cressona Ordnance Plant conducted two special operations; 1) a fifth eschelon repair plant for power train assemblies (all equipment from engine and wheels, including gear-box, transfer ease, differential and front and back wheel axle-drives and assemblies; with a planned ultimate capacity of 1,500 power trains, weekly), and, 2) clean-up and parts replacement of 600, 90 mm., A.A. Guns, M1, on M1A1 Carriages, complete with parts (with a planned ultimate capacity of 100 guns per month.

Fifth eschelon activities at Cressona; in view of the foregoing, included the following activities:

1. Power trains rebuilt, as noted
2. Small arms repairs
3. Battery rebuild
4. 90 mm. Gun and Mount repairs and reconditioning
5. Electrical assembly repair, consisting of generators, starters, etc.
6. Carburetor, fuel and water-pump repairs.

An early and a very critical necessity at Cressona was that of providing personnel, the greater part of which was not at all familiar with Ordnance or its nomenclature, with a means of identifying and classifying the thousands of varieties of incoming materiel, of recognizing its practical applications, and of knowing how to process it. To that end there was provided for the plant what very likely was one of the largest technical working libraries in the United States.

To speed up the checking of parts nomenclature and status, the office of the Chief of Ordnance—Detroit provided in March 1945, at the request of the contractor, an IBM Master File of approximately 350,000 index cards conforming to those in use in Detroit and in several of the Ordnance Depots. Subsequently, some 50,000 cards in addition were received; these, to enable Cressona to keep its identification files up to date.

As the methods used in reclamation work varied at different Ordnance plants, meetings of Ordnance and civilian personnel who were interested were held during January and February 1945, in Detroit and Washington to discuss the need for greater standardization of procedures and for a training program to develop Reclamation Specialists. It was decided as a result of the meetings that schools should be established for training in such subjects as segregation, identification, classification and technical inspection of Ordnance materiel. As Cressona already was functioning as a reclamation center it was decided that this would be the logical place for a school. The opening date was scheduled for 15 March 1945 and was expected to cover a period of from 60 to 90 days. Instructors were provided by Office, Chief of Ordnance—Detroit. The courses subsequently were extended from 18 April to 9 June 1945; and the second course started 18 June, for a period of six weeks. Certificates of proficiency were awarded to 27 graduates in the first class; 22 in the second class.

To handle the many and diversified items of materiel arriving at Cressona, it was necessary on many occasions to improve equipment and routines in order to speedily keep production in line with incoming volume, and to return the material to points where the need was critical; also, where equipment and tooling was in short supply or of inadequate capacity for volume requirements. Originally it had been thought that incoming materiel would fall into a limited number of specific categories, and the thinking of that period was directed toward the setting-up of production lines of more or less conventional types. But it didn't work out that way. The "stuff," as it was named in the plant, piled in a hetergeneous mass, often badly packed, and not readily identifiable; and for which there did not exist any standard means of processing. Plant procedures, therefore, and equipment, had of necessity to be sufficiently flexible to meet the needs imposed by infinite variety and unpredictable volume of incoming shipments. Quick shifts in plant arrangement and in procedures became the rule rather than the exception. Facilities had quickly to be adapted to new needs. Improvisations were frequent and, often, unorthodox; but exceptional results were obtained.

Against that background Major Howard P. Klair was informed that his objective should be the production of the greatest possible tonnage at the lowest attainable cost, and the design and integration of processes and procedures essential to that end.

As a result of his earlier administrational and engineering experience, to say nothing of his tremendous energy, Major Klair was able to fully meet his responsibilities. There was not time at the beginning for extended planning. Materiel was pouring in. The plant had to absorb during its first eight days of operation more than 1,600 tons of incoming materiel.

In the matter of reclamation cost: from October through December 1944, cost per pound of reclamation averaged out at $.31335. In January 1945, cost dropped to $.28187 per pound. In February 1945, to $.18450 per pound. In June 1945, to slightly less than $.05 per pound. At one time during June cost reached an all-time low of $.03 per pound.

Then there were the amazing processes developed under the pressure of time and necessity and in connection with which it was easy to trace the "Klairian" influence. To mention a few—there was the battery line, set up to quickly recondition the many types of batteries daily arriving at Cressona; an automatic sawing machine for sawing crosswise and lengthwise the lids of loaded boxes as they rode along a conveyer belt; a tunnel-type jet washer which carried parts in baskets, subjected to hot water under exceedingly high pressure, striking the moving basket of parts from all angles and flushing off surface dirt and grease.

The first of four automatic preserving machines was installed in March 1945. A second machine was ready for operation in June. These machines also were of the tunnel-type, applying preservation solvents followed at different stages by drying operations as the parts passed through while suspended from a conveyor or carried in baskets. During one operation the metal surface was neutralized against corrosion from fingerprints.

A paint line on small parts was another Klair installation. Here, parts were hung on wire hooks and moved along in front of a sheet of water. Paint was sprayed on the parts, the excess paint carried off by the water and later reclaimed.

Fourteen belt conveyor packaging lines with packing tables alongside of each were built to suit the varied needs and, in general, following the standard practice for package delivery belts. Two additional lines were installed to wrap electrical and other equipment with metal cloth. In the latter procedure there was inserted in the package a desiccant, such as silica gel, to prevent formation of moisture. A special packing line was installed for the handling of bulk packages, especially painted items or those requiring anti-rust treatment or protection.

The cutting of bevel edges on solid rubber tires on bogie wheels was greatly speeded by use of hot electric cutting tools. When the wheels were rotated, one at a time, in a sheel-lathe, the pair of cutting tools mounted at the proper angles could be pressed against the tires to quickly remove the rubber not required.

Many other tools and mechanical appliances were made for special needs as they developed.

It is the middle of January 1945. The war is biting into its fourth year—for us. Cressona was doing very well for a young industry. Already the contractor's payroll carried 2,057 names covering all the categories of Operations, Inspection, Administration, Industrial Engineering, Planning, Industrial Relations, Plant Protection, Plant Engineering, Traffic, Procurement, and the Comptroller's Unit. In addition, 357 personnel were on hand for the Defense Plant Corporation—and a fair squad for P. O. D.

For the week ending 13 January 1945, 88 Purchase Orders had been written, for material and equipment worth $54,359. Total Orders placed to this date totalled $485,205. During the same week, 93 carloads, 30 less-than-carloads, and seven truckloads of materials were received, and of materiel on hand, in the Finished Stores ready for shipment, there were 113.8 tons, or 227,600 pounds. The contractor's operation payroll for the week was of $77,369.00.

And of what did the outgoing shipments consist? Well, there were 11 carloads and two truckloads shipped to various Army installations—including 496 engine assemblies, 664 dual tire chains, 1,402 cylinder assemblies, 10 fifth-wheel assemblies and 75 batteries.

Coming over into February 1945. The week ending 10 February, saw 46 carloads, 37 less carloads and five truckloads of materiel moved in; in an aggregate of 1,238 tons. On the outgoing line there were 16 carloads, two truckloads and one express shipment, to various Army installations. Shipments included anti-friction bearings, automotive parts, single and dual chains, batteries, gun maintenance parts, tools, spare parts, crankshaft assemblies, hydraulic hoist assemblies, etc., etc., etc.—ad infinitum. Employment by the contractor now was of 2,398 persons; by Defense Plant Corporation, 486 persons; by P. O. D., six officers, 31 civilians. Contractor's payroll for the week, $113,751.00.

The training work was coming along. In Visual and Dimensional Inspection Training, now 82 enrollments; Identification and Classification, 131 enrollments and, Carburetor, Tank Heater and Water Pump Repairs, 12 enrollments.

Business continued good at Cressona. During the week to 10 March, there were received 1,025 tons of materiel; 742 tons were processed; 778 tons shipped out. There was accumulated 415 tons of unserviceable materiel; 1,246 tons of scrap. Contractor's payroll listed 2,947 employees and a payroll of $127,469.00. Three truckloads, 86 full tanks and 23 winches were delivered to the Hahn Motor Company in Hamburg, Pennsylvania.

During the week it was reported that the very unique high pressure jet cleaner that blasted, with live steam, the rusted surface of gun barrels, leaving them clean as a whisker, was 65 per cent complete and would be in operation in a matter of days. Also, that design and construction of the various shops required for the overhaul and repair of 90 mm. Guns and Mounts; the battery line, power train assembly units, electrical and miscellaneous small assemblies, bogie wheels and other assemblies were in operation.

One week later, Frank P. Gallagher of the P. O. D. staff reported for his Chief, Major Howard P. Klair, that during the then recent past ten days a separate small arms reclamation line had been set up. Approximately 300 guns, Model 1919A4, Caliber .30 Machine Guns were disassembled, examined, all defective parts replaced, and the guns reassembled. Rather good. During the same period there were received 90 mm. Anit-Aircraft Guns with Mounts designated as M1 or M1A1, bringing to 532 units the total to date of this item. Of them, 18 were completely disassembled. Four were reassembled and were waiting upon test equipment from Frankford Arsenal. Two thousand five hundred and twenty-one persons were paid for the week, a payroll of $127,469. During the week, 67 Purchase Orders were written, for material and equipment valued at $52,616.00, bringing to $1,373,483.00 the total of orders placed to date. To 18 November 1945, and the transfer to the Field Service of the Cressona operation, the total dollar value of Purchase Orders issued during P. O. D. occupancy, was $2,491,960.00.

Employment was gradually upward to a high in August of 4,010 persons, exclusive of Ordnance personnel. From VJ Day, the trend was definitely down, and a little swifter than the climb. As of 28 November, the total of Cressona personnel, including the lads of Defense Plant Corporation but not including Major Klair's group, had leveled off at 2,587 persons.

It would have been something slightly short of a miracle if Cressona had gone more than a few months without shift or change in its organizational set-up. It would have been so contrary to the nature of Ordnance, and of war, as to have been unthinkable.

April found Major Klair and Captain Waite still in command. Mildred A. Bonin, formerly secretary to Major Klair had been succeeded by Anne Oracko, and had been named Administrative Assistant with Frank E. Gallagher. On the staff, Captain Giles P. Wetherill appears as Public Relations Officer, and as Assistant, in Charge, 90 mm. Gun Expediting Section; Fiscal Audit Section still the charge of Joseph E. Hatch; Lieutenant Frank F. Hagenbuch continues as Chief, Inspection Section; Captain F. J. McCusker still on OVM Expediting Section; Captain J. M. Harding, Assistant Property Officer, is Chief, Material Control Section, with Lieutenant Stanley B. Honour, Transportation Officer, as Assistant; Bert Krause heads the Property Section and Willmer Allam still is Property Disposal Section Chief.

Under Joseph E. Hatch of the Fiscal Audit Section appears Mary A. Tomes, Secretary; John O. Glover, Auditor; Stanley J. Ward, Labor Checker. Serving with Lieutenant F. F. Hagenbuch, of the Inspection Section is Secretary, Lillian Cain. In the General Inspection Unit, the following Inspectors: John O. Dixon, Leonard A. West, Bynum H. Jones, Leon F. Hickman, Charles W. Rickard, Enoch A. Laukitis, Michael C. Cosen, Thomas J. Doyle, Jack F. O'Brien, John A. Reifsnyder and John F. O'Neill. In the Packaging Unit: Gerald B. Jacobs, James O. Harrison, Charles M. Beckett, Jack J. De Long, Raymond V. Reckmack, N. D. Hickson and Helen D. McKeone. Under Captain McCusker, Ammon T. Stahl, who also served with Captain Wetherill, as Inspector.

Material Control Section: Helen B. Bergen handles the secretarial assignment. Marion A. Donavon, Clerk; Virginia V. Rowan, Teletype Operator, Charles H. Reese is Checker for the Disposition Unit. Traffic Unit is directed by Elizabeth M. Uleckie with the assistance of Emma M. Cerullo. Identification Unit is charge of Roy D. Miller; Library Unit Staff includes Eura B. Schnerring, Virginia R. Eifert, Margaret M. Kelly, Betty A. Klein, Pauline S. Stefaneck and J. L. Trout.

Assisting Bert Krause as secretary is Mary T. Varano, Auditors are George H. Hart and Earl L.

Fennelly. Charles F. Wildonger is Inspector; Morgan O. Edwards, Anna E. Wommer, and Marilynne E. Miller, Clerks. Under Willmer Allam is the Property Disposal Section, Elizabeth M. Wheeler has the secretarial post; Ralph A. Fisher appears as Property Disposal Agent.

And now for a bit of statistical data which will reveal something of the scope of operations at Cressona. The heaviest week in regard to incoming material was that of 4 August 1945 when 162 carloads and 18 less-than-carload shipments rolled in. The low week during Ordnance operation was that of 28 April 1945 when 27 carloads and 40 l-c-l shipments were checked in. On the reclamation and outgoing side, the high week was that of 25 August 1945 when 70 carloads and 6 l-c-l shipments were moved back into circulation. The weekly average for incoming materiel was 61.9 carloads; outgoing 31.1 carloads. The foregoing figures are based upon weekly reports for the period 5 January 1945 to 25 November 1945.

Employment at Cressona Ordnance Plant continued on a fairly even keel to the end. As of 13 January 1945, personnel on the contractor's payroll stood at 2,414 persons. The week following saw an increase of 426 persons.

By steady weekly increases the total moved to its high point, 4 August 1945, of 4,010 persons. From this point there was a gradual falling off to 25 November 1945 when the final reported total of plant personnel registered at 2,587 persons.

Labor turnover was in good control, considering the time, the job and a few other factors such as labor supply, transportation and the pressure under which Cressona operated. For the greater part of the period of operation, weekly labor turnover was only slightly in excess of 1.0 per cent. It was not until the 22nd week of operation that a 2.0 per cent turnover was registered. For ten weeks following turnover ran along at 1.0 per cent or less, then it picked up to three per cent. There was a sudden jump during the week of 24 August 1945, to 13.6 per cent. The following week it was 10.3 per cent, then back to the 2.0 per cent level. Again, during the week of 21 September, the highest point reached during the program was marked up— 18.7 per cent, followed by a sharp decline, to 2.8 per cent; then, gradually to 1.0 per cent, as of 18 November, to 1.0 per cent.

Absenteeism at Cressona did not register so many fits and starts. The highest weekly percentage for the first 11 weeks, was 6.8 per cent.

Then a rise to 8.5 per cent, for one week, followed by a drop to 6.1 per cent, then to 5.3 per cent. The high point for the program was in May, when absenteeism registered at 10.1 per cent. From then on the weekly total fluctuated between 5.2 per cent to 8.8 per cent, a point reached only once during that period.

Weekly scrap tonnage totals read about like this: Early in January 1945—1,246 tons for the first reported week, and a steady weekly climb to 3,145 tons. Six weeks followed during which scrap received 1,600 tons and less per week, then a quick rise to 2,543 tons. Six weeks later the total was down to 889 tons; then back to 1,163 tons, 1,647 tons, 1,911 tons; and then a quick drop to 779 tons. Five weeks later tonnage had recovered to 2,305 tons, then 2,919 tons, 3,172 tons, 2,439 tons and finally, under Ordnance, 1,615 tons.

The weekly reports of Unserviceable Scrap, beginning at 415 tons climbed by weekly stages to 18,796 tons in late September 1945, from which point it dropped to the last reported total of 14,-750 tons.

Materiel charged to Finished Stores, beginning at a weekly level of 113.8 tons, had reached early in February 1945, a total of 2,094 tons. By weekly increases, the total moved to 22,255 tons, as of 26 October 1945. As of November 1945, the total had dropped to 17,430 tons.

Purchase Order totals indicated frequent if not wide variation. The weekly high of 98 PO's was reached early during the program—running along somewhat in this fashion: 90, 72, 46, 67, 67, 57, 74, 90, 72 per week until August 1945 when there was a sharp decline to 48, and in several weeks, to 28, and finally, the one week in October, 18—the lowest. In dollars, the weekly variation was wide, as could be expected. Starting at $28,717.00 there was a somewhat jumpy advance over a period of seven weeks to $195,022.00. The preceding week had registered $58,993.00. The highest weekly total was credited to June, when the total was of $220,711.00. For the following week the total was $33,320.00. The low week was in October 1945, when only $1,345.00 was earmarked.

On September 1945, Day & Zimmermann, Inc., were notified by the Contracting Officer that the operating contract would be terminated at midnight, 18 November 1945. However, the plant was to be continued in operation after that date, but as an Ordnance Depot and Fifth Echelon Shop under the Storage Division of the Ordnance Department.

Surplus property now in the Treasury Stores aggregated 500,500 pounds, or 250 tons, including tool cabinets, Hull and Sponson boxes, wire rope cables, single-bitted axes, funnels, cross chains, bicycle chains, glazing compound, hydrometers, tin measures, shovels, saws, cross bars, cartridge elements, picks, portable forges, files and miscellaneous automobile parts.

On 7 November, Colonel S. P. Huff was appointed Commanding Officer at Cressona, and at his request, arrangements were made with the contractor for interviewing Day & Zimmermann employees for employment by Civil Service. A questionnaire prepared by Colonel Huff's staff was distributed to all plant employees, including those employed by the Defense Plant Corporation. Approximately 1,700 employees responded.

As of midnight 18 November 1945 materiel on hand at Cressona was as follows:

Army Finished Stores	17,634 tons
In Process	8,627 tons
Backlog	10,164 tons
Total	36,425 tons

Serviceable material aggregating 1,057,791 pounds, or 529 tons, was ready for shipment to Army installations.

Unserviceable materiel was to a total of 29,500,-961 pounds, or 14,750 tons.

Scrap was to a total of 3,230,910 pounds, or 1,615 tons.

Surplus Property in Treasury Stores now aggregated 1,049,462 pounds or 525 tons.

All construction for Ordnance now had come to an end, and property of the Reconstruction Finance Plant Corporation and the Defense Plant Corporation was in process of preservation, removal and shipping according to instructions of the Senior Engineer.

Phillip Morris' Johnny gets it straight about the progress of the war from Lt. Colonel, then Captain, William L. Stephens, Property Branch head

Chapter XLI

FRONT PAGE FOR POTTSTOWN

IT IS certain that had the war gone on for another year Pottstown would have had an even larger place in the Victory drive, for then the Pottstown Ordnance Plant, activated 20 July 1945, would have been piling up in channels to the battle-fronts, mountain-high supplies of critical materials and equipment reclaimed from the scenes of earlier strife.

At any rate, the Pottstown Ordnance Plant was ready, a wise precaution of the Ordnance Department, designed to supplement with its big brother plant at Cressona, the increasing tonnage of fighting equipment and supplies pouring out of the Nation's war plants.

The contract (W-36-034-Ord-7140) for the operation of the plant was awarded the Firestone Tire and Rubber Company, under the administration of the Philadelphia Ordnance District. Three Ordnance officers, together with seventeen male civilians and seven females were assigned. In addition, there was assigned from Frankford Arsenal Field Service Sub-Office for temporary duty, to advise on operations and procedures in reference to Fire-Control materiel, a total of nineteen military personnel.

The Pottstown Ordnance Plant originally was activated to serve as a Returned Material and Reclamation Center for all Ordnance General Supplies materiel to be received, segregated, identified and inspected, to which extent it supplemented the job already being done at Cressona. Materiel found to be unserviceable, but repairable, and which could be reclaimed within reasonable cost, would be repaired and returned to channels. Materiel found upon receipt to be serviceable would be packaged, if necessary, and returned to appropriate supply depots. Unserviceable and unrepairable materiel would be turned over to the Salvage Officer for disposition. Material no longer required by the Armed Forces, yet having a civilian value, would be turned over to the Department of Commerce for disposal.

The P. O. D. organization at the Plant consisted of Major Howard P. Klair, also Commanding Officer of Cressona; Captain Robert D. Scarlett, Officer-in-Charge; Fiscal and Property Officer, Captain Clair A. Kilgore, a 6 September 1943, P. O. D. acquisition who came East from the Chicago Ordnance District, following graduation from the University of Minnesota with a B.A., and six years of CPA activity; Christine Borland, Clerk; Robert H. Bowman, Inspector; Russell M. Gerhart, Clerk; Ross E. Guthrie, Property Disposal Agent; George H. Hart, Administrative Assistant; Virginia Irey, Clerk; Donald W. Knauer, Industrial Specialist; Edith L. Kramer, Payroll Clerk; Harry J. Kressler, Inspector; John J. Lombardi, Inspector; William F. McLaughlin, Inspector; Ralph A. Morgan, Inspector; Thomas R. Morris, Inspector; Ruth I. Shoup, Clerk; Edwin O. Snyder, Administrative Assistant; Francis A. Stevens, Jr., Inspector; John R. Taylor, Administrative Assistant; and Claude F. Walter, Inspector.

The various functions established at Pottstown were as follows:

1. Material Control Division: controlling incoming shipments, directing flow through the various operations, issued disposition instructions in reference to "what to do with it"—and, through the Traffic Unit, to work with the contractor's Traffic Department. Too, there was a Production Facilities Unit that rooted out equipment needed by the contractor.

2. Property Disposal Division, disposing of property no longer needed by the Armed Forces—consigning it to the Department of Commerce or to salvage.

3. Inspection Division: with its staff of "peekers and feelers" to check the work of the contractor's employees, during the flow of material through the plant operations. There was also in this division a Technical Data Section which

procured technical publications and such needed in the operation of the various processes.

4. Field Audit Section: concerned with invoice examinations, payroll and special examinations and labor checks on the contractor.

5. Property Division: making materiel checks of Property and property audit.

Then there was the matter of training. Forty employees of the Firestone Tire & Rubber Company were sent to the Cressona Ordnance Plant for a six-weeks' course in segregation and identification of Tank-Automotive On-Vehicle-Materiel. In addition, twenty contractor employees were sent to the Rock Island Training School, for segregation and identification of Artillery items. Special training by representatives from the Field Service Sub-Office of Frankford Arsenal was given a group of employees in Fire-Control segregation and identification.

It was a great organization, carrying the Kelso-Gadsden touch for thoroughness, for precision in organization—lacking only the opportunity to do the job for which it had been planned and manned. Immediately following VE Day, 8 May 1945, there was received from Brigadier General Edward E. MacMoreland, a teletype in which it was advised that the extent of repairs to Ordnance materiel would be greatly reduced and that concentration would be in reference to segregation and identification.

On 22 August 1945 Brigadier General E. L Ford, Brigadier General John K. Christmas and Brigadier General F. I. Gilbert dropped by Pottstown long enough to give the plant an optical going over and to decide that henceforth work would bear mainly on the segregation, identification and repair of Fire-Control Material, but not high-hatting general Ordnance items that might be received at the plant.

On 27 September, came a letter (File No. SPX 681, dated 24 Sep. 1945, OB-1-SPMOC; if you must be technical) from Lt. General Brehon B.

Somervell in which announcement was made that, effective 18 November 1945, the contract with Firestone Tire & Rubber Company for the operation of the Pottstown Ordnance Plant would be terminated and the Plant redesignated as the Pottstown Ordnance Department, to be operated as a Class IV installation, under the Chief of Ordnance.

Then, 23 October 1945, Teletype, SPOFM, Manlove, TT25596—the straw that broke the camel's back. Suggested the fateful teletype: "All plans for setting up the Pottstown Ordnance plants are cancelled." This was followed, 25 October 1945, by a telegram from 150 South Broad Street, second floor, second door to the left, informing Firestone of immediate termination of the operating contract.

However, Captain Bob Scarlett and his boys did have an opportunity to show what they could do under pressure. During the period, 20 July 1945, through October, there were received at the Plant, 222 carloads of material. Of this total, 26 carloads were processed and shipped to other destinations. To 30 September, the preponderance of materiel received was in the Tank-Automotive category. From 1 October to the final curtain, the greater part of the materiel handled bore a Fire-Control label.

Completion of the final production lines and shops had never been effected—possibly not more than 50 per cent.

Immediately upon notice of termination, clearance of the plant was begun. The first outgoing shipments were made 25 October. Personnel of Frankford Arsenal Field Service Sub-Office remained at Pottstown, and with their assistance, the flow of other installations of Reclamation Materiel was quickly established. All materiel received under P. O. D. supervision was clear of the plant by 20 November.

And so, Pottstown and its big brother, Cressona, become at about the same time, casualties of peace.

☙

Chapter XLII

THE REDISTRIBUTION CENTER

Periodic data bearing on the Redistribution Center appears throughout the NewsReel
Sections of this Manuscript. The following material is for completion of this story.

THE Redistribution Center was established early in the Fall of 1944, in the Government-acquired warehouse at Pencoyd, Pennsylvania, and was made an adjunct of the P. O. D. Property Disposal Branch. It was established to function as a central point to which small lots of excess property could be shipped for further redistribution. It was the declared policy of P. O. D. to move to the Center excess termination inventory which otherwise would remain in contractors' plants subsequent to final settlement of their terminations. However, when a considerable amount of termination inventory should be involved, the material would remain at the contractors' plants under storage agreement until final disposition should be made.

It would likewise be District policy to remove from contractors' plants excess Government-owned non-termination material if immediate disposal should not be possible.

The Property Disposal Branch would assign to the Center, the necessary personnel, who would review the excess property received, to determine appropriate disposition, to issue requests to the P. O. D. Packaging Section for packaging service and to request the Property Branch for shipment of property, cr reporting property as surplus to the Treasury Department or the Reconstruction Finance Corporation.

Property Disposal Branch Officer-in-Charge was designated as Contracting Officers Representative on all property disposal matters and was held responsible for the administration of all his personnel and the Salvage Board established at the Center. Also there was appointed a Redistribution and Salvage Officer. In November 1944, Captain, then Lieutenant Neal W. Slack was named Redistribution and Salvage Officer; Captain, then Lieutenant Philip J. Fields, Assistant, sometime later, was named Officer-in-Charge.

Officially, by Office Memorandum No. H-9-44, dated 11 December 1944, Subject: "Redistribution Center," signed, C. Jared Ingersoll, District Chief, the Redistribution Center was established.

It was ordered 31 October 1944, that the following Sections be set up at the Center:

     a. Inspection Section
     b. Property Section
     c. Property Disposal Section

Shortly thereafter, the complete organizational line-up appeared thus:

Operating Chief: Sidney S. Press, who succeeded Lt. Colonel H. K. Kelley.
Officer-in-Charge; Contracting Officer's Representative, Major, then Captain Welles H. Denney.
Assistant Officer-in-Charge; Assistant Redistribution and Salvage Officer: Captain Philip J. Fields.
Salvage Board: Anthony Fendo, John E. Cellars, Harold L. Fritz, Marie A. Walsh.
Inspection Section: Anthony Fendo.
Identification: John E. Cellars.
Packaging: Harold L. Fritz.
Property Section: Captain John B. Jones.
Property Disposal Section: Sidney S. Press.
Transfer: Wilks H. Douglas, Morris L. Wolfe,
File: Harry D. Given, Margaret T. Higgins.
Review and Statistics: Thomas A. Nyland.

Changes shortly thereafter show an Inventory Folder Section with Anthony Fendo, Harry D. Given and Marie A. Walsh; Margaret T. Higgins taking care of an Order Section; Captain Frank J. McCusker attached to the Transfer Section; and a Section labeled Shop Disposal Men, with John E. Cellars and Harold L. Fritz.

The Inspection Section was held responsible for

the identification and inspection of parts and components; for inspection of outgoing shipments, and for recommending that property be declared non-repairable.

The Property Section, consisting of the two units—a Property Record Unit and a Traffic Unit—the former responsible for maintenance of accountability records, employed as stock control and location records: the Traffic Unit, responsible for obtaining or executing bills of lading and Vendors Shipping Documents.

The Property Disposal Section was held responsible for effecting the disposition of the property in the warehouse.

During the first full quarter of operation—January through March 1945—the Center disposed of materials to the total of $2,800,000.00, of which $1,500,000.00 represented transfers to Government agencies; $300,000.00 of which represented sales of serviceable items; $300,000.00, Sales of Scrap; and $700,000.00, declarations to S. W. P. A.

On 28 April 1945, J. I. Schwabe, Steel Marketing Unit, Service Section, of the Property Branch, was to write:

"In the three months we operated at Pencoyd, disposition was accomplished of 7,656,610 pounds of steel stock having a total value of $476,782.82.

"We actually received at the Center a total of 4,841,000 pounds with a dollar value of $225,607.61. Of this, 3,804,033 pounds were transferred to other Government agencies. We sold 405,906 pounds at a 98 per cent realization. One hundred and forty-four thousand six hundred and fifty-three pounds of material was scrapped, consisting of all armor plate in process. We reported in surplus to the Surplus War Property Administration, 486,408 pounds, completing disposition of all raw materials shipped into the Center during the three months."

Further on, Mr. Schwabe wrote:

"As we were located right at Government Warehouse No. 2, I spent quite a bit of my time locating items of steel upon which, in some cases, no action was being taken. Some other items I had withdrawn from Reconstruction Finance Corporation after I found a market for the material. The total weight of this material was 2,529,906 pounds, having a cost of $188,568.62. We sold 1,191,241 pounds at a 97 per cent realization. I might mention that all the sales made were either to war contractors or suppliers having war contracts. Included among these sales were all billets which had been shipped into the Warehouse from the Baldwin Locomotive Works. Of this lot of material we transferred to other Government agencies, 546,036 pounds, and reported as surplus to RFC, 792,629 pounds."

The foregoing letter is offered as evidence of one phase of activity at Pencoyd—and not with any thought of covering operations in detail.

Future students of Ordnance, and of the Redistribution Center in particular, may be interested to learn what happened to some of the material moved out of that installation into commercial channels.

Of Government material, a considerable amount was transferred, without funds, to hospitals for occupational and physio-therapy activities. This material included chains and snaps which were used for making jewelry, watch chains, etc.; plastic items of which veterans fashioned ash trays, jewelry and other items; Plexiglas and mirrors converted for use in vanity sets, checker and chess sets, among other items; rayon cordage and rayon cloth cuttings which veterans employed for weaving, making scarfs, handkerchiefs and aprons; and webbing, which the boys conjured into mats, carry-all bags and numerous other items.

Then, of course, great quantities of brass, bronze and copper went back into industry, some to the Coast Guard, some to the Navy and to Ordnance Arsenals. Even waste gasoline was salvaged and sold.

Inasmuch as Pencoyd was one of those gawking structures of wide open spaces there was difficulty during the winter of 1944–1945 in keeping the place warm and the workers, particularly the girls, in a state of even reasonable comfort. Captain Fields, with frosted fingers, and in a fitful mood had frequent occasion to remind higher authority that something needed to be done.

One of his communications, fortunately salvaged during the "consolidation of files" period in 1946, is reproduced herewith, in full. It rates a place with other epistolary items of the war period. Here it is:

ARMY SERVICE FORCES
Redistribution Center
PHILADELPHIA ORDNANCE DISTRICT
3730 Main Street
Philadelphia 27, Pa.
Phone—MANyunk 3760

IN REPLY REFER TO   P. J. Fields/dmb

PHA No. 400.99   19 January 1945

MEMORANDUM TO: Mr. S. S. Press, Property Disposal Branch
SUBJECT: S. O. S. for Heat at Pencoyd

1. The first month at Siberia Paradise was uneventful—nobody died of chilblain, though it was expected that the small band of Eskimos quartered there would all certainly perish from the severe climate.

2. During the past six weeks, the U. S. Army Engineers have ventured by dog sled to this remote corner of the Polar Region several times with promises of supplying enough cans of steam heat so that a hot time could be had here throughout the Winter months. However, these promises have not materialized. In fact, their promises sound like a lot of hot air, which is the only heat supplied to date by the Engineers.

3. Now Mr. "Anthony" Press, my problem is—"Should I get angry with the Engineers, or should I just let my Eskimos freeze to death?"

S/P. J. FIELDS
T/P. J. FIELDS
1st. Lt., Ord. Dept.
Officer-in-Charge
Redistribution Center

Chapter XLIII

THEY GOT WHAT THEY WANTED

WE HAD it. They wanted it. They got it. But it wasn't a half-bad deal for us—or them. We are speaking of Lend Lease, a "turn-about-is-fair-play" arrangement with our Allies that had its inception in P. O. D. in the Spring of 1941, not too long after that fateful moment, 3:50 P. M. 11 March 1941, when the late President Roosevelt put his name to H. R. 1776, that made us partner with the nations lined up against the Berlin-Rome mob.

Prior to Lend Lease foreign orders were placed direct by Purchasing Commissions of the interested governments. One of the largest of these was an order placed by the United Kingdom with the Baldwin Locomotive Works for 685 Medium Tanks, M3, at a cost to Brother Jonathan of $40,035,408.-06. These tanks were manufactured concurrently with an order for a like number of the U. S. War Department. Agreements were made with the United Kingdom representatives for the joint use of the $3,000,000.00 worth of machine tools which had been supplied through the agency of the U. S. Government to Baldwin's.

The Britishers did not have at the time an organization for design and engineering work, consequently, we had to interpret specifications as best we could. Differences of opinion with U. S. Ordnance engineering soon developed, the British ordering radical changes which were widely at variance with those ordered by Pentagon topside. As the Eddystone Regional Offices had assumed responsibility for inspection of the United Kingdom contract, the changes caused many difficulties in reference to production and inspection. Requests for changes came faster than the Seilers, the Disneys or even Joe Cook's "four Hawaiians" could have kept up with them.

Captain Jesse C. Jessen of the Tank-Automotive Branch recalled that the British contracts came to P. O. D. via Washington without any distinguishing characteristics, except in a few instances. These were dealt with here in the same manner as the general run of U. S. Ordnance contracts, with the exception of spare parts orders, which usually were marked for Belle Mead Storage until needed. On occasion, they were "borrowed" by P. O. D., and later replaced. On some contracts, the British gave a list of spare parts with certain quantities indicated, and an entirely different list to the manufacturers. At times, they permitted deviations and later refused them on identical parts.

The first U. S. made British Tanks were designed with a cupola. Since overhead passages in the areas where these tanks were to be used had not been built enough to allow clearance, there were some unfortunate accidents. This resulted in prompt redesign.

"In the early days," quoth Cap'n. Jess, "time spent producing and inspecting any part of a foreign order was made a matter of record." This was done with the expectation that the U. S. would be reimbursed. Following Pearl Harbor, such particularizations were discontinued. It was our war, now—in earnest.

Because of the frequent changes, the United Kingdom tank contract did not get under way as promptly as the U. S. contract, and it ultimately became necessary to freeze design changes in order to get into quantity production. With many parts which were common to both the British and U. S. tanks under divided ownership, diversions from one contract to the other occurred frequently and was a cause for confusion. It was therefore decided in December 1941, to expedite the British contract, giving it preference over U. S. needs. This was the earliest instance of borrowing or exchange.

In July 1941, all then existing British contracts in the District were assigned to P. O. D. for production follow-up and inspection.

EARLY PROCUREMENT

With the initiation in the District of Lend Lease procurement there was received from O. C. O., a directive bearing upon Defense Aid procedure. Procurement at the beginning was pretty much confined to machine tools, but subsequently was extended to a wide range of materials and end items. Separate funds were alloted by the Government for such procurement. This continued to 1 July 1943, from which time payments were made from one general fund—ours.

As Lend Lease got under way in P. O. D., there were periods of urgency during which materials and items purchased for U. S. contracts were in part diverted to Lend Lease contracts. Only exhaustive analysis of many files and the exploring of many P. O. D. minds would disclose the full data.

In August 1941, there was developed by the Chief of Ordnance a special form for reporting all negotiations in reference to the procurement of Defense Aid tools. It was made clear that bid mistakes were the responsibility of the contractors. The District did not take advantage of obviously typographic errors in bids. For strategic reasons every effort was made to assure the contractor a fair profit. The Ordnance Department was at that time building all Lend Lease heavy machinery for Russia; all Lend Lease light machinery for Britain. Approximately one contract in a hundred had a reimbursement clause.

There was compiled late in 1942 by the British Purchasing Commission, a schedule of differentials in connection with requirements for machine tools which were purchased for the United Kingdom from Lend Lease funds. The list of differentials represented the difference between domestic list prices on tools to be procured and foreign net prices. Subsequently, machine tool builders were instructed to show commissions paid to foreign agents or representatives; sums which were liquidated wherever possible.

"I recall," Major Bill Eadie told us, "that the early purchases by foreign governments for materials of war were made at exorbitant prices as compared with prices charged after these contracts were turned over to Lend Lease. It was thought that this condition existed because foreign purchasing agents did not have proper knowledge of negotiation systems in the U. S., nor that they were familiar with U. S. custom of bidding before placing an order. On the other hand, manufacturers had not taken orders for such items in quantity since World War I, and could not figure

a margin of profit as closely as it must be done today.

"The original figures on Russia's contract with a manufacturer in the District for a High Pressure Pump Accumulator System are not now available, but it is recalled by negotiators of P. O. D. that several months were spent in negotiation before the U. S. S. were able to agree on the price which would be paid under Lend Lease. The price finally agreed upon, $125,000.00 was a great reduction from the original. The same high prices prevailed on a contract with another manufacturer for Projectiles, 75 mm., A.P.C., Shot, M61. The price per projectile was figured at $23.00, as against $7.00 in February 1945. Of course, increased "know how," and integrated production on a wartime mass basis accounted in some measure for the lower figure.

"They were great days, back then," said Henry Marcus, a trace of nostalgia in his voice. "I recall," he continued, "that the Russians purchased through Lend Lease (on Contract W-679-Ord-3320) from the Florence Pipe and Foundry Company, a number of hydraulic presses. When ready for delivery it was noted that there were small "blow holes" in the large castings that made up the rams. The manufacturer made mention of these. The presses however were "passed" by P. O. D. Inspectors on the basis that such conditions in the rams did not make the presses less useful. But the Russians said "Nix!" even though they were given the manufacturer's guarantee. On 16 December 1943, Henry "Show-me-a-radio-set-I-can't -fix-quicker, etc., etc." Marcus, and Lieutenant Kron went to the plant to meet the Russian inspector, Mr. Malinin. There was much discussion followed by many tests. The manufacturers and P. O. D. Inspectors agreed to be entirely responsible to the Russians for any failure of the rams, or the presses—so, Mr. Malinin said whatever is the Russian word for "okeh." Tools were not included in this order, but the Russians were so insistent on having them that the manufacturer supplied a number."

"And here is one for the book," said Tom Potts. "The British had purchased from an up-state Pennsylvania manufacturer $250,000.00 worth of drills for which they had not furnished funds and for which they had requested Lend Lease financing. I went to the plant, examined the drills, and reported the price 'too high.' I then went to see the company's foreign purchasing agent, and the conversation which ensued went something like this:"

POTTS: These are standard commercial items and I would like to have a list of quotations.

AGENT: Well, we don't have a list, guy.

POTTS: We must have a list.

AGENT: We can't get you a list, guy.

POTTS: The price is much too high.

AGENT: Don't you know there is a war in Europe, guy?

POTTS: Yes, but we are not going to pay such prices.

AGENT: That's the price, guy, and you will have to pay it if you want the drills.

"Later, Manuel Cole of the Fiscal Branch, and Lieutenant Ed Lynch went to the company's main office and had a talk with the president who was very cooperative. Together the three "guys" went over the cost sheets, settling upon a price which appeared satisfactory all around."

"Britain," continued Tom Potts, "made some of their earlier purchases of machinery from the Sherman Safe Company of Philadelphia. Before the deal could be finalized the company was merged with the O'Brien Machinery Company. The British had furnished $500,000.00 against the contract, but later requested the U. S. to finance the remainder on Lend Lease. I was sent out to check over the materials in order to determine whether all items were as reported. Many were not, and were therefore stricken from the list. There were approximately 200 pieces of machinery involved. These were for use in Africa and Australia—and our Government financed on Lend Lease all of the approved items."

"Take it from me," said William J. "Bill" O'Brien of the Ammunition Branch, "procurement under early Lend Lease was something to try the patience of a Sphinx. Back during those days, Ordnance Inspectors worked at a disadvantage. Russian representatives in plants sometimes made "side arrangements" with manufacturers, thereby increasing inspection difficulties and causing price changes from the original.

"The Russian Government ordered late in the Summer of 1942, for instance, a machine for use in the final inspection of shell-casings. The price was approximately $1,000,000.00. Before production was got under way, P. O. D. was re-

quested to send representatives to meet and discuss with the manufacturer, with greater thoroughness than before, various factors involved. Captain John C. Pyle, Jr., and I accepted the assignment. We met with the manufacturer and the Russian representatives with their interpreter.

"The machine in question was to be used for detecting imperfections in the casings, thereby preventing possible premature explosion in the firing chamber, with resultant loss of life. The cost against advantages, was thoroughly gone into; but the Russians decided to cancel the order. The general opinion among Americans concerned was, that the machine would cost more than it was worth to the Russian Government since men, at that time, were more expendable than dollars.

"The very large orders for wheel-lathes placed by the Russian Government confounded men in the Ordnance engaged in Ordnance procurement. On the surface there could not possibly have been a need for them in Russia, in such quantity, for they were of the type ordinarily used for locomotive wheels. These orders exceeded anything approximating the needs of railroads even in the United States. The one possible solution of the enigma was the probability of shipments having been sunk in transit.

"The large number of reamers ordered by the United Kingdom for delivery to Australia caused wonder in P. O. D. as to whether the reamers were being used in place of bullets. Here, also, was the possibility that some of the shipments were not reaching destinations."

Still on the trail of machine tool notes, we took the stairs at 150 So. Broad, three at a time (we had seen Major Bill Lafean do this) and were, in seconds, at the desk of Al R. "Superman" Testa. Here is the story he gave us:

"Way back in December 1940 the Miscellaneous Materials Branch began the handling of foreign orders for machine tools. These orders were for presses, the greatest number, from Russia. Henry Marcus was responsible for Inspection. My job was Production. Each month a War Aid Tool Progress Report was issued.

"The first presses for Russia were the largest ever manufactured; one press required sixteen freight cars for hauling to Port of Embarkation. Some of the presses were to be used in the manufacture of a plywood of two inches in thickness.

"It developed late in 1942 that much of the material being delivered to foreign governments was, more often than not, received in bad condition. Occasionally, the damage had been so great as to be beyond repair. Many tons of material had been shipped before notification of condition at point of acceptance had reached us in Ordnance. Items had always been boxed or crated, and the use of corrugated paper had provided some surface protection. However, no thought had been given to the matter of moisture and waterproofing.

"The need for something new, and special, in packaging was thus made apparent, and early in 1943, a Packaging Section was established in the old Miscellaneous Materials Branch. Contractors generally did not relish the prospect of change. Some of the larger manufacturers had for years been shipping somewhat similar items by the old method. Complaints, they said, had been negligible. Ordnance men pointed out that former shipments were not made under war-time conditions, time was not of the essence, and repairs and replacements, when necessary, could be effected.

"At any rate, schools of Packaging Instruction were established in P. O. D. and were attended by contractors as well as Ordnance personnel. The new Packaging requirements were pretty rigid.

"Proper marking of packages had not been standardized and, as a result, much incorrect marking was noted at points of acceptance. However, as we advanced into the war years, this too was corrected, if not entirely, then with infinitely less confusion at the moment of end use."

Difficulties in reference to inspection, and inspectors crop up with interesting frequency in the records. We do not quote experiences with the Russians and the British, or their representatives, with any feeling other than one of sympathy for differences in language and philosophy, as far as the Russians were concerned; and unfamiliarity with American procedures and techniques, in reference to the British. Incidents quoted herein were selected from those which were convenient at the time this chapter was written.

One instance of trouble was recalled by William J. Jeffries, P. O. D. Metallurgist. He made mention of a contract for spare parts for the British M3 Medium Tanks, and some difficulties in reference to corrosion on the malleable iron castings used. P. O. D. engineers were consulted and it was decided that British inspectors were justified in requiring the change of metal requested. Thereafter, a higher quality of metal was used in fulfilling the terms of this contract. Cast steel occasionally had

been substituted on British contracts for cast iron, particularly where the parts would be subjected to a great amount of shock.

Generally, however, inspection, as many other phases of Lend Lease routines, was taken "in stride," Inspectors handling Lend Lease matters along with U. S. Ordnance inspections.

A case in point was that of a shipment to the Soviet Government of several two hundred and fifty (250) ton Presses, EG 53 Type, Parts, Spare Parts and Lubricating Systems. Walter A. Stoever, Senior Inspector for the Philadelphia Regional Office, of the District, would make routine inspections of the Russian items during his regular tours of duty. The Russian Inspectors, however, insisted upon being present at all inspections; never, under any circumstances permitting Ordnance to have final responsibility, even in order to expedite shipments and to clear plant areas for further production. Lieutenant William F. Rathgeber, Jr., reported 8 January 1945: "A Russian representative was always present for final inspection, and the British, occasionally. Russians were very particular in monetary matters, whether charges appeared too much or too little."

Russian inspectors often complicated the joint inspections by failing to keep appointments. "They would," according to Inspector Stoever, "appear at another time and appear greatly annoyed if I should not be there. They seldom acknowledged mail queries or explained broken appointments.

"The Russians had their own ideas and would insist upon deviations from design and specifications while items were in production. They had a peculiar way of ordering spare parts. It frequently happened that parts packed with shipments had no relation to the item, or that other parts were ordered packed with parts belonging to the end item. On one occasion they ordered a grease gun packed with a two hundred and fifty ton Press. To meet the request I purchased a fifty-cent grease gun in a local hardware store. That seemed to please the Russian inspector, and the shipment was accepted.

"The British inspectors, on the other hand, were prompt in keeping appointments, which they usually followed with courteous notes thanking us for our interest and cooperation. They were amenable to suggestions and frequently sought our counsel."

Other Inspectors of the Philadelphia Regional Office whose rounds included Lend Lease Inspections, included Joseph Singer, Julian F. Rehnstrom and Samuel T. Riggins.

A major problem in the early Lend Lease era, a hangover from November 1940, was in reference to an option obtained by the British Purchasing Commission to have a certain manufacturer produce a large number of 75 mm. Guns and spare parts, to be used on M3 Tanks. The British agreed to make an advance payment of 25 per cent of the full amount of the contract. Inspection difficulties lost no time in snarling the routine. These difficulties appeared chiefly to be due to lack of co-operation on the part of the contractor who appeared to be more concerned with production than with quality of output.

A high stage of annoyance was reached in October 1941. This was discovered to be the result of mutilation of parts in order to make them fit and, in some instances, interchangeable. There were difficulties in final assembly as a result of mutilation. Three examples are quoted from a report by the Inspector to Lt. Colonel, then Captain, Art Seiler, Industrial Chief:

1. Breech ring holes were filed to an oval in order that pins could be inserted.

2. Detent grooves in operating crank were ground beyond tolerance so that the detent pin might be inserted.

3. Contractors had placed two rejected cranks in two guns and had mutilated both cranks to secure interchangeability.

and 146 of 200 handle latches which had been rejected later were found in the stock room with rejection tickets removed. Rejected firing pins later were found in assembled guns. And trouble did not end there. Facilities charged with assembling the guns constantly were reporting their difficulties. Points of friction occurred between British and P. O. D. Inspectors.

Steps of course were taken. As with all other problems attendant upon Lend Lease contracts, and all other contracts for that matter, this one finally was adjusted to the credit of the District, if not to the contractor. The incident as sketched here is one indication that "it wasn't all honey"—back when.

SPARE PARTS

The matter of concurrent spare parts had from the start been one of continuing difficulty. Though alleviated somewhat by increasing experience, it never was got completely out of the way.

It was decided back in the Defense Aid days, August 1940, by agreement between the Field Service Section and the Traffic Section, both of the Property Branch, that all related material and Spare Parts distribution activities first would be cleared by the Field Service Section for issuance of bills of lading. Out of this grew the Lend Lease Unit in the Branch which was, as a matter of fact, the only unit in the District Office devoting its entire attention to Lend Lease matters. The Unit was set up in June 1941.

Lend Lease shipments at the start were the responsibility of John Baisley. Part of his task was to maintain contact with Inspectors, and expediting Shipping Documents. Later, the Shipping Documents were forwarded by the Property Section of the Branch.

The larger problem encountered by the Unit, grew out of the scarcity of shipping facilities. Time and again material authorized for transfer could not be released by foreign representatives because of ship shortages.

Another problem to provide a target for the Unit, was that in connection with the marking of material. It was called to the attention of O. C. O. that marking instructions forwarded to P. O. D. by the various foreign government representatives very often revealed in uncoded form the final destination of the shipments. Thus, when shipment was made, material classified as restricted, or even as confidential, inquisitive persons quickly could learn what was going on.

And that, too, was taken care of by the "boys of the old 9th floor."

Came time, somewhat later, when Captain Bob Vogelsberg took charge of Lend Lease shipments, and when John Baisley "shoved off" from P. O. D., his work was taken over by Harold J. Turtle and Lawson Gotwals.

Just how much of Lend Lease funds was spent in the District is not known. Payments, as already noted, came for the greater part out of a general fund allotted by Washington. As a clue—Bill Rathgeber noted that 473 Machine tool contracts of record carried 507 requisitions. Several gage contracts were included. All contracts were 90 per cent or more complete by early 1945. "In the beginning," the Lieutenant told us, three per cent was added for packing and handling. This later was increased to 25 per cent.

The Treasury Department took over all Lend Lease, 15 May 1944, but had no interest prior to that time.

A list of contractors in the Philadelphia Ordnance District who contributed in one way and another to the Lend Lease program would cover this page and a few pages following—a veritable "who's who" of manufacturers in the seven state District area. And orders were in quantities of astronomical dimension.

At the war's end it was a far cry from that day long before when the President had said in reply to critics of the impending Lend Lease Bill:

"We must be the great arsenal of democracy."

And Winston Churchill had sent rocketing across the world this never-to-be-forgotten challenge:

"We shall defend our Island, whatever the cost may be; we shall fight on the beaches, we shall fight on the landing grounds, we shall fight in the fields and in the streets, we shall fight in the hills; we shall never surrender, and even if, which I do not for a moment believe, this Island or a large part of it is subjugated and starving, then our Empire beyond the seas, armed and guarded by the British fleet, would carry on the struggle, until, in God's good time, the New World, with all its power and might, steps forth to the rescue and the liberation of the Old!"

That the New World did release its power and its might, without stint, without limit—is now a matter of glorious record—Lend Lease—and men.

L. to R.: Captain Arthur J. Seiler, Lt. John H. Derickson, Martin Sandler, Captain Ernest J. Langham
(Rank indicated is at time of picture)

Chapter XLIV

ENDING IT ALL

SOMEONE once said, "The end lies in the beginning. In the game, it is the final score that matters. In war it is the victory . . ."

The first termination attempted in the District bears an October 1942 date line. The contract, that of Triumph Explosives Company, was not actually settled until several years later. At the time of the first audit the Contract Settlement Act had not been written into the termination procedures. Anyhow October 1942 gives us a beginning—a jumping-off spot.

This is not to be a chapter on the laws, and rules and directives that came in increasing volume with the progress of the war. A file of this data would reach seven times to the moon and four times around Tony Galento.

The big forward spurt of interest in Terminations came in December 1943, with the advent in P. O. D. of Colonel Fred A. McMahon, as District Chief, succeeding Colonel D. A. Hauseman. Colonel McMahon was all for more attention to Terminations as an important preliminary to the flood of cancellations which sooner or later would come. Subsequent to the Staff Meeting during which the Colonel had turned on his oratory, the Control Board met in solemn conclave and gave proper heed.

To 1943, Terminations had been a Legal Branch function. Lt. Colonel Joseph A. Whelan, Chief, and Lt. Colonel, then Major, Albert W. Gilmer, Assistant, were running the business—and all very well.

A Terminations Branch was established in the District, in December 1943. This, as it was explained at the time "was in recognition of an increasing need for quick and equitable settlement of an ever-increasing volume within the District of contract terminations."

Major Gilmer was named Chief of the new Branch and Contracting Officer with power to finally commit the Government contractually with the terminated contractor.

The Branch was set up as a part of the Purchase-Termination Division of which, Martin Sandler, until then Director of Purchase, was appointed Chief. A Termination Section charged with the responsibility of handling all terminations "for the convenience of the Government" was established under Terminations Branch jurisdiction in each of the three Commodity Branches—Artillery-Small Arms Ammunition, Tank-Automotive, and also in the Production Service Branch.

In line with P. O. D. policy and that indicated by higher authority, of handling all terminations on the basis of true negotiated settlements based upon strict accounting substantiation of every item in contractor's claims, the District topside appointed to the Section posts men of demonstrated experience of industry and, whose backgrounds as Ordnance officers, suggested resultful relationships with contractors in their respective fields of operation. Selectees for the sectional posts were as follows:

Artillery-Small Arms: Major Joseph I. Wexlin
Ammunition: Major Harold L. Vennell
Tank-Automotive: Major Oliver C. Conger
Production Equipment: Major Arthur B. Allison

Fact-finding and routine duties in reference to terminations were not exclusively the function of the Terminations Branch Commodity Sections. Certain functions officially were assigned to other Branches where existing experience assured efficient procedure. (1) Fiscal Branch; (2) Legal aspects with the Legal Branch; (3) Redistribution and Salvage functions under Major Paul H. Carlson, a section of the newly formed Property Disposal Branch under Lt. Colonel Hayward K. Kelley, formerly Chief, Ammunition Branch, and at one time P. O. D.'s Production Director; (4) much of the initial investigation and routine follow-up work on the presentation of claims was delegated to the Regional Offices.

In effect, practically every Branch, Section and Field Office of the District was given its share of the terminations work. In addition there was established a review board, labeled the Board of Terminations, whose duty it became to review proposed settlements following completion of negotiations between negotiators and contractors. The board, in accordance with Procurement Regulations—good old PR—made final recommendations to the contracting officer before final authorization of settlement. The original Board of Terminations had for its members: Martin Sandler, as Chairman, Lt. Colonel Joseph A. Whelan, from Legal, Major Charles W. Sorber, from Fiscal, H. Paul Gant, Planning Director, and Lt. Colonel Gilmer, Terminations Chief and Contracting Officer.

In January 1944 there was established in the Branch a Review and Statistics Section; its job to conduct routine reviews of all recommended settlements prior to their submission to the Board of Terminations, and to maintain statistical records required after preparation of reports. Members of this board were John Watt, Chief, Allen McK. Beecroft, Herbert Effiger and Mrs. Powell.

The first edition of a Philadelphia Ordnance District Termination Manual (H-1-44), now a collector's item, if you go in for that sort of thing, was issued 8 May 1944. Later came other publications—bulletins, memoranda, lectures.

The great aim, often impressed upon Branch personnel, was to get Uncle Samuel out of the war, in so far as possible, "on the double." A recurrence of the chaos trailing the Armistice of 1918 was to be avoided at all costs.

The need for a considerable period was for training of both Ordnance and contractor personnel. The former, to be properly prepared to absorb, and to expedite settlement of a great volume of terminations; the latter, to set up their organizations to carry the major part of the termination burden. Consequently, there was established in the District a series of schools (of which more later) to accomplish these ends, and to lay the foundation for continuation by District Branches and Sections, and by prime contractors and subcontractors, of day to day training, through experience "on the job."

Forums and conferences were held in various manufacturing centers within the District area, in cooperation with Chambers of Commerce and other groups. Likewise, a Termination Forum held during January and February 1944 in the Auditorium of 150 South Broad Street, for District personnel. Similar forums were held in the Regional Offices. There was issued during this period a publication, "Instructions to Prime and Sub-contractors Relative to the Termination for the Convenience of Government of fixed price supply contracts," which served the dual purpose of training, and as a notice accompanying Notices of Termination.

In breaking the ice for the series of forums at 150, Mr. Ingersoll said, in his introductory talk:

"This Termination job as I see it is one of the most important things that we have got in this war effort. We have heard an awful lot about winning the peace, but this is certainly, as I see it, one of the most vital things as far as the United States is concerned in the winning of peace. In other words, as we believe in private industry and Government, as we understand the Government, this termination job must be done effectively and well. If it isn't, Lord knows what will happen to us. There are a few angles that show you that this is the truth. When you think that if the war stopped as of that time there probably would be $75,000,-000,000 worth of contracts that would have to be stopped. The working out of that job quickly is a great deal worse than the job we had two years ago in building up to that figure. We want justice to industry, we want justice to the Government, and those two can go right side by side and are not in any way in conflict with each other."

The ratio during the first three months of 1944 of completed to outstanding Terminations changed unfavorably. The principal bottle-neck was in reference to the disposition of excess contractor-owned material. This was a matter of national as well as P. O. D. record. The main cause was the unwillingness of Government agencies to incur heavy losses in salvaging and scrapping materials without stronger backing through general regulations. Difficulties also were met in clearing, through other Government agencies in order to obtain usable outlets, before selling at scrap or salvage prices, such circularized materials as spare parts and partly completed work. It was believed at the time that Ordnance Procurement Circulars recently distributed would facilitate (1) streamlining of exchange between Districts of service; (2) facilitate storage of Government owned property, or property transferred to Government account (3) set a time limit of 60 days after which the contractor might request and obtain permission to transfer to the Government, title of excess materials (4) permit delegation to the contractor of blanket authority to dispose of materials at 65 per cent of value (7th inning, all stretch). Three full years of this sort of goings-on. No wonder Terminations personnel went in suddenly for hair dyes.

There was appointed during the Summer of 1944 in each of the Regional Offices, a Property Disposal Manager whose responsibility it was to maintain close relationships with the contractors in disposing of property and filing of inventories; as well as, in many cases, in checking inventories listed in contractors' claims. It worked. Claims and inventories arrived in P. O. D. in better condition, and contractors were receiving better information.

Considerable headway was made in July 1944 in inducing prime contractors to accept the delegation of authority to settle sub-contractors' claims up to $10,000.00. To 30 September, 67 contractors had accepted this authority.

The experimental program in the training of contractor personnel, in July 1944, had been put into actual operation. The first course, which was got under way during the first week of July with an enrollment of 75 persons, was a marked success. Difficulties were experienced in obtaining the necessary funds for financing the program. However, through the efforts of the District, a contract was let with the University of Pennsylvania, to finance the program for a period of approximately eight weeks.

Subsequent to the first two training meetings at the University, difficulty was encountered in the enrollment of contractor personnel. It became necessary, as a result, to allocate to each of the participating agencies, earlier set up as a "combined operation"—Navy, Quartermaster's, Signal Corps, etc., a certain number of persons, thus putting it purely on a solicitation basis. And this plan worked. The increase from then on, in enrollment, was encouraging.

The War Contract Termination Training Program through August and September had gathered momentum. Enrollments now were of more than 100 persons. Credit for this and other of the training programs belongs to Lt. Colonel Gilmer and to his right hand man, Captain Phil M. Andress. The Colonel prepared all instructional data, ar-

ranged and supervised class sessions, stirred up interest of industry personnel, and personally and otherwise obtained enrollments in sufficient number to encourage U of P to continue the course. He also prepared publicity releases aimed at the stimulation of an advance interest on the part of industry in the inevitable victory rush into terminations.

In September 1944, the Branch was giving over much of its time to the matter of Pre-termination Planning. Under this procedure various negotiators were each assigned a number of contracts and they, in turn, established the necessary files and accumulated essential data pertaining to each contract under their respective assignments. Arrangements then were made by the negotiator for meetings with the contractors inviting, when necessary, Property Disposal Branch, Fiscal Branch, Legal Branch and Regional Office representatives; this "team" discussing matters of primary interest to their respective branches, and determining ways and means of setting up and adjusting their records in the event of Terminations.

The plan was well described in a letter SPOGL —Contract Termination Branch, from Harold Shepherd, Lt. Colonel, Ordnance Dept., Assistant, dated 16 August 1944. Subject: "Pre-termination Planning." Quoting, in part:

"It is believed that much more can be done *at once* to prepare ourselves and the contractors with whom we do business. Specifically, it is believed that each of the contractors with whom your volume of contracts is sufficiently great to justify the anticipation of a substantial number of terminations should be requested immediately to prepare and present to you a statement of its termination plan, describing its preparations for the settlement of its termination claims and the termination claims of its sub-contractors, listing specific problems as to which it requires answers, and making concrete proposals as to matters upon which advance informal agreements could be reached by you."

Assignments to the negotiators, for example would be about like this:

To Lieutenant F. W. Boege who, with Blythe J. Minnier, J. S. Rettig, Michael A. O'Neill, Captain Paul Caldwell, E. F. R. Wood, was a negotiator on ammunition, would go a list such as this: American Tin Plate & Supply Company, American Can Company, Atlas Powder Company, Charles D. Briddell Company, and possibly 21 others.

Another negotiator, say, Blythe J. Minnier,

might have been assigned, for instance, Coplay Cement Company, Crown Can Company, General Electric Company (York, Pa.), and others.

By October 1944, Pre-termination Planning had become one of the most important activities in the Terminations Branch, looking toward the cessation of hostilities on some on-coming VE Day. Negotiators were planning Pre-terminations meetings with contractors who, in all probability, would be affected. Branch topside after receiving pertinent data from the negotiators, was endeavoring to tie in problems which were to be answered by O.C.O. For example, questions in reference to "practical cut-off points," and what was to be done with items which were in the "ninety (90%) per cent incomplete stage."

Came December 1944 and there had been a change of thinking in reference to Pre-termination Planning. The Nazi crowd were blasting through us in E.T.O., and interest in the District made a quick shift to production. In order that nothing might interfere with the production schedules of P.O.D. war contractors, all discussion of Terminations was held to a minimum. This development took the edge off the good results following the work of the Inter-Agency Committee on Terminations Training held back in October 1944, at the University of Pennsylvania. The event was a mass meeting on Pre-termination Planning. The Inter-Agency project was initiated by the Readjustment Division, A.S.F., and was to be the first of a series of 17 meetings throughout the country. This Branch, with Captain Andress doing a good chore in the arrangements, had been playing an important part in preparing for the event; the Army, the Navy, 39 Boards of Trade, and a variety of manufacturers' associations lending a hand.

Saturday morning meetings of the Terminations Branch began way back when the Branch was young, continued through the end of the year and into 1945. A typical meeting would find present, in addition to Colonel Gilmer and Captain Andress— such dignitaries as—Major Bill Lafean, successor in Ammunition to Major Vennell; Major Joseph I. Wexlin, of Artillery-Small Arms Terminations; Captain Paul B. Caldwell, of Ammunition Terminations, later, Chief; Lieutenant George T. Hall, Artillery-Small Arms Terminations; Lieutenant Guy D. Beaumont, Property Disposal; Lieutenant Gerald F. Welles, special assistant to Colonel Gilmer; Lieutenant Walter R. Griffin, negotiator of Tank-Automotive Branch Terminations, later, Chief.

Lieutenant Elvon R. Hamilton, who did a masterly job in compiling a record of the Mack truck termination, on which he was negotiator; Lieutenant Wm. M. Hall, Property Disposal; Fred F. Corleto, who did some good publicity work for the Terminations Branch and for a time served as a termination instructor at U of P; Fred D. Sarkis, Negotiator on cost-plus-a-fixed-fee contracts; John E. Chevalier, negotiator for Artillery-Small Arms Terminations; Herbert Effinger, of the Review and Statistics Section of the branch; Paul W. Williams, negotiator, Artillery-Small Arms Terminations; Blythe J. Minnier, negotiator, Ammunition Branch; Alfred Koch, negotiator, Artillery-Small Arms Terminations; William C. Sutherland, Jr., negotiator, Production Service Branch; Elias Vander Horst, negotiator, Artillery-Small Arms Terminations; Michael A. O'Neill, negotiator, Ammunition Terminations; James J. Keleher, negotiator at Autocar Company; J. S. Rettig, Negotiator, Ammunition; Cyril E. Hepburn, negotiator, Terminations Branch; John Watt of the Review and Statistics Section; Mrs. Evelyn Duncan, branch statistician (and darned good) and Miss Irene M. Tiller who joined up with the Marines in March 1945.

The list did not appear to be "hard and fast," but varied from week to week. No doubt according to the responsibilities of those expected to attend.

A month to be long remembered, certainly by Lt. Colonel Gilmer, was that of December 1944, when the Baldwin Locomotive Works, cost-plus-a-fixed-fee contract, the now famous W-670-Ord-1814, was settled. This was the first contract of its size, and possibly of its type, ever written. The final negotiation meeting was held 13 December in the offices of the company. Attending, for P.O.D. were Major Oliver C. Conger, Chief, Tank-Automotive Termination Section; Captain Bernard M. Zimmerman, Legal branch, Tank-Automotive section; Fred D. Sarkis, negotiator for the Tank-Automotive Branch, and J. J. Tierney field auditor.

Not only could the Termination Branch attach to this settlement, a brace of "firsts," but, even beyond such distinction, the Branch could lay claim to something of a record for speed in bringing the settlement to a conclusion. It is recalled that actual work on the settlement was initiated in March of 1944, covering a series of four notices of Terminations from 10 April 1943. And in view of the December 1944, windup, it is well to remember that the company was in production almost to the "farewell hour"—actually, to deep in November 1944.

Originally, October 1941, W-670-Ord-1814, was written to the estimated cost of $22,000,000. With amendments and additions, the total slithered to a grand high of $295,725,108—and this did not include fee. Of the total, Baldwins produced to a dollar value of $92,197,000. The amount cancelled was $203,532,108. There were involved, some 400 sub-contractors. The big ones were referred to the Districts where they belonged. The others, 230 of 'em were handled right here at home. Involved on the sub-contractor side were approximately 125,000 Purchase Orders, and amendments. In P.O.D., we disposed of somewhere in the general vicinity of $24,000,000 worth of material: some to field service, some to tank manufacturers and some to scrap.

During the negotiations and discussions, Branch and other interested P.O.D. personnel "microscoped" every item: decided which were allowable; which were not. Too, this group of "surgeons" reckoned within 1%, the total of G.I. material in the plant—while the job was running. And every pertaining piece of material, every component in the plant, had of necessity to be examined for scrap.

Of course, this was more than a one-man, two-man, or even a corporal's guard. Twenty-five P.O.D. mental wizards, here in the home office had a go at it. Down at Baldwins, 100 P.O.D. assistant wizards were steadily at work—and it was all hard line-plunging; no fancy open-field running and, incidentally, no fumbles.

There were difficulties, plenty of 'em. The War Department and the General Accounting Office did not always, at the beginning, see optic to optic. All in the interest of efficiency, y' understand. There were difficulties in reference to agreement upon the language. It also developed that the procedures, and methods of payment in connection with the work performed by the contractor were new to just about everyone concerned and, therefore, both the Government and the contractor ran into some hitches during the early stages. But everything came out in the wash and there was no "tell-tale gray." "Duz Gilmer" does everything.

Quoting from a letter, 11 January 1945, from Colonel Irving A. Duffy, Chief, Legal Division, O.C.O.

"While I know the settlement was the result of Ordnance teamwork, I also know that two individuals in particular, Major O. C. Conger (assistant to the then Major Gilmer) and Major A. W. Gilmer were the main sparkplugs who, by their drive and untiring efforts, to a great extent made possible the settlement of this case . . . . "

And kudos came from Baldwin's president, Ralph Kelly; all of which made it a very nice affair, all the way from scratch, and, as a flattering finale, O.C.O. had copies of the Termination procedure in this case committed to paper, 80 copies of it, which were sent around the U. S. as an example of clear thinking and incisive, efficient action. Upon receiving news of this, many faces in the Terminations Branch assumed a wholesome pink.

It now is 1945. Captain Andress, who is all over the Terminations Branch like a heavy fog, and up to his good-looking locks in training work, is only two-and-one-half jumps ahead of digitalis and thyroid extract.

Substantial effort was made through the early months by the Branch in negotiating advance binding agreements with ten contractors of the District. This was not the first attempt to make such agreements. Experience has shown the contractors were too much concerned with the current pressure upon production to take seriously the matter of agreeing in advance upon the use of formulas which would permit immediate determination. Delegations of authority, such as authorization to settle sub-claims of less than $10,000 and authorization to dispose of terminations inventories had further lessened the need, of binding agreements, in many cases.

To the end of March 1945 a total of 265 Ordnance contractors in the District had been delegated authority to finally settle with sub-contractors, Terminations claims, in those instances in which the sub-settlement was not in excess of $10,000. The extent of final authority of the contractor in reference to claims of more than $10,000 had been increased in those cases in which the Property Disposal branch had been delegated authority to effect and dispose of inventory in lots of $2,500 or less at the best price obtainable; or of $10,000 at 75% or better.

There was instituted in January 1945, at Heintz Manufacturing Company, a Sub-contractor Training Program, proposed and developed by the Termination Branch in co-operation with the Inter-Agency Training Committee. It was hoped that the experiment would be of benefit to other committees and organizations laying plans for Termination training with the smaller war plant contractors.

It has been recognized that none of the Termination Training Programs effected to this time had been reaching a sufficiently large number of smaller contractors, a situation to be faced, not only in Philadelphia, but, as well, throughout North-South-East-West. Out of the Heintz experiment grew what later became known as the "Heintz Plan." The opening meeting was given its impetus by Dr. V. S. Karabaz, University of Pennsylvania, director; Wm. J. Meinel, Heintz president, and the omnipresent Captain Andress, who later authored a very comprehensive report of the proceedings, and the plan.

In March 1945 *The Terminations Branch Handbook*, fell upon a waiting world. This was the result of two months work; its basis, an analysis of the relationships of the Terminations Branch with other branches of the District. The project involved in particular, the development of specific procedure to be followed by the Regional offices, to the end that clearly defined allocation of responsibility might be assured.

By far, the greater portion, approximately 80% of termination cases processed during the period resulted in "no charge" settlements. This was due, it was reported, to a greater percentage of small cut-backs, and a ruling of the Bureau of Internal Revenue permitting the charging off of Termination costs for income tax and renegotiation. Principal cut-backs of the period included among many others:

Heavy Shell
Shot, 90 mm., A. P.
Boosters for Medium Shell
Adapter, Cluster (for Frag. Bomb)
Shell, H.E., 81 mm.
Shell, T-16, 105 mm.
Guns, 57 mm., 76 mm., 90 mm., 155 mm.
Heavy trucks and Spare Parts
Transporter, 6 Ton
Fuze, P.D. for Medium and Heavy Shell
Cartridge Cases, 105 mm.
Fragmentation Bomb, 20 lb.
Practice Rocket, 2.36
Shell, H.E., 240 mm.
Howitzers, 240 mm.
Mortars, 60 mm.
Trucks, 7½ ton Prime Mover
Recovery Unit, Tank, M32

The greater number of Terminations during May 1945, were in reference to spare parts items. Difficulties hinged, mainly, on the fact that neither the Commodity Branch or Field Office production records, nor the Office, Chief of Ordnance—Detroit Supply Control, had been organized to permit quick determination as to the status of these items. In particular, terminations affecting authorized items of issue called for acceptance of completed articles regardless of the delivery status. In certain situations, as long a time as 30 days was required to determine the quantities cancelled. Over 50% of such cut-back notices resulted in no cancellations, all affected items on the contract having been completed. On the other hand, O.C.O. required that immediate cut-back information be given the contractor. Accordingly, cut-back notices affecting spare parts items now were classified as "indefinite" notices, and such notices were not registered or given standard distribution until both the contractor and Field office had made an exact determination of the quantities to be cancelled.

The District now had applications from several of the larger prime contractors for assignment to the Consolidated Termination Program. This program, we almost forgot to tell you was established back in September 1944, and included various of the services. The idea was, according to a Memorandum SPRCD, 25 September 1944, Subject: "Co-ordinated Termination Program," signed D. N. Hauseman, Brigadier General, General Staff, Readjustment Division, in which it is explained:

"To provide at the field local level the means of an interchange of such information and, to the extent feasible, otherwise co-ordinate activity so as to minimize independent dealings with contractors when information desired exists in another independent contracting office, local Termination Coordination Committees composed of representatives of the Services having district offices in the area, should be formed. Normally, the head of the District Termination Unit of each such Service will represent that Service on the Termination Coordination Committee. It is suggested that the Termination Coordination Committees be formed in the metropolitan areas shown on the attached list, (*Editor's note:* No need to name them here. Just think of all the towns—and some important smaller ones, and there you are) and such other areas as are considered desirable. . . . . ."

Of course there was much more of this sort of thing. Everyday, every situation brought its problems which in turn lead to solutions which lead to more problems leading to more solutions—to the end of the war and beyond.

And about the end of the war, V-J-Day: Here again the Terminations Branch and its No. 1 men covered themselves with honors. "Way back in October 1944, Martin Sadler, Major Gilmer and other topside called meetings to get contractors interested in what would come when the shooting had stopped. This helped. Then came the Summer of 1945. Many minds still were bearing down on production, which was according to orders. But that man Gilmer. It was really early in August that he could smell something cooking in the Pacific. He confided to the District Chief, Colonel Kelso that, although the time might not be ripe for mass terminations, "maybe we had better trim ship, clear the decks for action, set our sights and be ready to shoot." Said the Chief—"I agree. It may be my rheumatism, or the price of butter—something tells me you are right. Let's call a meeting!" So—back to his Ivory Tower went Major Gilmer, where he drew up an air-tight plan for V-J-Day Terminations. Major Joseph C. Hoffman, Fiscal Chief gave the plan a going-over; put on some finishing touches.

The call went out to the Commodity Branches, Production Service Branch and other interested groups to turn in with "sudden immediateness" a complete list of all existing contracts. Two days later he had the lists. Asked Washington if any telegram forms had been prepared for the purpose of ordering terminations. None. Major Gilmer and his warriors drafted one in order to be in readiness. Sent it to Washington for approval. Washington not satisfied; said we'd have to use a message different from the one submitted. So, destroyed all we had prepared and given to Western Union. We made up new ones. One Washington dictated over the telephone was practically the same as the one submitted in the first place.

Now, we were all set. Telegrams at Western Union—ready. Came a teletype—"Stand by for important announcement." Waited, that night, August 15, assembled in P.O.D. President Truman spoke over the radio. We were in the clear—and the first District to get its telegrams in circulation. Many of the confirming letters dropped in the P.O. same day, reached contractors ahead of the telegrams.

Terminations personnel wrote history that night.

Perhaps on one far day, someone will ask—"Did the contractors come out on the long end of the terminations?" The answer to that is, they received their full due, based upon some pretty hard facts taken into consideration. The aim was, always, to do the fair thing. Contractors knew that we meant it, and more often than not accepted P.O.D. findings. There were differences of opinion, of course; and in some instances, "blood, sweat and tears"; but in the end, there were no hard feelings.

Anyway, to give you an idea, here are some figures, taken from straight through a report of the Board of Terminations, for the months of January and February, 1944. Names only are changed. They are all prime contracts:

Date Approved	Contractor	Total Contract	Terminated Value	Settlement
January 1	X Company	$ 320.00	$ 90.00	$ 15.50
January 6	XX Company	394.50	197.50	35.07
January 7	XYZ Company	1,119.00	675.00	374.00
January 7	MYM Foundries	112,700.00	70,505.12	8,351.84
January 7	Doe & Brothers	1,120.00	140.00	59.00
January 7	Blank Industries	992.00	776.00	336.10
January 7	Yule Logs, Inc.	2,985.00	880.00	185.70
January 10	On the Beam, Inc.	41,580.00	41,580.00	25.25
January 10	Triple A. Company	3,750.00	3,750.00	842.67
January 15	Double D. Inc.	949,000.00	427,300.00	72,068.38
January 18	Mansize Industries	1,482.00	291.00	109.65
January 24	Metals, Ltd.	225,000.00	57,600.00	16,582.80
January 27	Tin Tab Tub Co.	148,750.00	140,000.00	800.00

January 27	Whassis Foundries	338,350.00	166,384.00	30,173.00
January 27	Long & Lane Sons	1,080,000.00	781,898.40	58,826.22
January 28	Target Works	1,544,000.00	729,230.00	6,066.59
February 2	Oldtimers, Inc.	1,241,423.79	854,631.29	16,883.47
Febryary 12 . . .	Make 'Em Good Corp.	44,214.94	39,458.54	324.63
February 23 . . .	Tom. Dick & Harry Co.	100,000.00	100,000.00	5,356.74
February 23 . . .	AAA, Corporation	252,000.00	252,000.00	5,538.74
February 23 . . .	Jones Company	433,500.00	261,421.89	2,205.67
February 23 . . .	Jones Company	433,500.00	261,421.89	2,205.67
February 23 . . .	Smith, Smith & Smith	276,512.72	192,755.62	13,886.94
February 25 . . .	East-West Ordnance Supply Co.	11,007.45	1,052.25	635.91
February 25 . . .	Tool & Gage Mfg. Co.	874,800.00	251,950.00	50,371.66
February 25 . . .	Eastern Company, Ltd.	317,480.00	311,150.00	53,158.56

What was the net of all the Terminations work? Well, during the full spread of Branch activity, and including the early days in Legal Branch, there were reported 3,918 settlements authorized, to the total of $1,020,789,768. Of these, 3,359 were settled in the amount of $87,716,733. Rescinded cases numbered 559. Of the latter dollar total, $29,193,191 was for Government Account. And the foregoing totals did not include cost-plus-a-fixed-fee contracts and their sub-contract settlements.

There were eight of the CPFF contracts representing deliveries in the amount of $206,790,000. And these terminations cost the Government $10,512,805—according to the gentleman who fell heir in 1946 to all that remained of the Termination Branch and the Property Disposal Branch—Paul Williams.

In closing this chapter, recognition must be given those other earnest individuals, not elsewhere mentioned, who made their contributions to the total Terminations score; among them—Captain Oliver K. Hearte, Jr., Assistant Chief, later Chief, Tank-Automotive Terminations Section; the late Harry E. "Dick" Snyder, Negotiator, Baldwin cost-plus-a-fixed-fee contract; Fred D. Sarkis, Negotiator, on the Baldwin Contract; Major J. M. Teasdale, Negotiator; Lt. Colonel Oscar H. Hansen, Negotiator,. American Car & Foundry Company; Kenneth C Trauger, Negotiator, Artillery-Small Arms, Terminations Section; Leutenant Albert E. Smith, and Louis H. Seip, Negotiators, Tank-Automotive, Terminations Section; Chester M. Graves, Negotiator, Artillery-Small Arms, Terminations Branch.

As of 1 September there were 1,767 Terminations in process. By October ,the total had been reduced to 1,199 cases; by November to 872. This would be reduced, by 1 December to 500 cases, and by 1 January 1946, to 125 cases, approximately.

Captain Theodore C. Sheaffer

Lt. Neal W. Slack

Chapter XXXXV

WHAT TO DO WITH THE STUFF?

ON THE heels of the formation of the Terminations Branch came the Property Disposal activity—the other half of the job of getting P. O. D. contractors out of the war and quickly back in commercial production.

[For a time, Property Disposal existed as the Redistribution and Salvage Section, under Major Paul H. Carlson. It was then part and parcel of the Industrial Division during the regime of Colonel A. Donald Kelso. Getting a bit big for its boots, the larger activity, Property Disposal Branch, was set up, and switched to the Contract Settlement Division where Martin Sandler "pulled the strings." Lt. Colonel H. K. Kelley, Ammunition Chief, was requisitioned for the Property Disposal assignment, Major Carlson continuing as Assistant Chief, and with the Redistribution and Salvage Section his principal activity in the Branch. All clear? Captain, then Lieutenant Howard S. Gallaher, came along as a Salvage Officer. Also came Lieutenant Neal W. Slack as Assistant to the Chief; Lieutenant James R. Aydelotte, Captain Oliver K. Hearte, Jr., Lieutenant James H. Nisbett.

From time to time other Military and Civilian personnel were assigned; among them, Lieutenants Eugene R. Carson, Oren H. Persons, Jr., LeRoy M. Bissett, Lloyd H. Diehl, Richard S. Edmonds, Stanley B. Honour. Other names to appear were those of Lieutenant Howard D. Ginsburg and Lieutenant James I. Kelley, Jr., Donald B. Kimmell, Captain Frank J. McCusker—and the great Major Welles H. Denney. Showing up mid-year of 1944 on a then recently established Salvage Board were the names of Emil Mathias, Leonard L. Eyster, Chester W. Graves and William J. Jeffries. Later, Hugh B. LaRue joins the Board. Many other names appear, in many capacities through the life of the Branch: Richard M. Keator, John McDowell, H. Rex McKnight, John I. Schwabe, Lieutenant John D. Adair and Lieutenants Earl H. Lentz, Francis M. Watson and Laur G. Wheaton, to mention a mere handful.

The start . . .

The new Branch was set up 28 February 1944 by order of the District Chief, C. Jared Ingersoll, acting on urgency expressed in a teletype dated 25 February, signed by Lt. General L. H. Campbell, Jr., Chief of Ordnance. As indicated at the opening of this narrative, the Property Disposal Branch took over all functions and personnel of the Redistribution and Salvage Section of the Production Service Branch. The Section had its inception in the Purchase Branch where it was known as the Salvage Section. On 7 November 1943 it was taken out of the Purchase Branch and established as a unit of the Production Service Branch, Industrial Division, where it continued until its complete reorganization as the Property Disposal Branch, Contract-Settlement Division.

For two weeks following establishment of the new activity, Colonel Kelley, Major Carlson and Major Denney investigated bottlenecks which had developed in connection with the disposal effort, and devised means of overcoming these bottlenecks; interviewed and assigned personnel and clarified the procedures and responsibilities of the Branch. A principal discussion was in reference to the removal from the Commodity Branch Disposal Sections of the administration of Property Disposal activities within the scope of the Commodity Branches. It subsequently was decided, 30 March 1944, that administration of the Property Disposal Section of the Ammunition Branch and Artillery-Small Arms Branch would be transferred to the Property Disposal Branch. Change of administration of Tank-Automotive Disposal Section was withheld until May. These changes had the effect of raising the total of Property Branch personnel from 38 to 65 persons as of 31 March 1944.

Functions of the Branch were to (1) establish P. O. D. policy for the redistribution and salvage of excess contractor and Government property, (2) receive from the Termination Branch and Property Branch inventory lists of excess materials and equipment and in connection with such inventories:

a. Make analyses and determine the appropriate disposition to be made.

b. Guide and assist contractors in negotiating proposals for disposition of contractor-owned property; and submit such proposals to the Contracting Officer for authorization, such submission to be made through the Board of Sales.

c. Upon determination, arrange for the disposition of Government-owned property.

(3) Administer the Salvage Board which would review and approve or reject recommendations for the determination as "non-repairable" of Government-owned property submitted for such review prior to certification by the Redistribution and Salvage Officer.

There were many problems during the "getting started" months. To meet them, "Ground Rules" were established. Problems embracing such matters as:

1. Packaging preparatory to storage of Government-owned excess property.
2. Need for a common list of sales outlets, and means for maintaining this list.
3. Examination of factors retarding the disposition of excess property.
4. The need for a set of standard records to be used by the Redistribution and Salvage Units in handling distribution of property.
5. Cooperation with other Government agencies.
6. Sales of Salvage material for export.

To mention a few:

At the end of February 1944, the Branch was able to report the following:

1. Contractor-owned Property

Inventory value.....................$506,169.00
Sales value........................ 336,547.00
Percent of realization—66%

2. Government-owned Property

Sales completed....................$ 38,647.00
Material transferred............... 535,865.00

Here, as in other areas of P. O. D. operations there sprang up a crop of units. In April 1944, there was added to the Material Marketing Section a Commercial Marketing Unit to assist in the disposal of commercial items. Late in May came a Scrap Marketing Section. Then there was an Inventory Costing Unit, Steel Warehouse Panel and a Steel Marketing Section. As an indication of the success of the latter, note the following results of June 1944 efforts:

Raw Steel received for
disposition...............1,722,090 pounds
Value......................$96,095.25
Sold or transferred............1,447,007 pounds
Cost of Steel disposed of........$73,718.65
Return of Amount sold or
transferred...............51,993.59
or a return to Government of 70.52 per cent.

The property Disposal Branch, now, 30 June, had a personnel of 81 persons, 13 of whom were officers; three, enlisted men.

And it was during this period the Salvage Boards were established at Baldwin Locomotive Works and at the Berwick Inspection Office. Others would follow. Terminations inventories were beginning to come in from other Districts. New rules were being adapted. The Branch already is up to Ground Rule No. 38. Changes in Procurement Regulations make necessary changes in the reporting of disposal activities. Matters of packaging for storage yowl for attention. A pretty warm month for all this, too.

Inventory sold during the three-month period ending 30 June, was marked up at $3,802,537.00. Sales value was $3,051,329.00. The backlog as of 30 June stood at $7,749,184.00. These figures represent total embracing all Commodity Branches.

Now we do a little merging: the Scrap Marketing Section joins hands with the Commercial Marketing Section to become the Scrap and Salvage Section. Richard M. Keator—the old Mask and Wig Club Keator—is named Chief of the new set-up. The Steel Marketing Section still is riding along on its own. In September 1944, that operation reported:

Raw Steel received for
disposition...............916,313 pounds
Value......................$29,504.00
Steel sold or transferred in
September...............1,389,062 pounds
Cost of steel disposed of........$117,455.84
Return on amount sold or
transferred...............79,158.16

Late in July 1944, "Bundling" goes to war for Ordnance. Lt. Colonel Kelley initiated efforts at this time to establish in the Branch what, for want of better designation, he labeled "Bundling." In essence, this was the grouping in one inventory of all items, each having a value of $25.00 or less; and disposing of these in a single lot. The procedure clicked from the start, and by the end of August there had been put into effect a similar procedure involving items whose individaul values were not over $100.00.

Steps were taken in August 1944 by the Property Disposal Termination Branches to formulate a Pre-Termination Plan which, when put into effect, would process before actual Termination should be initiated, all preliminary steps in reference to a termination settlement. Pre-termination meetings were held. A Pre-termination Planning Section was set up in the Property Disposal Branch, with Captain F. J. McCusker as Chief.

There had been announced in July 1944, a job to be done at Baldwin's. This was something in the nature of a "meanie"—the disposition of all excess property resulting from the operation, completion and the termination of Ordnance contracts with the Baldwin Locomotive Works. The disposition was to be accomplished within three months from 10 July.

The major contracts placed with the Baldwin Locomotive Works, beginning back in the "Educational Orders" days, were for the production of Medium Tanks, Heavy Tanks, Recovery Vehicles and Spare Parts, with a total value of approximately $437,000,000.00, all of which contracts, with one exception, were cost-plus-a-fixed-fee contracts, in addition there were awarded several other CPFF contracts, as well as many fixed price contracts, for Artillery materiel and War Aid machine tools.

It should be recalled that the Baldwin contracts still were in production—into November, in fact— and the CPFF contract on the way to final termination.

As of 10 October 1944 three months later the mission had been substantially accomplished. During the three months period approximately $5,000,000.00 worth of excess property had been disposed of, and it was estimated that less than $2,000,000.00 of such property still remained. It was expected that most of this would be disposed of by 1 December 1944. The amount disposed of to

10 October 1944, compared favorably with excess property to the approximate value of $12,000,000.-00, disposed of by all other disposal units of P. O. D. during the same period.

The property of which disposition was made during the three-month period at Baldwin was distributed as follows:

40% transferred to the Army, Navy and CPFF contractors
40% sold as scrap
10% sold to continuing contractors
6% reported to SWPA as Surplus
4% placed in standby

It was a big job. Only men trained to "think big" could handle it. With that in mind P. O. D. topside knew exactly what to do—they picked Sidney Press for the top assignment, and Captain Neal W. Slack as Contracting Officer's representative. Sid Press, it will be recalled, once stung by the wanderlust bug that seeks out so many discontented little bugs, decided to see the world— and took it the hard way; two years on a tramp steamer. Returning, he invested his savings in a business. Prosperity followed him. Restlessness again developed, and Sid, this time, took to the air. Achieving, in his own plane, a sufficient number of flying hours, he took the test for a commercial license, and passed. It was while flying as a mail pilot that Sid met Colonel Seiler who, at the time, also was an aerial letter carrier. Next came a barnstorming tour; then the purchase and operation of an airport. Later, the Government decided to teach some college students to fly. Sid offered his services as an instructor, and was accepted.

In February 1941, Sidney Press came to the Philadelphia Ordnance District by request of the Executive Officer. There was a special job in procurement of M3 Medium Tanks which needed to be done, and fast, so Sid went down to Baldwins. Followed two years of "close-up" of all that goes into the production of a tank. Sid was transferred to the Philadelphia Mobile Shop Depot. Did a grand job there, returned to 150 South Broad Street and subsequent assignment to the Disposal job at Baldwins—right back home.

The staff assigned to Sid at Baldwin's left little if anything to be desired by a hard-hitting efficient executive. The staff consisted of 131 individuals, military and civilian. Forty-two of the civilian staff were secretaries, typists and general assistants, all on the distaff side. It was an "all star" team. On it we discover Ed. T. Berdge with Anthony Fendo as assistant; Howard B. Biles, was Administration Assistant and Security Officer; Captain Philip J. Fields appears as Staff Assistant; J. J. Tierney Chief, Terminations Section; Ed Berdge, again, as Chief, Inspection Section; Sanford C. Wickline, Chief, Government Property Disposal Section; Lieutenant O. E. Kritter, heading the Property Section and the Fiscal Section; Mary E. Lange, Chief, Purchase and Sales Control Section, and Wilks L. Douglas, Chief Production Section.

Of course, each of these sub-divisions boasted its complement of Units. Under J. J. Tierney for instance in the Terminations Section, is a Contract Property Disposal Unit with Wilks H. Douglas, William E. Higgins, and Donald A. Duncan; and a Termination Control Unit with James J. Tierney and Harry J. McLaughlin. Under Ed Berdge in the Inspection Section where he is assisted by August H. Austin, there is a Machine Tool Unit with Anthony Fendo, John E. Cellars, Kurt Mullenex and Edward N. Hill; a 602 Shipments Unit with Pat Masticola; a Record and Inspection Unit with William J. Schwartz, Raimond T. Guernsey, Francis J. Keville, Francis E. Ressel, Howard E. Ransom and Alvin V. McCormick; a Spare Parts Unit with Mahlon J. Mercer and Albert E. Miller; a Government Storeroom Inspection Unit with John E. Eshelman, Andrew H. Watson, Albert Noren, George Beswick, Harry Robins, Donald A. Yealy, Ed E. Boyle, Dan M. Miller and Roy C. Adams. A Government Storeroom Records Unit boasts Jim J. Brady, Charles Mahon, William J. Murray, Leo Paci; and on Special Assignments, Ralph E. Campbell.

Under Government Property Disposal Section, comes a Transfer Unit with Lieutenant Stanley B. Honour, M. L. Wolfe and J. D. Whitehead; an Order Unit with N. H. Banning; an Inventory Unit with H. D. Given and, finally, an Expediter, E. T. Hazard. In the Property section, under Lieutenant Kritter, W. A. McCracken appears as Civilian Chief. There is a Property Records Unit with J. M. Trimble, B. R. Thompson, H. A. Gaston, F. J. Fodsy, E. E. Massimaine and T-Sgt. J. Devney; and a Traffic Unit with P. E. Cooper and E. S. Varnadore.

In the Fiscal Section, J. Walker is listed as Field Auditor; a Material Audit Unit includes W. Jaffee, S. D. Steward, E. S. Sayler, E. D. Martin, S. J. Ward, E. H. Britton, F. Malatesta, S-Sgt. B. R. Dall, Pfc. A. R. Guidi and Pvt. S. Howell; an Overhead and Labor Audit Unit, includes L. Hacker, L. B. Atlas, R. Fordyce, E. N. Hill and N. Wetheim; and a Termination Claim Review Unit with J. M. McGunagle. Under M. E. Lange of the Purchase and Sale Control Unit we discover T. A. Nyland. In the Production Section under W. H. Douglas, with W. P. Hutcheck as Expediter, H. F. Stevens as Contract Superintendent, and a Spare Parts Unit with E. R. Stahl and F. A. McCosker.

"The main lessons learned at Baldwin's," reported the Press-Slack Combine upon completion of the mission, "are as follows: (a) great quantities of material could be redistributed to productive channels through transfers, without funds, between two Government agencies and, (b) that redistribution of material would be facilitated by accumulating and disposing of it at one central location. Based on these lessons, a Redistribution Center, located at Manayunk, was conceived and organized.

The return in October 1944, to the District Office of Sidney Press, and Captain Slack did not impair the property disposal activities remaining at Baldwin Locomotive Works. The power formerly delegated to Captain Slack as Contracting Officer's Representative to authorize the disposal of excess property was left entirely under the able jurisdiction of Captain John P. Grimwade, down from the York Regional Office. The authority formerly delegated to Captain Slack as Assistant Redistribution and Salvage Officer to declare excess property non-repairable was redelegated to Captain Phil Fields—excellent preparation for this young officer's subsequent assignment to the Redistribution Center.

On 3 November, Martin Sandler, Chief, Purchase-Terminations Division, wrote Captain, then still Lieutenant, Grimwade:

"I see by the October report that once again the Baldwin Disposal Team has come through with a victory. By exceeding your October quota of $1,500,000.00 by over $800,000.00 you have not only disposed of more property than during previous months, but also you have surpassed the property disposal records of all other P. O. D. Disposal Units.

"I congratulate you who are in property disposal work on this splendid record."

Two days following completion of the original assignment, Baldwin president Ralph Kelley wrote Sid Press:

"The very difficult work that has been done in your recent tenure here has been done mainly due to your energy, and knowledge, and the cooperation you have developed with your operating people. It has been a splendid job."

Property Disposal accomplishments at the Baldwin Inspection Office were widely reflected by the "press" (not Sidney). At the request of the Chief of Ordnance, Lt. General L. H. Campbell, Jr., local newspaper reporters were invited to the Baldwin plant for the purpose of securing facts

and pictures concerning the losses which would be incurred upon the arrival of V Day. In addition to highlighting the substantial losses to be expected, the newspaper articles commented upon the high percentage of realization which had been accomplished.

Swinging into 1945 we discover the Branch in top form, its 15 officers, 18 enlisted men and 71 civilians "going great guns." The Redistribution Center, Pencoyd, a Branch activity, was doing an excellent job in disposing of Government-owned excess steel.

More merging: In March 1945 there was established a Service Section, a combination of the Steel Marketing and the Scrap and Salvage Sections. This move was in line with the reorganization of the Branch. Under the new plan, the Commodity Sections of the Branch were broken down into units under a single Section (Termination Inventory Disposal Section) which would handle all types of commodities resulting from terminations in the Regional Office areas; all except the Baltimore Regional Office Unit which would handle all disposals originating in that area.

Philadelphia Electric Company puts on exhibit to show what the District is doing in the "Victory Drive"

O, yes, there was a Policy Unit attached to the Property Disposal Branch. It was a dependent of the Staff Section. Early in the period the Unit issued its new Property Disposal Bulletin, No. 3, summarizing the then latest developments within the Branch; new procedures, rules and regulations. The Property Disposal Branch had now issued Handbook No. 13, bearing upon the establishment of steps to be followed in achieving plant clearances and in providing a convenient means of maintaining a record of procedures in follow-up on the part of the Inventory Manager.

Another new Unit to appear during the period was the Government-owned Disposal Section, taking over all projects not then (January) assigned to the Redistribution Center. This was in line with the general plan to entirely segregate from contractor-owned termination inventory, all Government-owned property disposition. The Unit would handle, in conjunction with Government-owned property, the disposition of half-track material placed in standby. Office, Chief of Ordnance—Detroit was closely checked during January to have rescinded, instruction on this material. Formal notice came along in February.

The end of March 1945 saw completion of all shipments from ACF-Brill Motors Company of excess materials from two terminated contracts. This material which had been stored by the company and which weighed more than 2,000,000 pounds presented something of a moving problem. Approximately $30,000.00 worth of spare parts were shipped to the St. Louis Depot; 17 large shipments of steel were transferred to the Redistribution Center from whence transfers to other points were made.

Textile Machine Works, Reading, Pennsylvania, received a visit in March from P. O. D. personnel. The object of the visit was to dispose of an inventory of approximately $374,000.00 worth of Government-owned gages, dies, tools and fixtures. Plans were made to photograph various of the items involved as an aid to disposal. Some of the material was sold to the company, some shipped to the Gage Laboratory, some to the Reconstruction Finance Corporation and the remainder to scrap.

There was a marked decline in April 1945 in the volume of excess Raw materials transferred or sold. This was held the result of a decline in terminations; also to the fact that less time now was allowed for disposal. It was expected that with the

advent of VE Day, raw materials would become available in increasing quantities. However, the materialization in May of VE Day, did not set loose the expected flood of terminations. The increasing intensity of the Japanese war was offered as an explanation.

In June 1945 there was added to the Branch set-up a Special Facilities Section which was made the responsible unit for the disposition of material now becoming available at special facilities; among others—Mack Manufacturing Company, Baldwin Locomotive Works, and Autocar Company. The Government-owned Disposal Section thus was relieved of functions in reference to facilities in this category. However plans were made effective whereby the Government-owned Disposal Section would assume responsibility for disposition of production equipment inventory which was in excess as a result of contract termination. Clearance from the Production Equipment Section of P. O. D. still would be necessary to make the equipment available for disposal; and it would be the responsibility of the Production Equipment Section to inform the Property Disposal Branch of needs throughout the District for machines for use by contractors or for Arsenal rehabilitation.

Disposals during the three month period, April-June 1945, at the Redistribution Center were to a dollar total of $1,432,569.00. A comfortable portion of this total included donations to schools engaged in pre-induction training.

Now, up to Schuylkill Haven, and over to Cressona: A procedure was put in motion here in June 1945 by which bids for sales at Cressona Ordnance Plant, of accumulating scrap, would be solicited by Day & Zimmermann, Inc., Philadelphia, operators of the plant. The procedure required CPFF contractors to do all work incident to request for bids for scrap or salvage accumulating at their respective plants. This procedure also applied to the Chester Tank Depot (Ford Motor Company) Chester, and Tacony Packing Plant (Barclay White Company) Philadelphia, as well as to other CPFF contractors.

Regretably, your narrator cannot cover more than a few of the developments, however interesting and however vital to the disposal activity, which featured discussions within the Branch over the spread of its existence as a going concern. We can touch only upon an incident or proceeding here and there and trust to the reader's memory to fill the gaps. Matters of plant clearance, "Blanket Letters of Prior Approval," procedures of Use Analysts, "Shot-Gun" inventories, disposition of terminations inventories, revisions of forms, reporting surplus property to disposal agencies; these and many other matters came to vex and challenge and keep Property Disposal personnel on their respective toes.

As of 1 June 1945 the Property Disposal Branch had on hand for disposal material valued at $1,809,891.00. During the month an additional $3,269,443.00 worth of inventories was received. An additional $53,452.00 worth of material was released from standby and placed in active inventory. Of the grand total $3,457,826.00 worth of material was disposed of during the month leaving a backlog of $1,674,961.00.

By June 1945, Lt. Colonel Kelley had sometime since departed for a turn in Cleveland with RFC, on his way back to the Kelley enterprises. Sidney S. Press had moved to the top of the Property Disposal Branch, with Captain Slack in the capacity of Assistant Chief. Lieutenant Earl H. Lentz, Chief, with Lieutenant Louis Stein, was heading up the Staff Section. The Procedure Unit of the Section was the responsibility of W. Charles Swingley; the Control Unit directed by Lillian Phillips, assisted by Anne F. McAleer; the Reports Unit under Staff Sgt. Harold Winetsky; the Review Unit under Betty Kuhn assisted by Harry D. Given, Staff Sgts. Seymour Jarvis, Walter B. Hunter, Tarumianz and Daly and Mrs. Lois C. Rudy.

The Termination Inventory Section under Captain Phil Fields, assisted by Dorothy M. Burns, boasted a Pre-termination Planning Unit, with Captain Fields, assisted by Lieutenant Gerald F. Welles, WOJG Martin C. Barrell and Marguerite Bond; a Baltimore Unit under Thomas J. Morrison, assisted by Staff Sgt. Charles M. Wentz; a Bethlehem Unit, under H. R. McKnight assisted by William A. Seery, Benjamin S. Thorpe, Master Sgt. J. Wilkinson, Elizabeth M. Brady and Catherine M. Hoge; a Philadelphia Unit with Lieutenant LeRoy M. Bissett as Chief assisted by Nicholas C. Mirras, Walter C. Lytle, Staff Sgt. Guy D. Womack, Mrs. Catherine R. Vogt, Sarah E. Armstrong, and Anne M. McCarey; a Richmond Unit, with Lieutenant Don Kimmell as Chief and Dorothy M. Burns as assistant; and a York Unit under George D. McCool, assisted by Joseph H. Kloke and Madeline T. Derringe.

There was the Special Facility Section with John McDowell; his assistants, Chester E. Sawtelle, Henry L. Stoddart, WOJG Ludwig R. Aberle and Dorothy P. Katz. The Service Section was blessed with a certain Captain Howard S. Gallaher assisted by Rita H. MacDonald. The Scrap Unit of the Section had been assigned to Lieutenant Francis M. Watson assisted by Mr. Charles Schectman, Sgt. Sidney M. Fabian, Francis T. Boyce and Pauline Malin. The Redistribution Unit was headed by John Schwabe, with the assistance of Alvin T. Raynor and Mary C. Kindt; the Surplus Property Unit, by Thomas F. Palmer, assisted by WO Philip W. Silverman, and Jean Ashby; the Gage and Production Equipment Liaison, by Technical Sgt. John S. Shaffner.

The Government Property Section was the responsibility of Lieutenant James H. Neisbitt, assisted by Marguerite L. Bole, Secretary, Lieutenant Robert J. Hinchman, James E. Tucker, Thomas L. Bishop, Staff Sgts. Joseph Christy and Merle E. Kuns, and Mrs. Beatrice Goldman. The Redistribution Center under Lieutenant Eugene Ayres, Assistant Chief Herman Barthel, and James F. Gibson, Anthony Fendo, Anselm K. Fitzgerald, Frank C. McCollian, Staff Sgt. John F. Keefe, Frances Walsh and Jean Niederman.

In July 1945 there was a general transfer to the Branch of the property disposal work and related activities previously listed among the duties of the Commodity and other Branches of the District. Also, transfer was made in July from the Production Equipment Section, Industrial Division, to the Property Disposal Branch, of responsibility of all Part III property and all capital machine tools and equipment for which there was no longer need for war production. Some problems developed as a result of the latter switch, particularly in reference to the fixing of responsibilities between the Sections.

From 117 persons in August 1945, personnel of the Property Disposal Branch climbed to a total in December 1945 of 134 persons.

The end of the Japanese war had brought to the Branch a substantial increase in responsibilities. New Joint Termination Regulations had been issued. Blanket Prior Approval Letters were rescinded. Contractors holding Government-owned Production Equipment were advised in August by letter of the conditions and the terms under which they might purchase such equipment.

Bottlenecks trailed the inability of RFC, due to limited personnel, to keep pace with inspection requirements.

In September 1945 there was initiated a procedure by which disposition of property now would be undertaken by the Terminated War Contractors under the guidance of the Philadelphia Ordnance District and Regional Offices. The Property Disposal Managers of the Termination Inventory Section subsequently were relieved of all active disposal work and now would act as Liaison Managers between the two offices, to the end that Regional Offices would conform to policies of the District Office. It became the duty of Liaison Managers to see that material was turned over to RFC, and to put pressure on the issuance of shipping orders when and as requested by the Regional Office.

The Government-owned Disposal Section of the Branch developed in August 1945 procedures with school districts of Pennsylvania and Virginia for donation and use of excess production equipment. As much as possible of production equipment would be applied to this purpose.

In December 1945 the Section was confronted with the problem of packaging in connection with the donations to Educational Institutions, it having been ruled that the receiving school should pay in advance all packaging charges.

The volume of disposition in August 1945 of production equipment was the largest the Government Property Disposal Section had ever accomplished.

The first action of the large Government-owned facilities which were being declared in their entirety to the RFC was also effected during the period. Conferences were held with RFC, Engineer Corps and leasing contractors, in reference to preparation of equipment, repair of buildings and dates for actual turnover to RFC of the various properties. The installations involved were the Lycoming Division, Aviation Corporation; Koppers Company, Henry Disston & Sons, Inc., and the Danville and Williamsport, Pennsylvania, plants of Rheem Manufacturing Company.

The Government Property Disposal Section was seriously handicapped in November 1945, in effecting disposition of production equipment, due to the inability of the Packaging Section to reach an agreement with various contractors in reference to the packaging for long-term storage of machine tools.

Earlier in the period there had been established in the Property Branch an RFC Unit whose duty it became to conduct liaison with the Reconstruction Finance Corporation, iron out problems, and facilitate declaration to that agency of property to be shipped or otherwise transferred to it. Just about this time, redistribution and sale by the Steel Marketing Service of steel was discontinued. Emphasis on the sale of steel now was being placed with the contractor in possession. In those cases in which the contractor should be unable to make sales, the steel would be turned over to RFC for disposal.

The RFC Unit experienced hard going for a time. The corporation had, it seemed, been taking an excessive amount of time in supplying shipping instructions after a declaration had been submitted. It was taking a lot of time to properly code declared material in accordance with RFC standards. There were difficulties in reference to nomenclature; differences in reaching conclusions and disagreements regarding saleability, to mention a few hurdles, all of which subsequently were adjusted.

The Special Facilities Section was assigned in August 1945, the additional responsibility of disposing of material located at Heintz Manufacturing Company, Barclay White Company and Ford Motor Company, Chester, Pennsylvania. Other facilities handled by the Section were Baldwin Locomotive Works, Mack Manufacturing Company and Autocar Company. VJ Day terminations immediately were initiated at these facilities, with the exception of Ford Motor Company. All property at Ford (Chester Tank Depot) was Government-owned and, inasmuch as this contractor was on a CPFF basis, plans were being laid to make disposals under CPFF termination procedures. Liquidation of all property, and Plant Clearance, at Ford were accomplished in November.

A substantial portion of the October and November disposition was designated as scrap. An increased volume was marked for donations to authorize schools and colleges.

With the separation early in the Fall of 1945, of Sidney Press and his consequent relinquishment of his post as Chief, Property Disposal Branch, Contract Settlement Division, Assistant, Captain Neal W. Slack moved up a notch and carried on from that point, with the assistance of Lieutenant

L. R. Aydelotte. The Records Section now was the responsibility of WO Philip W. Silverman, assisted by Staff Sgt. Seymour Jarvis, and Staff Sgt. Harold Winetsky. On the ladies panel, Ann E. Boyle, Genevieve Janulis, Gloria L. Panzera, Maire F. Redmond, Frances Walsh, Mary M. Wysock and Dorothy A. Medvic. The Staff Section was the charge of Lieutenant Louis Stein, with the assistance of Mrs. Betty Dickerman. The Administration Section carries Cecelia McNarama at the masthead assisted by Inez A. Smith and Mrs. Olive M. Sprows. The R. F. C. Liaison Section, with Lieutenant Alexander Zeeve, and Harry D. Backall, Ralph F. Hartz, Howard F. Stevens, Helen M. Reardon, and Patricia Quigley, Michael T. Sullivan. The Government Property Section, with Lieutenant James H. Nisbett, Chief; Mrs. Regina C. Rose, Captain Albert E. Lee, Jr., and Mrs. Eunice C. Howver, The Control Unit of the Government Property Section was directed by W O John S. Schaffner, with assistants: WO Merle E. Kuns, Staff Sgt. Joseph F. Christy, Regina Ashby, Mary K. Burke, Avis L. Hughes, Mrs. Marie T. Strang and Virginia P. Williams. The Residual Inventory Section under Lieutenant Laur G. Wheaton, with James J. Brady, Rose R. Barsh, Beatrice Goldman and Mary T. Watson; the Sales Unit under Thomas S. Potts with Norman H. Banning, Anna M. Moran, and Mrs. Caroline L. Trauger; the Scrap Unit with Lieutenant Francis M. Watson, and Sgt. Sidney M. Fabian, John S. Merrill, John Schwabe, Helen R. Begley, Elizabeth S. Bewley, Helen Bugera, Doris Hopfenthaler, Mrs. Marcella L. Mackiewicz, Pauline Malin and Ruth Wilson. The Baltimore-Richmond Unit under Frances J. Stress with Howard H. Stock, Ralph T. Stone, Bernice L. Abramson, Elsie Dinardo and Mrs. Mary R. Dorazio; Bethlehem Unit with Lieutenant James J. Law, Jr., and Harold L. Fritz, Mrs. Margaret C. Held, Mrs. Margaret M. Rhodes and Beatrice H. Young; the Philadelphia Unit with Lieutenant Gerald F. Welles in charge assisted by Lieutenant Robert J. Hinchman, Lieutenant Jerome W. Kaufman, Ernest L. Biddle, Anthony C. Calabresse, Dudley Cozad, George Kazansky, Alice L. Baker, Jeannette M. Bennett, Elizabeth A. Conroy, Katherine R. Macrillo and the York Unit with Chester Loveland as Chief, Marguerite Bond as Assistant.

Under the Special Facilities, John McDowell, Chief, and Dorothy P. Katz as Assistant, there was a group of Liaison Managers headed by Bill Bunker assisted by Ferd C. Graham, Norman E. Hildreth, Chester E. Sawtelle, Henry L. Stoddart, Gertrude M. Durkin and Mary R. Feckno; and an Accounting Unit, WO Ludwig R. Aberle, Technical Sgt. Cecil Annette, Leola D. Bryant and Betty Kuhn.

At the Redistribution Center, Lieutenant Earl H. Lentz, Chief, and Marie A. Walsh, Secretary. The Disposal Unit in charge of Mr. Herman Barthel assisted by WO John F. Keefe, James F. Gibson, Anna M. Cunningham and Jean Neiderman. The Roll Shop with Anselm K. Fitzgerald in charge, assisted by Frank C. McCollian.

The Termination Inventory Section is the responsibility of Captain Philip J. Fields assisted by Lieutenant LeRoy M. Bissett and Marguerite L. Bole. The Administration Unit of the Section is the charge of Jacob L. Gordon assisted by Marie C. Cesaro, Madeline T. Derringe and Patricia H. Smith. The Recap Unit is assigned WO Amos W. Brewer assisted by Staff Sgt. George C. Wilt, Harry D. Given, Samuel Sondberg, Anna M. Contino, Anna D. Kennelly and Ruth L. Purnell. The R and A Control Unit with Staff Sgt. Charles M. Wentz, supported by Master Sgt. Theodore J. Wilkinson, Dorothy M. Burns, Mary J. Emma, Mrs. Catherine M. Hoge, Anne M. Lachall, Mrs. Ruth E. Lefler and Rita V. Tatu. Liaison Managers for the Section are as follows, Baltimore Unit, Thomas J. Morrison; Bethlehem Unit, Howard R. McKnight; Philadelphia Unit, Nicholas C. Mirras, Wm. J. O'Brien and Sarah E. Armstrong; Richmond Unit, John McLean; and the York Unit, George D. MacCool.

Into January 1946 more and more changes, faster then your historian can keep up with them. Officers and civilians departing. Familiar names now appearing unfamiliarly in new posts. One instance: Captain Neal W. Slack tells Ordnance and Property Disposal Branch "farewell," all in one breath in February 1946; Lieutenant Aydelotte steps into the breach. Came June 1946 and Paul Williams takes over the entire Contract-Terminations Division including the Property Disposal Branch, (following a brief tenure by Sid Press) and in practically no time at all the complete operation was down to a personnel total of two persons—Paul Williams and his secretary.

Before the final curtain there were such matters

to attend as the closing of the Regional Office disposal files; winding up C. P. F. F. remainders; clearing up problems in reference to terminations in the final stages; plant clearances obtaining Formal Scrap Certificates; errors of contractors in computing claims and other odds and ends—by way of mopping up. And as of June 1946 came to an end it was reported that during the month the Property Disposal Branch had disposed of material valued at $251,358.00 leaving a backlog of $914,-670.00. Also during June, property to the value of $600,936.00 was declared to other disposal agencies.

Top row: Major Eugene H. Uhler, Captain Joseph I. Wexlin, Captain Robert H. Andrews, Lt. Wm. F. Rathgeber.
Bottom: Lt. Marvin C. Jilbert, Captain Victor W. Smith, Charles O. Guernsey, Major H. K. Kelley.
(Rank indicated is at time of picture.)

Chapter XLVI

TELLING THE WORLD

A CONSIDERABLE literature bearing upon Public Relations had been developed over the years by the War Department. During the war the P. R. bulletins, instructions and manuals issuing from Pentagonia compared favorably in volume with the gross tonnage of "paper" coming out of other departments. Much of this had a vital part in final victory for it was by means of the flood of press releases that the public was kept reliably informed and inspired to the all-out effort which finally spelled victory.

Wartime Public Relations in P. O. D. dates from sometime in 1940—shortly on the heels of the arrival in the District of Lieutenant Charles R. Madary, the first P. R. Officer. However, it was not until March 1941 that the name of this Officer appeared in the reporting of an event of P. R. importance. This was in connection with a broadcast, 15 March 1941, over the 83 stations of the Red Network, National Broadcasting Company, from American Car & Foundry Company, Berwick, Pennsylvania, of a National Defense Program, a dramatization of tank production. Lieutenant Madary is listed among those attending from Washington and P. O. D.

A month later Lieutenant Madary was recounting to Lt. Colonel, then Captain Fred E. Smith, Administrative Officer, a busy hour or two of his reception of the Irish Free State Minister, Frank Aiken, who flew up from Washington was properly met, hustled out to Frankford Arsenal, shown the works, amply fed, and catapulted back to the airport for the 3:45 P. M. plane. The Lieutenant's narrative also included a visit to ACF with movie-reel cameramen; a visit with "high brass" to the Danville, Pennsylvania, plant of the Kennedy-Van Saun Manufacturing and Engineering Company to view the production line of the 81 mm. Trench Mortar; such another to the Harrisburg Steel Corporation to take a peek at the company's manufacture of 100 pound and 500 pound Demolition Bombs—a visit followed by pleasant even-

tualities at the Hotel Hershey, Hershey, Pennsylvania; a tour of the Empire Ordnance Corporation plant where a British contract was in process; a visit to Baldwin's; another to Read Machinery Company, at York; one to Merchant and Evans, at Lancaster.

Then there was the presentation, 24 April, by Baldwins to the Ordnance Department, of the first M3 Medium Tank, to which numerous references have been made throughout this narrative. There was held on the "great day" a fitting field demonstration planned and directed by Lt. Colonel Arthur J. Seiler. The tank crew was commanded by Captain McClelland of Aberdeen; the "gunnery crew" by Captain Wetherill. Attending the ceremonies were the Hon. Robert P. Patterson, then Under Secretary of War, Brigadier General Burton O. Lewis, Colonel W. W. Warner, Colonel, then Major, Emerson L. Cummings, Colonel, then Lieutenant, David R. Stinson, Colonel Robert A. Ginsburgh, C. Jared Ingersoll, P. O. D. Chief and more than 200 industrialists of the District area.

A few weeks before, Lieutenant Madary had written of a visit by Brigadier General Russell E. Maxwell, Administrator of Export Control, and one time P. O. D. Executive Officer.

More in May, including a junket down to Koppers Company, to celebrate the initial delivery of the 37 mm. A.A. Gun Carriage, with Generals, Governors, Mayors, P. O. D. topsiders and company big-wigs. Speeches galore and entertainment by District Chief, C. Jared Ingersoll. On the 16th there was the Philadelphia Post, Army Ordnance Association meeting and banquet, broadcast by Radio Station WPEN. Major W. S. Broberg directed the affair with assistance by Pat Rayport and Dorothy Carroll with Lieutenant Madary pulling the publicity strings.

This was a busy month with the Lieutenant addressing a convention of Building and Loan Associations in Baltimore, Major Hauseman addressing a meeting in Quakertown of the Lehigh-

Bethlehem Post of A. O. A.; a day at Henry Disston & Sons, in dedication of a new power house, and a trip to York to arrange the script for a National Association of Manufacturers "Defense for America" broadcast. Colonel Hauseman, S. Forry Laucks, President, York Safe & Lock Company, the late Graham MacNamee and Major, then Lieutenant, Howard P. Klair had parts in the testing range phase of the broadcast.

And of course there were many speeches to be ghost-written, all of which kept Lieutenant Madary on his P. R. toes. And all of which is indicative of the furious activity then under way, and which would continue with growing intensity with the progress of the war. Lieutenant Madary and his successors were given no opportunity to let down. There were battles of public opinion to be won, labor to be inspired, workers recruited, transportation problems to be met, "share-the-ride" campaigns, conservation of fuel, bonds to be sold, blood plasma to be procured. The pen and the sword had a team job to do from 1941 into 1945.

The P. O. D. United Service Organization drive came along in June 1941 to engage Lieutenant Madary's abilities. On 2 July, down to Baldwin's with Life Magazine photographers to do a pictorial tank-line series; a 104th Mechanized Cavalry parade from Indiantown Gap under command of Colonel A. H. Stackpole; Ordnance displays set up in Gimbel Brothers windows; celebration at American Car & Foundry Company of the 1000th Tank produced by that facility—and more speeches, more "Defense for America" scripts reviewed and more and more press releases.

And early in August a sham battle commemorating the 1000th ACF Tank broadcast over NBC. Christening was by Mrs. Charles J. Hardy, the wife of ACF President; Movietone, Metro-Goldwyn-Mayer and other newsreel services were well represented. Twenty-two bands took part, and the attendant parade through Berwick lasted two and one-half hours. It was the town's big day.

The newspapers of the area now were beginning to "front page" Ordnance activities and accomplishments in a big way. Radio long since had joined the drive. Graham MacNamee, Fulton Lewis, William L. Shirer, Lowell Thomas and others.

Exhibits were cropping out, just about all over the United Gas Improvement Company Building, The York Fair Defense Exhibit, another P. O. D. display at the convention of the American Society

of Metals at the Benjamin Franklin Hotel, one in the lobby of the Corn Exchange National Bank and Trust Company for the Bok Vocational School and another in the Broad Street Suburban Station Building.

Midway of November came the appointment of Captain, then Lieutenant, David H. McIlvane as Public Relations Officer succeeding Lieutenant Charles R. Madary, transferred.

December rolls in, a month of great publicity events, including the reception at Baldwin's of Lord Halifax who came accompanied by Colonel Angus MacDonnell and Mr. Charles Peake. Lt. Colonel Hauseman, and C. Jared Ingersoll represented our side, with the assistance of the then Baldwin President, Charles E. Brinley. Following a track test demonstration, Lord Halifax mounted an M3 and was given a ride around the field. News pictures of his "Ludship" atop the monster were flashed from papers across the world. Also at Baldwin's and also in December the first Heavy Tank T1-E1 was formally presented to the Ordnance Department. Baldwin vice president, William H. Harmon made the presentation. Major General Gladeon M. Barnes delivered the speech of acceptance. Following a sham battle involving three Light Tanks and 2 Medium Tanks, with land mines, boom boom and everything—all broadcast over a Coast-to-Coast hook-up by the Mutual Broadcasting Company. Attending were Lieutenant Colonel D. N. Hauseman, C. Jared Ingersoll, Brigadier General, then Colonel, J. K. Christmas, Lt. Colonel, Felix J. Atwood, Brigadier General James Kirk, Brigadier General William A. Borden, Colonel Grant A. Schleiker, Colonel Emerson L. Cummings and other important topside.

Earlier in the month Radio Corporation of America, Camden, New Jersey, staged an elaborate ceremony; named it, "Beat the Promise Pledge" to celebrate the delivery to the Signal Corps of the 8,500th Tank Radio. P. O. D. Lieutenant Madary obtained the services of Brigadier General Burton O. Lewis to substitute for the high ranking Signal Corps Officer who could not be present. P. O. D. also had an M3 Medium Tank driven up from Baldwin's for the affair. The "doings" extended into the evening with Anti-Aircraft Searchlight demonstrations, a battalion of troops from Fort duPont, Delaware, on parade. During the demonstration, carrier pigeons of the Army Signal Corps were released, carrying messages to Lt. General Hugh A. Drum, Commander of the First Corps

Army on maneuvers in South Carolina. The messages were to tell the General that RCA had "Beat the Promise."

Down in Elkton, Maryland, a Christmas Banquet for the employees of the National Fireworks Company was occasion for the announcement of production by the company, of the 3,000,000th RYG Fuze. Colonel Hauseman, Captain A. W. Hamilton and Lieutenant Madary smiled pretty for P. O. D., and the latter giving forth an even more beaming smile over his successful direction of the Red Cross drive in the District.

Final reports were in on the Defense Stamp sales in November by 500 newspaper boys of the Philadelphia Evening Bulletin. High scorers had received medals presented by Lieutenant Colonel Hauseman.

The new Public Relations Officer ran into a busy January. The year 1942 started off with a bang. The final moments of the old year found Captain Dave McIlvane in Wilkes-Barre, Pennsylvania. The occasion, a luncheon marking completion of the 1000th 77 mm. Gun Mount for the M3 Medium Tank. The day following, 30 December, tank drives were provided for the newsboys who had made the largest sales in November of Defense Stamps. The drive had netted $13,400.00.

The Civilian Personnel Branch was "aided and abetted" in its Scranton, Pennsylvania campaign, to round up good inspection talent.

Captain, then Lieutenant, John F. Carson, Civilian Personnel Branch head, directed the "on the spot" operations. The Public Relations Branch previously, and during the hunt, saturated the area up there with press releases. Results, 350 applicants interviewed during one day, ninety hired. Similar jaunts subsequently were staged in Hazelton, Pennsylvania, Richmond, Virginia, and Wilkes-Barre, Pennsylvania. Captain McIlvane gave a talk before a meeting of the Eastern Pennsylvania Industrial Advertisers' Association on the importance of obtaining clearances on advertising copy concerning Ordnance contracts and related matters.

On 25 January, Captain McIlvane personally conducts through P. O. D. offices, Alfred Friendly of the Washington Post, Mark Watson of the Baltimore Sun and Edwin A. Lahey of the Chicago Daily News, here to obtain much detail regarding District activities and the conversion to war work of industry hereabouts. Early in February a somewhat similarly purposed visit by Charles Hurd of

the New York Times, Jerome Green of Time Magazine and Charles Purcell of Columbia Broadcasting Company. The latter used much of the collected material in connection with a broadcast interview of Donald Nelson, War Production Board head.

The District was honored in February with a visit by Lt. General William S. Knudsen and his Executive Officer, Colonel A. B. Quinton, The General addressed P. O. D. Officers; pointed out Philadelphia's manufacturing possibilities; stressed all-out production.

Also, in February 1942, arrangements were made through P. O. D.'s Public Relations Office for representatives of Fortune Magazine to gather war story data at York Safe & Lock Company.

Rallies at War Plants dot the March sky in P. O. D. One, 25 March 1942, at the Philco Corporation plant. Employees to the number of 4,800 attended. Much military topside in evidence. Principal speakers were Colonel Robert A. Ginsburgh, aid to the Secretary of War, Philco president Buckley, Brigadier General, then Colonel Archie A. Farmer, Commanding Officer, Philadelphia Signal Depot, Colonel Hauseman and James Carey. National Secretary for CIO. In the afternoon, a similar rally at Bendix Aviation Corporation with 3,000 workers attending.

And on 26 February, Lord Halifax was back for a visit to the Empire Ordnance Corporation, with Lieutenant Colonel Hauseman doing the honors.

The plant rallies increased in frequency during the months following. There were rallies at the plant of Triumph Explosives, Inc., Chestertown, Maryland; American Car & Foundry Company, Harrisburg Steel Corporation, York Ice Machinery Corporation, Armstrong Cork Company, E. G. Budd Manufacturing Company, J. G. Brill Company, Doehler Die Casting Company, Henry Disston & Sons, York Safe & Lock Company and many, many more over the course of the Ordnance program.

More and more representatives of the press make P. O. D. headquarters for Ordnance Data. Hugh O'Connor, New York Times; Tom Henry, Washington Star; Clark Beach, feature writer of the Associated Press; Cy Peterman, Philadelphia Inquirer and Frank Chase, Saturday Evening Post.

During April, the Public Relations Branch took over responsibility for one phase of the Army Day Parade, obtaining one Medium Tank, two Light Tanks and two Gun Motor Carriages. The Branch also assisted to obtain for the parade, from the

Ordnance Training School, at Aberdeen, 1,000 picked troops. In June 1942, Captain McIlvaine assisted Colonel A. D. Elliott, Ordnance Officer for the Army War Show, in obtaining the use of six new Light Tanks. Among other items obtained was a rejected 75 mm. Gun and Recoil Mechanism on the Medium Tank at the Show. Two windows of the Wanamaker Men's Store were obtained for Army War Show publicity. And for the Army Day Parade at Chester, other Light Tanks were provided by P. O. D.

On 18 May 1942, there was held in the Ballroom of the Benjamin Franklin Hotel, a P. O. D. luncheon commemorating the 20th Anniversary of the Ordnance District Procurement System. The luncheon was attended by 725 Officers and civilians of the District Office. O. Howard Wolfe, Chief of the Administration Branch served as Toastmaster. Lt. General Brehon Somervell, Major General Charles M. Wesson and Lt. Colonel David N. Hauseman were the speakers. Eleven similar luncheons were simultaneously being given across the country.

Baldwin Locomotive Works welcomed in May, 20 newspaper writers from as many sections of the U. S., come to gather material for a tank story. The newspapers, among them some of the country's largest in point of circulation, later printed an impressive story, with pictures of operation in the plant, and emphasized P. O. D.'s relationship with the Tank Program.

A few days before his visit with the newspaper men to Baldwin's, Captain McIlvaine had given a hand to Radio Station WCAU personnel in preparation of two, one-half hour installments of that Station's "Industry Goes to War," series of broadcasts. On the 14 May broadcast the Station announced its Merit Award to the Animal Trap Company of America, Ltd. The second broadcast featured the work of the Model Tool and Die Company. Also during this period, a series of Ordnance broadcasts over Station WDAS, was moving along through the arrangement stage. Warren Webster Company featured the third presentation. Another featured Ocean City Manufacturing Company—and there were more to come.

Other May 1942 items of interest concerned a talk before a banqueting group of the Easton-Phillipsburg Chamber of Commerce by Captain McIlvaine. His subject, "The Ordnance Program." An interesting Ordnance display of the month was that at the Philadelphia Zoo, in connection with

that institution's annual May Day celebration. Colonel Hauseman attended and greeted the more than 35,000 persons viewing the exhibits. Lowell Thomas acted as Master of Ceremonies.

The scrap drive in the District which had been gathering momentum with the increasing material shortages was high-spotted in the Sunday, 14 June 1942 rotogravure section of the Philadelphia Inquirer, featuring the presentation to the District by the American Legion of old World War I guns and the subsequent reduction to scrap of these items.

A War Heroes Parade was held in Philadelphia on 9 June. This was in conjunction with the Treasury Department. The Public Relations officer obtained for this parade, which was conducted as a War Bond sales stimulant, two Tanks and a Half-Track Gun Carrier. A few days later, the P. R. shop was busy assisting press photographers and newsmen in obtaining clearances for pictures and stories of the visit to Baldwin's of Colonel R. M. Mayhew, British Ordnance Officer for Libya.

More displays. As "Snozzle" Durante would have said, "Everybody wants to get into the act." A window display was provided in June for the Benjamin Franklin Savings & Loan Association, and another for Snellenberg's Philadelphia department store.

The Public Relations Officer, very much concerned with War Bond sales in P. O. D., reported in June, that to date 2,366 Officers and civilians of the Districts combined total of 3,479 personnel, of 68 per cent, had subscribed a total of $361,760.00 (maturity value).

The press was continuing to do right well by P. O. D. During July newspapers over the District published releases on, among others, Gages; Scrap Metal Collection; Dollar volume of June production; Pictures and Stories concerning the Baldwin tank lines; Strikes in P. O. D. areas; the Recruiting Drive—and a surprise story covering the gifts by the Pennsylvania Joint Board, Amalgamated Clothing Workers of America, of a check for $50,-000 for purchase of a Tank and other equipment. The presentation ceremony was held in Hazelton. Major Brendan D. Walsh delivered the acceptance address.

In July, Captain McIlvaine got out into the territory to assist the newspapers of the Baltimore and Richmond areas in organizing publicity releases in connection with the scrap drive and other

Ordnance objectives. A scrap drive in Maryland to collect old guns and relics was bearing fruit. A deposit pile in front of the War Memorial Building in Baltimore, initiated with the blessing of the War Production Board, was fast becoming a menace to the Axis.

It now is August of 1942 and the Army-Navy "E" Awards are on the march in the District. The first ceremony was held 14 August at the Philadelphia plant of the Philco Corporation, and was in recognition of that contractor's record on production of Fuzes, P. D. M48 and M51.

The "E" Awards were made on the basis of the recipient's ability to meet schedules on both a quality and quantity basis; and with searching consideration for such other critical factors as ability to meet and overcome production obstacles; prevention of work stoppages by control of raw materials and ability to meet new equipment requirements, and, successful negotiations with pertaining labor groups. Matters of employees training were considered, as were management policies, particularly as regarding overall in keeping abreast with requirements.

Just two weeks to the day following the Philco Award, fortune smiled upon the Autocar Company. Again, 5,000 enthusiastic workers, many carrying small flags, came to cheer. In this instance the "E" Award flag was presented by Major General Charles T. Harris, Jr., then Commanding Officer, Aberdeen Proving Ground. The "E" pins for the employees were given out by Colonel Hauseman. Again, the press responded, and the National Broadcasting Company sent the story out over the Nation. A few days later, the Harrisburg Steel Corporation received its award; Lieutenant Colonel Hauseman speaking for the Army; Lieutenant Harold Hentz for the Navy.

Before the war should come to an end, many "E" Awards would come to contractors in the Philadelphia Ordnance District area.

"Star Awards," came later. These, added to the flags, would indicate contractor's ability to keep in stride, and for added accomplishments.

A double-header baseball game, Sunday, 23 August, at the Philadelphia American League Baseball Park, in which the Philadelphia Athletics were a participant, was for the benefit of Army and Navy Relief. Attendance was in excess of 28,000. Between games, a troop of mechanized cavalry of the 104th Cavalry Regiment gave a demonstration.

Captain McIlvaine had much to do with the arrangements.

It also was in August that Lt. General William S. Knudsen gave the District a six-day going over, calling at 40 plants in the area, studying, inspecting, passing out "gems" of the Knudsenian wisdom. Captain McIlvaine planned the General's travel, made all arrangements with contractors for the visits, and all contacts with the "press."

Before the year ended there would be more displays; one in a window of the Wanamaker Store, another at the Girard Trust Company, and one during Philadelphia Bock Fair Week, at the Bellevue Stratford; there would be an Ordnance contingent with two Tanks, a Gun Carrier and a Half-Track Personnel Carrier in the Army Unit of the Navy Day Parade, and similar equipment provided for the Armistice Day, Army Recruiting Campaign; Lt. Colonel, then Major, Robert G. Allen, Executive Officer would speak at an H. W. Butterworth Company, Service Flag raising, and Army and Navy "E" Awards would fall to the lot of: Ford Motor Company (Chester Tank Depot), General Steel Castings Corporation, E. I. duPont De Nemours Company (Neoprene Division), York Safe & Lock Company (Navy), Solvay Process Company, Hopewell, Virginia, Martin & Schwartz, Ind., Mack Manufacturing Company, Armstrong Cork Company, Henry Disston Sons, Inc., United Specialties Company, Peco Manufacturing Company and E. I. duPont DeNemours Company, Inc. (Repauno)—all of which meant speeches to be written, to be rehearsed, and ceremonies to be arranged, speakers provided, as the "E" Award routine practically was a business in itself, if all of the preliminaries are considered—the surveys of contractors before the final approval.

It was not possible during these mad days to pick up a newspaper almost anywhere in the P. O. D. area and not have your eye fall upon a brazen headline of some District activity and accomplishment. There were stories for instance, of the organization of Industry Integration Committees; stories of materials, conversions, of "Tremendous Trifles" which were just that; of the Citations presented to Lehigh Foundries' president Frank Shuman, and Philco Company engineer-mastermind Charles H. Godschall; a field day at the Chester Tank Depot: Colonel Hauseman's reception tendered the city editors, the managing editors and chiefs of the news wire services; the .30 Cal. Carbine and the Bazooka; female employees replacing men inducted into the services; promotion of P. O. D. officers; the visit of Major General Williams of British Ordnance; Lt. General, then Major General Levin H. Campbell, Jr., Chief of Ordnance, addressing a meeting of the Safety Council of America—to mention a few such stories, and to say nothing of editorials and picture features appearing almost daily, together with "over-the-air" stories of radio commentators of the area.

In March 1943, Captain David H. McIlvaine packed his duffle up to the Fiscal Branch leaving in his wake a record for high accomplishment in never for a moment permitting his public an opportunity for overlooking P. O. D. and the job it had to do. Vrest Orton, Vermonter, who had been giving the historian a hand, was named to head the Public Relations Branch, under the appraising eye of Lewis H. Van Dusen, Jr., later heading the Censorship Branch of which P. R. was a unit.

Vrest Orton, "could write good," as Corey Ford, noted author, might have said in sizing up this speed demon from the North.

It was at this time that the Public Relations Section was assigned the additional responsibility for surveying plants and preparing data essential to the Army-Navy "E" Award recommendations. The first group of Awards made "under the new management" of P. R. were those to Metlab Company, at which Major Victor W. Smith, Chief, Philadelphia Regional Office, was the principal speaker; the Hendrick Manufacturing Company, where Lt. Colonel, then Major, Albert W. Gilmer, then of the Legal Branch, occupied the "podium," as one reporter put it; and the National Fireworks Company, Colonel, then Major, A. Donald Kelso, slammed down the gavel. Rallies during that first month under the sign of Orton included E. F. Houghton Company, Crown Can Company, Atlantic Elevator Company, F. C. Castelli Company, and the Abrasive Company.

Attention was given in April to discussion concerning a central Public Relations Office to clear stories out of the various services. A meeting in P. O. D. headquarters was attended by Colonel William Wharton of the Third Service Command and Lt. Colonel William Slater, Bureau of Public Relations, Washington. P. O. D. objection was overruled.

Decentralization of Public Relations activities got under way in June 1943. The Public Relations Officer began his swing around the Regional Office circuit, appointing Public Relations representatives in the various offices and holding conferences with local newspaper publishers and editors.

June 1943 also saw the first shaping up of plans for the "Ordnance for Victory" Show to be opened during July following. Major Lorin E. Warlow, who arrived in P. O. D., 10 May 1943, was assigned as Officer-in-Charge. The Show, on the 8th Floor of the Wanamaker Store opened its doors to the public on 24 July. Attendance on the opening day was 17,250 persons.

More help came in preparation of "E" Award data, with the appointment of Andrea Farnese and Mrs. Louise Soliday, formerly of the Civilian Personnel Branch.

Appointments were made during July of Public Relations representatvies in the Regional Offices, as follows:

Ben L. Grier, Baltimore
Jack Dalton, Berwick
F. L. Shankweiler, Bethlehem
Christine R. Borland, Reading
Captain, then Lieutenant, William B. Wellborn, Richmond
Captain, then Lieutenant, John P. Grimwade, York

In September 1943, a Central Public Relations Office through which press matters of the various services were cleared, was set up in Third Service Command, with Major Carter Glass, Jr., son of the late Senator, in charge. Later, this assignment would go to Major Thomas Richter and, in turn, to Lieutenant John Dougherty and WAC Lieutenant Hattilu C. White.

First repercussions from the "Ordnance for Victory" show were numerous requests from stores, banks and other sources for material for use in local Ordnance exhibits. These had to be denied, in view of critical material needs at this time.

The late Patricia Rayport, long of Ordnance Public Relations, and of Welfare, was lost by transfer in October. Fay Hirst resigned and Olga Legnini was assigned. In November, Dorothy Whitaker, secretary to the Public Relations Officer was assigned to the Gage Section.

By January 1944, Public Relations were well integrated. The "E" Awards represented the number one function of the Branch. The newspaper groups now knew where and how to gather Ordnance stories of general public interest. Such outstanding writers as Murray Cassidy and John La Cerda of the Philadelphia *Evening Bulletin* were getting out into the plants, and, under the guidance of the Censorship Branch, doing an excellent job in romanticizing the war production effort.

Late during the winter, Vrest Orton was reassigned to the Readjustment Division, O.C.O. under his former superior officer, Lt. Colonel D. N. Hauseman. Andrea Farnese stepped into the gap, carrying on until amost the end of the year

and the appointment of Lieutenant Albert T. Collins. In April 1945, Captain David H. McIlvaine who had meanwhile been transferred from the Fiscal Branch to Third Service Command, was reassigned as Public Relations Officer, P. O. D., a post which he held to his separation, 1 December 1945, at Indiantown Gap. Lieutenant Collins remained until August 1945, as Assistant. As of 1 January 1946, the Public Relations work became the added duty of the historian.

Top row, L to R: Lt. William J. Feigley, Lt. Wm. J. Bright, Lt. Oren J. Persons, Jr., Lt. Augustine Edwards.
Second row: Captain Cecil Bentley, Captain Roland C. Disney, Captain David B. Robb, Lt. R. Paul Fugate.
(Rank indicated is at time of picture.)

Chapter XLVII

ORDNANCE FOR VICTORY

HAD you been in the region of 13th and Market Streets in Philadelphia, at 2 P. M., 23 July 1943, you might have been puzzled by the huge crowd "packing" into Wanamaker's, one of America's great retail establishments. And had Army regulations and the canons of good taste permitted, you might have heard something like this:

"This way, Ladies and Gentlemen, this way to the Big Show! The greatest show on Earth. Nothing like it ever before seen in the United States! Come one! Come all! The Admission? It's not a dollar, Ladies and Gentlemen. Not fifty cents. It's free! Folks, it's free!

"Come on! See what Industry in the Philadelphia Ordnance District area is making to rock Mussolini, Hitler and Hirohito back on their heels! See the great guns and tanks and small arms and other fighting tools Uncle Sam is giving your boy overseas. The best in the world—the best boys, the best fighting equipment! Don't miss it! It's free!"

Well, that was the "Ordnance for Victory" Show, held from 23 July to 18 September 1943, and it was estimated that during that period more than 1,000,000 persons came to stare in open-eyed wonder, and to leave, more confident than ever that, with the amazing accomplishments of Industry hereabouts, America could not fail.

It was late in May 1943, that Brigadier General, then Colonel D. N. Hauseman, District Chief, conceived the idea of an Ordnance exhibit whose objectives should be:

1. To reveal to the great body of the public what the Ordnance-Industry Team had done, was doing, and to give a hint of what would be done to win the war.

2. To show the Mothers and Fathers, Wives and loved ones of the boys in the war services, the quality of Ordnance their boys were using.

3. To show Mr. and Mrs. Public just how its War Bond and War Stamp dollars were being used.

Satisfied that this was the thing to do, Colonel Hauseman sought from Colonel L. A. Codd, Executive Assistant, Public Relations and Information Section of the Office of the Chief of Ordnance, the authority necessary to initiate such an enterprise. There followed a trip to Pentagon by C. Jared Ingersoll, P. O. D. Deputy Chief, and Major Lorin E. Warlow who had been selected to help in the enterprise, if and when.

Authority promptly was forthcoming, and to get the ball rolling, without further delay, which was the manner of all P. O. D. undertakings, a meeting was called for the purpose of "talking turkey." In attendance were Colonel Hauseman; Wanamaker president, Charles R. Shipley; Wanamaker Estate attorney, Maurice Saul, C. Jared Ingersoll, Major Warlow, Captain John Stevens of the P. O. D. Legal Branch. The fruit of the meeting was a tentative agreement.

Mind the dates. They will provide an example of Ordnance speed—and efficiency. On 7 June 1943, a second meeting was held. This time the subject was "principles of operation." In attendance were Charles R. Shipley, Thomas L. Prendergast, Wanamaker Treasurer; Karl Knipe, Advertising Manager; Donald R. Funk, Store engineer; Major Warlow, and Vrest Orton of the P. O. D. Public Relations Branch.

On 10 June, Major Warlow visited the New York Ordnance District Office and the Ordnance exhibit then being held in the Chrysler Building. There he obtained information and data which later proved helpful.

On 14 June, Hugh L. Adams, president of one of the largest Ford agencies in Philadelphia, and a well known industrialist, was invited to Colonel Hauseman's office to discuss the P. O. D. exhibit where he was asked by the District Chief to head up the show. As a result of this meeting, it was decided that the exhibit should be primarily an Ordnance exhibit (no side lines), and the contract was so drawn. It was also decided that all exhibits offered should be held subject to the approval of a special committee. This was done in an endeavor to prevent either undesirable exhibits or duplication of exhibits.

A tentative opening date of 15 July was set. On 15 June, Colonel Hauseman wrote to 85 contractors in the P. O. D. area, inviting participation in the show. On the day following a P. O. D. Show Office was established on the eighth floor of the Wanamaker Store. The entire eighth floor was taken over—an area of 83,000 square feet.

Telephone cost was equally divided between Wanamaker's and the Philadelphia Ordnance District. Power installations were provided by the Store. Special elevator service to the floor also was provided.

Letters were mailed on recommendation of the Commodity Branches and Officers-in-Charge of Regional Offices to additional lists of contractors.

Thomas S. Potts, P. O. D. engineering genius, was assigned as of 25 June, in charge of scheduling the movements of incoming materiel, to check floor loads and rigging, and work with Wanamaker engineers and those of the exhibiting contractors.

Captain, then Lieutenant, Phil J. Fields of the District Communications (Mail and Records) Branch was assigned to assist Major Warlow in interviewing contractors.

It now had been discovered that a considerable amount of Government Issue materiel would be required to complete the exhibits. On 3 July, Captain Lewis A. Smith, Jr., recently of the Tank-Automotive Branch, and formerly of the Priorities Branch, joined the P. O. D. group at Wanamaker's. With him went Lieutenant Oren H. Persons who had been in Priorities prior to his assignment to the Baltimore Regional Office. The job of these two officers was in reference to the expediting of G. I. Materiel. Just previous to his show appointment Captain Smith had accompanied Colonel Hauseman to Washington where arrangements were made to have the needed G. I. materiel cleared. Shipping orders had of necessity to be issued and forwarded to Arsenals and Depots scattered across the country. Upon its arrival in Philadelphia, completed units of materiel were disassembled, cleaned, then reassembled on the floor and put in proper locations. Captain Joseph Tampico and Lieutenant John Procopi of the 15th Ordnance Company furnished invaluable assistance in this work.

Opening of the Ordnance Show originally was scheduled for 15 July 1943, but due to the fact that some of the displays would be delayed, the opening date was set ahead—to 2:00 P. M., 23 July—and P. O. D. kept the date.

Henry P. Patchett of the Philadelphia Regional Office was assigned to contact city officials regarding the movement in and out of Philadelphia of heavy Ordnance equipment; obtain permits for pertaining parades; provide police and military escorts for visiting big-wigs; arrange with exhibiting contractors for the showing of tanks, jeeps, desert trucks, etc., to their employes as morale builders. H. P. also was assigned charge of Safety and accident precautions and plant protection for the show; issued all passes for show personnel, and for equipment removed from the floor.

A suitable name for the show was the next item on the agenda. A luncheon, with food calculated to induce thought, was staged, 6 July, in the office of the Wanamaker president, Charles R. Shipley. In attendance were C. Jared Ingersoll, Colonel Hauseman, Colonel Leo A. Codd, up from D. C., Major Warlow, Warrant Officer Eisner, of O. C. O., Hugh L. Adams, Thomas L. Prendergast and Philadelphia newshawks. Many names were proposed; one was chosen—the contribution of Colonel Codd: "Ordnance for Victory" Show.

Subsequent to the luncheon, Richard Potter of Conversion Engineering was elected to "spot" on the huge draft of the Show floor plan, the names and locations of exhibitors.

Now, on 6 July, with the problem of a name out of the way, the basic plans well integrated, and all space spoken for, there was only one piece of exhibitor's material on the floor—a Mobile Shop from the Thornton-Fuller Company; and the process of getting this item into the Wanamaker Store was worth a picture feature in *Life* Magazine. The Store freight elevator, the largest in the store, and one of the largest in the city "could not take it." The truck had therefore to be completely disassembled, carried piecemeal to the 8th floor of the store and there put together again; a procedure later followed with the installations of tanks and other large exhibits. The Ford Motor Company furnished a crew of riggers under the direction of George Likona, all of the Chester Tank Depot, to handle these assignments.

The Wanamaker Store employed publicity-minded John Gerahty and his secretary to open the publicity campaign, which later had the added support of Major, then Captain, Morden R. Buck who, from 1933, following his "release" from Duke

University, and to 1941 had been a radio program director. Major Buck came to P. O. D. in time to do an excellent job throughout the show. At the close of the shindig in September 1943, he was assigned to duty with the Army Public Relations Section, Third Service Command.

The telephone problem was quickly dispatched. Public booths were installed as an aide to the men in charge of the various exhibits. As a further assistance, P. O. D. contributed two messengers for the purpose of "Calling Philip Morris" or any other of the wanted gentry. Too, a reception room was established to serve as a meeting place for contractors, carpenters, electricians and others with materials or services to offer.

Decorations? The Decorating Department of Wanamaker's under the direction of Herbert Faber made display signs used in connection with the exhibits and the store's Ordnance window displays. Donald R. Funk of the Store was in charge of the Wanamaker workmen.

Arthur Munn, long experienced in staging commercial and industrial shows, came to the Show to set up the Philco Corporation exhibit which consisted of Shell, H. E., 40 mm. MK II; Shell, H. E., 75 mm.; Moving belts showing break-down of Shot, 40 mm. A. P., M81; Shell, 40 mm. H. E., MK II; Fuzes, P. D., M48 and M51A1; Bomb Tail, AN–M100A2, and other exhibits. Many of the exhibitors had discovered at this time that they had been allotted inadequate space. As a result, there was some complaint, and dissension among the exhibitors. Arthur Munn, who had worked with Hugh L. Adams some fifteen years before in connection with an E. G. Budd Manufacturing Company exhibit, was asked to assist in adjusting differences. To complicate his assignment some of the exhibitors wanted to enclose their spaces with high murals which would have obscured neighboring exhibits. Others had gone in for flood-lighting which would have confused and blinded visitors in adjoining booths. A few had moving picture machines, some with sound-tracks, loudspeakers and other noisemaking devices which easily might have blotted out nearby vocal programs. Still other exhibitors had brought large flags which they desired to drape in such positions and at such angles as to overshadow the "man next door," thus disturbing "good neighbor policy." It is not on record that Arthur Munn received the orchids, plaudits and other tokens of high accomplishment he so overwhelmingly had

earned. Later, he was employed by Wanamaker's to work with Major Buck on the Show publicity job.

An interesting side development of the Show was the sale by the Store to exhibitors of various items. It started in the Heintz Manufacturing Company exhibit. The exhibitor felt the need of a good rug. He purchased it. Other exhibitors were impressed; bought more rugs. Some went in for inlaid linoleum. Altogether 12,600 square feet of floor space thus was covered.

Came in due course, 2:00 P. M. of Friday, 23 July 1943. A dinner and private preview had been planned for visiting royalty, heads of facilities and newspaper representatives. This took place at the dinner hour—and convenient to Lowell Thomas' daily broadcast time. The famed commentator was made Master of Ceremonies. Present, among the 900 persons in attendance were Colonel Hauseman who took to the "mike" to be interviewed by Lowell Thomas, Pennsylvania's Governor Edward G. Martin, the Honorable John E. Sheridan, 4th District, House of Representatives, Philadelphia's Mayor, Bernard Samuel, Major General Gladeon M. Barnes who had come in Lt. General Campbell's stead, Members of the P. O. D. Advisory Board, Industrialists and Bankers and representatives of many other phases of the country's activities.

A parade in the afternoon, under the direction of Captain Lew Smith and Henry P. Patchett was announced to a waiting world that the "big show" was just around the clock by a few hours. A smart Aberdeen Proving Ground Band gave with the music. Up and down nearby streets and around pigeon-splashed City Hall, the marchers high-stepped. Upon reaching each corner of City Hall Plaza, tanks, jeeps and trucks were rolled up runways, to remain for duration of the Show. The band returned to the Wanamaker Store where it rendered several selections before going inside, to the Grand Court. A feature of the Band was the "Ordnance for Victory" March. Harl McDonald, manager of the Philadelphia Orchestra, wrote it.

The Show was opened to the Public, 25 July 1943, at 10:00 A. M. A record crowd of 17,250 persons attended. Attendance figures were arrived at by means of a daily check of the eight express elevators assigned to the 8th floor of the Store, and adding 15 per cent, a conservative percentage representing those who used the stairs.

There were special attractions daily to attract

visitors, beside the full page and smaller announcements run in the Philadelphia and outside newspapers. For instance, on 26 July, an Amphibian Jeep, manufactured by the Ford Motor Company was demonstrated taking to the water from a dock in League Island, with Colonel Hauseman a willing passenger. Of course it was a good newspaper story.

On 27 July, an 8-in. Mobile Gun was brought in from the Erie Proving Ground, paraded through the streets to Rayburn Plaza; and at 4:45 P. M. there was a 15-minute radio broadcast from the store during which two veterans from Valley Forge Hospital were interviewed.

At 12:00 noon, Wednesday, 28 July, an M-7 Tank was given a police escort around City Hall. During the same day, there were two broadcasts from Radio Station WFIL, with Hugh L. Adams; Roy Porter, CBS Newscaster, and Major Buck, the guest speakers. These programs were sponsored by the Ford Motor Company.

There were more radio broadcasts than one complete top sergeant could count on all his fingers and toes, and those of the Color Guard.

The only sour note in the whole affair, and it soon was forgotten in the greater glamour of the Show, was the detonation, 10 August 1943, of a fuze which had been employed as a noise-maker in a Booby Trap Display. A short circuit did the trick. The detonation threw sand among a group of onlookers, causing minor cuts and bruises. Prompt attention by the Wanamaker Store physician, plus tetanus shots for all persons involved averted serious results.

And parades, no end. On 13 August a cavalcade of tanks and jeeps rolled out to the Philco Corporation plant where there was flag waving with huzzahs. In the evening, 50 members of the Philadelphia Lighthouse for the Blind visited the Show.

Presentation on 18 August, to the Ordnance Department by the Ford Motor Company, of the 50,000th Tank processed at the Chester Tank Depot drew Lt. General Levin H. Campbell, Jr., to Chester. At 8 P. M., same day, Earl Godwin, dean of Washington commentators, interviewed Colonel Hauseman at a broadcast from the Ford exhibit. This interview was transcribed and rebroadcast on a later program.

On 20 August, another parade. This one to the Heintz Manufacturing Company and the E. G. Budd Manufacturing Company. On 25 August, Electric Storage Battery Company was similarly

honored. Two days later, the parade marched out to give J. G. Brill Company a few cheers. Three days following the marching and rolling host travelled down to Baldwin Locomotive Works, where Major Charles T. Michener, P. O. D. Adjutant, held forth as the principal speaker.

Then there were feature days—a York Safe & Lock Day, a Lee Tire Day, an Electric Storage Battery Day, a General Motors Day, a Chrysler Corporation Day, a Peco Manufacturing Day—all with appropriate "goings-on."

September 17th, wrote finis to the broadcasts and gave notice of the official closing just one day off. Successful beyond all predictions; productive of countless square yards of newspaper space and hours of broadcasting time; and beyond this, a story of the materials of Victory, convincingly told to more than a million 8th floor visitors and thousands more along the streets and at the big plants hereabouts. During this final broadcast, Colonel Hauseman presented Hugh L. Adams with an antique tankard for a job superbly done. A scroll of appreciation was presented to Charles R. Shipley of Wanamaker's for the store's unstinted cooperation in making the "Ordnance for Victory" Show the success that it was. Major Buck made the introductions. Joseph Cunningham of the York Safe & Lock Company represented the exhibitors.

The Show closed officially, 5:45 P. M. Saturday, 18 September 1943, after a successful run of 49 days. Ten days later all materiel had been removed from the Store, the exhibition floor cleared, and the old 8th floor was back in action with "business as usual."

The Exhibitors? Ninety-one of them—more than 650 separate items—in addition to the items making up the exhibits of German and Japanese materiel.

The Exhibitors were:

Theodore Alteneder & Sons
American Car & Foundry Company
American Meter Company
American Viscose Company
Animal Trap Company of America, Ltd.
Armstrong Cork Company
Atlantic Elevator Company
Autocar Company
Lycoming Division, Aviation Corporation
Baldwin Locomotive Works
Barclay White Company

Bethlehem Steel Company
Black & Decker Manufacturing Company
Board of Education, Philadelphia
Bonney Forge & Tool Company
Bonschur & Holmes Optical Company
J. G. Brill Company
E. G. Budd Manufacturing Company
Bunting Glider Company
F. C. Castelli Company
Chipman Knitting Mills
Chrysler Corporation
Coplay Cement Company
Cordomatic Corporation
Crown Cork & Seal Company
Darling Valve & Manufacturing Company
Davison Chemical Company
De Walt Products Company
Dienelt & Eisenhardt Company
Henry Disston & Sons, Inc.
Drever Company
E. I. duPont De Nemours & Company
    (Remington Arms included)
Eastern Malleable Iron Company
Eastern Rolling Mill Company
Electric Storage Battery Company
A. B. Farquhar Company, Ltd.
Ford Motor Company
Frankford Arsenal
General Motors Corporation
L. F. Grammes & Sons, Inc.
Gulf Oil Corporation
Hamilton Watch Company
Harrisburg Steel Corporation
Heintz Manufacturing Company
E. F. Houghton & Company
International Business Machinery Company
Jesse Jones Paper Box Company
Kennedy Van-Saun Manufacturing & Engineer-
    ing Company
Koppers Company
Lansdowne Steel & Iron Company
Lee Tire & Rubber Company
Lehigh Foundries
Karl Lieberknecht, Inc.
Line Material Company
Mac-it Parts Company
Mack Manufacturing Company
Mail Oil Burner Corporation

Merchant & Evans Company
Milco Undergarment Company
John J. Nesbitt, Inc.
Owens-Illinois Can Company
Parish Pressed Steel Corporation
Peco Manufacturing Company
Philadelphia Ordnance District—Gage Labora-
    tory
Philadelphia Ordnance District—Materiel
Philco Corporation
Proctor Electric Company
Read Machinery Company
Red Cross
Thomas Royal Company
R-S Products Company
R. F. Sedgeley, Inc.
S. K. F. Industries, Inc.
Standard Pressed Steel Company
J. B. Smith Company
Sun Oil Company
Taylor-Wharton Iron & Steel Company
Textile Machine Works
Thornton-Fuller Company
V-Mail Booth: U. S. Post Office Department
War Bond Booth
War Manpower Commission
Warren Webster Company
Radio Station WCAU
York Corporation
York Safe & Lock Company
L. A. Young Spring & Wire Company

The exhibits included just about everything from drafting instruments to big guns, bombs of various types and sizes, shells, forgings, tank turrets, machine guns, Bofors, personnel mines, engines, parachutes, flares, cartridge cases, gun mounts, batteries, adapter clusters, rifles, helmets, Mobile Shops, Jeeps, shoe tracks, weldments, forgings, projectiles, gun tubes, electric tools, optical elements, cartridges, ammunition boxes, generator units, automotive and tank parts and components, trucks, machinery, gages, directors, small arms, flyers' armor, fuzes, camoflage nets and so on and so on and so on. It was an Ordnance exhibit with a vengeance—enough to initiate a fair-sized Central American revolution.

Chapter XLVIII

OVER ON THE CULTURAL SIDE

IT WAS in late 1940 or early 1941 that certain blythe spirits of Philadelphia Ordnance, either feeling the need of a means of relieving a state of ho-hum, or of setting Ordnance personnel off to one side as a distinctive and privileged class, turned to cultural, benevolent, literary and other pursuits as accesses to their Utopia.

The first blush of the "new life" appeared in the form of the Sunshine Club. Appended to a fiat issued 2 January 1941, appear the names of Mister Bill A. Eadie, President; the late Mrs. A. Pat Rayport, Secretary; Mrs. Helen Hermann, Treasurer; Evalyn De Woody, Assistant Treasurer, and Mrs. L. Rudnick, Purchasing Agent. The Club grew out of a suggestion by the late Pat Rayport.

In December 1940, the Sunshine Club "threw its first Christmas Party." Cost, 50 cents, on the line, and a package (dry)—and no admittance unless you had the "4 bit piece" and the bundle. Mrs. Nora Dougherty acted as "Collector of the Port."

The Club turned in a good job over the spread of its active life. Note these data from an early Eadie approved bulletin:

"Inasmuch as the Sunshine Club is in its infancy it has been necessary to make the following revisions in benefits in order to maintain a workable balance: In the event that the balance in the treasury reaches $200.00, payments in dues will be suspended; when the fund decreases to $100.00, payments of dues will be resumed."

"a. Illness of Member for one week—Gift or Flowers—$2.00
"b. Death of Member or Member's Immediate Family—Flowers—$5.00
"c. Marriage of Member—Gift—$5.00
"d. Birth of Child to Member—Cash—$5.00"

To give the reader an idea as to how this program worked out, your narrator offers the following tabulation of some early emergencies, happily met, with extra payments when needed:

Wedding Gifts:
Mrs. Miriam Brown—Cocktail Set
Alfred Testa—Sandwich Grille
W. A. Cosalesky—Sandwich Grille
James G. Price—Telechron Clock
Harold Fritz—Carpet Sweeper
L. B. Kramer—Carpet Sweeper
John Rollins—Carpet Sweeper
Cyril Cosgrove—Electric Kitchen Clock

"Bundle from Heaven" Gifts:

K. M. Jones	John J. Target
J. B. Centola	Edward Kirk
Julius Gussman	

Flowers:

J. A. Whelan	E. E. Tucker
N. Deutschman	C. R. Boreland
Charles Brennan	John J. Target
Frances Cleary	LeRoy Hodgson
Mary Ambrosini	Walter Hagen

It appeared late in January 1941 that the Democrats were out, and the Republicans were in; for now, the official line-up went like this:
President—Lieutenant W. L. Stephens, Jr.
Secretary—Louise Evenson
Treasurer—Madelein F. Beil
Asst. Treasurer—Lieutenant Jack Carson
The then policy board of the Club included Lieutenant Carson, Captain Eadie, Nora Dougherty, Margaret Mannian and Anne Fitzgerald.

Hospitalization activities already were under way. In February 1941, Blue Cross monthly payments were being made to Captain then Mr., Richard S. Edmonds, VMI, 1934, with a B.S. in electrical engineering. Dick subsequently saw service in the Artillery Branch, the Berwick Regional Office, American Car & Foundry Company

Inspection Office and, finally in the Terminations Branch.

Anna Ragni, gal of all work, came along later to collect for Blue Cross and about everything else— between Spring Dances and Parties and amateur dramatics.

History has not given the Sunshine Club the credit it deserved. The record of its accomplishments and "good in its time" will no doubt be pleasurably recalled by the P. O. D. oldtimers who watched it wax and wane. In May 1943 the Club's worthy successor, the Welfare Association, was got under way by O. Howard Wolfe, Chief, General Office Division, who felt that the principal features of the Sunshine Club should be revived, in view of a now increasing need. Welfare sprang to full life almost over night. Its services, some of which extended far beyond the end of the war, included the sponsoring of entertainments of various kinds, theatricals, collections for Red Cross Hospitalization, cashing checks for employees, emergency loans to employes. Postage stamps and War Bonds were sold, and apartments found for Ordnance personnel.

In September 1943 a Lending Library was established. In May 1944 a special drive within the District for blood donors was initiated—and to February 1945, 1,500 pints had been accounted for. And through all this activity appears the constantly alerted and tireless figure of Anna Ragni, who continued to her separation in 1946, and the succession of Anne Almeida. Income from the Library, from the entertainments and theatricals was chiefly used to maintain the Infirmary, under, for the greater part of the war, the able administration of Nurse Mary Lenny.

Of the literary phase: *Time Phews*, so named by Lt. Colonel, then Captain Fred E. Smith. The first issue appeared in October 1940, a mimeographed affair sparkling with chit chat, quips, and vital trivia of the day. For a time the little magazine came along twice a month, but as the Defense program got under way, and news was coming in from more and more sources in increasing volume, it became necessary to change *Time Phews* to a monthly and to change the title to *Time Fuze*.

Time Phews was another Pat Rayport idea; and in suggesting it, she carved out for herself no end of extra work, for the "magazine" "had to be done" after hours. Uncle Sam did not include Ordnance District house organs among the materials of war.

That first issue did some nice commemorating, considering that it was the first U. S. publication to announce the birth of Bill Bright's first born—a boy; the Lownsbury-Van Horn nuptials and the current anniversary of Helen Sherrick's advent on earth.

Many names grown memorable in P. O. D. appear through the many issues of *Time Fuze*. That the topside took it very seriously is borne out by the fact that from time to time, as one thumbs over issues grown old with age, one runs across items over the signatures of C. Jared Ingersoll, Brigadier General Hauseman, Major W. S. Broberg, O. Howard Wolfe, Lt. Colonel Arthur J. Seiler, Captain Charles R. Madary, Charles O. Guernsey, Malcolm White, Lt. Colonel Fred E. Smith, Captain Giles P. Wetherill.

The issues, until suspension in July 1943 at the behest of Lt. General Campbell who had in mind the setting of an example in the conservation of paper, were replete with biographies of P. O. D. dignitaries; stories of facilities and of items under manufacture; reports of weddings, and celebrations, the 10,000th this and that, and the 1,000,000th of these and those; and reams upon reams of the doings of just about everyone anywhere in P. O. D., its various divisions and out among the facilities. Here is history, as it should be written—about real people doing a real job.

During the early days the names of Pat Rayport and Dorothy M. Carroll appear prominently at the editorial masthead with Captain Stephens coming through with some of the smartest cartoons of the war. Al Stopes appears slightly later as Camera man. Bill Casella did quite well in the picture category, too.

Contributors of those days included Pat Uhniat, Isabella Swartzkopf, Libby Rudnick, E. W. Loudon, Edward C. Engleman, Peg Hendrick, Louise Evenson, Cy Cosgrove, Sally Sloan, F. A. Beccone, Major Vic Smith, Irene T. Farrell, Lt. Colonel H. K. Kelley, Sidney M. Gartmann, Evelyn Short, Richard Dressler, Helen Druzek, and many others.

By September 1942, the list of contributors, those contributing poetry and other items, and those very active reporters of the various Branches and other divisions of P. O. D., and in the plants, had grown so long that publication here is next to impossible. However, just to give you an idea, note the following:

A. Patricia Rayport, Editor
Helen Druzek, Associate
Co-Editors:
    Major C. T. Michener, Military Personnel Chief
    O. H. Wolfe, Chief General Office Division
    J. M. Neville, Public Relations Division
Assistant Editors:
    Major, then Captain, P. H. Carlson
    Captain, then Lieutenant, P. J. Fields
    F. B. Hutchins, Production Division
    Max Dunning, Production Division
Photography:
    Lt. Colonel, then Major, R. H. Andrews, Fiscal
    Robert H. Poe. Jr., Artillery
    Al Stopes, Public Relations
Artists:
    Lt. Colonel, then Captain, W. L. Stephens, Jr.
    Mrs. Georgia Boudreau, Civilian Personnel
    Vera Kronberg, Fiscal

Of regular reporters, or correspondents within
P. O. D. central office, there were thirty-seven,
and out in the Field, in Regional Offices, Inspection
Offices and in the facilities there were fifty-five
enthusiastic news gatherers working feverishly and
voluminously to monthly publications deadlines.
Here was a staff that would have been a credit to
any commercial publisher.

The editorial content of *Time Fuze* left little
to be desired. There was no end of all kinds of
talent among P. O. D.'s 4,000 and more people.
S'matter of fact it wasn't long before professional
writers were borrowing (?) our stuff and turning
it over to the "slick" magazines at top prices, as
rumor had it. Note the following, a concoction of
a P. O. D. poet, which appeared in the October 1941
Time Fuze:

> *Little girls like pretty dolls*
> *And little boys like soldiers:*
> *The years pass by—*
> *And my, O my*
> *The boys they like the pretty dolls*
> *And the girls all go for soldiers.*

The blow hit us full force come February 1942,
when, scanning the column of a well known
magazine hereabouts we read:

> *Little girls choose dolls for toys,*
> *While soldiers are the choice of boys:*
> *But when they've grown up you'll find*

> *That each has had a change of mind.*
> *The girls prefer the soldiers then,*
> *And baby dolls attract the men.*

Aside from the fact that plagiarism burns us up,
that garbled version is about as exhilirating as a
glass of warmed-over beer.

Of poets there were enough to pack a fair-sized
$2.00 anthology. Who does not recall the ring-
ing lines of Carl Phillipi's "Remember Pearl
Harbor," or Dan J. Farrell's verse in which Samp-
son appeared as a one-man Army Corps? Then
there was Arthur Tinney's "So Shall They Reap,"
the "B. S. O." Song, by Miriam S. Uman of the
Baltimore Regional Office; the scintillating verse
of Peg Hendrick, Roberta Hedrick, Flo Diffenderfer, Sam Marx, J. W. Paradis, E. W. Louden
and scads upon scads of rhyme by poets too shy to
acclaim their authorship.

In May 1943, *Time Phews*, its label now changed
to *Time Fuze*, as being more in line, came to full
magazine stature. Pat Rayport and Helen Druzek
had taken on other and heavier regular duties,
with the result that little time was left for their
voluntary contribution of energy to the *Time Fuze*
job. The editorship passed to a group widely
experienced of magazine publishing: Vrest Orton,
Managing Editor, and one time book publisher;
Gordon Barber, writer and publisher, and key man
of the Development Visualization Branch, under
Major General G. M. Barnes; Samuel Marx,
writer; Robert T. Gebler, formerly editor of *Judge*,
and Jeanne Cramp, daughter of the New York
Herald Tribune's top cartoonist; Circulation Manager, Fred W. Harvey, of the Office Service Section,
and publisher of the *Confectioner's Journal*, Advertising Manager; and Alymer Stopes, one time
Canadian Flying Ace, Staff Photographer. And
Time Fuze now was carrying "paid advertising."

Unhappily, the glorified Time Fuze was not long
for this world, as previously reported. Paper was
short, so the monthly which held so much promise,
which so long had been a great morale builder had
to go. And, as best it could, it made its exit with a
smile.

It was inevitable that our researches anent the
late lamented Time Fuze should bring to light the
spoor of earlier efforts of publications. Simple
mention to Major Bill Stephens of our desires was
enough to fetch out of dusty retirement a batch of
issues of a long-forgotten Bulletin, of which Volume
I, Number 1, appeared with a November 1935 date

line. This was a good looking "sheet," alive with news concerning the movements and activities of Reserve Officers, historical data and what not. And running through all the issues, full page cartoons by Bill Stephens himself, featuring those unforgettable black-face characters, Smokey and Bud.

The original editorial staff of the ancient Bulletin included Major W. A. Holland, Captain W. B. Williams, Captain H. E. Schofield, the then Lieutenant A. W. Hamilton, Lieutenant James J. Maloney and, inevitably, cartoonist Stephens. Somewhat after Number 1, Major, then Captain, Charles T. Michener took over Major Holland's job, and Lieutenant R. T. Mancill succeeded to Lieutenant Hamilton's post. And of course, time brought other changes.

The Policy Bulletin, successor to the original Bulletins, first appeared 17 March 1937. This was largely an instructional affair, somewhat along the lines of the later Office Memorandum. It was of irregular issue and followed no particular pattern. It was employed by Major Walter C. Hamilton then Executive Officer, as a means of conveying orders, routines and instructions to Officers. The Policy Bulletins covered such matters as the use of passes in crossing the Delaware River Bridge, Military and Civilian Personnel Records, and Reports, Responsibility for Property, Purchases, Report on Apportionment, Efficiency Reports and so on.

Beginning with the 5 December 1938 issue, a single Bulletin was typed, then passed down the line to be read and initialed. The earlier of the initialed bulletins picked up the initials of John H. Beyer, William H. Crown, Jr., Richard S. Edmonds, H. S. Koenig, F. I. Naughton, John W. Ogden, S. R. Shadel, Nelson E. Spurling, M. M. Bigger, Frederick Feldheim, M. L. Hodgson, J. E. Zortman, Carl T. Gohn, Sam McClenahan, William J. Bright and Elizabeth E. "Betty" Tucker who remained with P. O. D. to become secretary at one time and another to a succession of District Chiefs.

The last of the Policy Bulletins of which we have evidence is No. 21, dated 10 February 1940—and this was given over to a ruling on Educational Orders and Production Studies. And from this point the Office Memoranda carried on.

Bowling popped up late in 1941 in P. O. D., regularly organized of eight teams, enough to form a league. The first panel of Officers were as follows:

L. Richard Dressler—President
LeRoy Hodgson—Vice President
Frank G. Ferrell—Secretary
Sidney Horner—Treasurer

The idea and the league were expedited into existence within so short a space that difficulty was experienced in obtaining quickly, in a central location, and for a time which would be most convenient for the entire tribe, a battery of the eight required alleys. However, after much search the necessary arrangements were made with the topside at J. R. Creeley's Philadelphia Recreation Company Alleys on the 6th floor of 1005 Market Street, for play every Monday at 6:25 P. M.

Creeley donated the use of the Alleys, effective, beginning 22 September 1941. Twenty-seven P. O. Ders came out and bowled. On 29 September, forty-five men turned up and the league was immediately formed. Colonel Hauseman was to have blessed the opening tournament with his presence. Couldn't make it; so designated Jack Carson to come over and roll out the first ball.

Creeley did a good job of cooperating. He supplied printed schedules, Alley Cards, and team standings on the Bulletin Boards—also lockers.

At the end of the second league night, 6 October, the situation was as follows:

Team	Won	Lost
Bombers	8	0
Mortars	8	0
Rifles	4	4
Grenades	3	5
Cannons	3	5
Fuzes	3	5
Howitzers	2	6
Gunners	1	7

Rolling into the sixth week, we find the standing changed somewhat:

Team	Won	Lost
Cannons	19	5
Rifles	15	9
Mortars	14	10
Howitzers	14	10
Bombers	10	14
Grenades	10	14
Fuzes	10	14
Gunners	4	20

Lieutenant John Spiegelhalter, Captain of the Mortars was setting the pace with a high single game of 234, and high three of 568. The Gunners and Fuzes were tied for high team with 801, and the Fuzes had 2283 for high team three games.

At this time the Prize Committee Chairman, Bill Benat, and Banquet Committee Chairman, John Target were working out a plan for a successful spring wind-up. Other plans in the making were a handicap sweepstakes for the Colonel's prize, and a special match between picked teams from the P. O. D. League and the U. S. Army Engineers League.

Came the 11th week and more shifts in the scoring line-up:

Team	Won	Lost
Cannons	34	10
Howitzers	28	16
Mortars	25	19
Rifles	22	22
Fuzes	22	22
Grenades	18	26
Bombers	15	29
Gunners	12	32

Came finally the end of that first season, the banquet at Club Bali, congratulations and the Award to Captain Bill Feigley of the Colonel's much coveted cup.

For the 1942 Season, the club officials lined up thus:

L. Richard Dressler—President
Cyril Cosgrove—Vice President
Larry Meyers—Secretary
Sidney Horner—Treasurer

The only subsequent change during the existence of the league, which went out of business in the Spring of 1945, was the succession of Paul Williams to the Larry Meyers post.

At the end of the 1942 season, the teams wandered over to the Club Bali for another go at the groceries, and to toss a few hurried hurrahs for Walter White of the Philadelphia Regional Office,

1942 Cup Winner. The 1943–1944 season wrote finis at Shangri-La where Jack Norton, Inspector at Barclay White annexed the trophy. For the final season, 1944–1945, celebration again was at the Shangri-La with Sam Kinney capturing the honors.

Among others who contributed to the bowling fame of P. O. D., we recall George S. Bickle, Bob Wilson, William Benat, Walter Mullin, Harvey Battersby, Russell A. Lizzio, Jack Norton, William Neil, Charley Egolf, Vic Strohlein, Pat Mc-Donough, Robert Church, Paul Guthrie, Benjamin Murphy, George Kazansky, Walter White, John Hoar, Oliver Foxworthy, Harold Turtle, Fred Dubbs, Arnold Patterson, Dudley Cozad, Ed Moore, Don Wear, Howard Stock, Dick Keator, William Gould, Charles Dresch, Bernie Gallagher, John Gillespie, Gordon M. Bitterlich, George Suther, Maurice Weil, Robert Bauer and Bill Bright. Captain, then Lieutenant, Howard Gallaher; Captain, then Lieutenant, William Nicholls; Lieutenant Alvah Thomas, Captain, then Lieutenant, Ross Henderson, John Rooney, John Watt and James Farell.

As the war progressed more and more of the players departed for the Services, their places taken by Ordnance members from the glamour side; and as suddenly compacts and mascara became accessories in the Alleys. Among the girls were Ann Alexander, Helen Pfender, Cass Palmer, Audrey Abbott, Bunny Roberts, Emily Magee, Mary Trinity, Mary Callahan.

And no end of other pleasant and remembereble activities. Softball for instance; and the Glee Club and Quartet, and that once a year outpouring of talent by the Carolers. Truly these P. O. Ders were a hard plugging bunch, for what, with a war on their hands and plenty of work, they could still find time to refresh themselves— and the entire P. O. D. organization. They had learned to "whistle while they worked," and by so doing, made an important contribution to the morale that put this District out in front in more ways than one.

Chapter XLIX

GLAMOUR, GLAMOUR EVERYWHERE!

IT STRUCK you plumb between the eyes the moment of your arrival at 150 South Broad Street—and you asked yourself, "Where am I? Is this the MGM lot, or first row center at the Vanities? This can't be real," you mumbled, as you staggered forward, clutching your brief case. However, you soon were brought out of your tail-spin, by a clear, liquid voice which sweetly inquired: "May I help you?"

You might have been Lieutenant General Campbell, up from Pentagon, the Ambassador to the Court of St. James, a G. I. come to help out in Fiscal, the boy from a nearby coca cola emporium delivering an order, or just plain John G. Citizen—it was all the same to P. O. D.'s Eleanor Armstrong— the best known, most favored receptionist hereabouts. Everybody who knew Eleanor—and everybody did—loved her. Her's was the very critical assignment of speeding wanted visitors to their objectives; unwanted visitors on their way. This she did, smilingly, efficiently; and it is not on record that so much as a single complaint ever was aimed in her direction. Eleanor came to P. O. D. when the organization was beginning to bulge at its Mitten Building seams—and she remained just days short of a full five years. It might have been longer; but you see, her young man had come marching home and into her life forever—and she, out of ours for the same length of time.

Being a practical person and knowing in the ways of business, you very likely arrived at the conclusion that this idea of having a very beautiful girl at the "front desk" was purely a matter of window dressing, "putting on a good front," placing one's better foot forward." "It will be different when I get upstairs," you said to yourself. But it wasn't. You soon discovered how wrong you were. And how much more amazed you were when you learned that Ordnance women were outstandingly efficient as well as pleasing to the eye. Wherever you went in P. O. D. you were im-

pressed with the wonderful work these women were doing—and how well, and how enthusiastically they were doing it. Many had husbands, brothers, sweethearts or sons in the Services. These women were on the job with their hearts as well as their heads and hands. Their contribution to the war effort was important—whatever their assignments— secretaries, typists, stenographers, file clerks, record clerks, machine operators, mail girls. Who they were and what they were spoke well for the painstaking procedures of personnel selection and training—only the best was good enough for P. O. D.

Who of wartime P. O. D. does not recall, among a considerable list of very capable secretaries, Peggy Butts, Secretary to John Baizley; Isabel Swartzkopf, Secretary to David McIntire; Dorothy M. Carroll, one time Secretary to Major Ogden; Claire Gallagher who married her boss, Lieutenant E. J. Lynch; Helen Conlan, one time Secretary to Lt. Colonel Andrews, preceding Dorothy M. Stewart, who was to assist, in turn, Major Joseph C. Hoffman; Olga Fecanin, who became Mrs. Don Wear, Secretary to Robert R. Rimsky; Emly Lineman, Secretary to Captain Peterson; Ann Boyle, Secretary to Captain Morton Fetterolf of Safety and Security; the late Pat Rayport, as Secretary to Major Broberg; Helen J. McCabe, Secretary to Lt. Colonel Joseph A. Whelan; Virginia Bigelow, Secretary to O. Howard Wolfe; Martha "Mitzi" Sharon, Secretary to Captain Bob Merz; Elizabeth E. "Betty" Tucker, Secretary to Colonel Hauseman—later, to C. Jared Ingersoll; Virginia Smith, Secretary to Major Michener; later, "Polly" McKinley's assignment.

Then there were Helen Newbold assisting William J. O'Brien in the Machine Tool Section; Rita O'Brien, Secretary to Art LeBon; Ruth Mebs, editorial assistant and Secretary to the Historian, Robert T. Gebler; Regina Ashby, "multiple secretary" at Baldwins, serving in turn, Lt. Colonel Arthur J. Seiler, Major Roland C. Disney and Major Wilmsen; later coming uptown to assist Lt.

Colonel A. W. Gilmer; Betty Armstrong, Secretary to Captain Paul Grumbly of Legal; Betty Dickerman, Secretary to Captain, then Lieutenant Neal W. Slack; Ruth Tuttleman, Secretary to Major Disney while Chief of the Tank-Automotive Branch. Continuing: Grace J. Gallagher appears as Secretary to Henry B. Reinhardt of Fiscal; Rose Kuhn, sometime Secretary to Lt. Colonel Seiler; Helen B. McNally, Secretary to Captain John "Dutch" Derickson and Roberta Hedrick, "wording 'em" for Captain John F. Carson.

The list grows, revealing Marguerite "Peg" Hendrick of the Malcolm H. White Office, assistant to Colonel Hauseman; Eleanor Madden, assigned to George T. Francis, Jr., while Control Chief; Norma Innaurato, Secretary, in turn, to Lieutenant Jilbert, K. E. Butler, Captain James R. Stewart and Victor Strohlein, all of Technical Data and, later, to Blythe J. Minnier; Mrs. Lorraine Roderick, Secretary to Captain Edward C. Peterson; Alice Young, Secretary to C. Jared Ingersoll, sharing that honor with Rose Kuhn and Betty Tucker; Lucille Allessandroni, one time Secretary to Colonel Hauseman; Helen Druzik, Secretary, in turn, to Major Ogden, Lt. Colonel Robert G. Allen and Lt. Colonel Henry W. Gadsden. She was succeeded by Ruth Cunningham. Mary (Quigley) Steffler, Secretary, in turn, to District Chiefs, Colonel A. Donald Kelso, Colonel John P. Harris, Colonel Gordon B. Welch and Lt. Colonel Tyler D. Barney; and Rosemary Mooney, Secretary to Lieutenant Jack Walsh of Labor; and Mrs. Helen MacFarland who kept the Board of Awards out of trouble.

Shall we go on? Well, there was Cecilia McNamara long time Secretary to Lt. Colonel Ken Kelley; Patricia Moore, Secretary to Major Joe Baxter; Alice Keenan, assisting Major Joseph C. Hoffman while Control Officer; Leona Hyland, Secretary to Major Art Allison; Lucy Knoblauch, Secretary to Joseph Stone of Office Service; Mary Casey, Major Lafean's indispensable aide; Kay Byrnes, who helped uphold the Major Feustel reputation; Joy Spohrer, who jumped to the Wexlin call; Marie (Callahan) Silk, who kept the Major Beyer, and, later, the Captain Buerger shop in order; Florence Keisel, Secretary to Charles O. Guernsey of Inspection; and Captain Cecil Bentley's right hand, Lorayne T. Kesel. And include Betty Bauder, Sid Horner's comely young lady; petite Mary Ryan of the Bogert department; Dorothy Burns, giving a lift to Captain Jesse C.

Jessen of Tank; Winifred Connolly, Secretary to George Thomas and Lawrence Larson of the Philadelphia Regional Office; Dorothy Shady helping J. S. Reddick down at Eddystone; Mary Spack, Secretary to H. L. Wilson; Loretta Walker supporting Ramsay G. Regester; Concetta D'-Ettore, Secretary to Captain Lewis A. Smith, Jr., and so on, and so on, and so on.

It is not to be assumed that all the fine ladies held continuously from start to finish the assignments wherein they are here listed. Officers and men came and went. Units and Sections were shifted and merged. Work assignments changed—and secretaries and the other charmers were shifted along with the rest. There was little of standing still during wartime in P. O. D.

Then there were all those others on the distaff side who held responsible posts—in addition to those whose names are recorded elsewhere in this narrative. Remember Libby Rudnick, Chief, Purchase Office Supplies and Netta Davis and Mary Magee who also did their turns in the same Section? Too, we recall Irene T. Farrell, Key Punch Operator in Property; Nan Coffey of Public Relations; Mrs. Bertha Berry, Chief, Typing Pool before Ann Almeida took over that job; Dorothy Short, receptionist down at the Mitten Building; Ruth Woodring, assistant to Pat Rayport and custodian of the "coke" machine's nickels; Mrs. Harold R. David, C. M. P. Chief in Artillery; Wilhemina Hecksher, Chief, Survey Unit in Property; Evelyn S. Duncan, Chief, Reports Section of Terminations; Jane Rich of Communications; Margaret "Peggy" McKay of the old Sub-Office Administration; Agnes Stetson, Chief, Contract Section of Legal; Sue Bombaro, who shared responsibilities with Mrs. Elizabeth Graffen, Alice Smith and Ann Hayes in the Library Section; and Jean Randino, of the Specifications Section, Technical Data.

And let us not pass by Mrs. Anne Hilliard, Chief Clerk at Eddystone, later to do secretarial for Captain Lew Smith, George T. Francis, Jr., Captain Howard Gallaher and others of the "Broad and Walnut Mob"; Gladys B. Kovesy, Chief, Report Control, Cardex Unit, Reference Book of Current Production—Statistics and Reports Section; Helen Diskin, Chief, Postage Stamp Unit; Margaret Murphy, Special Assistant to Captain Jessen; Mary McCabe, Classification Analyst, along with Elsie De Camp; Kay McCaughey, Telephone Conversations Typist; Mrs. Marie

Jackson, Legal Branch, Mrs. Lourainia Vrooman, Counsellor; Lucille Fideli, Assistant in Gage Section; later, to Carl Phillipi.

Topping another list comes the name of Mrs. Lela Friel whose various assignments included that of Chief Clerk, Ammunition Section of Terminations Branch, War Bond Program header-upper, along with Dorothy Wall, Upper Darby Beauty Prize Winner; Mrs. Merrill S. Helms, one time master-mind of Files, later Assistant to the Historian; Anne Fitzgerald, Chief, Control Unit, Fiscal; Mrs. Bernadine Kleinhans, Gage Section; Mrs. Rosa Brady, Bills of Lading Unit; Mary Falls, Mary E. Brady, Margaret Hanna of Travel;

Betty Buehle of Plant Protection. Then the telephone operators—Jean Evans, Catherine T. Lynch, Margaret T. Brennan, Helen G. Ball, Lois N. Blair; Rosemary Curran, Frances T. Fair, Blanche Hunt, Jeanne McCracken and Ann McConnell.

From Berwick, from Baltimore, from Richmond, from about everywhere we hear of the splendid service turned in by, among so very many others, Christine R. Borland, Dorothy E. Martin, Bernice Bauman, Charlotte M. Keefer, Ruth A. Miller, Dallas I. Weiser, Anna Brophy, Ruth A. Hagenbuck, Mildred A. Bonin, Marian C. Ritts, Mary Spott and Catherine Connolly.

Thanks to all of you, very much.

❧

Opening night, 23 July 1943, for "Ordnance for Victory" Show in Wanamaker Store. L to R: Maj. Gen. Barnes, Chief of Technical Div., O.C.O.; Col. Hauseman, Chief of Phila. Ordnance District; Brig. Gen. Kutz, Chief of Military Training Div., O.C.O.; Col. Wilson, Executive Officer, ORTC, Aberdeen P. G.; Lt. Col. Rivkin, Public Relations Officer, A.P.G., Md.; Maj. Moore, Aide-de-Camp to Gen. Campbell, Chief of Ordnance; Lt. Haight, Aide-de-Camp to Col. Hauseman

Chapter L

THEY KNEW THEIR WAY AROUND

NO LESS conspicuous than other branches of District service were the chauffeurs. Certainly their contribution was important to the expedition of war's needs hereabouts. They were always on call, cars and trucks kept as bright as floor samples, and mechanically alerted for whatever emergency might strike.

Who will not readily recall William—William R. Johnson who saw service under every District

Few worked harder for P.O.D. and Victory than William Johnson, chauffeur to Philadelphia, Washington and other visiting topside through the war years and after

Chief from Brigadier General Hauseman to Colonel Kelso during the war years, and under Colonels John P. Harris, Gordon B. Welch and Tyler D. Barney—far into the Peace years.

We will also readily recall David Eugene Mock. "Gene" was drawn into the Army, serving from 28 September 1943 to 25 October 1945, returning to the District. On 26 July 1946 he moved up to Temple University to become chauffeur to Brigadier General Hauseman. Then there was Arthur W.

Parsons, Herbert H. Turner, LeRoy Kelley and Charles Brennan.

The transportation strike of 11 February 1946 found these men on their toes. During an earlier strike transportation was provided P. O. D. workers by car owners who volunteered the use of their cars. Routes were assigned. In the 1946 breakdown of service arrangements were made with the Navy for use of buses. There were five of these pressed into use, but before we could use them they had to be brought up from Baltimore, from the Storage Pool at Schultz Farm.

William Johnson was assigned to head the caravan which left Philadelphia early during the afternoon of the 10th and were back in Philadelphia with the buses by 9 o'clock in the evening. During the short period of their absence there was completed, with Captain Lewis A. Smith, Jr., George T. Francis, Jr., and Joseph Stone collaborating, a complete city transportation plan. Routes were marked out, stations established, and a signal system for District employees who might be picked up on their way to the stations. The men handled the buses superbly well. No time was lost to the District and everyone appeared pleased with the working out of the plan, and with the work of the chauffeurs. All of which brought high praise from the District Chief, Colonel John P. Harris.

Back in April of 1945 there was a trip to the Cressona Ordnance Plant at Cressona, in connection with which William Johnson and Herbert H. Turner were charged with the safe delivery at destination, and back at 1950 South Broad Street, with Lt. General Levin H. Campbell, Jr., Chief of Ordnance, Major General H. B. Sayler, and Brigadier Generals Coffey and Ford. Too, there was District Chief, C. Jared Ingersoll, and Lt. Colonel A. Donald Kelso.

Yes, these men knew their way around

Army and Navy "E" Award Day at Autocar Company, 27 August 1942. L. to R: C. Jared Ingersoll, Major Brendad D. Walsh, Major General Charles T. Harris and the late Robert P. Page, Jr., President of the company

Workers of Philco Corporation gather, 18 March 1942, to hear Colonel A. Robert Ginsburgh, Aide to the Under Secretary of War, visiting Philadelphia with a group of officers and enlisted men from Washington and Fort Dix

PART II

Chapter LI

NEWS REEL, 1941

THOUGH not yet in the war, and still sharing with the President the hope that no American boy would be sent to fight overseas, the country was at least beginning, in 1941, to smell powder, and getting a close-up view of what American industry would be able to accomplish, just in case. Great plants and small already were turning out in great numbers for Lend Lease and the Defense program, tanks and various motorized vehicles, guns, bombs, planes, ships and countless components, parts and small items.

As early as January 1941 the District, with a personnel, including the military and civilians, of 446 individuals was administering contracts to a value of $103,503,793.10. At the end of the year the records would show 598 prime contracts in force at a value of $378,496,275.66 in force. Before the end of the war the personnel total would reach 4100—the number of contracts 16,240 and the total of awards would exceed $2,900,000,000 spread over the seven-state District area and bringing employment to thousands.

An early step in the activation for war of the District was the award in January 1941 by the Office of the Chief of Ordnance of a negotiated contract for the establishment of a Proof Testing Range. In a matter of days a Range was under construction at the York Safe & Lock Company and the company awarded a contract for proof-testing 37 mm. Gun, M3; 37 mm. Gun Carriage, M4 and for road-testing of the carriage. A proof-range at American Car & Foundry Company, Berwick, Pennsylvania, also immediately was got under construction.

Intrigue early claimed the spotlight with the announcement in January 1941 that blueprints of a new shell forging machine smuggled out of the great Skoda Works of Pilsen in Czechoslovakia just ahead of the German invasion now had been put to use under an Educational Order granted by the War Department to the Baldwin Southwark Corporation, Philadelphia. The pertaining machine, which permitted production of a finished shell in two operations already was turning out 150 shells per hour. Story was that three Czechs stole the plans, fled to London where they set up a plant for shell manufacture. Subsequently, the Baldwin Locomotive Works acquired the U. S. manufacturing license.

A visiting Ordnance officer said, when told of the stolen plans that, "a production rate of one hundred and fifty shells per hour was not substantially better than could be obtained by other methods. "Preference," he added, "was a matter of opinion."

In February 1941 Ray P. Farrington came into P. O. D. as Chief Inspector. At this time the District had more than 3,500 items under inspection. It was in February that the Baldwin Locomotive Works turned over to Ordnance the first 8 in. Railroad Gun Mount* manufactured by American industry since 1918, and it was during the same month that the District was to experience its first strike.

March winds of 1941 blew hot and cold. Difficulties appeared at one plant where the quality of steel and heat treating of 155 mm. Gun Forgings, M1, were factors holding up production. At another plant cracks in 37 mm. Breech Ring Forgings were irritating production experts. On the brighter side, Philco Corporation had completed its Educational Order for 5,000 of the M48 Fuze and had immediately turned its equipment to production of fuzes on a $2,000,000.00 prime contract.

On the 24 April there rolled out for its initial test at Baldwin Locomotive Works, just nine

---

* Combined weight of Gun and Mount was 227,500 pounds. The Gun fired a 260 pound shell. Range 18 miles. All-over length 49 feet 6 inches. Clearance 13 feet 4 inches. Built at Watertown Arsenal. Mount described as 8″ Barbette.

months ahead of schedule, the Army's new hard hitting Tank, the 29 ton M3, a 225,000 pound weapon, carrying one 75 mm. and one 37 mm. Semi-Automatic Cannon and four .30 Cal. Machine guns. This new engine of destruction was powered by a 400-horsepower radial, gasoline-fed, Wright Cyclone Airplane Engine, which could attain a speed of thirty miles an hour, and a cruising range of one hundred miles without refueling.

This event was heralded the length of the Nation. Under-Secretary of War, Robert P. Patterson said, speaking before the more than five hundred notables attending the demonstration, "This is more than just a tank. It is a tank the design of which embodies the fruit of lessons learned in the Battle of France. One can almost say that this tank has been through fire. The Battle of France was fought and lost less than a year ago. The drawings for this tank were completed less than six months ago. Yet here it is, ready to be manned by a crew from the new Army, which itself was not in existence a year ago."

A few days before the birth of the M3, newsreel men and cameramen were swarming through the Armor Plate and Tank production plants at Berwick, Pennsylvania, of the American Car and Foundry Company, where thirteen-ton M3 Light Combat Tanks at the rate of six complete tanks per day were rolling from the production lines—and where a $70,000,000 order involving 3,089 tanks had been placed. The original order at Berwick had been for 329 tanks. Two months later in June 1941, A. C. F. was turning out thirteen M3's a day. In October came an order for an additional $30,-000,000 worth of these tanks—1,200 of them, and the production aim now was of five hundred units per month.

By April 1941, Baldwin Locomotive Works already had working on Lend Lease and Defense contracts in its 500 acre plant at Eddystone, more than 6,800 persons. Before December, more than 9,000 persons would be at work. To this time, E. G. Budd Manufacturing Company, Philadelphia, Pennsylvania, had produced and shipped to Arsenals, 1,250,000 Fragmentation Bombs, 20, No. M40. This was a new type of aerial Fragmentation Bomb, one of the deadliest in use—spreading hundreds of jagged steel fragments over a two hundred yard area upon explosion. The essential feature of this weapon was its casing, made of seventeen feet of half-inch square wire.

Speaking 11 June 1941 at a meeting of top in-

dustrialists of the District interested in National defense production, C. Jared Ingersoll, then P. O. D. Chief, keenly sensitive to world conditions and developments, said, "I wish war would be declared so that we would all wake up to what facts are on the present international situation . . . we are too slow in this District in the production of the necessities for National defense, although I do admit that the Philadelphia District is away ahead of any other area—the Army is now setting tough delivery dates to hurry production and we feel that it will bring results."

How right the District Chief was—P. O. D. did get results as the late Lt. General William S. Knudsen, then Chief of Production of the Office of Production Management was to affirm, 11 February 1942, on a visit to Philadelphia. Quoth the motor-man: "The Philadelphia Ordnance District, which is handling $700,000,000 worth of contracts for tanks, arms and munitions, is one of the largest districts in volume of production in the country. In less than six months," he said, "contracts would total $1,500,000,000" . . . and they did!

It was during 1941 that the descriptive term "gun limber" was added to Army chatter. What in tarnation was a gun limber, someone asked H. S. Lewis, Vice President of the Parish Pressed Steel Company, Reading, Pennsylvania, whose company earlier had received an order for $1,600,000 worth of this hefty gadget: "A 1941 gun limber (M2A3 Gun Mount, 73 mm.)," he replied, "is a rubber-tired baby-buggy built to race across country at fifty miles an hour with an eight foot cannon nestled in its cradle, and to bounce over rocks, ditches, mountain roads, river beds and Maginot Lines without a squeak. It consists of more parts than a Swiss watch, machined to an accuracy of one-half of 1-1,000th of an inch, gathered from 187 manufacturers and put together with loving care and microscopes in a factory that specialized in stamping out truck frames."

Any thing could happen during a period of American life when a New England flute manufacturer could switch over to rifle barrels; a Lancaster, Pennsylvania, watch-maker turn out on short notice small firearms parts; and a builder of cake-mixing machines could conjure up 66 mm. Trench Mortars. It all sounds so topsy-turvy; but even greater conversion miracles were performed during the war years.

Take those 66 mm. Trench Mortars: Read

Machinery Company had received its initial order 8 November 1940. A new building had to be erected, production lines installled, and not a move could be made until January 1941 when specifications finally were received by the contractor. Then, in addition to the building and equipping of a plant, machines were of necessity to be obtained, and one hundred and thirty complex parts fashioned from ten different metals and alloys—yet the first mortar came off the line in July 1941, seven months from the date of contract. In July 1941 these 37 pound "hell raisers" were leaving the plant at the rate of one hundred a week. These Mortars, with lateral as well as vertical adjustments, were rated the most powerful weapons that an individual soldier could carry. Their accurate range was almost one mile—three times that of World War I Mortars. The four pound projectile sprayed hot metal over an area of one hundred and fifty yards diameter.

Comes to Autocar, Ardmore, during the month from Washington, instructions that Company engineers are to solve problem of mounting a 75 mm. Gun on a T-12 half track chassis with especial reference to taking up the recoil. One gun was mounted on the double-quick and sent to Aberdeen. Proof results brought Autocar a full-size allocation. This was the first plant to mount so heavy a Gun on a half-track chassis. Some of these Guns saw action at the time of the first Japanese attacks on the Philippines.

On 2 August 1941, a crowd of 25,000 persons closed in upon the American Car & Foundry Company, Berwick, Pennsylvania, to witness the christening of the 1,000th 13-ton Tank to leave the assembly line of that company. Six thousand workers with their twenty-eight bands and fife and drum corps escorted the tank, painted white for the occasion, to the airfield where fifteen sister tanks in full battle array engaged in a realistic sham battle. Highways and Berwick's flag decked streets were jammed. The parade through the town was viewed by 60,000 persons. Distinguished guests and military topside were everywhere.

At the sham battle, fifteen tanks with their 37 mm. guns roaring, jockeyed back and forth across the field, crashing through defenses, into pillboxes and over booming land mines. From his position in the control tower, Captain, then First Lieutenant, Giles P. Wetherill supervised the firing of the more than three hundred powder charges. It was all very real.

Another event of newsreel importance in 1941 was the dedication, 23 June at Tacony, Philadelphia, Pennsylvania, of $1,250,000 Henry Disston & Son, Armor Plate Mill. This huge Armor fabricating plant, together with a $675,000. boiler house was put officially into operation before a distinguished group which included Brigadier General C. T. Harris, Jr., assistant to the Chief of Ordnance, Brigadier General John B. Rose, Commanding Officer at Aberdeen Proving Ground; Brigadier General Walter P. Boatwright, Commanding Officer, Frankford Arsenal; Lieutenant Colonel David N. Hauseman, Deputy Chief, and C. Jared Ingersoll, Chief, Philadelphia Ordnance District, and newsmen.

S. Horace Disston, President of the Company, lighted the fires under the great boilers, marking the entrance of the plant upon the expanded Plate program which would, it was announced, lead to a tripling of the company's output of Armor plate. C. Jared Ingersoll spoke to the guests and employees—3,400 of them; and as he spoke there were ranged about the speaker's stand, one of the new 31 Ton Medium Tanks which had made the trip under its own power, via Central Philadelphia, from Baldwin Locomotive Works at Eddystone; a new M-2 Half-Track, caterpillar tread Scout Car from the Autocar Company plant at Ardmore, and a 37 mm. Gun from York Safe & Lock Company at York, Pennsylvania.

While all the fanfare at Disston's was in progress, came word from the American Car & Foundry Company that production records on the 13 Ton M3 Tank again were being exceeded. "Now," said the dispatches, "the plant is completing and submitting to a seventy-five mile test, thirteen tanks everyday." These tanks, be it noted, resembled the light tanks Russia had at first used in Finland, and bore other resemblances to tanks sent into the campaign in Greece and Albania by the Italians. They had a speed of thirty-five miles an hour, carried a 37 mm. Gun and a revolving turret—and for those interested in paper work there is a suggestion of full employment in the fact that this tank boasted 2,865 parts.

The reel spins and there flashes upon the screen one of the most exciting industrial accomplishments to come out of the war—the building at York, Pennsylvania, by the York Safe & Lock Company, in the short space of sixty-one days of a complete, modern, Armor Plate Plant. "From Cow Pasture to Armor Plant in 61 Days" had announced newspapers from coast to coast. Morley Cassidy was to write for the Philadelphia *Evening Bulletin* of 9 October 1941:

"If any axis spies have been wondering how many months American Ordnance-makers would require to build and equip a plant that would whittle out Armor Plate for 25 Ton Tanks, they did not have far to go.

"Here is the answer all written out for them: 61 days!

"And that means starting from scratch in a cow-pasture—with cows in it.

"Spies may doubt this, so here is the chronology of what has been happening in one particular cow-pasture, just two miles north of York's Continental Square:

June 17—Cows are chased out.

June 18—First steel is placed for the new plant.

July 1—Machine tools begin arriving.

August 17—Plant is turning out Armor Plate.

"A steel and concrete building was erected, 120 feet wide by 600 feet long. A half-mile railroad spur was built. Material from more than 200 sub-contractors was assembled. The floor was filled with 80 of the biggest machine tools used in modern industry—including a 500 ton hydraulic press that bends Armor Plate like tinfoil. All this was set up in three production lines, tooled up, and powered.

"And today the plant is in full-blast production, finishing every pound of Armor Plate needed by the Baldwin Locomotive Works for the giant M3 Army Tanks it is building at its Eddystone Plant."

Event crowds upon event. The place of modern war is swift. October 16th found Lieutenant Colonel Hauseman at the plant of E. G. Budd Company, where he attended a ceremony marking the production by that company of the 1,000,000th No. 20 Fragmentation Bomb which was said to be one of the deadliest bombs yet devised. Many of the 10,000 employees of the company cheered and waved flags outside the shop as President Budd presented the bomb to Colonel Hauseman, a token of their all-out drive for Victory.

Five days later, Colonel Hauseman was on his way to the Philco Corporation plant in North Philadelphia to receive from the hands of Philco Vice President, George E. Deming, the 1,000,000th detonating fuze turned out by that company, the M48. This fuze was used with 75 mm. field guns and Howitzers, the 105 mm. Howitzer and 3 in. Sea Coast Guns. To the end of production, following VJ day, the Philco Corporation was to produce a total of fuzes in excess of 17,200,000 units.

Almost in a matter of hours later, Colonel Hauseman received in fitting ceremony from Frank Shumann, Lehigh Foundries, inc., vice president, the 1,000,000th 60 mm. Shell dropped from the "line" in that company's Lancaster, Pennsylvania plant; and at just about this moment, the Animal

Light Tanks, Medium Tanks, Heavy Tanks—all get a workout during maneuvers at Baldwins

Trap Company of America, Ltd., Lititz, Pennsylvania, was marking with a vivid "okeh," the 1,500,000th core of a contract for 25,000,000 similar units. These cores were for .30 Cal. and .50 Cal. Armor Piercing Bullets, and to meet its requirements the contractors had, in view of the growing shortage of equipment and tooling, to adapt and improvise machinery designed for an entirely different purpose.

Miracle-workers were cropping up everywhere in P. O. D. industry. Records were made only quickly to be shattered as more and more of the contractors got into the spirit of the Defense program, and as mass production techniques in connection with strange items were acquired. Records were no longer news.

Distinguished visitors from overseas now were beginning to appear. On 21 November 1941, Lord Halifax, Britain's six-foot-four Ambassador, crowded his Ingersollesque frame inside a 28 Ton Tank at Baldwin Locomotive Works to see what sort of doodads Cousin Sam was turning out for his embattled country. To give His Lordship some first-hand experience with American made tanks, the vehicle he was riding was skittered over the plant's purposely rough proving ground—his only point of vision being that provided by an observation slit. A few minutes later, riding atop another tank, but travelling at a more restrained pace, he had opportunity for leisurely observation. However, he did not release his death-like grip on the tank's 75 mm. Gun.

A few days later, on 8 December 1941, the Army's first 60 Ton Tank, T1-E1 Tank, with its 1,400 horse-power motor was piloted across the Baldwin Locomotive Works proving ground by Lt. Colonel, then Captain Arthur J. Seiler. When the giant tank first hove into view Army officers cheered, workmen cheered and officials from other plants engaged in defense work cheered. A Navy Blimp from Lakehurst, the L1, circled overhead. Land mines to simulate real war were blasted on the test field. Commercial Air-Liners from the Philadelphia Airport soared overhead without concern. The tank was delivered by Baldwin vice president, William H. Harman, to Brigadier General G. M. Barnes, then Assistant Chief, Industrial Service, Research and Engineering.

And for good measure, came word 26 December from Elkton, Maryland, that the National Fireworks Company had gaged and accepted its 3,000,000th fuze for the British.

Ellis Mather 73 in '43 and still
going strong in property

Chapter LII

NEWS REEL, 1942 — PART ONE

A New Year's resolution, 31 December 1941, was that the Districts persuade more and more plants to change over from peace-time production to the production of some kind of Ordnance materiel. Orders from General C. M. Wesson, then Chief of Ordnance, were that district offices extend the services of their engineering staffs to "more of the smaller manufacturers, to assist them in getting work for their plants, and to expand district's engineering staffs if necessary to accomplish this." That was S. W. P.'s job later on, but at this early movement the task fell in the lap of the then recently established Special Projects Section whose activities are reported elsewhere in this narrative.

Significant among the early conversions of small non-Ordnance plants was the switch to the manufacture of 75 mm. Shells of a Baltimore, Maryland, manufacturer of gas ranges and bath tubs who had been experiencing increasing difficulty in obtaining raw materials. A study of the plant's facilities was made under the direction of Major, then Lieutenant, E. H. Uhler. The study indicated that the company already possessed certain of the required machines and that, with the addition of a few others, the plant would be "set" for Shell production.

Another instance of successful conversion was that of the facilities of Martin & Schwartz, Inc., Salisbury, Maryland, manufacturer of gasoline filling station pumps, to the manufacture of 37 mm. Shot.

One more: The H. W. Baker Company, of Bryn Mawr, Pennsylvania. This contractor had been making milking machines and hair-clippers for cattle. The plant soon was deep in production of 20 mm projectiles. From butter to bullets, so to speak.

It was activity such as the foregoing that keynoted the New Year—an activity that was to persist through all the maze of activities and problems that were a part of getting out "enough and on time."

First news-making event of the New Year was the progress, 26 January, through Philadelphia of the largest Mobile Artillery piece in the world, the 240 mm. Howitzer—on its way from Wisconsin by way of Chicago, Buffalo, Albany, New York, Trenton, Philadelphia and Wilmington to Aberdeen. This huge gun fired a projectile weighing 350 pounds, and in general use would be employed for fire over intervening hills. The gun was accompanied on its journey by a block long cavalcade, including troops from Fort Bragg, Ordnance engineers, all under the direction of Major Elton V. Stallard of the Chicago Ordnance District. Two 10-Ton Diesel-motored Army trucks towed two trailers, one of which carried the 20-foot long gun tube. Also in the convoy was a self-propelled crane with an overall weight of 26 tons; and there were four prime movers, two of which were needed to manouver the gun.

If the route appears a circuitous one this was made necessary by all the precautions that had to be taken—the arrangement with officials of municipalities, surveys of bridges, underpasses and highways; the spotting along the route of State and Local Police—all took time and study yet the entire journey of 1,200 miles was accomplished in only 11 days. P. O. D.'s part in the "show" was the furnishing of a special escort which met the convoy at Elizabeth, New Jersey.

By 1 February, P. O. D. was gathering production momentum. In its issue of 12 February, the Philadelphia *Inquirer* was proclaiming in blazing headlines: "Arms Production Rises 2,500 Pct. in Philadelphia Area: Conversion Speeded." Even the New York *Times* sat up and took notice, with the announcement: "Philadelphia Setting Fast Pace in Arms Production: Deliveries of Material Have Multiplied 20 Times in Year to $22,176,000 a Month." Actually, as of 28 February 1942, 764

P. O. D. Prime Contracts were being inspected. These were to an Award dollar value of $636,407,-799.21. Yes, P. O. D. was rolling: one month later the figures stood at 819, and $1,157,656,041.08.

Congratulations were in order 10 February 1942, in the District when orders elevating Lt. Colonel David N. Hauseman, Deputy District Chief, to a full Colonelcy. Industry had by this time discovered the Colonel an understanding friend and a topnotch jacker-upper on the production front.

Another view of the giant 60-Ton T1-E1 Tank launched during maneuvers at Baldwin Locomotive Works Proving Ground, 8 December 1941

Chapter LIII

NEWS REEL, 1942 — PART TWO

"THE kitchen-gadget man," according to a newspaper story of 23 March 1942, "was tearing his hair. 'I can't get steel. I can't get aluminum. I can't get copper,' he wailed. All they want is war goods—but what do they think I can make? Tanks? Guns? Bombs? I haven't got machinery for such things. I'll just have to fold up!"

And then, as the story goes, someone told him of the Ordnance Museum on the 15th Floor of the Mitten Building in Philadelphia; and there, after walking about among the exhibits of Ordnance end items, components and parts, which was to grow to more than 2,300 separate units shortly after P. O. D. had moved, in April, to larger quarters in the old Manufacturers' Club building, he suddenly, and excitedly exclaimed: "There is something I can make!"

"Blueprints and specifications," said Colonel Hauseman, "do not always give the clearest possible picture. Small manufacturers aren't always skilled at reading blueprints; but let him see the article, and hold it, and he can tell you in an instant just what machines he'd need for the job and how the work would be handled."

Plants which might have been much longer in coming into Ordnance production, because of priorities effecting their commercial lines, or because they believed they were not equipped for Ordnance work, needed to spend only a little time in the Museum to be convinced that there was a place for them on the program.

On the executive end of the Museum, Major Charles T. Michener, Chief of the Military Personnel Branch, and his assistant, Lieutenant Maurice H. Felton, did an outstanding job. It was their assignment—and they made the best of it—right to the moment of dismantling early in 1944 when it had been decided that the Museum had served its purpose and the space now better could be used to relieve crowded conditions elsewhere in the District Offices.

Recollection of the Museum brings back to mind the opening, 6 January 1942, in the Pennsylvania Railroad's Broad Street Suburban Station Building of what was popularly termed the "Cafeteria" for distributing small war orders to P. O. D. area manufacturers. The idea was evolved by the Office of Production Management, who believed that visiting manufacturers might, between trains, discover among the two thousand and more items on display, something they would be able to produce for the war effort.

The newsmen had much to keep them on the jump those mad March days. For one thing there was the fire that destroyed the annealing and cleaning building of Lehigh Foundries, Inc., plant at Easton, Pennsylvania. That was late in February, and it was feared at the moment that here was a critical program gone smash, but anyone who really thought that reckoned without the spirit and energy of the men who later were to earn for that Company its Army and Navy "E" Award, for just one week and two days after the fire all debris had been cleared away, foundations were dug and steel work going up for a new fireproof building—and all the while the plant was running at full capacity.

The work leading to reconstruction was begun before the embers had cooled. Annealing ovens were operated in the open, to mention one among many improvisations which, with the speed of putting the plant back in shape, marked this as one of the engineering marvels of the war days.

On 8 April 1942, Philadelphia, for the first time since 1918, was parading in full dress. This was Army Day. Fifteen thousand warriors were in line, viewed by at least a half-million enthusiastic citizens. But there was a note of sadness, too, as wave after wave of Army men, Army Aviation Cadets, Navy men, Marines, Veterans, ROTC Units, Veterans and members of civilian services marched by. Ordnance, too, was much in evidence with tanks and guns and other equipment. This was more than a shot in the arm for Philadelphians; it was beyond this a promise.

By early May, the Baldwin Locomotive Works was exceeding tank quotas by three and one-half times earlier estimates. District awards had topped $1,387,000,000. The District was working a seven-day week. Donald M. Nelson, Chief, War Production Board, ordered that every mill and lathe, forge and furnace, wheel and turbine be kept in operation over the Memorial Day holiday as the workers' own special tribute to our boys overseas. The M3 Tanks now were heard to be tearing into Rommel on the Libyan Desert. Came the first report of War Bond Pay Deductions with the total at $361,700 and still going strong, and on 22 June 1942, war in miniature but with full size equipment and standard munitions came to Franklin Field, Philadelphia. There was a full week of it. Sixty-eight thousand persons tried to crowd into 65,000 seats on opening night and almost made it.

The Army War Show, with its nucleus in Franklin Field, overflowed into Fairmount Park and over the Schuylkill River. The booming guns, racing scout cars hurtling into old cars, screeching dive bombers, flame throwers spewing liquid fire, searchlights ranging the skies, the ceaseless staccato of machine guns. Also on the Field or on display were the 28 Ton Tank produced in U. S., also a Baldwin product; light tanks from American Car and Foundry Company, 75 mm. Gun Carriages from Autocar Company, 37 mm. Anti-Aircraft with tubes by Midvale Company, machined by Baldwin's and assembled in Baltimore on Mounts manufactured by the Barlett-Hayward Division of Koppers Company. Also on display were demolition bombs, 100 pounds, 300 pounds, 500 pounds, 1,000 pounds, 2,000 pounds, produced by Bethlehem Steel Company; and 20 pound fragmentation bombs from E. G. Budd Manufacturing Company, now one hundred per cent on war work. And there were 90 mm. Anti-Aircraft Guns—but why go on? The sponsors of the demonstration and exhibit were good showmen. They had thought of everything, and Philadelphia caught on. The proceeds were turned over to Army Emergency Relief.

Parades and Bond Rallies now were the order of the day all over the P. O. D. area—Lancaster, Berwick, Hazelton, Easton. Scrap drives were getting under way on the grand scale. Iron scrap already was critical. Several steel mills in the area were on a day to day basis. National leaders gathered 19 July 1942 in Chester, Pennsylvania, to inaugurate a country-wide scrap collection campaign which was expected to make available for the winter 8,000,000 to 10,000,000 tons of badly needed iron scrap.

By this time more than 12,000 Salvage Committees spread across the country were working with Civilian Defense Councils. A $2,000,000 advertising campaign had been launched to stir public interest.

Late in July 1942, Richmond, Virginia, there rolled out of Byrd Park, where it had been mounted for sixteen years, an 8 in. German Howitzer, trophy of World War I. Following brief ceremonies attended by Colonel Hauseman and Major Samuel H. Franklin, Jr., Officer-in-Charge, Richmond Sub-Office, the gun was moved to the junk yard, later to be turned into a "General Lee" Tank Hull.

The first Army and Navy "E" Award to be made in the District was presented 14 August 1942, to the Philco Corporation. Four thousand employees and their families attended the colorful ceremonies. Colonel A. A. Farmer, commanding officer, Philadelphia Signal Depot, made the presentation of Award. Lapel insignia were presented by Colonel Hauseman to employees and representatives of the management. A few days later, 27 August 1942, the Autocar Company became the recipient of the coveted award. An estimated 3,000 workers cheered throughout the proceedings. Dr. Robert L. Johnson, president, Temple University, was the principal speaker. Master of Ceremonies was Penn Mutual Life Insurance Company's president, John A. Stevenson. Major General Charles T. Harris, Commanding General, Aberdeen Proving Ground, and Colonel David N. Hauseman also were importantly in attendance. Robert P. Page, Jr., Autocar president, received the Award on behalf of the company.

Back in the District Office the girls were beginning to sport the new, trim, brown gabardine uniforms designed for the Services; tailored-to-measure, $37.50; slightly more with a matching topcoat. Stores enter competition, and a uniform appears at $24.75. Girls claimed the uniform a great wardrobe stretcher, saving wear and tear on "pretties." Good business until, a year later, Government said: "No insignia or 'flaming bombs' on other than authorized military uniforms, and when these are worn by members of the Military."

Chapter LIV

NEWS REEL, 1942 — PART THREE

ABOUT now, Army and Navy "E" Awards were popping all over the place; 30 September it was the Ford Motor Company's Chester Tank Depot and the Trojan Powder Company, Allentown; 3 October, it was the General Steel Castings Company at Eddystone, Pennsylvania; and a few days later, the E. I. duPont De Nemours Company, Inc., plant at Deepwater, New Jersey. From here on, the "E" Awards, which proved of high value in stimulating activity in the plants, were popping up almost daily in the news.

Arrangements were made early in October 1942 with the Service Commands whereby the clearance of visitors to the plants of Ordnance contractors became the responsibility of P. O. D.

Shortages of material through October 1942 gave contractors cause for concern. Many of the contractors were experiencing difficulty in finding sufficient work to keep skilled and semi-skilled employees busy. The War Manpower Commission and other government agencies were in a huddle at the time over a plan by which skilled employees might be loaned by a not-so-busy plant to one "up to its ears."

Business booming, too. Baldwin Locomotive Works received, in October, authorization to build 150 Tank Recovery Vehicles.

A contract for 226 Half Track Cars, M2, was awarded Autocar Company . . . Koppers Company delivers its first 40 mm. A.A. Bofors Gun Carriage . . . Chipman Knitting Mills turns out 32,000 60 mm. Shells—75,000 Anti-Personnel Mines . . . First M4A2 Medium Tank leaves Baldwin's . . . American Pulley Company ships its first M6 Grenades . . . L. A. Young Spring & Wire Company begins 75 mm. H.E. Shell production . . . Later, Martin Sandler and the Board of Awards would call the foregoing an "appetizer," a sample of things to come.

Early in November the Textile Machine Works, up Reading way, completed the first M5 Director.

Civilian personnel problems had their innings during November 1942. First off was the announced War Department policy in reference to deferments which caused certain male personnel to question whether they should not immediately switch to highly-paid industrial jobs until drafted. Another and more critical disturbance was in reference to the cessation of overtime pay. This meant a minimum wage reduction of 20 per cent, accentuating the discrepancies in pay between Ordnance and industrial employees. The situation was particularly acute, where because of plant hours, Ordnance inspectors were required to work 60 hours. In such cases the pay reduction amounted to 50 per cent.

A substantial increase in production at Darling Valve & Manufacturing Company of Shell 105 mm., M1, was explained by the installation of a bonus system and increased employment of women.

Pilot lot of M66A1 Fuzes by Bulova Watch Company passes inspection at Picatinny Arsenal. Virginia Steel Company, now manufacturing trunnion bands, were in critical need of 19 tons of seven-eights in. steel bars, while Captain Art Allison, Officer-in-Charge at Reading Sub Office, was loudly clamoring for a two drawer card file.

More magic! L. A. Young Spring & Wire Corp., makers of wire coat-hangers, coiled springs for auto seats, furniture, etc., and with no previous experience of hot die forging, bring in first production of 75 mm. Shell Cases. The hydraulic presses, pumps and other equipment used in performing this contract were salvaged from junk yards, covered with rust. They formerly had been used in the rubber industry. By adaptation and improvisation, and by dint of outstandingly good management, this company was able to keep its scrap losses within 0.5 per cent over the war production period, earning its Army and Navy "E" Award by a comfortable margin.

First quantity requirements for Cal. .50 A.A. Mounts were met by M3, a new design of Heintz Manufacturing Company, first of a long list of

Research and Development projects assigned this contractor.

December 1942 brought a production drive on 49 of the then 58 critical items. Requirements were met or exceeded on all forty-nine. Two of the outstanding accomplishments were the increase at Kennedy Van-Saun Manufacturing & Engineering Company of 60 mm. Mortars, and the attainment at York Safe & Lock Company of a "new high" for the month of 261 units, 37 mm. Carriages, M4A1.

A History Section is set up in P. O. D. with Robert T. Gebler as Chief.

Public transportation systems in widespread areas now approaching saturation point. In six of the larger cities the situation was critical and further increases in the passenger load would, it was feared, make necessary drastic reallocation of equipment. Bad weather on the way was expected to cut the use of private automobiles and add to the headaches of public carriers.

Total value of Prime Contracts under administration in P. O. D. now at $1,756,283,741.31. In this, this year of astronomical figures, the Sun, with a mere 96,000,000 miles separating it from 150 South Broad Street, is a poor contender.

75 mm. Gun Motor Carriage parked in front of P.O.D. headquarters, 150 South Broad Street, during Bond Drive

December was carbine month in P. O. D. More than one hundred plants were contacted and tentative schedules for a number of them submitted to the Carbine Integration Committee . . . Tank Automotive Branch was reporting a sizeable job in handling inspection on 1,053 prime contracts, 2,599 sub-contracts and 459 requisitions from other Districts . . . Production initiated at Armstrong Cork Company on adapter clusters, M3 . . . Colonel Hauseman decides coffee will not win war; declares ban on 10 A. M. exodus to nearby drug-stores and sandwich bistros.

Gages of glass now were expected to replace more than half the steel gages used in machine shops. Brigadier General Hermon F. Safford, Chief of Production Service, O. C. O., appeals to manufacturers at Frankford Aresnal meeting to offer suggestions for substituting materials to augment the supply of diminishing materials.

It was announced by Colonel Hauseman at the Arsenal meeting that P. O. D. had topped $90,-000,000. in production in November 1942. He warned the visitors against leaning too hard on Ordnance inspectors. "Our staff has been depleted considerably, and from now on you are going to have to do your job in assuming the responsibility of inspecting."

Thornton Lewis, civilian engineer, Deputy to General Safford, told the manufacturers "the problem of conversion is so vast that it cannot be handled by Ordnance alone." Thornton Lewis was well known in the District. He had once been associated in the Carrier Corporation, Syracuse, New York, with H. Paul Gant, P. O. D. Planning Director. When Colonel Hauseman left for Washington in November 1943 to become Chief of the Readjustment Division, Thornton Lewis was reassigned from the Industrial Division to the post of Public Relations Director to assist Colonel Hauseman, a work which he continued to within a few months of his death, 4 July 1945. The War Department, recognizing the high importance of his contribution to the war effort, awarded him posthumously the Citation and Emblem for Exceptional Service. Presentation was made 12 March 1946, at his late home, "Holiday Hill," Newtown, Pennsylvania, by Colonel J. P. Harris, P. O. D. Chief.

Civilian employment, including 242 on terminal leave, now stood at 4,098 persons, down 202 from all-time District high in August 1942 of over 4,100 persons.

So much for 1942—a year of great accomplishments, of spectacular production "firsts"—of young officers growing to executive stature within a few months—of civilians hailing from all departments and all levels of industrial and commercial life, tackling strange problems in unfamiliar fields—of events of great moment—activities of such magnitude and in such number that in these few chapters we can little more than skim over a few; but these few, it is hoped, will recall something of the spirit of the time and bring to memory those who labored in that spirit.

$\mathcal{C}\!\approx\!\mathcal{O}$

90 mm Gun Shop of Cressona Ordnance Plant where weapons and other war items were cleaned, adjusted, repaired and otherwise rejuvenated for further service

Chapter LV

NEWS REEL, 1943

CAME January 1943 and industry and about everyone in the U. S. and his Cousin Elmer knew we had a war on our hands. We were remembering Pearl Harbor with a vengeance.

Early production in 1943 was featured by completion in January at Textile Machine Works of 25 Directors, M5, at Kennedy Van-Saum Manufacturing and Engineering Company, of 600, 60 mm. Mortars; and at Read Machinery Company, of 573 Mortars, to mention a few high spots.

Newspapers the country over proudly were flashing pictures of the General Sherman Tank, a powerful fighting tool that General Rommel, the Desert Fox, discovered in Libya. This was a Baldwin Locomotive Works product. P. O. D. now was digging in at the Mobile Shop Depot, recently moved over from Rahway, New Jersey, with Brigadier General H. R. Kutz, Chief of the Ordnance Field Service Division early up from Washington to look over the operation.

February, and critical labor areas begin to steal the show. The eight hundred and more Ordnance contractors in P. O. D. area now functioning through more than seventy-five Industry Integration Committees. Charles H. Godschall, Philco Corporation engineer, first to be honored in this area by the Ordnance Department for "marked contribution to the vital war production program to conserve critical material and machines." He lead way to savings of 166,000,000 pounds of brass, enough to build a solid brass tower 24 feet square as tall as Washington monument.

Rocket Launcher Research and Development Program awarded Heintz Manufacturing Company. To end of war all artillery type launchers which saw duty from the ground or ground vehicles were of this company's design and manufacture. Included was the "Calliope" 60 Tube, T34, 4.5 in., firing electrically. Said by Major General Barnes, wartime Research and Development Branch Chief, to deliver greatest fire power in the history of firearms.

It was announced that four tanks built at American Car & Foundry Company were first vehicles of the victorious Eighth Army to crack way into Tripoli. Small firms in area are to get war orders.

March 1943. Unveiling of Chester Tank Depot makes headlines. On hand were Brigadier General J. S. Hatcher of the Field Service and Brigadier General John K. Christmas, Chief, Tank-Automotive Center, Detroit, later christened Office, Chief of Ordnance-Detroit. Baldwin Locomotive Works moves into the Army and Navy "E" Award column.

April—War expenditures by U. S. top staggering total of $52,000,000,000, and the end is not yet . . . Strick Company of Philadelphia produces a pilot model of a bomb-handling trailer which cut from 11 to 3 the number of men required to handle a 2,000 pound bomb. Voluntary reductions effected during month exceed $4,000,000.00 . . . Metallic Belt Link facilities in initial production; General Aviation Equipment Company turns out 14,000,-000 units.

May—The month saw the delivery of the two first 7-in. Barbette Carriages by Baldwin Locomotive Works. P. O. D. Ordnance Show plans take shape. Safety Council of America meets in P. O. D. Office; Major General L. H. Campbell, Jr., Chief of Ordnance, principal speaker. District honored by visit from Major General L. H. Williams, C. B. M. C., Controller Ordnance Services, United Kingdom, and Brigadier General E. P. U. Hardy, Deputy Controller of Ordnance Services in North America. Guests visited Chester Tank Depot, Philadelphia Signal Corps Depot and Frankford Arsenal. Eastern Pennsylvania Congressmen Gallagher, Myers, Scott, Miller and Sheridan and Philadelphia Mayor Bernard Samuel tour District, visiting Thornton-Fuller Company, G. K. Garrett Company, Ocean City Manufacturing, American Meter Company, Heintz Manufacturing Company and Bulova Watch Company. Tour was for purpose of acquainting Congressmen with efforts being made by P. O. D. to utilize all available facilities, particularly smaller war plants.

Further gains were made during May in rating P. O. D. actual production to forecasts. Acceptances of 93.1 per cent of all major items covered by production orders were within 10 per cent of forecasts, comparing with 90.5 per cent in April; 89.5 per cent in March. Frankford Arsenal experiencing difficulty placing $2,000,000. worth of orders for small parts and special tools authorizes P. O. D. to permit expanded gage facilities in District to use Government-leased machine tools in the manufacture of these items should any be called upon to do so. Deferment cases processed by P. O. D. Labor Branch greatly reduced as a result of Replacement Schedules being filed and accepted by Selective Service Headquarters. Fewer cases of labor piracy during May. Migration of labor also on the down side. Baldwin Scrap Drive salvages 116,000 pounds of scrap and 75,000 pounds tool steel. With 40 mm. Barrel Assembly Program now on production basis, proof-firing at York Proof Range "ups" to 5,329 units, from April total of 4,463 units. P. O. D. personnel down to 3,150 from August 1942 "high" of 4,149.

June 1942—Quality Control Inspection, authorized by P. O. D. Ammunition Branch, is adopted by the Ammunition Branch, Office, Chief of Ordnance. Plan included 100 per cent critical dimension inspection for a period of two weeks, with understanding that if no defects were detected, the pertaining plant would be qualified as a Quality plant, and would revert to a sampling method requiring less personnel. If defects cropped out later, the plant went back on another two weeks' trial. American Viscose Company makes initial delivery of 60, 20 mm. Mounts, M1A1. Artillery Branch retained award for 100 per cent accuracy of scheduling and production control. Nelson Hall, P. O. D. Physical Director gets headlines in Philadelphia newspapers . . . Baltimore Sun does a three-column exultation of job done by the District. Five final agreements forwarded Washington by Price Adjustment Chief, Charles P. Stokes. Total Cash Refunds agreed upon totaled $18,719,213. Paint peels from ceiling in Chief Stokes office. "That's where contractors 'hit ceiling' during renegotiations visits," claimed assistant Lt. Colonel, then Major, W. Fred Feustel.

Procurement Planning Section does sweet job

in corralling large number of Research and Development contracts. Production of Philadelphia Mobile Shops Depot hits 1,000 units. Metallic Belt Link production for June hurdles 91,000,000 units. Two hundred twenty-eight war contractors in area report 186,506 persons employed; up 12,000 plus from April. Hepburn of Production Engineering Section submitted an idea covering use of 20 mm. Steel Case rejects on Rifle Grenade, replacing the then present use of tubing, and at a great saving in machinery. Result: Enthusiastic response from O. C. O. and four jobs requiring this type piece assigned to P. O. D. for development. Baldwin Scrap Drive nets 477,879 pounds of brass scrap . . . Carney's Point Inspection Office put 1943 scrap goal at 1,000,000 pounds. P. O. D. assigned administration of Research and Development contracts at Franklin Institute and the University of Pennsylvania.

Arrangements conditionally were made at the request of Captain D. F. Ducey, U. S. N., Naval

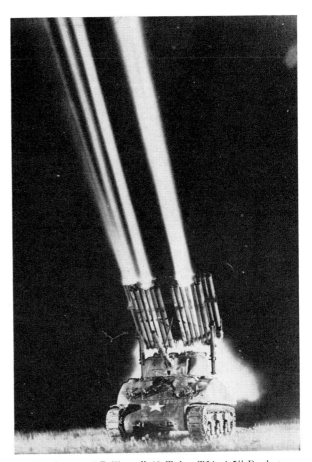

The famous "Calliope," 60 Tube, T34, 4.5″ Rocket Launcher establishes a record for fire power

Inspector of Ordnance at York Safe & Lock Company, to turn over to Captain Giles P. Wetherill of P. O. D. for supervision, the Navy Proof Range, adjacent to the Army Proof Range. Contracts and Purchase Orders under administration, 1,920; dollar value, $1,958,624,464.06.

July 1943—The critical list now was humming along in high and hitting on all twelve cylinders, with Major General Theodore J. Hayes, then Chief of the Industrial Division, down Pentagon way 'giving it the gun" and demanding all-out production on all "criticals." In the Ammunition Branch alone, where Major H. K. "Ken" Kelley was pulling the strings, thirty-eight contracts were affected. These included the 105 mm. Brass Cartridge Cases, at Eastern Rolling Mill Company, Baltimore, 20 mm. Cases at Proctor & Schwartz, Philadelphia, 40 mm. Steel Cases at Armstrong Cork Company, M42 Aircraft Signals at Triumph Explosives Company, and so on and so on ad infinitum.

Heintz Manufacturing Company sets production record in 6-day conversion to Pedestal Mounts of Motor Truck Anti-Aircraft Gun Mounts, Caliber .50. The converted units were used in pairs on light landing craft.

And, in July, Major Johnnie Beyer, Dean of Artillery, hits 100 per cent of accuracy of scheduling and production control—an old Beyer custom—not ignoring the parts played by co-pilot Captain Joe Buerger, Genial John O'Rourke, Dave McIntire, Lieutenant E. C. Peterson, Elias Vander Horst, Mrs. G. S. David in charge for the Branch of the newly concocted Controlled Materials Plan, and a whole host of other worthies.

Before the end of the month six new "E" Award flags would fly in the District—Dollar value of materiel produced and accepted during the month would exceed $66,324,900. Awards would top $91,490,500, with Contracts and Purchase Orders under administration, 1,552 of 'em, "figger-in' out" at $2,041,623,647.83.

Came to the District this month, such well remembered Officers as Captain T. Elliott Wanamaker, Captain Morden R. Buck, Lieutenant Philip S. Durfee, Lieutenant Bernard G. Fortmann, Jr., and the handsome Lieutenant John S. Haight. Barclay White Company cries "T-i-m-b-e-r!" for current crating needs: gets 800,000 feet of it with help of Welles Denney's lumberjacks. Armstrong Cork Company leases space at Millersville State

Normal School for 1,500 newly recruited plant personnel, putting heavy burden on local transportation.

Baltimore Regional Office feels labor pinch; working staff is down to 136 persons. Berwick reports 222 on office rolls, and 141 at facilities, to a total of 363 persons; Bethlehem reports 150 at work; Eddystone, 206; Philadelphia Regional Office, 510; Richmond, 109; Reading, according to Captain Art Allison, then in Charge, 133; York, 261 . . . all of which is just to give the reader a rough idea of what it takes to run a Regional Office in wartime; and these are not peak figures.

On 24 July, the "Ordnance for Victory" Exhibition formally opened its doors to a first day attendance of more than 35,000 persons who crowded the 8th floor of the John Wanamaker store to gaze in open-mouthed wonder at the eighty-five great displays of materiel brought from as many District manufacturing plants. This materiel ranged from the 90 mm. Anti-Aircraft Gun to the Garand Rifle, from the 4,000 pound "Block Buster" to Cal. .30 Small Arms Ammunition—displayed together with numerous German, Italian and Japanese weapons; but more of all this later.

August, still in 8th place in the Calendar League came up to bat in due course, bringing in Lieutenant James F. Bush, Jr., from Aberdeen, Lieutenant Vincent L. Fisher and Lieutenant Clair A. Kilgore, the two latter named coming from AFS, Duke University. Five more "E" flags ran up as many freshly painted poles . . . On the 19th the Chester Tank Depot delivered its 50,000th Vehicle. On the 23rd the Autocar Company demonstrated tanks for newsmen. Later, Standard Oil Company magazine devotes two pages to special grease developed by P. O. D. boys as requests pile in from stores, banks and others for Ordnance materiel for exhibition purposes. Major L. E. Warlow, Chief of the Censorship Branch, is relieved and assigned to help in the "Ordnance for Victory" Exposition.

Now, they're tightening up inspection methods. French E. Dennison pitches hot liners to Regional Offices on Quality Control and master-minds meetings on Packaging in these installations. Fifty-seven facilities needle District to assist in rounding up additional labor. Value of month's production was marked up at $80,083,147.92. Ordnance Department announces expectation that contractors will produce a minimum of 100 per cent of scheduled production, but that they should endeavor to turn out up to 130 per cent of critical items, and up to 110 per cent of all others.

Women workers in war plants show signs of tiring. Housekeeping and care of children reported as factors. Accidental explosion of Booby Trap at "Ordnance for Victory" exhibition injures fourteen onlookers . . . Al Stopes, P. O. D. cameraman, discovered to be godchild of Prime Minister Churchill. Bazooka pictures begin to break out in the news.

"September hath thirty (30) days," children were rhyming. Ordnance could have used sixty. During the month, 6,882 units of 37 mm. and 40 mm. materiel were proof-fired at York Proof Range, up 800 units from August. Ninety-four per cent of all major items production within plus or minus 10 per cent of schedule; non-critical items were at 99.4 per cent of that scheduled. Chester Tank Depot sets new high record with processing of 6,300 vehicles; almost one and one-half vehicles per man employed. Morale tours move more prominently into the news with Lieutenants Henderson and Walsh of the Labor Branch officiating. Records kept by the Office, Chief of Ordnance reveal that as of 1 September P. O. D. leads in meeting gage

delivery dates: 67 per cent for us, 35 per cent for other districts.

Procurement Planning Section wrestled with forty-six new allocation, ammunition items, principally. "Wexlin Branch" accepts a portion of allocations of the Springfield, 1903, Rifles. "Wex," reports Flyer's Armor Schedules "on the dot," but there is no confirmation from Dot. "Wex," because P. O. D. receives allocation, after much work, of only 9,500,000 Clay Pigeons, then goes out and picks up 2,675,000 from shelves of hardware stores. With no tires on hand and 2,000 applications on file, and more in prospect, Captain W. S. Canning, Transportation Chief, joins Headache-of-the-Month Club. Audit requested by Charley Weiler, Chief, Miscellaneous Vehicle Section, Tank-Automotive Branch, of contractor's stocks resulted in a saving of $325,000. which was half of the price quoted; additional savings, due to changes in material, were $53,000.

On 8 October came to South Broad Street for a District Chiefs' Meeting, a complete set of Ordnance bigwigs; among them, Lt. General L. H. Campbell, Jr., Chief of Ordnance; Major General T. J. Hayes, Chief, Industrial Division; Brigadier

District Chief, Brig. General, then Colonel, D. N. Hauseman, in command of Amphib test, takes off the hard way at League Island. Vehicle was traveling at 45 m.p.h. when picture was snapped

General W. P. Boatwright, Chief,Tank-Automotive Center; Brigadier General R. E. Hardy, Brigadier General James Kirk, Brigadier General H. C. Minton, Brigadier General H. F. Safford, Brigadier General J. K. Christmas, Tank-Automotive Center; Brigadier General G. M. Welles, Colonel C. E. Davies, Colonel I. A. Duffy, Colonel J. C. Raaen, Colonel H. B. Sheets, Colonel O. M. Jank, Office, Chief of Ordnance; Colonel E. L. Cummings, Tank Automotive Center.

Textile Section of Ammunition Branch completes a Classification of Defects and Plan of Inspection for Bomb Parachutes, the first attempt on the part of any District to establish such a procedure. An orchid for "Ken" Kelley. Fire drills introduced in District Office. Officers' Insurance up $60,000. reported First Lieutenant Philip J. Fields, then Chief, Communication Section. The District flying the Minute Man Flag of the U. S. Treasury signifying that 90 per cent of personnel were investing 10 per cent or more of gross salary in War Bonds.

Deputy District Chief C. Jared Ingersoll heads War Chest Drive in the District. O. Howard Wolfe, Chief, General Office Division, resigns. Total civilian personnel now at 3,327 . . . Military at 121. Forty-two more facilities seek P. O. D. help in obtaining labor . . . Four strikes reported. Five "E" Awards made. Lieutenant Howard L. Burns arrives in P. O. D. Captain Howard A. Cressman leaves P. O. D. Fiscal for FDRP, Duke University.

Captain Gene Uhler reports 24 new allocations requiring special planning action . . . Captain Lew Smith goes from Priorities to the Sales Section, Purchase Branch, with Concetta C. D'Ettorre, one of P. O. D.'s top flight secretaries, trailing. C. M. P. invades Production Service Branch. Major Joe Hoffman of Cincinnati Ordnance District, later to be assigned P. O. D., visits District to study processing of Purchase Action Reports. O. C. O. asks P. O. D. to produce 21,000,000 Metallic Belt Links —and fast—and P. O. D. quickly did! Rheem Manufacturing Company receives an RAD contract for 1,000,000 heavy Anti-Tank Mines, T6E1. Accuracy of Prediction? Still in the "gay nineties," of course. Julius Gussman of Ammunition and Charles R. Marsh of Purchase first in P. O. D. to receive civilian awards.

November . . . Thanksgiving Day with an encore. What is left over of the brown October ale and Cornell leaving Franklin Field on the short end of a 20–14 score. Five new "E" Flags

unfurled. Ten Officers move to higher levels— Paul H. Carlson, Roland C. Disney, Henry W. Gadsden, and Wilbur L. Lafean, Jr., get Gold Oak Leaves; J. Albury Fleitas, Robert D. Scarlett and Charles W. Sorber each add a Bar while "West Virginia" John S. Haight, Henry S. Sekerak and Robert O. Watson move up a peg to First Lieutenant. Automobile mileage tops 100,000. On 8 November General Hardy cancels all Steel Cartridge Case Contracts; later, cuts Textile contracts. Ammunition Branch urged to analyze difficulty of processing Bangalore Torpedo components in the District. Explosive noises on 4th Floor, 150 South Broad Street traced to self-applause of Captain Johnny Beyer upon the Branch's accomplishment of 95 per cent accuracy of Prediction for six months running. At same time, Captain Joe Wexlin claiming 99 per cent for November on Small Arms. Eight strikes reported. Lieutenant Frederick W. Boege ties up at P. O. D. dock. Military Personnel procures 150 Pennsylvania Liquor Control Cards, shocking the Historian. "Pat" Rayport of Welfare and *Time Fuze* Magazine resigns.

Production Service Branch now boasting 114 civilians and seven Officers.

December . . . P. O. D. says "Farewell" to Colonel Hauseman; greets the new Chief, Fred A. McMahon, formerly Chief, Cincinnati Ordnance District; Colonel Hauseman going to Washington to organize and direct the Readjustment Division, O. C. O. Twenty automobiles returned to 1362nd Service Unit, Command Shop, Reading, to be immobilized. P. O. D. fleet now down to 81 vehicles. Captain Wannamaker takes temporary charge and reorganizes the Powder, Explosives and Pyrotechnic Section in Ammunition. Captain Dave McIlvaine, Public Relations Chief, transferred to 3rd Service Command. Promotions carry John R. Armstrong, John H. Derickson, Jr., and William A. Dilks to Captaincies. Display at 150 South Broad Street is dismantled to provide additional office space. Adjutant Charlie Michener and Company moving upstairs. WAC Detachment established. Miscellaneous Materials Branch dissolved and all but one member going to Production Service Branch, Captain Welles Denney stepping into the No. 1 position. Gage Section mates up with the Gage Laboratory to form a new section in the Production Service Branch. Under administration, 2,480 contracts, to a dollar value of **$2,344,-178,809.82**. Dollar value of Production, major end items, components and spare parts reaches $65,424,375. Shipping tonnage of 175,915 tons is 35,000 over November. All duties and functions of Eddystone, except Ordnance Contracts at Baldwin Locomotive Works, transferred to other divisions of P. O. D. Control Branch set up in December by Colonel McMahon, headed by H. Paul Gant, decides District Branches, Regional Offices and others are to drop Monthly Activities Reports; must, however, furnish a Monthly History Report: "A rose by any other name, etc., etc. . . ."

Merry Christmas, Everybody!

Close co-operation between British and U. S. Army Ordnance: left to right, Brig. General G. P. U. Hardy, Deputy Director of Ordnance Supplies for the British Army, in North America, and Major General L. H. Williams, Controller of Ordnance Service for the British Army, and Brig. General, then Colonel, D. N. Hauseman, District Chief

Chapter LVI

NEWS REEL, 1944 — PART ONE

JANUARY! Control Board goes to work in earnest. French E. Dennison appointed Liaison Representative for all Industry Integration Committees to succeed Charles O. Guernsey. *Time Fuze* Magazine nominated for oblivion by Control Board. Motor pool established in central Philadelphia under jurisdiction of Third Service Command. Automobile mileage tops 68,263 miles. Ammunition Branch scores 92.9 per cent accuracy of Production; Artillery-Small Arms Branch, 100 per cent. Anti-Concrete Fuze, T-105 makes its first appearance in P. O. D., experimental contract going to Bulova Watch Company. Fuze, Rocket, M4A2, new to both O. C. O. and P. O. D., comes to town. Fragmentation Bomb production looking up. Almost 23,000,000 Yards Rayon Cloth for Parachutes now on order with twenty-two contractors faces cancellations. Embargo by Railroads threatens shipments from Chester Tank Depot.

P. O. D. Deputy Chief C. Jared Ingersoll named by Chief of Ordnance, Levin H. Campbell, Jr., to succeed Colonel Fred A. McMahon as District Chief. Ten thousandth Mobile Hospital Unit processed at Mobile Shop Depot for Overseas Service. Contract Change Unit and the Change Unit of Artillery combined and placed under direction of Charles O. Guernsey protege, Arthur LeBon. Artillery Branch now administering 203 contracts. O. C. O. Award for Accuracy of Prediction comes to Branch for seventh time in ten months.

Heintz Manufacturing Company brings in first production of their development of the 4-legged, M3, Cal. .50 Gun Mount. Fast schedule kept up with Jeeps and trucks from Camp Mackall assigned to get mounts to embarkation point to sail two days later with the 82nd Airborne Division.

Fourth War Loan Drive gets under way— January closing with employee participation at 95.9 per cent of total; cash sales at $21,225. Reclassification of all jobs in P. O. D. begins.

Forum meetings to be held every Tuesday and Thursday at 4:30 P. M. in Auditorium, 150 South Broad Street, initiated in January—average attendance 175 Civilians and Officers. Heavy response received to P. O. D. endorsement of ESMWT (Engineering-Service-Management-War Training Courses) conducted at Temple University and at two public schools, six hundred P. O. D.ers enrolling.

District Chief C. Jared Ingersoll heads drive in District Office to round up through employees urgently needed personnel for inspection. P. O. D. workers asked to canvass relatives and friends. Frankford Arsenal contributes sixty inspectors to the drive. Recruiting begins in District to aid O. C. O. Second Lieutenant Rena Friedman, designated Commanding Officer of P. O. D. WAAC Detachment. Navy ready to take over direction and operation of York Safe & Lock Company, but company to continue Ordnance production. Conversion Engineering Section forwards 459th Suggestion to Washington. Packaging Section begins negotiations with contractors in connection with O. C. O. campaign for salvage of fibreboard cartons. Purchase Action Reports transferred by Control Board from Statistics and Reports Section, to Fiscal Branch. Property Branch completes manual, "Property and Traffic Operating Procedures," covering the new Vendors' Shipping Document.

February. More Valentines to Tojo and "Dolfie." Major Albert D. Kelso, Chief, Industrial Division, promoted to rank of Lieutenant Colonel. Colonel D. N. Hauseman comes up from Washington to receive degree of Doctor of Science at Temple University. Record shows 97 per cent of P. O. D. employees now participating in Pay Reservation Plan for War Bond Purchases. Monthly total up to $64,436.50 or 12.2 per cent of Payroll. Cash Bond Sales for Drive, $103,021. Three "E" Awards this month. Automobile mileage 49,069 miles. Ammunition Accuracy of Prediction hits 92 per cent.

Artillery-Small Arms reported in February, 192 contracts, covering 210 items, in 116 plants. Rocket launchers "bullish," with Heintz Manufacturing Company, Philadelphia, much to the fore. "Blitz" Program of Spare Parts launched in Tank-Automotive Branch. Regional Offices each assign a "Blitz Specialist." Shortage reported to Officers with adequate training. Planning Section and the Conversion Engineering Section combine to form the Planning-Engineering Section and assigned the Production Service Branch of the Industrial Section.

The Planning-Engineering Section, under Captain E. H. Uhler, now embraced the Procurement Planning, Smaller War Plants, RAD Liaison, Transportation and Fuel, and the Labor Liaison Units. Twenty-four allocations on which planning was required bore February dates; for the most part these were drill cartridges, grenades, and fuzes. Ninety-three RAD active contracts register at $9,396,170. Suggestions to O. C. O. by Conversion Engineering Unit reach 463 to date. Machine Tool Inventories, Major Arthur H. Allison conducting, begin to click. To end of month, 35 surveys completed and forwarded Property Branch for further checking. Property Branch under Major W. L. Stephens, Jr., stalking warehouse space for future needs. Pencoyd Iron Works building a possibility. Termination Branch now boasted Review and Statistics, Ammunition, Tank-Automotive and Artillery-Small Arms Sections. The first edition of a Philadelphia Ordnance District Termination Manual was in preparation for issue in March 1944. Play given at Bellevue-Stratford, "Papa Is All," nets Dispensary $255.92, thus making no longer necessary the 10 cent visiting charge.

March. Thirty-six enlisted men assigned for temporary duty in order to offset critical shortage of qualified civilian accountants to perform contract termination work. As month ends P. O. D. has 232 contract terminations in process; only one over six months old. Property Disposal Branch a going business with 38 personnel, bearing down hard on the critical job of redistribution, sale and storage of all excess contractor and Government-owned property resulting from the termination of contracts. March property disposals reach $1,295,-261, reducing backlog to $1,929,793. Termination schools conducted in Wilkes-Barre, Richmond and Baltimore for contractor and Ordnance personnel. District Accuracy of Production at all

time high of 94.5 per cent. Ammunition Branch scores 94.6 per cent. Salt Bath at a P. O. D. facility blows up. Company had 125 of 425 Shields for 57 mm. Gun Carriage, M1A1 still to go. Some fast P. O. D. thinking by P. O. D. lads plus cooperation of Henry Disston & Sons Company saved the month's production quota. A month lacking in quips and cracks anent paper-work and red-tape; but it still was with us. March automobile travel, 43,609 miles. Gas? Two thousand eight hundred and twenty-three gallons. Bulova Watch Company awarded 610,000 more units of the new T-105 Fuze, bringing total to 710,000 units. All CMP Sections in Commodity Branches consolidated in Material Control Section of the Production Service Branch. P. O. D. personnel at 2,978 as compared with 3,499 in March 1943. Purchase-Terminations Division born, fathered by Martin Sandler. Procurement Planning Section initiates planning in March on twelve items; down twelve from February. One hundred thirty-four Smaller War Plants split $29,622,000. Labor Liaison Unit notes increase in deferments. Conversion Engineering Section rings up four more ideas for O. C. O. CMP Unit reports lumber in critical supply. Demand for steel heavy. Contracts and Purchase Orders under administration, 2,183, total $1,907,693,064.77. Dollar value of production Major End Items, Components and Spare Parts, $49,367,880.00. Contracts and Purchase Orders Awarded in March, 274, to a dollar value of $24,617,140.05.

April. Military personnel of P. O. D. on the move, Captain Ernest J. Langham is promoted to the rank of Major; Lieutenant L. B. Redmond is appointed Captain, and Second Lieutenants Howard L. Burns, P. S. Durfee, Bernard G. Fortmann, Jr., E. L. Pearce, W. F. Rathgeber, Jr., Jack Walsh and E. L. Young, Jr., move up a notch . . . P. O. D. is honored by visit of Major General L. H. Williams, Controller of Ordnance Services for the United Kingdom. Principal interest of visit was in spare parts and adequate packaging and identification. Accompanied by Colonel P. M. Seleen, Executive Assistant to the Chief of Ordnance. Mr. C. Jared Ingersoll, General Williams visited the Chester Tank Depot and the Electric Storage Battery Company, following which visits the Major General addressed key personnel of the District . . . On 8th April, C. Jared Ingersoll has fifteen minute spot on Radio Station KYW program of Federal Business Association of Philadel-

phia. His topic: "Victory Rides on Wheels" . . .
P. O. D. job classification completed with a maximum or journeyman's grade designated for each
job. Philadelphia Regional Office, Safety and
Security Branch, O. C. O., discontinued; Inspection
functions transferred to O. C. O.; all others to a
Liaison Representative. Terminations in process
down to 182, bettering March by 50. Termination
personnel complete series of talks to contractors'
representatives. Major item production schedules
accomplished, plus or minus 10 per cent, on 93.5
per cent of items involved. Rifle, Grenade, A. T.,
M9A1 requirements considerably upped. Facilities
given only five weeks to get set. However, J. J.
Nesbitt Company and Electric Power & Equipment
Company take all hurdles. Property Disposal
Branch move $1,187,000 worth of contractor-
owned equipment, leaving $1,214,000 worth to
be disposed of. Captain Lewis A. Smith, Jr.,
Signal Officer, goes after excessive telephone calls.
Automobile travel consumes 2,231 gallons of gas,
rolls 39,916 miles.

Heavy Shell program receives further impetus,
with Harrisburg Steel Company and The E. G.
Budd Manufacturing Company scheduled to carry
the burden of 8 in. M106 production; and Rheem
Manufacturing Company booking Shell H.E., 155
mm. General Hardy gives Emergency Urgent
status to Fragmentation Bomb, AN-M41A1, 20 lb,
American Locomotive Company, E. G. Budd
Manufacturing Company participating. To Bethlehem Steel Company goes complete requirement
on 1,025,000 Shell 3 in. H.E., M42A1. Overall
Ammunition Branch Accuracy of Production,
92.7 per cent. Cancellation on all Rayon Parachute
Cloth contracts completed.

Julius Gussman, Seymour Preston, J. C. Miller,
George D. Keller, W. E. Ross, Laurence A. Larson
and Lieutenant Frank W. Kron of Ammunition
running all over the lot. Why? Schedules were
being set up for Canisters, redesign of Adapter,
Grenade, Projection M1, trouble with the Fin for
155 mm. Mortar Shell, redesign of Mine A.T. T6E1,
design changes in Non-Metallic Mines M6 and T3,
method of sealing Burster Well Assembly into the
Body of Rifle, Smoke Grenade, T5E1, failures of
Rocket M6A3, engineering problems in reference
to Mine Crate, T-24 . . . Artillery-Small Arms
Branch reports 196 contracts covering items in 131
plants. Midvale Steel Company and Bethlehem
Steel Company step up heavy Gun Forgings.

Artillery-Small Arms Branch received its 9th
O. C. O. Award for Accuracy of prediction.

Tank-Automotive Branch notified 28 April by
Office, Chief of Ordnance-Detroit that Thornton-
Fuller Company, operating the Philadelphia Mobile
Shop Depot, vacate Commercial Museum by 1
June, as space was urgently needed by the U. S.
Post Office. (On 19 May, Detroit advised that
Contractor would not be required to vacate and
that arrangements should therefore be got under
way to reestablish the Depot in the Museum.)
Car load shipments of Spare Parts at Autocar
Company at all time high. One hundred carloads
were shipped. Captain Jack F. Carson, since July
1940, Chief of Civilian Personnel Branch, assigned
to active field service; succeeded by Samuel Mc-
Clenahan, relieved as Administration Chief, Industrial Division. Three hundred nine supervisors
who had been designated as personnel rating and
reviewing officials attend training classes in efficiency rating procedure. War Bond Sales Report
reveals 96 per cent of P. O. D. personnel investing
12.4 per cent of pay. Personnel at 3,008 as compared with 3,417 for April 1943. Total Officer
strength at 163.

Eighty-nine prime Smaller War Plant contrac-
tors divide awards of $29,871,000. Conversion
Engineering Unit discontinued by order of Major
General T. J. Hayes. Functions were distributed
among the interested operating Branches. Eight
Transportation Contracts terminated. Labor
Liaison Section handles 40 requests for increases
in manpower. Requested by O. C. O., R. J. Bothwell, Packaging Section, visits Paramount Studios,
Astoria, Long Island, to assist in making a Signal
Corps Film on packaging and prevention of corrosion. Property Branch arranges to transfer
to Gage Section all gages and measuring instruments then within the District, Section Chief
Lieutenant R. O. Watson held accountable.
Property Branch prepares for efficiency of shipping
instructions in connection with the accelerated
Heavy Shell program, already at a monthly level
of 150,686 tons. Branch still on the hunt for future
storage. Pencoyd Iron Works now definitely an
Ordnance Installation, to be known as Army Ordnance Warehouse No. 2.

Termination Branch sets in motion a program
which it was believed would result in the establishment in Philadelphia of a central termination
group for contractor personnel. First plant-wide
settlement termination organization in P. O. D.

is set up at American Car & Foundry Company, Major Howard P. Klair, former Berwick Regional Office Chief, assigned to handle all terminations at ACF for all Services. Termination Branch establishes a procedure for handling terminations services to and from other Districts.

May. Bumper crop of kudos looms . . . Colonel E. L. Cummings of Office, Chief of Ordnance-Detroit starts off with praises to Tom Beattie and Dave E. Clark of Tank-Automotive Branch for DUKWorthy performance on the Landing Craft Program. Peco lauds Captain Corb S. Hoffman for 18 months "front page" performance as Assistant Chairman, M110 Bomb Fuze Committee; and from Major General T. J. Hayes, and others, salvos for Jim G. Price of Property, daddy of the Vendors' Shipping Document—says General Hayes: "James G. Price is a recognized authority on both the War Department and the Vendors' Shipping Document; and he has performed a valuable service in writing the Ordnance manual of Procedure." Ordnance automobiles rolled off 42,273 miles in May; burned up 3,019 gallons of gas. Telephones cost at high for the year to date: $18,969.48. Large allocations were received during the month for Fuze, P. D. M51A3, Plunger Body Assemblies for Fuze M48, and Booster, M20A1 . . . P. O. D. facilities attended meeting called in Cincinnati by Brig. General R. E. Hardy on 81 mm. Shell and Fuze Programs. Powder procurement up: Atlas Powder Company, Hercules Powder Company and Du Pont figure in procurement 13,700,000 pounds of Dynamite. Atlas adds 10,000,000 pounds of TNT to its production schedules; Du Pont, 6,400,000 pounds. Ammunition Branch Accuracy of Prediction, 93.9 per cent. Picatinny Arsenal places contracts in P. O. D. for Cotton Cartridge Cloth. Ammunition Branch's Jack C. Miller, Julius Gussman, George D. Keller, Seymour Preston & Company again on the loose. Research in progress in reference to possibility of etching cross-sections on High Explosive Shell; Sections to be selected at the rotating band location in order to determine tight seating of the rotating band to the shell body: A John Target enterprise. G. & A. Aircraft Division, Firestone Tire & Rubber Company, completes pilot lot T57 Rocket Launchers. Heavy Gun Forgings still merrily skyrocketing. Eight in. Howitzer Carriages classified "Emergency Urgent"; S. Morgan Smith Company complete three . . . Tank-Automotive Branch received and processed 21 "Blitz" Spare

Parts requests from Office, Chief of Ordnance-Detroit, and 96 Critical Spare Parts Requests.

Job descriptions are written of 2,408 positions, reviewed during Classification Survey. From 1 May to 30 June P. O. D. personnel give to American Red Cross 500 pints of blood. Officer strength remains at 167. John C. Pyle, Jr., "the pride of Legal," moves on to a Captaincy. F. B. I. Agents turn in approximately 300 rounds of stolen ammunition and parts of Rocket M6 for investigation and disposal. P. O. D. begins to feel the "pinch" of expanded Ammunition Programs. There was begun by the Production Equipment Section a survey of all machine tool accessories and dies, jigs and fixtures within the District. As the month ended the Terminations Branch had in process 141 Terminations, as compared with 182 for April. Three "E" Awards go to P. O. D. contractors. To date 42 Awards had been made.

June. The District Chief, C. Jared Ingersoll, announces "next six months critical for munitions." William P. Schmid, production trouble-shooter of the Industrial Service Division, receives from the Chief of Ordnance the Meritorious Civilian Service Award. Newspapers, Radio Commentators and some Congressmen sure of post-war job chaos. That Automobile mileage business again: 44,646 miles and 2,604 gallons of gas. Telephone charges at $20,338.33, still on the way up. Gussman, Kemper and Bill Schmid, Inc., begin survey of all P. O. D. plants on conversion to M104 of Shell, 155 mm. H.E., M102. Purpose: to determine changes in existing requirements as a means of eliminating bottlenecks. Du Pont picks up orders for 2,069,205 pounds of Dynamite; Bethlehem Steel Company rates 1,025,000 Shell, H.E., 3 in. M42A1; Atlas Powder Company takes on 2,436,-500 Electric Ignition Squibs and 3,000,000 Blasting Caps. Accuracy of Prediction in Ammunition Branch clicked at 83.3 per cent for criticals; 95.8 per cent for non-criticals . . . District changes from production M40 Chester Type Parachute to the M4 Individual Type: first time in P. O. D. for the latter. Regional Office Inspectors trained in the new requirements. Contractors told to improvise and manufacture own gauges until Ordnance Gages should be available.

No let up in Training work. For instance, 65 new employees attend Orientation classes; 130 contractor personnel received Contract Termination instruction at the Contractor School, University of Pennsylvania; and excellent progress was made in laboratory training for Gage Checkers, and in the classes conducted in the Property Disposal Branch for its personnel. P. O. D. personnel total now at 2,969 against 3,370 in June 1943.

Seven days from first notice of requirement Heintz Manufacturing Company delivers 450 sets of "surfizing" equipment for preventing landing tanks from becoming immobilized in the surf. Weight, one ton each. Delivery made on tight schedule with P. O. D. officers with handbags and sealed orders riding on truck-cab seats.

First Lieutenants have an inning: Josef H. Buerger, Frederick C. Wedler and Bernard M. Zimmerman step out with the Captains, while Second Lieutenants James F. Bush, Jr., Theodore L. Hayes, Clair Kilgore and Adrian M. Strachen are promoted to the rank of First Lieutenant.

Smaller War Plants awards of $68,016,000.00 spread over 159 Prime Contracts. Artillery-Small arms administering 247 contracts covering 298 items in 211 plants. In Property Disposal Branch: Sales, $2,174,000; Backlog, $7,749,184. Personnel at 70. Pencoyd (Pa.) Warehouse in process of renovation—87 per cent complete. Contract to Autocar Company calls for conversion to Personnel Carriers, M3A1 (Half-Tracks) of 1,247 75 mm. Gun Motor Carriages. Prime Contracts and Purchase Orders over $1,000 under administration numbered 1,726 to a dollar total of $1,866,206,101.80 . . . Awards to the total of 458 and a dollar value of $101,037,588.14. Dollar value of production major end items, components and spare parts, $43,418,726. District Chief announces 1,819 contracts placed from 1 January to 15 June; dollar value, $267,163,000. During same period 335 contracts representing a value of $64,335,000 were terminated.

❧

REQUEST

God give us shells, the while,
The battle nigh is won.
God give us shells, and 'planes and guns
That you may sooner see again—
Your sons.

God give us strength to bend
Unto this greater need.
Give us the will to do; the heart,
And steady hands to quickly speed—
The end.

Yet, "Give us shells," we plead;
"For time moves on apace,
And we who keep this rendezvous
Would one fair day return again—
In Peace."

                                    R. T. G.

Chapter LVII

NEWS REEL, 1944 – PART TWO

JULY . . . Nelson Hall, P. O. D. Physical Director, dies following brief illness. Thus comes to an end a colorful career during which he made many friends. From Major General Gladeon M. Barnes, Chief, Research and Development Service, a letter to Lieutenant Thomas E. Bogert, P. O. D. RAD Liaison Officer, hailing P. O. D. as the "outstanding leader in all RAD Liaison Work" and Tommy Bogert as a great "head man." Said General Barnes: "It is desired that subject Officer be commended for his outstanding work, his resourcefulness and well planned execution of the assignment, and for the superior manner in which all his relations with this office have been conducted." Fifth War Bond Drive came to an end with 153 per cent of quota pledged.

Plaque bearing names of 36 P. O. D. winners of Awards for ideas is unveiled in the lobby of 150 South Broad Street; C. Jared Ingersoll, Major Henry W. Gadsden and Captain Lewis A. Smith, Jr., officiating. Indoctrination Course takes on 29 new employees. Starner-Scrugham Act, the "G. I. Bill of Rights" setting up "rule of 3," now in effect. Bill required three eligibles for each job, and that each eligible be given consideration for three vacancies before exhaustion. Training Courses going strong; they include "Bomb Reconnaissance Instructors' Course," at Aberdeen; "Contract Termination Course," Army Industrial College, Washington, D. C.; "Contract Termination Course," Judge Advocate General's School, Ann Arbor, Michigan; "Component Training Program for Gage Checkers," in P. O. D. Gage Section; "Indoctrination of New Employees," Civilian Personnel Branch; "Disposal of Contract Termination Property," P. O. D. Property Disposal Branch; "Cost Analysis and General Engineering," Tank-Automotive Branch; "Military Correspondence." Administration Branch; "Termination Procedures," Terminations Branch; "Accounting and Auditing Procedures," Fiscal Branch; "Payroll Procedures," Fiscal Branch; "Preparation of Legal Documents Relative to Ordnance Contracts," Legal Branch; "Maintenance of Property Records," Property Branch, and "Inspection Procedures," at Autocar Company Inspection Office.

Lieutenants on the march: Hamilton Page and Maynard H. Patterson acquiring their second bars, and Vincent L. Fisher, John J. Geraghty, Charles J. Grant, Jr., Oliver K. Hearte, Jr., Mahlon C. Hoy and Paul Jones advancing to the rank of First Lieutenant . . . Oliver C. Conger, W. Fred Feustel and Edward M. Lafferty go to their Majorities. Pay date for P. O. D.'s "faithful" moved back one day; the ghost walking on the 8th and 23rd of the month instead of the 7th and 22nd as formerly. Overtime now paid at the end of the period during which it was performed. And just to give you an idea, Advance Payments authorized in July totalled $8,187,135; Liquidated, $2,174,587.38.

Ammunition planning continues upswing in the face of a sharp decrease in available plant capacity. Smaller War Plants receive 127 Prime Contracts valued at $48,757,000. RAD Contracts to the number of 127, valued at $7,147,063.00 (including $4,000,000 Mine Contract at Rheem Manufacturing Company). Gun tubes in use in ETO wearing out faster than they can be replaced. O. D. asked to develop method of lengthening the tubes of rifle. RAD inherits the problem. William J. Meinel, Heintz Manufacturing Company head said, "Can't be done!" but did it—within two weeks! . . . Supreme Headquarters in England clamors for a 3 in. Armor Piercing Shot to stop Kraut Tanks. On 18 July, RAD of P. O. D. takes over; 2,000 units required. (H.V.A.P., 3 in., T–4) Jacob Noll and George Thomas assigned to live with the job. They do—delivering the shot 3 August.

Pencoyd warehouse fast filling up—12 shipments in July total 739,102 pounds. Property Disposal Managers appointed in Regional offices. Prime contractors urged to accept delegation of authority to settle claims up to $10,000 of sub-contractors:

32 accept during month. Seven new officers and 9 new civilian assignments to Termination Branch— to act as negotiators and assistant negotiators. Scrap Marketing Section with Richard M. "Dick" Keator as Chief set up in Property Disposal Branch. Special Salvage Boards established in Regional and Inspection Offices. "Bundling" comes to Property Disposal Branch: Under this procedure all items of less than $25.00 on a given single inventory would be grouped and disposed of in one lot. Property dispositions in July were to a total of $8,219,297, of which $5,423,658 represented Government-Owned property. Automobile travel covered 43,045 miles; gas, 2,553 gallons.

Sixty-two ammunition contracts awarded in August. Fuze items "hot." Bulova Watch Company has 100 per cent step-up on fuze C.P., T–105. Philadelphia becomes No. 1 labor area. Ammunition accuracy of prediction—85 per cent for criticals; 90 per cent for non-criticals. George D. Keller; W. J. "Bill" Dorsey, Chief of Production, Ammunition Branch, Julius Gussman, Lieutenant T. E. Bogert, Lee Matter, Seymour Preston and others of ammunition continue witch-hunting. Atlas Powder Company's Reynolds, Pa. plant turns out 8,000,000 blasting caps and squibs. DuPont accounts for 1,000,000 pounds smokeless powder. Trojan Powder Company reworked 800,000 pounds of scrap TNT.

Artillery-Small Arms Branch reports 255 contracts covering 325 items in 153 plants. A critical procurement falling into the lap of the Tank-Automotive Branch was one for asbestos grease to be used as a caulking compound. None had ever been made in U. S. and the requirements of approximately 1,000,000 pounds appeared too large for any facility to accomplish in the required time. Undaunted, Captain J. Albury Fleitas of Purchase, working with the Standard Oil Company of New Jersey, turned the trick for a photo-finish overseas. (More of this story is found in another chapter). Another "impossible" was a requirement for 978,000 feet of wire-enforced hose to be delivered in 60 days, Port of New York. You have guessed it: the hose was procured and it "hit the deck"—on time! Number of awards in July, to a total of $56,659,334.64 of which $39,975,143.47 was absorbed by ammunition requirements. . . . Production "let-down" in July held due to hot, humid weather, and general feeling of optimism as a result of Allied successes.

August. Dog days, again: Four "E" Flags catch the District breeze. Production slump continues as transportation strike and increasing absenteeism take their toll. For "scientific and engineering achievement," Franklin Institute was announced to receive, 13 September, the Ordnance Distinguished Service Award. Philadelphia Port of Embarkation freight tie-up blame placed on stevedores by War Manpower Commission. A Personnel Utilization Program, under the direction of J. J. Gordon, was aimed at full and proper utilization of the time and efforts of clerical and stenographic employees. P.O.D. personnel total of 3,011 as compared with 3,374 for August 1943. Officer strength at 159. WAC Detachment at 38. P.O.D. made advance payments during the month of $545,407.42: There were no liquidations . . . . Problems of getting P.O.D. people home during transportation strike assigned by Mr. C. J. Ingersoll to Captain L. A. Smith, Jr., Lieutenant J. H. Spiegelhalter and Sam McClenahan. They did a great job. No one suffered. Smaller war plants divide 156 prime contracts with a value of $77,542,000. Union objections prove a hurdle to the use in Ordnance production of prisoners of war. RAD contracts, numbering 153, are to a dollar total of $6,268,200, including two mine contracts with Rheem Manufacturing Company, for $4,000,000 and $400,000 respectively.

Spurred by an "extreme urgency" warning from Lieutenant General Levin H. Campbell, Jr., William A. Gilbert, production director, and Captain John Derickson, with John Rodgers of the Bethlehem Regional Office, hightail it to Bethlehem Steel Company to discuss a procurement of 5,000 Shot, 105 MM, T–13. Boss Uhle of the Coplay Cement Company joined the party. Arrangements were made by the Packaging Section for 50,000 reusable wooden containers for Government-Free-Issue to Lehigh Foundries, Inc., for shipping 155 MM Illuminating Shell.

Procedures begun for establishment at Cressona, Pennsylvania, of a Reclamation Plant (See special chapter on this project). Packaging Section to provide technical training and counsel in reference to packaging at the Cressona project. Seventy per cent of Gage procurements now classified "Emergency Urgent." As of 31 August Gages acquired by Government through contract termination were to a dollar value of $102,979. Property Branch to assume property responsibility in reference to the Cressona Ordnance Plant. Captain J. M. Harding named Assistant Property Officer, following plant visit by Lt. Colonel A. D. Kelso, District Chief; Major W. L. Stephens, Jr., Chief, P.O.D. Property Branch, and A. J. Donahue and S. S. Horner of the Branch.

Pencoyd Warehouse absorbs 88 freight shipments grossing 3,083,693 pounds. Terminations Branch provides comprehensive instructions to incoming personnel. Looking to VJ-Day, Terminations Branch contemplates expanded personnel needs, and the assignment of new military personnel then in training at the Army Industrial College and University of Pennsylvania. Steps taken by Property Disposal and Terminations Branches to formulate a Pre-Termination Plan which entailed consideration of and processing of routines before the actual termination or disposal should take effect. Disposals for August compared favorably with those of July, with backlog reduced from $5,481,718 to $3,296,271. Survey reveals 766 forms in use in P.O.D.—a peak to date. Auto travel registers 47,061 miles, consuming 2,742 gallons of gas.

Telephone charges touch a new high—$21,759.81. Ammunition Branch also at peak with 100 awards, including RAD contracts. Increased program included 1,326,240 Shell, 81 MM, M43A1 to Kennedy Van-Saun Manufacturing and Engineering Company, Danville, Pennsylvania; new allocations were for Fin assemblies for the 81 MM and 60 MM Mortar Shells; continuity of the 3 in. Shell, to the tune of 339,479 units, to Bethlehem Steel Company; 1,055,000 units to L. A. Young Spring & Wire Company, Trenton, New Jersey; 187,641 units to Armstrong Cork Company. Of M2832–T27 Primers, 4,873,000 to Ocean City Manufacturing Company, Philadelphia. Then there was a little matter of 3,343,000 non-electric blasting caps to Atlas Powder Co., Wilmington, Delaware. The AN–M110A1 bomb fuze at Peco Manufacturing Company, Philadelphia, and Karl Lieberknecht, Inc., Reading, Pennsylvania, was extended through April 1945 for a total of 2,000,000 units. The 20 MM, T9E5, Shot, continued in "hot" demand with 1,439,000 to Armstrong Cork Company. A surprise continuity allocation in August was that for the T–24 Heavy Mine Crate.

Other "Urgencies" included the M38A2, 100 pound Practice Bomb, the T–24 Ammunition Crate and the M85 Concrete Bomb, the latter rating AAA and AA–1 ratings. P.O.D. brain-trusters swarm over area needling critical schedules, adjusting production and inspection difficulties: Reports

sparkle with the names of Julius Gussman, W. J. Dorsey, John J. Target, French E. Dennison, Inspection Chief; L. C. Sneed, Lee C. Matter, Seymour Preston, Harry Allison, Captain Frederick C. Wedler, L. H. Seipp, George Kazansky, W. L. Bunker, A. J. Volmer. Artillery-Small Arms now buzzing along with 288 contracts covering 330 items in 149 plants. Battery deliveries critical. Schedules for September set at 24,000.

DuPont has contract for 1,038,000 gallons of Ethylene Glycol anti-freeze. Shortage of battery cases a production hurdle . . . . Reported that 90 per cent of batteries shipped overseas were being received in an unserviceable condition. For the third consecutive month the value of undelivered items to be produced under contracts of the District rose, though the increase in August was less than that for July. The increase in August was of $9,500,000 as against $36,070,000 in July. Fifty-four terminations authorized, reducing backlog to 82. Prime contracts and Purchase Orders under administration—1,870, divided among 573 contractors—to a dollar total of $1,933,706,751.80.

September. Labor Day work urged by Army. "Forty-eight hour work week goes into effect on Friday." (1 September 1944) announces WMC area director Carl B. Harr. Sharp decline in new cases of procurement: down to 307 from August level of 461. New cases of terminations up six from previous month's 54. Automobile travel registered 2,086 miles over quota of 46,000, with gas consumption at 2,833 gallons. Telephone charges on the upside at $21,759.81. Slight dip in ammunition procurement. Lehigh Foundries takes on a Shell, 60 MM, M49A2 award.

Ammunition production results a shade better than August, rated worst month in scoring in history of the Branch: September all-over score, 87.2 per cent—based on 188 items of which 24 were missed (22 were critical). William E. Gilbert and William J. Dorsey went after the "bugs." "Bill" Dorsey visits O.C.O. to discuss the new Concrete Practice Bomb Program. Certificates and Bars awarded at Baldwin Locomotive Works to Ed T. Berdge and Roy S. Adams by Lt. Colonel A. D. Kelso. Regional WMC Director, Frank McNamee in a blanket order to area directors in Pennsylvania, New Jersey and Delaware authorized all industries to assign limited staffs of engineers, technicians and experimental workers to post-war planning. Letter Purchase Orders go to P.O.D. contractors, Lieutenant Julius Mahalek was named key inspector on the

Integration Committee for the 100 lb. Practice Bomb, M85 program. Critical demand for shaped charges and black powder continues.

Announced that from October on, Rheem Manufacturing Company, Danville, Pennsylvania, would be exclusively engaged with production of 720,000 Shell, 155 MM, H.E., M–107. We've been neglecting the Ammunition Branch's Price Change Section. The record is a proud one. In September alone this alert group saved $66,339.22 to Government. The month saw more excitement in Terminations than in Procurement when 15 heretofore "hot" items, 4 of which were RADs, were cut back. The list included the 4.5 in. T–22 Rocket Components at Crown Can Company, American Can Company, General Electric Company and E. G. Budd Manufacturing Company; the M2A3 Mine at Lehigh Foundries; the Bangalore Torpedo; the M141 Fiber container at Cleveland Container Corporation; T–3, Electric Detonator; the Stabilizer Tube Assembly for the 2.36 Rocket M6A1 at American Pulley Company. Artillery-Small Arms Branch reports 286 contracts, covering 337 items in 150 plants.

Ordnance Supply Control now in effect. Battery manufacturers miss by 4,075 critical September schedule of 24,138 units. Failure due to lack of cases for which 9,748 were promised: 1,881 delivered. Barclay White Company, packaging facility, turn in excellent performance during entire life of contract: In September, for example, the facility packed or crated 10,976 items—shipped 10,940; these included 6 and 10 ton Mack Trucks, Cargo Trailers, Jeeps, Mobile Shops, Deep Water Fording Kits and Batteries. Tank-Automotive Branch hears from Detroit that 619 mixed medium tanks M4A1 and M4A3 designated in August for conversion were to be converted (100) to M32B1 Tank Recovery Vehicles and (519) M32B3 Tank Recovery Vehicles. Production Order issued for the conversion to Personnel Carriers of 331 K–67A Semi-Trailers. Production achievement at 89.8 per cent—up 3 per cent over August.

Machine tool shortages impose hurdles. Civilian personnel total at 3,277 as compared with September 1943 total of 3,020. Military personnel at 191, up 9. Advance payments authorized during

1944 Critical Ammunition schedules call for many conferences; in this one, sitting left to right—Jack Miller, Lt. Colonel H. Ken Kelley, Ammunition Branch Chief; Captain, then Lieutenant, William J. Feigley, Captain Corbit S. Hoffman, Jr., John J. Target, Julius Gussman and Captain, H. Melvin Gingrich. Standing, left to right—Cy Cosgrove, Daniel Murphy and Edward Nahill

the month were to a total of $2,580,000: Liquidation, $79,090. Upon request through channels from Lt. General Brehon B. Somervell, the Fiscal Officer, Major J. C. Hoffman, was required to prepare work sheets, schedules, flow charts, reports and related data applicable to Fiscal Branch operations; the result bringing "Greetings and Salutations" from Major J. C. King of the O.C.O. Fiscal Office and from Colonel James D. McIntyre of the War Department General Staff. Lieutenant F. W. Sinram relieved of duties as Officer-in-Charge at Harrisburg Steel Corporation.

Decrease reported in number of items requiring planning. Capacity lacking for Fuze and Shell items. With smaller war plants activities on decline, Unit Chief, Caleb F. Fox, III, is assigned additional planning duties. Smaller war plants prime contracts to the number of 171 divided $79,865,000. Labor continues in critical shortage. Procurement Planning Unit lends a hand in preparing the operations of Cressona Ordnance Plant. Selective Service was adding difficulties to RAD "must programs." One hundred and fifty-eight RAD contracts are to a dollar value of $3,698,000. Packing Section importantly concerned with the preparation for extended storage at the warehouse of material to which title on terminated contracts had been taken by the Government. Gage procurements drop from 1,554 in August, to 752 units in September; with dollar total dropping from $76,550. to $41,010.70.

As War Aid Tool Equipment now was a Treasury Department activity, contracts were no longer being received by the War Aid Tool Unit of P.O.D. Production Equipment Section. Distribution was made of machine tools returned by England to the United States. Shipped overseas on Lend-Lease, these tools had been found in excess of needs. Captain D. B. Robb and Lieutenant Paul Jones of the Property Branch conduct a "Property School" as an aid to interested members of the Property Disposal and Terminations Units of the Commodity Branches. Other classes in the Property Branch were for the training of Branch personnel in IBM machine operations: Seventy persons attended.

Prime Contracts and Purchase Orders under administration supervision were to a dollar total of $1,980,565,138.74 covering 1,954 awards divided among 595 Prime Contractors. Dollar value of Production of major end items, components and spare parts were to a value of $37,766,738.01. Four hundred thirty-two awards added up to $78,461,597.72. Sixty-seven contractors now had accepted delegation of authority to settle subcontractors' claims up to $10,000. Terminations Branch now providing training for all Branch personnel. Cheers for the competency and courtesy of W. M. McKee, H. G. Stewart and T. H. Roth of the Price Adjustment Board, in reference to a clearance for the year 1943 under the Renegotiation Law, come from H. W. Prentis, Jr., President, Armstrong Cork Company.

Chapter LVIII

NEWS REEL, 1944 — PART THREE

OCTOBER, a fast war, and a fast P.O.D. By October 1944 we were shipping out obsolete files in mounting volume. This month, 6,375 pounds of 'em were heading toward Curtis Bay. Third Service's Philadelphia Motor Pool was stamping a "must" on mileage reduction. P.O.D. responded with a 33⅓ per cent cut. But telephone charges still were hovering around $21,000. Under urging of General Eisenhower, ammunition programs again were given the needle. Undelivered machine tools were snagging Fuze and Booster quotas. "Accent on Ammunition" brought teletypes and allocations in dizzying volume. 500,000 M51A4 Fuzes, 500,000 M21A4 Boosters, 160,000 Fin Assemblies for the 100 pound M85 Practice Bomb, 3,750,000 60 mm. Shell, M49A2, 500,000 90 mm. Projectiles, M82, 5,000,000 Shell, 105mm., M1. No Pollyanna stuff, this. Under this pressure came a Knute Rockne change in line-up: Major Ernest J. Langham takes over the No. 1 post; Major Ed. W. Lafferty is assigned as Chief, Heavy Shell Section, Captain Fred W. Wedler to the Medium Shell Program. Fuzes to Captain E. H. Uhler, Bombs and PEP to Lieutenant Nieman; Julius Gussman and others remain at their old posts . . . . Comes hefty boosts in demand for 60 mm. Mortar M2, and Multiple Rocket Launchers, 7.2″.

Sid J. Trotter goes to Artillery-Small Arms Branch to head the newly established Spare Parts Control Section. Manpower shortage still a tough hurdle. On 18 October, Day & Zimmermann is formally awarded contract to operate Cressona Ordnance Plant; Major Howard P. Klair named Commanding Officer. To 18 October, 3,200,000 pounds of material is received from battle areas. Mack Manufacturing Corporation turns out 727 ten-ton trucks, up 183 from September level. United War Chest Drive launched in P.O.D. by the District Chief, C. Jared Ingersoll . . . . Twenty-seven P.O.Ders receive suggestion awards; the highest, $800, to Dave Clark of Tank-Automotive Branch

for a suggestion that spare links be supplied with tow chains. Now, 3,067 persons on District payroll. Same month, 1943, 3,327. Officer strength climbs to 194; WAC Detachment, to 37. Promotions move 1st Lieutenant Robert P. Fugate and Edward C. Peterson to Captaincies; James R. Aydelotte and Leroy M. Bissett into the 1st Lieutenant spots.

Fiscal Branch initiates a study of terminated cost-plus-a-fixed-fee-contracts, with a view toward granting partial payments which would be a means whereby advance payments could be liquidated and financial relief immediately given the contractor. Chief of Ordnance using Baldwin Locomotive Works' cost-plus-a-fixed-fee contract termination as a "guinea pig." Major, then Captain, E. R. Uhler, assigned additional duty as District Integration Officer on the M51A4 Fuze. Eighty-four Prime Contracts awarded in October to smaller war plants in P.O.D. topped $32,690,000. The month brings in $4,021,418 in RAD business. Increasing packaging complaints practically a barometer of increasing production. Blythe J. Minnier, one of long term P.O.Ders, goes to Rochester Ordnance District; but like Lassie, he soon comes home. As of 1 October, Property Disposal Branch had on hand $8,590,348 worth of material; this was upped by $3,847,876 during the month; sales were to $6,812,163, leaving a backlog of $5,626,061. Not bad. Cheers for Lt. Colonel A. W. Gilmer and Lieutenant Philip H. Andress from Brig. General Donald Armstrong, Commandant, Army Industrial College, for assistance during his exploration of P.O.D. Terminations routines.

November. Ammunition production still in high

Cecelia M. McNamara

Rose Sopinski

gear. Artillery-Small Arms Branch reports 213 contracts covering 235 items in 92 plants, the Branch still hitting around 100 per cent on Accuracy of Prediction. Bethlehem Steel Company notified to prepare for expanded production on 105 mm. Howitzer M2A1. A P. O. D. report states Baldwin Locomotive Works halted on Tank Recovery M32B1 program due to critical lack of "wrenches." Barclay White Company breaking their own crating records with 40,983 items including 10 and 6 Ton Trucks, Jeeps and Trailers 'wrapped up" for overseas delivery. Sixth War Loan Drive launched in P. O. D. 22 November. Lieutenants James E. Oyer and William M. Middledorf of the Army Air Forces are featured speakers. "Local" talent furnished by Elizabeth Zerone of the Tank-Automotive Branch, Betty Dawson and Mary L. McGonigle of the Property Branch and Margaret B. Dougherty of the Civilian Personnel Branch. Personnel total at 3,092, including attached units. Military personnel drops one to 193. Promotions up with First Lieutenants Thomas E. Bogert, Edwin G. Chambers, Howard S. Gallaher, Ross T. Henderson, and Jesse C. Jessen going up a notch. Second Lieutenants taking bows were William J. Crockett, Paul J. Grumbly, Stanley M. Levenson and James H. Nisbet. Fiscal Branch begins working out a procedure for handling interim financing on terminated contracts . . . Captain F. A. Pohl of the Office of the Fiscal Director, Office, Chief of Ordnance, declared P. O. D. Fiscal procedures to be one of the best among organizat'ons he had visited. Advance Payments liquidated reach $17,117,431.51 for the month, more than $15,-000,000 over October's total.

Procurement Planning Section on feverish search for facilities equipped to handle reinstated Ammunition items. Smaller War Plant Sections, Caleb F. Fox III, reports 68 Prime Contracts dividing $76,791,000. Because a Union allegedly objected to non-union carpenters patching a floor, 681 man-hours of production were lost in November in a P. O. D. contractor's plant on the 90 pound Fragmentation Bomb Program. The Tag on RADs for November read $4,924,391. Helen V. Meehan received ASF Service Ribbon marking 25 years' continuous service to P. O. D.

The Packaging Section is enlarged in November 1944, to handle terminated Government-owned materials and machine tools, both for shipment to other contractors, Depots and Government-owned

warehouses. Freight shipments top 148,000 tons. Property Disposal Branch started off in November with $5,626,061 worth of material on hand for disposal; "something new was added" to the extent of $3,526,930; of which $4,914,615.00 was disposed of, leaving a backlog of $4,238,376.

December. Ammunition procurement still "hitting on high"—Practice Bomb M38A2, Black Powder, Dynamite, M51A3 Fuzes, 60 mm. Shell M49A2, M100A2, and M103A3 Fuzes, Adapter Cluster M3A1, TNT, Demolition Blocks, to mention a few. Heavy Shell production victimized by undelivered machine tools. Fuze program invades E. G. Budd Manufacturing Company, Wright Automatic Machine Company, Fleetwings Division of Henry Kaiser, Bulova Watch Company and Ocean City Manufacturing Company. Major Wexlin acquires an AAA priority on headaches following failure of Clay Pigeon quota. Heavy-Heavy Trucks continue in heavy-heavy demand.

Barclay White Company, on basis of telephone instructions, begins construction of boxes for emergency deadline shipment of 365,000 yards of Cotton Fabric and 1,664,000 pounds of Carbon Black and kept the appointment. Production at ACF of 750 Howitzer Motor Carriages, M37, was estimated at $1,055,000 for Jigs and Fixtures and such; $3,598,000 for additional machine tools. P. O. D. Civilian Personnel at 2,888; Attached Units, 232. Military at new high of 208; Enlisted Personnel, 144, the WAC Detachment accounting for 41. Affable Art Allison and Donald A. Anderson join the Majors. Rationing of cigarettes is begun in P. O. D. Baldwin Locomotive Works cost-plus-a-fixed-fee contract Termination is accomplished: Another District first! Negotiated Settlement portion was of approximately $86,000,000; the terminated portion approximately $203,000,000.

Reversals in European Theatre have Procurement Planning Section on edge. One hundred and two prime contracts absorb 37,535,000 Smaller War Plant dollars. RAD Section lists 125 contracts, valued at $2,700,492.52. Material Control Section picks up 1,806,317 pounds of steel against a required 3,397,352 pounds—J. Ed. Moore, Chief, setting the pace.

In December, 7 cost-plus-a-fixed-fee contracts for packaging excess Government-owned property and termination inventory acquired for Government account were placed with P. O. D. facilities.

Seventy-five per cent of Gage Procurements now Emergency Urgent. Production Equipment Section given responsibility for Inspection and Segregation of a large quantity of British Shell Turning Equipment shipped to U. S. to expedite the Heavy Shell program. Pre-Termination comes in for some de-emphasizing in order that Production, now critical, might have right of way. Terminations training course set up for contractors. Heintz Manufacturing Company selected for the tryout. Fifty per cent of the Company's subcontractors and suppliers attended: Credit Captain, Lieutenant Phil M. Andress. Redistribution Center, Pencoyd,

Pennsylvania, now definitely in business, with Lieutenant Phil J. Fields as Officer-in-Charge.

Property Disposal Branch finds market for $6,812,163 of inventories, leaving backlog of $5,626,061. P. O. D. closes Sixth War Bond Drive with a score of 103.4 per cent of quota. $126,098.35. Percentage of employees participating now 99.9 per cent and with 12.7 per cent of payroll. Prime Contracts and Purchase Orders under administration, 2,032, valued at $2,015,423,174.86. The month closed on a total of 407 Awards—worth $48,398,693.82. Dollar value of Accepted Production—$46,206,337.

Making it hot for bad neighbors! The war economy
has taken over in earnest

Chapter LIX

NEWS REEL, 1945

JANUARY: Determined to throw a "haymaker," or a reasonably accurate facsimile thereof, at the Axis, 1,090 of the "faithful" in P. O. D. voted to contribute one day of work "for free." Sunday the 21st was the day selected. In addition, 200 went to work in the Bethlehem, York, Baltimore and Richmond Regional Offices. 'The effect on industry was good," said the District Chief, C. Jared Ingersoll. "The extra work will speed the delivery of $2,000,000 worth of combat equipment." Two hundred G. I.'s get 90-day furloughs to work in War Plants. Newspapers carry story of 800 men at Barclay White Company working 98 hours a week for three weeks in snow and rain, along with Lieutenant Oren H. Persons and his crew, to crate and ship critical equipment needed in ETO. Chester Tank Depot prepares and ships largest single high priority cargo of tanks ever shipped overseas—150 of the 32 Ton General Shermans.

To date, 130,000 Tanks, Half Tracks, Armored Trucks and Scout Cars had been processed through Chester and to Ports of Embarkation. Due to publicity given the "Work or Fight Bill," applications in January in the P. O. D. area, through the War Manpower Commission, increased approximately 35 per cent. The records pile up. This time, Cressona Ordnance Plant in period of ten days disassembles, examines, cleans, replaces defective parts of and reassembles 300 Machine Guns, Model 1919A4, Cal. .30. The District Chief receives for the District a citation presented by Lewis H. Bieler, Chairman Red Cross Donor Service in recognition of liberal P. O. D. blood donations. Obsolete files were now going to Curtis Bay to a monthly average of 2½ tons.

P. O. D. cars rolled up 39,011 miles; burned up 2,928 gallons of gas. Telephone conversations cost our Uncle $21,919.53 for the month. Ammunition Branch accounted for 135 Contracts and Purchase Orders. P. O. D. awards its first contract to Kaiser Industries, Incorporated—3,750,000

Boosters M21A4. Getting this contract under way was an achievement of the Colonel A. D. Kelso, Major E. J. Langham technique.

Heavy Shells roll off the lines—30,204 of Shell 8 in., M106 and 60,052 of 155 mm. Machine tool deliveries still a pain in the bottleneck. Experiments being made with electronic inspection of Shell Forgings. Heavy-Heavy Trucks by Autocar Company, Mack Manufacturing Company, and Corbitt Company add up to 1,355 units. Barclay White Company crated 5,741 vehicles—shipped 7,069. Resident Inspectors in training now numbered 121. As of end of month only six civilian employees were not participating in payroll Bond deductions. P. O. D. personnel now at 3,237 as result of drive to keep pace with expanded Ammunition and other programs. Officers count 224, and 102 for Enlisted men and 55 for the Army ladies. This was Ed Lynch's month—something was added to his single bar. For Joe Baxter, it now was: "Yes, Major," "Good morning, Major," etc. Fiscal Branch annexes thirteen Warrant Officers. As they might say in the financial reports: "Advance Payments and Liquidations firm to active"—with Advances at $1,000,328.79; Liquidations at $1,075,649.19. And here comes word that the 1944 Payroll grossed $7,118,013.12. Price Adjustment Section received largest single refund to date, $46,500,000—from ACF. The business of rooting out additional capacity for anything, these days, is a major activity: Now it is the 75 mm. Shell. Finally turn up sources for a combined 300,000 per month—at Bonney Forge & Tool Works and Coplay Cement Manufacturing Company. Smaller War Plants contracts total 138, to a value of $70,518,000. RAD Section reports 128 open contracts at $2,979,918.00. Material Control Section clicks on Steel procurement, corralling 3,868,467 of a wanted 6,883,535 pounds. New Gage procurement at $74,884.05. Redistribution Center disposes of $1,130,437 worth of material.

February: The month of "Production for Total Victory" from the dinner and speech-making fiesta of the same name. Held 5 February at the Bellevue-Stratford, under the auspices of the Philadelphia Post A.O.A. with the District Chief, C. Jared Ingersoll, waving the baton. Ordnance Chief Lieutenant General Levin H. Campbell, Jr., the speaker of the evening and first recipient of the John C. Jones Ordnance Medal, told of his visits with the Commanding Generals in the various battle areas—and stressed first-hand the needs for production as he received them. Other speakers were F. W. Stephenson, President, American Car & Foundry Company; Walter F. Perkins, Vice President, Bartlett-Hayward Division of the Koppers Company; Joseph Colen, President, Machined Metals Company, and Keen Johnson, Vice President, Reynolds Metals Company and former Governor of Kentucky. Henry P. Patchett, Major E. J. Langham, Captain Lewis L. A. Smith, Jr., and others did a stand-out job in arrangements.

P. O. D., once more, in February, witnessed the spectacle of entire programs being cancelled or, at least, retarded. At the same time, procurement was at top level, and Accuracy of Prediction at 95.4 per cent; a bit better than January. Acceptance by O. C. O. of realistic P. O. D. schedules accounted in the main for the step-up. Forgings moving out of the bottleneck area. Messrs. Julius Gussman, Kemper, George D. Keller, Seymour Preston, John J. Target, Lee Matter and other P. O. D. snoopers still turning in mileage—and results. Small Arms scores 100 per cent on graded contracts. Barclay White Company crated 7,910 Tank-Automotive Items—Trucks, Trailers, Mobile Shops and sundries—shipped 8,366. Civilian Personnel tips the scales at 3,322.

Efficiency ratings of 2,995 civilians were completed in February. Annual Red Cross Drive under way.

Civilian Awards for Suggestions still a popular feature; 12 reported. Mileage down to 36,819—gas to 2,928 gallons. Telephones up $2,000 to $21,919.53. Smaller War Plants contracts drop to 147; dollars to $58,998,000. Strikes becoming less a production hurdle. Only three in February. Still, however, a critical shortage of skilled labor. O. C. O. reports contractors turning out from 32 per cent to 15 per cent more Ammunition and components with increase in manpower of only 26 per cent. RAD contracts at 128—written in dollars, $2,979,000. Materials Control Section able to

supply only 4,096,027 of 16,921,997 pounds on S. O. S. Redistribution Center sales drop to $625,545.00. Property Disposal Branch moves out $3,010,327.00 worth of material, leaving backlog $3,494,465.00.

For the second successive month there was a sharp upturn in the number of terminations cases authorized: In February, 116—49 over January.

March: P. O. D. announces that 44 per cent of all new contracts were landing in Smaller War Plants employing less than 500 workers each. Ammunition Branch boosts its Accuracy record to 98.4 per cent. During month there were made 105 new Ammunition awards—to a dollar total of $35,100,000.00. District Accuarcy at 98.3 per cent is the highest yet. P. O. D. producers of Grenade, Rifle A. T. M9A1 received substantial cuts in quotas following Brigadier General R. E. Hardy's schedule readjustment meeting in Cincinnati. Bomb, Fragmentation, 90 lb., M82 also came in for some surgery. Harrisburg Steel Corporation exceeds by 8,200 units its scheduled production of 35,000 Shell, 8 in., M106, and now was set for 45,000 units per lunation—that's month, son. The 105 mm. Illuminating Shell, new to the District, goes to Elliott-Lewis Company, for 275,000 units.

Major Bill Eadie, returning to U. S. following service overseas, reports U. S. shells fired at Germans three weeks after leaving plants over here. Cancellations of gun forgings on the move, particularly the 90 mm. and 76 mm. Heavy Heavy Trucks up to 1,429. W. L. H. Bunker of the Tank-Automotive Branch, and W. E. English and Thomas Gallagher of Philadelphia Regional Office go witch hunting along Battery Row.

Civilian Personnel tallies 3,298. Officers 244. WACs still marking off 56. Red Cross Drive ending 31 March reaches $5,541.64. Military newcomers were First Lieutenant Albert E. Smith from the Alaskan Theatre; Second Lieutenant Louis Rosenstein reporting from the China-Burma-India Theatre. Advances reported at $11,360,400; Liquidations mark $11,042,792.53—the old Stokes balancing act—"There it goes! and Here it Comes!"

The thinking of the District now taking a turn toward the possibility of an early VE Day and attendant problems; among them, terminations, disposals, scrap, warehousing and such. Smaller War Plants procurements begin tapering off. SWP primes awarded in March, 159, worth $62,243,-000.

"Under-thirty" men deferred until now by Selective Service were receiving induction notices. Fewer RAD open contracts, but to larger dollar value—123, down 46 from February total of 169, but up $2,310,190.00 to $5,610,149.00. Material Control Section has orders for 16,912,997 pounds of Steel: rounds up a "mere" 4,096,027 pounds.

Captain Cecil Bentley, Packaging Section Chief, accompanied by assistant, W. W. Roberts, drops by Frankford Arsenal for a two-day chat in reference to Fire Control Major Items.

P. O. D. Termination Handbook issued—a Lt. Colonel A. W. Gilmer-Lieutenant P. M. Andress enterprise. Almost 80 per cent of terminations processed during first three months, 1945, resulting in "no-charge" settlements. Disposals at the Redistribution Center at $983,689 up better than 50 per cent from February. Property Disposal Branch unloads a volume of material tagged at $3,010,327 filing for April a backlog of $3,494,-654. Eighty-two terminations cases authorized during the month. There were 137 cases pending as the month ended.

Prime Contracts and Purchase Orders under administration, 2,602, to a dollar value of $2,146,-493,058.61. New Awards, 547, price-marked at $66,431,680.72. Accepted Production, $55,255,-991.

April: To keep the plants humming from VE Day to final Victory, the District Chief on 12 April wrote all contractors requesting that they review plans for handling VE Day announcement. ". . . vital for you," he wrote, "to take the necessary steps to insure such protection so that production may be continued after the period of celebration without delay or loss." The response was gratifying. Plants posted bulletins, distributed instructions, called meetings—got results.

A Work Simplification Program under the generalship of Major Joe C. Hoffman, Fiscal Chief, gets under way. In Ammunition Branch, John E. Ryan made director of the program; E. V. Barthmaier, assigned assistant. The Branch reported 163 Rated Contracts under administration; announced 105 new awards worth, approximately, $22,100,000.00.

District Chief C. Jared Ingersoll tells newsmen that production is up 35 per cent for the quarter.

Drive on to reduce at source sub-contract inspection on Ammunition items. Branch up .9

per cent to an Accuracy score of 97.5 per cent. Toluene still critical. Two facilities, Sinclair Refining Company and Barrett Division, produce 690,-081 gallons in April. New contracts to Barrett and Gulf Refining Company call for total of 4,900,000 gallons.

Cancellations included Adapter Clusters, AN-M1A3; Grenades, Rifle, Smoke, T-12, M22 and M19A1; Trunnion Band, M2A1. Artillery-Small Arms reports administration of 230 contracts covering 262 items in 75 plants. Autocar, Corbitt and Mack roll 1,197 military vehicles; 645 Commercial vehicles. Captain Lewis A. Smith, Jr., Chief, Administration Branch, again swings axe at telephone usage. Current charges, $19,658.77. Mileage skyrockets to 55,271; gasoline to 3,411 gallons. District Production for April at 96.9 per cent.

Civilian Award winners net $445.00 for suggestions. List includes Harry V. Ayers, Sam McClenahan and Craig Biddle. Released by request—Major Joseph L. Wilmsen, Captain Harold S. Willson, Captain George F. Dennis, Captain Frank McCusker and Captain Otis L. Evans. Promoted—Henry W. Gadsden to Lt. Colonel; Albert T. Collins, Louis Rosenstein and Charles H. Strong to First Lieutenant. Captain Bob Felch of P. O. D' later to serve with 102nd Ordnance Maintenance Battalion, forwards from Germany, a Nazi flag captured by his command, displayed in Lobby, 150 South Broad Street during the 7th War Loan Drive.

Major Art B. Allison, Chief, Production Equipment Section, and Major Roland C. Disney, Assistant Chief, Industrial Division, and former Chief, Tank-Automotive, depart for E. T. O.

Termination Interim Financing Coordination Committee formed in Fiscal Branch at the direction of Philadelphia Termination Committee. Major, then Captain, C. W. Sorber named P. O. D. representative; Henry B. Reinhardt alternate. Baltimore Audit Coordination Committee formed after not-too-much ASF urging. Lieutenant H. S. Sekerak named Philadelphia representative; Charles Barnard, alternate.

Fiscal Branch declares Work Simplification would save 1,565 man-hours. Caleb F. Fox III, who had been assigned from SWP to Chief, Procurement Planning Section, was relieved to direct Work Simplification in the Section. Search soon would be on for Warehouse space for VE and VJ Day cutbacks. One hundred forty-nine SWP contracts awarded total $44,319,000. Lieutenant Harry Corbin and Lieutenant Robert Bernheim of Labor Section move over to Major Vic Smith's Philadelphia Regional Office; Lieutenant Ralph Curley awaiting orders. Four minor strikes reported—and soon settled without noticeable damage. Value of 151 Active RAD projects placed at $4,839,746. Captain Eugene H. Uhler promoted to rank of Major.

Bonds? Well, 3,711 of 'em were processed in April. Advances authorized—just one, at $72,-000; Liquidations, $11,006,304.57. "This," said C. P. S., "is better than even break."

Production Equipment Section faces increased responsibilities as terminations make more and more machine tools available for disposition. Lists of available equipment were circulated among other Ordnance Districts and Government Agencies. Lieutenant J. A. McKinney relieved of his duties as Property Officer at Chester Tank Depot. P. O. D. requested to procure 25,000,000 pounds of Dynamite for Russia. Property Branch makes 296 per cent of its 7th War Loan quota. Disposals from Redistribution Center total $346,000. Personnel cut 50 per cent. Property Disposal Branch, though moving out material to the value of $2,-378,977, is left holding a backlog of $3,308,646. Termination cases authorized doubled March's total of 82; yet dollar value of items cancelled, at $36,537,703 was up only 60 per cent.

May: This is the month that Germany ran for shelter behind the biggest "8 Ball" in all Kraut History—May 8—with the Berlin radio silenced and the be-medalled Generals whimpering: "Ve haf been licked! Ve surrender! Ve is in der dog house! Nine?" Yah! Yah!! May 8—a day to remember. Cutbacks in production were in order; were forthcoming, and pronto. Philco announces release effective five weeks hence of 1,300 employees working on Artillery Fuses and Aircraft requirements. Production generally continued throughout Districts at high pitch. Ammunition Branch administering 172 Rated Contracts; made 98 new awards to a dollar value of near $6,990,820 Production score, 97.1 per cent. Tests at Aberdeen and Jefferson Proving Grounds indicate definite relationship between dispersion and surface finish, and shortness of range and band tightness—, articularly in the 75 mm. and 105 mm. range. Blasting Cap program drastically cut. Black Powder program slashed. 240 mm. Propelling Powder NH for Howitzer M1, and T.N.T. Demolition Black

bowed out. A number of Powder and Explosives plants expected to be sans Ordnance contracts by 31 July. Bombs and other items join the cutback parade.

Brigadier General R. E. Hardy heads up another Schedule Readjustment Meeting in Chicago. Some Fin Assemblies, Fragmentation Bomb Rockets, Grenade Adapters contracts feel the knife. Forging contracts feel the May blight . . . Barclay White crates over 120,000—about even with shipments—contents range from Batteries to Jeeps and Trucks. Terminations move in on Tank-Automotive items, registering reductions at Autocar of 4–5 and 5–6 Ton Trucks and Replenishment Parts, 1/4 Ton, 2 Wheel Trailers at Strick Company, Cargo Bodies, 80 in. by 144 in., at Mason Manufacturing Company; 7 1/2 Ton Truck, 6 by 6, and Replenishment Parts cancelled in entirety—and the same for certain batteries, to mention a few. P. O. D. production in May at 97.1 per cent.

Civilian Personnel dips to 3,044. Officer strength at 251, not to mention 69 WACS and 87 Enlisted men. By way of promotions, Albert W. Gilmer to Lt. Colonel, and Second Lieutenants Howard D. Ginsberg, James I. Kelley and Robert G. Tabors to higher echelon.

Catherine C. Conroy replaces Howard Biles as Civilian Personnel Branch Administrative Chief, who is reassigned with Mrs. Elizabeth Farnum, under John Wood, Chief, In-Service Placement Section, also Assistant Chief of the Branch. To 31 May, Civilian P. O. Ders purchase 111 per cent of quota in 7th War Loan Drive. Of Officers, 85 per cent participate; of Enlisted Men, 83.6 per cent, while civilians hold on at 99.2 per cent. Salvation Army Campaign tops $1,150. Mass production brings down materiel costs: M4 Medium Tanks drop from $70,459 to $45,846 per; the famous 76 mm. Gun Motor Carriage, M18, dubbed the "Hellcat", down to $43,287 from $53,449; the Multiple Caliber .50 Machine Gun Mount, M5, cut 55 per cent to $2,494. Kaiser Industries, $2,500,000 Booster Contract cancelled, and Scranton (Pa.) Armory procured by P. O. D. for this job turned back to owners. Cressona announces 2,000 tons of scrap lumber available free to anyone desiring any amounts of it for firewood. Civilian Pay Section, Fiscal Branch, reports delivery of 3,548 Bonds. Lump-sum payment of Retirement Deductions authorized. Advance payments, $723,353.70. Liquidations, $245,895.00.

Smaller War Plants awarded 114 prime contracts to a dollar value of $45,969,000. Three minor strikes occur. All quickly settled. Lieutenant Tom E. Bogert, RAD Liaison head, reports 151 Active Projects priced at $4,839,746. Material Control Section "puts the finger on" 2,514,909 pounds of a 7,186,417 pound Steel requirement.

End of War in Europe reflected in 50 per cent drop in overseas shipments from Chester Tank Depot. Terminations Branch personnel total upped to meet VE Day terminations. Authority granted P. O. D. to continue University of Pennsylvania contract in reference to Termination courses. The month recorded a substantial increase over April 1945 of authorized Termination cases. In April, 166 new cases; in May, 386. Dollar value of items cancelled for the cases in process rose from $36,537,703 to $137,519,023.

Property Disposal Branch parted company with material worth $4,276,485—leaving backlog of $1,809,892. Work Simplification Program completed 31 May—after 100 per cent Survey of P. O. D. jobs, covered 689,520 hours of work; saving was of 9.2 per cent man-hours. Prime Contracts and Production Orders under administration, 2,710, to a dollar total of $1,726,939,269.40. Four hundred thirty-seven new Awards total $22,789,044.34. Accepted production at $53,927,226.00.

June: Japs now seeing more of where bad little submarines go when they die. Brigadier General Alvaro Fiuza de Castro, Brazil's Chief of Ordnance and President of the Joint Brazil-U. S. Military Commission in Rio de Janeiro, and his staff, visit P. O. D., dropping in for a look-see and a chat at E. G. Budd Manufacturing Company, Read Machinery Company and A. B. Farquhar Company, Ltd. Major Ed. Lafferty, Ammunition Branch, was released by the Army for special services for the Government in China; Captain William A. Dilks, late of the Budd Field Office in Bustleton, takes over. In June the Ammunition Branch was administering 161 Rated Contracts; made 80 new awards . . . Artillery-Small Arms Branch reports 219 contracts covering 172 items in 71 plants. Survey reveals inspection standards relaxed during production drive. All save two gun forging contracts cancelled: those on Gun, 90 mm., T15 and Howitzer, 8 in., M1, at Midvale Company and Bethlehem Steel Company.

District Chief C. Jared Ingersoll resigns following a long illness—the penalty, no doubt, for his unselfish and enthusiastic devotion to his responsi-

bilities. Lt. Colonel A. Donald Kelso relinquishes his post as Industrial Chief to assume District command. Major Ernest J. Langham moves up to the Industrial post. "Spare Parts" still best stimulant of aspirin sales. Terminations slash remanufacture of Light Tanks at American Car & Foundry Company, Trucks, 4–5 Ton, 4 by 4 Tractor at Autocar, 10 Ton, 6 X 4 Trucks and replenishment "spare parts" at Mack Manufacturing Corporation; Cargo Bodies, 80 in. by 144 in. at Mason Manufacturing Company; Trailers, 1/4 Ton, 2 wheel Cargo, at Strick Company, and Surgical Bodies at York-Hoover Corporation. Comes word that a number of the Light M3 Tanks (General Stuarts) made in P. O. D. in 1942 were used through 1944–1945 by the 7th Light Cavalry Regiment of the 12th British Army in Burma, fighting all the way to Rangoon; the only armor included in the "impossible" operation of slashing through the Kabaw Valley in 1944. Colonel J. M. Barlow, Commanding Officer, stated not one of the M3s had become unbattle-worthy.

Production in June, according to W. E. Gilbert, Production Chief, at 98 per cent. Civilian Personnel at 2,923 is on the way down; dips 282 from May. Officers' strength in District, 265—in P. O. D. alone, 167. WACS make up 61 of total. Promotions, ten Second Lieutenants move up a notch: they are Walter R. Griffin, Elvon R. Hamilton, Donald B. Kimmell, Stanley B. Honour, Earl H. Lentz, John A. McKinney, Robert B. O'Reilly, John H. Schumacher, Francis M. Watson and Laur Don G. Wheaton. Old timers move out permanently: they are Lt. Colonel Hayward K. Kelley and Captain Corbit Hoffman, Jr. Also, Captain Cecil Bentley of Packaging. Master Sgt. Jacob J. Westerhoff of the Terminations Branch awarded Bronze Star for service in France. Major General Williams, British Ordnance Chief, pays P. O. D. a return visit. Bond deliveries in June put at 3,705. Advance Payments authorized during month, $1,114,578; Liquidations, $8,682,522.32 —nice business. Smaller War Plants Contracts total at 79, to a dollar value of $62,627,000.

No strikes in June. Two hundred and thirty-six Active RADs valued at $8,893,677. Material Control Section harvest 2,220,950 pounds of a needed 12,541,744 pounds of Steel. Gage procurement down to $20,752. During month, 272 Terminations cases were authorized; 480 pending as month faded out. The Redistribution Center at Pencoyd accounted for disposals to a dollar value of $425,309. Property Disposal Branch moves out $3,457,826 worth of material, leaving backlog of $1,674,961.

Sara Dailey and Emma Kerstetter, Ordnance Inspectors at Billard Machine and Tool Company, Mansfield, Pennsylvania, receive from the District Chief, C. Jared Ingersoll, Certificates of Commendation for saving Government property during a recent fire in the plant.

Army Public Relations reports 21,411,899 tons of supplies of all kinds were discharged in European ports during the late war; four times World War I deliveries. That mileage business again. This time, 50,561 miles; 3,085 gallons of gasoline. Telephone charges dip slightly to $12,217.89. Prime Contracts and Purchase Orders under administration, 2,637, to a dollar value of $1,654,269,507.26. New Awards, 398, worth $28,445,407.85. Accepted production marked up at $47,891,760.

July: Japanese weather note: "Increasingly warmer for Tokyo and environs, with showers— of what it takes." From Major General Henry P. Sayler comes the report that 11 months of ETO cost O. C. O. 865,056 weapons of various kinds— 81,379 vehicles including 13,056 Tanks, 1,625 Amphibious units. Hence the slogan: "By By Hitler; Buy Buy Bonds." Ammunition Branch achieves 100 per cent Accuracy of Prediction, administers 141 Rated Contracts and places 82 new awards worth $17,692,916.00.

Terminations roll merrily along. Artillery-Small Arms Branch again comes through to hang up a 100 per cent Accuracy record. Crating and Shipping at Barclay White Company misses 93,000 by the slim margin of 4 units. The 79th Congress passes the New Pay Bill. "Within-grade" promotions and reassignments in line with new rulings total 1,045. Tabulation of 7th War Loan results indicate 99.6 per cent civilians participating to average of 12 per cent of pay. District Chief Lt. Colonel A. Donald Kelso and John W. Thomas, Chairman of the Board, Firestone Tire & Rubber Company, announce, 21 July, that the company's new tire plant, Pottstown, Pennsylvania, which had been under construction for the preceding six months, in connection with the nation's tire program, will immediately be converted as an Army Reclamation Depot for the reconditioning of critically needed damaged war materiel. The plant later was to be known as the Pottstown Ordnance Plant; Captain Robert D. Scarlett in command. Principal items to be processed in the Pottstown Ordnance Plant

to include automotive and tank spare parts, tools, batteries, chains, generators, distributors, carburetors, fuel pumps, shock absorbers and other automotive and tank maintenance items. An employment of 2,500 persons is predicted.

Suggestions and Awards Committee is now constituted—Major Joe C. Hoffman, Fiscal Head, Chairman; Captain Lewis A. Smith, Jr., Samuel McClenahan, Civilian Personnel Coxswain, and Helen B. McNally of the silver voice, Secretary. Top award of the month was of $100 to Chester W. Graves of Artillery-Small Arms for his suggestion that, in view of the then surplus of forgings, all replacements be checked by teletype or telephone through O. C. O. Cannon Sub-Office to determine whether a surplus existed elsewhere. Suggestions received to date reach 1,122. Civilian total of personnel dips to 2,508. Strictly P. O. D. Military at 148; WACS at 57; Enlisted men tally 63. The indefatigable Philip M. Andress, John P. Grimwade and Neal W. Slack raised to Captain status. Frank P. Hagenbuch acquires a First Lieutenancy. Through the door marked "Exit" go Captain Frederick C. Wedler and First Lieutenant James I. Kelley. For outstanding record of discipline P. O. D. Enlisted Detachment is awarded the Special Meritorious Unit Plaque.

Civilian Pay Section loses genial Lieutenant C. W. Crockett to Office, Chief of Ordnance. Passes crown to WOJG Anthony O. Carter. Bi-weekly pay periods established.

Advance Payments register $279,048; Liquidations, $3,382,351.48. A Giant 45 Ton, M-26, General Pershing Tank from Chester Tank Depot spends 4th of July holiday in Philadelphia as part of celebration. To protect street surfaces, the monster was ridden in on 40 Ton Tractor-Trailer. Cancellations at Mack Manufacturing Corporation. S. W. P. does a July business involving 57 prime contracts to a dollar value of $17,899,000. Active RADs total 156. B. C. Bell, long of Steel Expediting Unit, resigns; a top performer all the way. When no one else could—he did. J. J. Brady, Surplus Property Liaison Officer of Material Control Section, joins Sid Press of Property Disposal Branch. In July, 7 cost-plus-a-fixed-fee and 6 Time and Material Contracts are placed with packaging facilities for packaging excess Government-owned property and termination inventory for Government account. Newspapers featuring pictures of tests, 57 mm. Recoilless Rifle—weighing 45 pounds, in contrast with 2700 pound 57 mm.

Anti-Tank weapon wheeled carriage. Hurls 3 pound shell 2 miles. Also pictured is 110 pound, 75 mm. Gun, contrasted with its 3700 pound ancestor. This "meanie" can chuck a 14 pound shell up to 4 miles with deadly accuracy. Used against Japs.

Production Equipment Section transfers to Property Disposal Branch, 416 items valued at $853,926.06 which it earlier had processed. Third survey of machine tools 89 per cent complete as month ended. Statistics and Progress Section down to a personnel of 6: a far cry from the boom days during the Lafean regime when the total hit a well rounded 55. Redistribution Center going full blast; now handling 2,000 and more items ranging from specialized screws to large equipment, in building almost half mile from stem to stern. Disposes of $521,000 worth of material during July; ships to schools and colleges for use in pre-induction training a quantity of equipment tagged at $135,000—all for free. Quantities of small items sent to Vet hospitals where occupational therapy groups wrangle out odds and ends of jewelry.

Franklin Institute inherits a 10 in. experimental rocket. From Washington comes word that to date a country-wide reduction in war contracts of $16,300,000,000 had been effected; 2,500 contracts involved. P. O. D. Property Disposal Branch disposes of $12,044,655 worth of material, leaving backlog of $2,532,829. During the month 271 Terminations cases were authorized, with 598 cases pending as the month ended. Pottstown plant of Firestone Tire & Rubber Company and Jacobs Aircraft Engine Company turned over to P. O. D. on reclamation project. Preparations rushed to receive trainloads of materials and equpment from camps and embarkation points. Prime Contracts and Purchase Orders under administration, 2,508 of them, figured in dollars reach $1,619,169,321.52. Three hundred and forty-seven new awards top $40,202,000. Accepted production at $38,795,572.54.

And that's the news to now.

August: With earth-shattering impacts came the blow that wiped from the face of time the ages-old city of Hiroshima and brought to its knees the once power-mad empire of Nippon. That was on 6 August, when an American plane dropped the first Atomic Bomb to be employed as a weapon of war. Before the enemy had an opportunity to recover, the second bomb fell; this one on Nagasaki.

The world was aghast. Man had torn from Nature the very secret of creative energy and had turned it against those who would destroy him, and by the same token had blasted his way into a new age for man. On 10 August the Japs offered to surrender. On 14 August Japan formally accepted the surrender terms but dawdled deep into September before her diplomats boarded the old Missouri in Tokyo harbor to bow to General Douglas MacArthur, and to sign on the dotted line. At any rate, the shooting war was over, VJ Day was here and, for the moment at least, nothing else mattered very much.

Greetings from Lt. General Levin H. Campbell, Jr., Chief of Ordnance, to the District Chief. He writes, 15 August: "May I extend to you in this hour of final victory my warmest congratulations and great admiration for the outstanding job which has been done by you and your staff, men and women, working in closest cooperation with industry to accomplish the greatest production of munitions known throughout history."

Lt. Colonel A. Donald Kelso advanced to the rank of Colonel. Captain Homes T. Case promoted to Major. P. O. D. goes on 40 hour week. Among other honors to the District Chief he is appointed ASF representative in War Production Board Region 3, succeeding Brigadier General A. A. Farmer, former Commanding General, Philadelphia Signal Corps Depot., to be charged with supervision and administration of ASF matters of procurement and production through ASF representatives. Captain Lewis A. Smith, Jr., Major J. C. Hoffman and Joseph W. Stone elected to develop plans for orderly liquidation of District Office space and equipment, and more efficient arrangement of Branches and Sections facing diminishing activity.

Ammunition Branch administering three Rated Contracts as compared with 141 in July. Approximate value of Ammunition Contracts cancelled following VJ Day—$92,998,229.52. George D. Keller resigns. The President declares a two-day holiday for Government employees to celebrate Victory. Civilian Personnel to 2,313. Military, in P. O. D., 143; WACs 65; Enlisted men, 65. One hundred civilian employees separated from the rolls; 500 additional being processed. Meritorious Civilian Service Emblem and Citations signed by General Brehon H. Somervell, Commanding General, Army Service Forces, and Lt. General Levin H. Campbell, Jr., were presented by Colonel A. D Kelso to

William E. Gilbert, Production Director; Marie M. Jackson, Legal Branch; Mary R. Lenny, Nurse; Samuel McClenahan, Chief, Civilian Personnel Branch; Sidney S. Press, Chief, Property Disposal Branch; William P. Schmid, Engineer on Special Projects; and Eleanor Armstrong, Receptionist, widely known and admired of Ordnance and Industry; darned pretty, too. Bond participation now, for civilians, 98.7 per cent, for Enlisted personnel, 92.3 per cent, and for Officers 86. per cent. Maintaining morale in the face of rapidly diminishing personnel becomes a problem. Veteran preference an increasing consideration.

The District Chief has "press" goggle-eyed with announcement that P. O. D.'s contribution to final Victory was made up of 19,000 Light and Medium Tanks, 44,800 Mortars, 58,200 Machine Guns, 25,000 Anti-Aircraft, Artillery and Anti-Tank Shells, 10,000,000 Bombs, 10,000,000 Rockets and Hand Grenades and millions of miscellaneous items of equipment such as Body Armor, Bomb Clusters, Cartridge Cases, Adapters for Rifle Grenades, Mobile Shops and a variety of vehicles. These and many others. Expenditure was well above $2,750,-000,000. H. Powell Patchett received Gold Medal Award of Army Ordnance Association for outstanding services in connection with Philadelphia Post, AOA "Production for Total Victory" Dinner, 5 February 1945, when the John G. Jones Medal was presented to Lt. General Levin H. Campbell, Jr., Chief of Ordnance, and for his successful drive for AOA Life Memberships. Automobile mileage skids off to 40,898; gas keeps pace at 2,328 gallons. Telephone charges also strive for new lows at $11,540.38. Drive in P. O. D. for contributions adds $313.50 to the Pfc. Jimmy Wilson Fund sponsored by the Philadelphia Inquirer. This soldier had lost part of all four limbs in combat.

Sensing early in August that VJ Day was in the offing, Lt. Colonel Albert W. Gilmer, Chief, Contract-Termination Division, put his house in order for the inevitable big cancellations push. Many of the procedures in reference to VJ Day Termination developed by Lt. Colonel Gilmer were adopted by the Office, Chief of Ordnance, and other Services. To VJ Day, the organization of 130 personnel which Lt. Colonel Gilmer trained and directed, terminated in due course more than 1,000 of the 1,767 contracts in process. Those terminated were to a value of $1,000,000,000, and of these, 80% were settled within the required period of four

months from the effective date of publication, and within six months, 99% were settled.

Among August departures were Captain Robert R. Hoffman, Captain Edmund G. Barbier, Captain William R. Wilson, and First Lieutenant Albert T. Collins, who had succeeded Captain David H. McIlvaine at the Public Relations post. Use Analysis Unit, Production Equipment, clears to the Property Disposal Branch for disposition, a total of 395 items to a dollar value of $1,667,126.17. Several hundred items of production equipment were released during the month to various Arsenals, Proving Grounds and other Ordnance installations. SWP manages to gasp out 28 prime contracts at an expenditure of a "mere" $4,930,000. To meet VJ Day impacts, Property Disposal Branch ups personnel by 30 persons to bring total to 117—sixteen of these were Officers; 13 were Enlisted men; 88, civilians. Special Facilities Section of Property Disposal Branch assigned responsibility for disposing of material located at Heintz Manufacturing Company, Barclay White Company, Ford Motor Company (Chester Tank Depot), Baldwin Locomotive Works and Mack Manufacturing Corporation. Subsequent disposition of this material effected a $14,500,000 reduction in the Property Disposal Branch backlog. Redistribution Center accounts for disposals to the extent of $154,000. Property Disposal Branch disposes of material to a value of $12,094,024, leaving a backlog of $9,760,651. RAD down to 35 Open Contracts. During the month there were 216 requests for Packaging instructions. Packaging Section places 7 cost-plus-a-fixed-fee contracts; 8 Time and Material Contracts. Prime Contracts and Purchase Orders under administration number 2,200; worth $1,521,342,489.90. New Awards, only 25, and to a value of $13,935,538.07 (from 1 January to 31 August 1945, there had been made a total of 3,594 Awards, with a total dollar value of $378,759,-126.49) . . . Accepted production ambles along at $22,452,346.57.

With war out of the way, our enemies humbled, the exodus from P. O. D. of those who served it so well. Industry holding its breath as it takes a sidelong glance at the conversion period ahead. Everyone asks: "What next? Depression? Unemployment? Boom? And what about Congress? Investigation in store? Will politicians in the coming election year tear down some spotless reputations in their yen for "goats?" Possible.

Certain, if Post-War-I is a criterion. So long, August, anyway.

September: The fade-out for P. O. D. as once we knew it really has begun. Public Relations Branch discovers that the "press" is no longer hot for Ordnance items. Disbursements $87,167.86 under August's total. Report requested by O. C. O. covering active Industrial Service Contracts and the total value of undelivered parts reveals 31 such contracts, to a dollar value of $25,531,091.02. Ammunition Branch reported 3 Rated Contracts under administration; worth $279,100. Overtime hours in September at 6,602, a decrease from August of 9,737 hours. Of 394 overtime hours worked by Military personnel of Fiscal Branch, 95 per cent was on Terminations.

Announcement is made that Army would take over Cressona Ordnance Plant 18 November. The Day & Zimmermann operating contract would be terminated. Cressona personnel accepted War Department transfer to the Depot, to be operated by the Field Service. As of 10 September the Research and Development Liaison Section closes its doors. Business is transferred to pertaining Commodity Branches. RAD Chief Captain Thomas B. Bogert is reassigned as Assistant to the Chief, Industrial Division. Lieutenant L. D. Wheaton is reassigned as Assistant to the Chief of the Property Disposal Branch. P. O. D. expert "spellers" spellbind Leeds & Northrup Team in contest broadcast by Radio Station KYW on A. H. Geuting Company (Shoes) program. Winners: Nora M. Dougherty of Production Service Branch, John A. Mitchell of Terminations Branch and Louise Evenson of Ammunition; Captain Bernard M. Zimmermann earlier gave the team a workout. No Advance Payments in September; Liquidations, $792,053.72. . . . To now, 7 cost-plus-a-fixed-fee, and 12 Time and Material Contracts had been placed with Packaging Facilities in the District. During the month the Use Analysis Unit of the Production Equipment Section cleared to Property Disposal Branch 3,368 items to a dollar value of $11,123,665.05. . . . Disposals at the Redistribution Center to the total of $249,939. Property Disposal Branch moves out material worth $9,874,340, leaving a backlog of $25,280,890. Captain Robert P. Fugate succeeds Lieutenant James F. Bush, Jr., as Security and Intelligence Officer. Officer strength, P. O. D. only, 136; WACs, 2; Enlisted men, 39. Promotions: First Lieutenants

Albert E. Lee, Jr., Philip J. Fields, Wm. J. Feigley to Captains; Second Lieutenants Jerome Bennett, Guy D. Beaumont, George M. Hall and Robert J. Hinchman to First Lieutenants. That noise upstage was adieus and hand-shaking of departees Captain J. Albury Fleitas of Purchase; Major Theodore C. Sheaffer, Purchase Chief; Major John H. Beyer, Chief, Artillery-Small Arms Branch, First Lieutenant John I. Spiegelhalter, one time Travel Section head, and First Lieutenant Henry S. Sekerak, Fiscal Branch.

It was announced 14 September by Colonel Kelso, that as a result of the general policy being pursued by O. C. O. in the post-VJ Day period, the operation and management of the Cressona Ordnance Plant, and its sister installation, the Pottstown Ordnance Plant, would be transferred on or about 18 November to the Field Service. It was believed permanent employment would continue at Cressona for 1,500 employees; at Pottstown, for 1,000 employees.

Mileage definitely on the low road at 36,344 miles; gasoline, 1,903 gallons. Telephone charges at $8,431.25 also reflect demobilization trends . . . And Civilian Personnel quietly eases off to 1,635. A total of 2,030 Bonds delivered in September. Payroll participation now at 96.5 per cent for Civilians, 62.5 per cent for Officers and 87 per cent for Enlisted men.

October: Newspapers hereabouts are bare of Ordnance news. Terminations, Property Disposal personnel now constitute the elite of P. O. D., with a nod to Research and Development, Price Adjustment and the rest. The War already is two months deep in history. A sign of the times: Smaller War Plants Section goes out of business as an independent unit. SWP activities now assigned to pertaining sections in the Production Service Branch. October awards amounting to $576,000 was spread over 7 Prime Contracts. The late Chief, Harvey R. Battersby, shortly after throws in the towel and moves up to J. J. Nesbitt Company; Caleb F. Fox III, his predecessor, already ensconced with American Pulley Company. Awards, generally, in October down to $195,898.39. Just 38 of them. Three RAD Awards in Ammunition items accounted for $12,119.85. Three Rated Contracts remaining in Ammunition are to a value of $104,997.65. Cancellations during the month of 64 contracts brought a saving in appropriations of

$2,952,556.09.Advance Payments liquidated registered $15,185,099.68.

Civilian Personnel Chief, Sam McClenahan announces P. O. D. Victory Loan Quota of $100,-000.00. Civilian staff reports 1,580 remaining on rolls. Tank-Automotive Branch alone down to 18 employees. Property Disposal Branch personnel up 25, to 131. Military personnel P. O. D. only, now at 136; WACs, 43; Warrant Officers, 44; Enlisted men, 39. Bonds are off: Deliveries of 1,639 Bonds are 391 under September. Civilian participation to 98 per cent. Officers to 80 per cent and Enlisted personnel 87 per cent. Seven Meritorious Civilian Awards were made in October, Colonel A. D. Kelso passing out the honors. Awards were to H. Paul Gant, Chairman of the Board of Awards; John C. Swartley of Purchase; French E. Dennison, Chief, Inspection; Harry V. Ayers, Philadelphia Regional Office; Thomas W. Beattie, Tank-Automotive Branch; Robert T. Gebler, District Historian, and John W. Magoun, Chester Tank Depot Staff . . . Lieutenant M. P. Felton and Sgt. C. W. Lewis of Price Adjustment depart P. O. D. Maury Felton is succeeded by WOJG O. A. Carlson who subsequently is named Legal Reviewer and Chief, Administration Unit. Mileage makes spurt to 43,000—up 6,687; gasoline, 2,457—up 554 gallons. But telephone charges do another nose-dive to $7,171.96—down $1,259.29. Price Adjustment Section processes 70 Applications for Partial Payments; total value, $15,185,099.68. Checking out in October were Major Paul H. Carlson, who came up to his Baltimore Regional Office Chieftainship by way of the Industrial Division; Major Charles T. Michener, Adjutant, and Specialist extraordinary; Major Oliver C. Conger, Chief, Tank-Automotive Section, Termination Branch, and one time Chief, Richmond Regional Office; Captain W. B. Wellborn, Officer-in-Charge at Richmond; Captain John B. Jones, Chief, Storage Section, Property Branch; Captain Ralph Farnum, Assistant to Officer-in-Charge, Philadelphia Regional Office; Captain Julius Mehalek, Assistant to Chief, Production Equipment Section; First Lieutenant Bernard G. Fortmann, Assistant to Chief, Artillery-Small Arms Branch; Captain Bernard N. Zimmerman of Legal; Captain Ross T. Henderson, Member, Industry Integration Committee on Rifle Grenades and Adapter, Grenades.

As of 31 October practically all Field Office Gages had been returned. Almost entire lot Gage Equipment donated Lehigh University had been shipped. Tool Room, Gage Section, reports 1,450 items remaining following shipments to Frankford Arsenal Gage Laboratory, to various University Laboratories of equipment alloted for War Industrial Reserve and the establishment of Laboratories in educational institutions. Redistribution Center reports disposal of material to a value of $1,543,347. Use Analyst Unit clears to Property Disposal Branch, 3,197 items valued at $9,731,314.48. By 31st October, 60 per cent of leases administered by the Lease Unit, Production Equipment Section, had been closed out. Contractors affected were: Bethlehem Steel Company, Rheem Manufacturing Company, Williamsport, Pennsylvania. Lehigh Foundries, Easton, Pennsylvania, and E. G. Budd Manufacturing Company.

November: P. O. D. now is heading with increasing momentum into a period of sudden and drastic change in the organizational set-up, and be it noted that due to the finicky personnel policy established by Mr. C. Jared Ingersoll and Brigadier General Hauseman, there was always ready qualified personnel to carry on at the vacated spots. Our luck seemed never to run out. Who will say, for instance, that Captain Neal W. Slack as Chief of Property Disposal, Captain W. T. "Bill" Young at the Purchase Post, Captain Norman L. Cavedo at Chester Tank Depot, Major C. W. Sorber, now wearing the "Hoffman purple," Major Rutledge Slattery, Legal high-light, to mention a few successions, were not aces in their own rights? And as these men "folded their tents like the Arabs and silently stole away," others were to step from the ranks, and still others. Truly, P. O. D. was marching into the sunset—proudly, heads up, and the satisfaction that comes with a job magnificently done. Topping the "out list" for November appear the names of Major Ernest J. Langham, Chief, Industrial Division, the final stage of a brilliant career in P. O. D.; and Captain Richard A. Furniss, one time Chief, Bethlehem Regional Office, and at the time of his separation, Chief, Production Service Branch. Still there was much to be done at 150 South Broad Street and out over the District area. Gage Section was dismembered in November and units and personnel transferred from 1420 Walnut Street to 150 South Broad Street. The Property Unit was transferred to the Property Branch. The Procurement Liaison and Property Disposal Units combined under one engineer . . .

All Gage Activities now practically were at an end. Liquidation of the entire inventory at Firestone Tire & Rubber Company (Pottstown Ordnance Plant) accomplished save for a few Shipping Orders. Contract Record Section, Administration Branch ships to Contract Record Branch, St. Louis, Missouri, 16 boxes consolidated contract files. Number of P. O. D. forms now at 206.

To date, 11,000 pieces of P. O. D. office equipment removed from Regional Offices, Inspection Offices and contractors' plants—4,400 pieces disposed of to Aberdeen Proving Ground, Veterans Bureau at Reading, Wilkes-Barre and Richmond, and other agencies. Telephone charges slip off to $7,741.61. Automobile mileage drops to 36,173 miles at a cost of 2,452 gallons of gasoline. It was necessary through the period to monitor a number of "veterans preference" employees—those with permanent status and veterans of World War II seeking positions. Many recently reported would soon be reached on Separation Lists. In behalf of these, it would be necessary to contact other War Department installations to the end that as many as possible might be placed. Civilian personnel checks off at 1,369. Of 14 new applicants employed, 12 were classified under "Re-employment after Military Service." Tank-Automotive Branch shyly admits to a present total of 8 personnel. P. O. D. Military at 124; WACs, 38; Enlisted men, 50. During the month, Detachment No. 39,354, T50, Cressona Ordnance Plant, was increased by 6 officers. Also in November, as elsewhere reported, the Cressona Ordnance Plant became the Cressona Ordnance Depot, under Field Service, and therefore discontinued operation under cost-plus-a-fixed-fee contract with Day & Zimmermann, Philadelphia engineering firm.

Ammunition Branch administering three Rated Contracts valued at $130,255 and 17 RAD contracts spread over 9 contractors. E. I. du Pont de Nemours Company completed Powder Propelling. Cal. .60 Ball, T-32 contracts. Tank-Automotive open contracts, completed VJ Day, 328. Acceptances, Tank-Automotive Branch, $912,382.63. Shades of Martin Sandler!—notices of Awards fetch only $1,057,698.39 worth of business for contractors. Advances liquidated in November reach $9,979,500. Fifty-eight Partial Payment applications processed to a total of $6,898,996.05; paid during month, $14,455,815. To end of month, 68.8 per cent of Victory Loan quota accomplished. Payroll participation in Bonds now

97.6 per cent for civilians, 81 per cent for Officers and 87 per cent for Enlisted men. Total of Bonds issued drop 224 to 1,415. Use Analyst, Production Equipment Section clears to Property Disposal Branch, 831 items worth $1,651,325.10; 252 items for transfer reported worth $635,226.50. Property Disposal Branch rids itself of material valued at $30,471,002, leaving a backlog of $35,600,150. Redistribution Center disposes of material to a value of $1,160,117. Included were ammunition components released from Standby—production equipment released by British Government and termination inventory forwarded for disposition.

November was like that.

December. Going! Going! but not quite Gone. That was P. O. D. in December 1945. The exodus now was swinging merrily along to a peak. One fifty South Broad Street was fast taking on the depressing air of a Summer resort hotel along about the second week in September. It was during this month that Colonel A. Donald Kelso, District Chief, who came to the District in 1942, put aside the mace and betook him to his first love. Lt. Colonel Gadsden, who did such a fine job in carving his name in the annals of P. O. D., stuck it out over Christmas. And it was in December that Captain Dave McIllvaine of Public Relations fame sang his swan song. It was farewell time, too, for Captain Thomas E. Bogert, Research and Development czar; Captain Robert W. Vogelsberg of Property; Captain William T. Young of Price Analysis; Captain Edward C. Peterson, of Artillery-Small Arms; Captain James R. Stewart who, after a round of responsibilities well met, landed at Chester Tank Depot, under the command of Captain Norman L. Cavedo, also a December departee. And so on down the list; Lt. Colonel Oscar M. Hansen of the Consolidation Section, Miscellaneous Termination Branch; Captain John A. McKinney, late of the Chester Tank Depot; Captain Josef H. Buerger, Jr., who succeeded Major Johnny Beyer as Artillery-Small Arms Chief; Captain Lawrence B. Redmond, Chief, York Regional Office; Captain Oren H. Persons, Jr., who had covered the circuit from Priorities to Barclay White Company; Captain John P. Grimwade, whose final assignment had been to the Production Equipment Section top job; Captain Edwin G. Chambers, Officer-in-Charge, ACF Inspection Office; Captain Robert D. Scarlett down from Pottstown Ordnance Plant; Captain John R.

Armstrong of the Ammunition Section of Legal; Major Howard P. Klair, Commanding Officer of Cressona and Pottstown; Major Joseph I. Wexlin, without whom no Ordnance District would be complete.

More? Add First Lieutenants Frank W. Kron, Philadelphia Regional Office; Robert G. Tabors, Assistant Chief, Production Service Branch. Major Homer T. Case, one time of Philadelphia Mobile Shop Depot; Captain William A. Dilks, late Ammunition Chief; First Lieutenant Louis Rosenstein, Assistant Officer-in-Charge, Baltimore Regional Office; Captain Charles A. Sinquefield, Chief, Richmond Regional Office; First Lieutenant Jack Walsh, Labor Chief, and First Lieutenant Robert D. Bernheim, also of Labor; First Lieutenant Robert B. Lowman and Lieutenant Richman Powers, both of Fiscal; First Lieutenant Guss Kass, Officer-in-Charge, Atlas Inspection Office. And over in the WOJG Sector: Gillis W. Uhler, Henry J. McCullough, William R. Bickley, Jr., Martin C. Banell, Charles E. Swingl.y, Arthur Schwartz, Allen Appel, Jack Bell, Max J. Gillens, Jr., and Meyer Auslander, CWO, Fiscal Branch.

Major Charles W. Sorber succeeds Major Joseph C. Hoffman as Control Officer. Captain R. G. Palmer named Fiscal Chief, and Lieutenant William F. Rathgeber named assistant. A day or so later they were addressing him as Captain. Development Visualization Branch moved from 1420 Walnut Street to 150 South Broad. All Ordnance equipment moved from Koppers Company; Baltimore Regional Office cleaned out. Lieutenant Mahlon F. Hoy comes up from Baltimore to iron out final details. Arrangements made in Washington with Veterans Bureau to transfer Richmond Regional Office equipment, also equipment remaining in Rheem Manufacturing Company's Danville, Pennsylvania plant. Some shipments made to Raritan Arsenal. Ten truck loads of miscellaneous items moved from Chester Tank Depot to Warehouse No. 1.

Total of forms now in use cut by Forms Design and Standardization Unit to 206. Automobile mileage at 22,607; gasoline, 1,924 gallons. Telephone charges up slightly to $7,741.61. Civilian personnel eases off to 1,057. Six new applicants were in classification "Restoration after Return from Military Service." Civilian purchases of Bonds represent 11.8 per cent of payroll and a participation of 96.9 per cent. All except three Artillery-Small Arms contracts now completed.

Advance Payments liquidated at a scant $71,000 . . . Applications for Partial Payments total 54, to a dollar final of $9,997,480.63; 40 were paid to a total of $8,794,138.83. Gage Section employment down to 2 individuals from the Section's high in July, of 67.

A particularly bright spot in the December sky was the Victory Mess held on the 7th, Pearl Harbor Day, at Kenney's Restaurant in Camden, New Jersey. The committee was composed of Major Joseph I. Wexlin, Artillery-Small Arms Termination Branch, and Master of Ceremonies; Major W. L. Stephens, Jr., Chief, Property Branch; Captain Josef H. Buerger, Jr., Chief, Artillery-Small Arms Branch; Captain R. P. Fugate, Adjutant; Captain Lewis A. Smith, Jr., Administration Branch. The presentation speech addressed to Colonel A. D. Kelso by First Lieutenant Howard L. Burns of Legal. Toast to the departing Chief, to the District and its Officers was given by Major W. F. Feustel, Chief, Price Adjustment Section. Major Stephens expressed the Officers' regret that the new Chief, Colonel John P. Harris, could not attend. Major Wexlin introduced Officers recently separated from P. O. D. The list included:

Major Charles T. Michener, Former Adjutant

Major John H. Beyer, late Chief, Artillery-Small Arms Branch

Captain W. E. English, late Chief, Philadelphia Regional Office

Major W. L. Lafean, Jr., Chief Ammunition-Production Service, Terminations Branch

Major W. A. Eadie, Jr.

Major J. M. Baxter, late Chief, Miscellaneous Terminations Branch

Captain M. H. Patterson, late Chief, Tank-Automotive Branch

Second Lieutenant James J. Law

WOJG Sidney Stransky, Fiscal Branch

CWO Samuel Kasdan

As Master of Ceremonies Major Joe was at his best. A hush came over the assembled group as he rose to his feet and began:

"Gentlemen, it has been customary for this Post to hold an Officers' Mess on particular occasion, where we gather to pay homage or do some honor to the several leaders and other outstanding men of our Post. This is such an occasion. Destiny has decreed that this is not only a final Mess, but also the occasion for the departure of a beloved friend and Commanding Officer, Colonel A. D. Kelso.

"I shall not make a formal speech; but since we are gathered here in finality it is the time that we will give thought to the men who are our leaders and the many stalwarts who have been able spark plugs of our District. No one man can claim all the glory. It was the fact that we were a hard-hitting team, fast on its feet going into action that was responsible for the glorious record of achievement within our District."

—and more of the same. Thunderous applause greeted Joe, when having divested himself of the sentiment that had been welling up within his great heart (and we really are not being facetious), he sat down.

There was singing—good, by Miss Isabelle Swartzkoft, one time of P. O. D. Music by a three-man orchestra that kept amazingly good time with the minestrone (and we don't mean metronome).

And when all else had been said and done that could be said and done, on such an occasion, Major Joe very capably delivered himself of the final salute with these now momentous words:

"With the permission of the Commanding Officer, I now declare the Officers' Mess of the Philadelphia Ordnance District dissolved."

And to this point we had come a long way from 7 December 1941.

PART III

Chapter LX

FOLLOW THE CHARTS FOR VICTORY

PERHAPS the background of the Ordnance Commodity Branch type of organization with its attendant Service Division Branches and other units, should be the Mobilization Plan of 1939 to which we earlier have referred. According to Major Hamilton's chart there would be in the District Office two main divisions: General Office Service, and Manufacturing Service, the latter one day to be charted as the Industrial Division. The Manufacturing Service was broken down into seven divisions: Artillery, Fire Control, Ammunition, Explosives, Gage, Machine Tool, and Executive. On the General Office Service side the breakdown is to seven sections: Office Section, Personnel, Contract, Legal, Publicity, Property and Traffic.

Provision was also made in the 1939 Plan for an Army Inspector of Ordnance comprising an Administration Division and an Inspection Division, the former with its complement of Sections, including Mail and Record, Property, Shipments, Personnel and Time, and Accounting; the Inspection Division with its Sections assigned to Drawings, Specifications, Gages, Progress and Statistics, and Assistant Inspectors.

It is to be recalled that the business of the District during this period still was chiefly concerned with plant visits, surveys, special investgations, educational orders, production studies and inspections. During the period, 1937 through 1942, the District completed 1,304 initial inspections; from February 1939, to December 1942, 10 Educational Orders, 16 principal Production Orders.

It was during the period 1938–1940 that inspection in P. O. D. began to show signs of becoming a major industry. The list of "greats" in that category now was carrying the following among other checker-uppers: Ed Berdge, Archibald Borbeck, William J. Bright, Michael M. Bigger, John A. Bosch, Jr., William H. Lownsbury, Charles

C. Koeneke, Lawrence A. Larson, Hugh B. La Rue, and Robert E. Layton.

Then there were John G. Centola, Cyril P. Cosgrove, M. Dudley Cozad, Charles M. Davison, Frederick S. Feldheim, Edmund L. Frank, Ivan L. Goff, Harold D. Goldberg, Bernard Hainiowitz, W. W. Henry, Maynard L. Hodgson, Charles P. Kerr and F. J. Kutilek.

And for good measure let us add Samuel McClenahan, David P. McIntire, Julius Mehalek, Walter J. Mullin, Joseph S. Musgrave, Joseph M. Pecarara, Carl L. Phillipi, Howard H. Stock, John A. Stinson, Harold L. Stoever, and Joseph W. Younger.

It was the impetus furnished in April 1939 by the passing in Congress of the National Defense Act that started Inspection on the march in a big way and at the same time pointed the need for perfection of the overall District organization and the induction of topside equal to the increasing demand for various types of administrative and technical skills.

Down in Washington David N. Hauseman early had seen the light and had been unsparing in his efforts to bring about in Ordnance the Commodity type set-up.

The Commodity Branch idea, succeeding the earlier functional type set-up, was given official status with the issuance 20 December 1940 of Office Order No. 7. The Order established an Industrial Service Division consisting of five Commodity Branches: Ammunition-Artillery-Automotive-Miscellaneous Machinery and Raw Materials; each with a Contract, Engineering and an Inspection Section.

The Industrial Service of that period had as its head Major W. S. Broberg. His immediate assistants were William J. Jeffries, on Inspection; John W. Ogden, in charge of Engineering, and doubling as Chief, Executive Branch of the Division, his staff in the latter capacity consisting of Major, then Captain, Ed H. Cahill, Chief, Priorities Section; Major, then Lieutenant, E. H. Uhler, Chief, Procurement Plans Section; Thomas S. Potts, Chief, Surveys; William A. Eadie, Jr., In-Charge Education Orders; and a Technical Data Section, a Gage Check Section and a Proving Grounds Administrative Section, all under the jurisdiction of Lieutenant Marvin C. Jilbert.

The Commodity Branch Chiefs were designated as follows: Ammunition, Major, then Captain, A. W. Hamilton, Jr.; Artillery, Major, then Lieutenant John H. Beyer; Automotive, Captain, then Lieutenant George L. Schiel, following a temporary assignment to Artillery; Miscellaneous Machinery; Frederick S. Feldheim, and Raw Materials Division, Lieutenant, then Mr., W. A. Mortenson. Out on the right wing, Major, then Lieutenant, Wilbur L. Lafean was heading up the Progress Division, later to be rechristened the Statistics and Reports Section, where in days to come would be hatched such notables as Lieutenant Neal W. Slack, Leonard Eyster, George T. Francis, Jr., Pierson Conrad, Robert Rimsky, Sydney J. Trotter, Walter C. White, Allen McK. Beecroft, Donald D. Wear, Ward P. Perry, John Slonaker, 3rd, Henry R. Clime, Robert C. Laurens, Charles Hunsicker— and not overlooking the ladies.

Among the "high-lights" of the Old Progress Division were Lieutenant R. S. Brill, who made way for Wilbur L. Lafean, Jr.; Colonel, then Captain Fred E. Smith, for a brief spell; Lieutenant Robert A. Scott who later was to move through Production, the Field Service Section and finally to the Baltimore Regional Office; Captain, then Second Lieutenant Philip M. Andress, who later would make history in Contract Terminations, and many others of equal calibre.

As of the end of 1940, Lt. Colonel, then Major, Fred E. Smith, was bell-wethering the General Office Division. Major Sam H. Franklin later was to head this Division; and later still, O. Howard Wolfe. Tracing down the chart from this point, we find, Captain, then Lieutenant, Jack Carson, Chief, Civilian Personnel; Miss H. V. Meehan, on Personnel Records; Major, then Captain, Charles T. Michener, Military Personnel Plans and Training. Dropping another notch we come up with Major, then Lieutenant, William L. Stephens, Jr., heading both Property and Traffic Divisions, with Sid Horner, Runner-up. Farther down, Lt. Colonel, then Lieutenant, Robert H. Andrews was making a

name for himself in Fiscal as Chief, with the assistance, of course, of such up-and-comers of that far day as Captain, then Citizen, William F. Rathgeber, and Captain, then Second Lieutenant, Philip M. Andress who, together, set up many of the procedures of that day in the Fiscal Branch, a work to which Frankford Arsenal and the Finance Office made generous contribution. Many of the forms initiated at that time persisted beyond VJ Day.

"Bill" Rathgeber, Philadelphia born, was a product of the Charles Morris Price School of Advertising and the Wharton School of Finance. He came into P. O. D. in February 1939, went directly to the Fiscal Branch and never left it. He originally was charted as Chief, Disbursement Section and Accounting Section. Later, under Branch Chief, Major Charles W. Sorber, he would appear as Assistant Chief of the Branch, continuing in that post through the administrations of Captain R. Gerard Palmer and Charles G. Barnard.

The other half of the team was Captain Philip M. Andress, Worcester, Massachusetts born, first attended University of Vermont, then slipped down to Harvard where he graduated in 1937 with his B.S. Became a prep school science instructor; three years later accepting an instructorship in Business, Mathematics, Science and Laboratory Technique at Boston University College of Business. On 19 September 1941 he turns up in P. O. D. an ROTC Second Lieutenant.

"The term 'Fiscal Branch' as applied to the unit of those early times was something of a misnomer," Bill Rathgeber told us. "The duties of the Branch then embraced Property, Property Records, Purchase, Payroll and Travel. As the volume of Ordnance Work increased it became necessary to divorce all Sections other than Payroll."

The first full-fledged Fiscal Chief, Robert H. "Bob" Andrews, landed in P. O.D. 26 August 1940, a First Lieutenant. He graduated at Rice Institute with a B.A. in Business Administration, attended South Texas School of Law 1936–1938; was dubbed a C. P. A. 1 January 1938. Much of his business acumen was garnered in the oil business. Some years of this, and thence into "pure accountancy" with Ernst & Ernst of San Francisco.

When Colonel David N. Hauseman was transferred in late 1943 to Pentagonia to head the newly formed Readjustment Division of O. C. O., Major Bob went along with him, as did Captain John

Stevens of Legal, Vrest Orton, Public Relations Chief, and, a bit later, Lt. Colonel Joseph A. Whelan, P. O. D. Legal Chief since 24 September 1940.

Next in line at the wheel in Fiscal was Major Joseph C. Hoffman, who came to P. O. D. in December 1943, from Cincinnati Ordnance District. Major Hoffman not only had successfully directed the Fiscal Branch back in Cincinnati, but had, at the behest of O. C. O., streamlined fiscal procedures in other Ordnance District Offices.

In July 1945, Joe was named to the P. O. D. Control Branch, as Chief, succeeding Major W. L. Lafean, Jr. This assignment followed his completion of the Work Simplification program—a survey of all P. O. D. jobs which embraced procedures, methods of handling, and time studies. The result was a net saving of thousands of work hours. On 1 January 1946, Major Hoffman was named Executive Officer, succeeding Lt. Colonel Henry W. Gadsden. The Major continued at the Executive post until 19 April 1946, when he checked in at the Separation Center at Ft. George G. Meade.

Both Lt. Col. Andrews and Major Hoffman later were to be recommended for the Award of the Legion of Merit, along with Lt. Colonel Gadsden, Lt. Colonel A. W. Gilmer, Major Ernest H. Langham, Major Howard P. Klair, Major Wm. L. Stephens, Jr., and Major W. Fred Feustel.

Good material never was lacking in Fiscal. When Major Hoffman came downstairs in July 1945 to tackle the job of Control Officer, Major Charles W. Sorber quietly moved his clock, chair pad and his pencils into the vacated office where he had the capable assistance of Dorothy Stewart who had served Major Hoffman and Major Andrews before him.

The new incumbent was the stork's gift to Dickinson, North Dakota. Following this sobering event in the Sorber menage we were not to hear of him again until 1929 when he completed his Liberal Arts course at Earlham College. Shortly thereafter he entered the Wharton School; went in for accounting. Graduating in 1932, he signed up with Ford Motor Company. Two years here and he was on to Ernst & Ernst for six years, resigning in 1940 to accept an important assignment with the E. I. du Pont de Nemours Company, as Traveling Auditor.

This noble son of the Flickertail State arrived in P. O. D., 25 June 1942, was commissioned First Lieutenant and assigned to the Fiscal Branch, as Field Auditor at Baldwin Locomotive Works Inspection Office. The system initiated by the smiling Lieutenant at Baldwin's for negotiating terminations payments became the basis for District procedure in that category.

On 1 March 1943, Lieutenant Sorber was transferred to the Fiscal Branch as Chief of the Audit Section, and ten days later, promoted to the rank of Captain. In April '45, he was named acting Chief of the Fiscal Branch. As the year ended, the chart revealed the now Major Sorber—he had received his Majority, 1 November—playing many parts; among them, Chief, Contracting Financing Section; Member, Board of Awards, Board of Terminations, and Treasurer, Philadelphia Post, Army Ordnance Association. On 1 January 1946, the Major appears as Assistant Executive Officer; Chief, Control Branch; Control Officer, Alternate Chairman, Board of Awards; Alternate Chairman, Board of Terminations and Member, Committee on Meritorious Civilian Awards—and that's all.

With Charley definitely out of Fiscal, Captain R. Gerard Palmer picks up the reins as Chief. Jerry had been in the Audit Section of the Branch from the early days of his arrival in P. O. D.—to be precise, 12 May 1942—a Second Lieutenant. As the earth turned into 16 January 1945, Jerry acquired his Silver Bar. On 14 July he received his Captaincy. Finally, 1 January 1946, he landed solidly on his feet as Chief of the Fiscal Branch.

Captain Palmer, born in the "land of the Dodgers," came the hard way, all the way. Four years at St. John's University School of Commerce where he sweated out his B.A.; three years in the same School roping his M.A. In October 1939 he passed the New York State Examination for Certified Public Accountant—and thence into business in earnest. On 15 May 1946 he was on his way out of the Army at Fort Meade.

On the 14 June 1946—direction of Fiscal destinies falls for the first time in P. O. D. history into the hands of a civilian—Charles G. Barnard who, since 17 April 1941, when he first punched the District clock, had been laying the greased rails which finally were to ease him into the top Fiscal assignment, and by the same token bring him appointments as Alternate Chairman, Board of Awards, and Alternate Chairman, Board of Terminations.

Charley Barnard was "York State Folks"; hailing from the town of Olean, finishing high school, he came down to take Wharton School in stride. Met up with Paul Grumbly who was studying law, and with whom he chummed through to graduation in 1935, surviving anti-Cornell rallies and assiduously side-stepping the last of the Rowbottoms. Back to Bradford to make his mark as a Certified Cost Accountant.

Seeking larger areas of achievement, P. O. D.'s non-military-Fiscal-Chief-to-be scampered through a tough Civil Service Exam; passed, and was told he might be sent to Porto Rico. Instead, a telegram from P. O. D. District Chief announced Philadelphia as his destination.

The Administration Division also embraced a Mail and Records Section. This was the responsibility of Raymond Ellis. Units of the Property Division were: Purchasing Section, under the indestructable Sid Horner; Storage Section with Captain, then Lieutenant, David H. McIlvaine; Field Service, directed by Lieutenant Robert Scott, and a Supply and Reproduction Section with William Casella. The Traffic Division, with a Passenger Section and a Freight Section, had commandeered Sid Snyder to head both.

Changes down the General Office Column were many and often; ranks are incorrect as of Jan. 1942, as are assignments. In January 1942, for instance, we find O. Howard Wolfe in charge. Captain Michener now is Adjutant. Lieutenant John "Dutch" Derickson comes in to assist Captain Carson. The Military and Civilian Personnel Branches are set up as separate units. The Legal Branch with Lt. Colonel Joseph A. Whelan as Chief, and Lt. Colonel, then Major Albert W. Gilmer as Assistant, has moved into this column. The Fiscal Branch, with Captain H. A. Cressman as Assistant Chief, has added a Contract Financing Section, under Charles P. Stokes; a Contract Disbursement Section for Bill Rathgeber's enjoyment; a Payment Travel Section with Captain Dave McIlvaine presiding; an Audit Section with Captain Sorber and a Salvage Section under Captain, then Howard S. Gallaher. The Property Division has added an Industrial Service Section under Captain David B. Robb; a Traffic Section under Lieutenant J. C. Hassett, Field Service Section with Lieutenant R. W. Vogelsberg, and, a Supply Section with Captain, then Lieutenant John I. Spiegelhalter in charge. The Mail and Records Section has rechristened the Communications Section and attached directly to General Office Division headquarters.

A few months later Ray P. Farrington is in the Civilian Personnel Branch directing the newly formed Personnel Training Section. Ray had to relinquish his assignment as Chief Inspector to take on this job. Lieutenant Gallaher now is in the Fiscal Branch where Charles P. Stokes is heading up the Advance Payments and Special Investigations Section and Captain Jerry Palmer, who was assisting Lieutenant Rathgeber, has been moved in to the General Office Section of Fiscal, and Major, then Lieutenant, Joseph M. Baxter has taken over the Audit Section.

The Legal Branch of the General Office Division has grown somewhat. The names of Captains, then Lieutenants, John R. Armstrong, Rutgers 1931, John C. Pyle, Bucknell; Rutledge Slattery, Princeton 1927 and Penn 1930; John Stevens, a combination of Harvard and Princeton; and Hamilton Page, Yale and Pennsylvania, now appear under the Whelan colors.

Deep into 1942 and more changes, more expansion and paper work in proportion. Lt. Colonel, then Major, Arthur J. Seiler now is Chief of Industrial Service with Major, then Paul H. Carlson as Executive Assistant. Higher up the chart Major Ogden appears as Executive Officer. Serving the Industrial Chief, we discover Charles O. Guernsey, as Inspection Consultant, William J. Jeffries as Engineering Assistant, French E. Dennison, Chief Inspector. Hooked up by devious lines on the chart to the Chief Inspector were the Gage Section under Captain Vernon, and Proof Range Section under Lieutenant Edward S. Tinley, Lehigh three degree man—B.S., M.S. and Ph.D., all in Electrical Engineering.

M. E. "Dusty" Miller was heading up a formidable group consisting of Major, then Captain Wilbur L. Lafean, of the Progress Reports Section; Captain Lewis A. Smith, Jr., of Priorities; Major, then Lieutenant, Lew Van Dusen on Labor Supply; C. J. Seyffer, Chiefing the Production Expediting Section; Roy R. Johnson on Machine Tools; Lieutenant Marvin C. Jilbert, Technical Data Section, and Sam Shadel, topping the Clerical Section.

Legal still was expanding. Now, Lt. Colonel Gilmer had under his charge a Contracting Section; Captain Bernard Lentz was signing himself Chief, Claims and Investigation Section; Major, then Captain John Stevens was directing the Facilities Section and Raymond M. Hendrick was pacing a Change Orders Section.

Under Major Walter C. Pew, we find Major Gene Uhler's Procurement Planning Section; Captain Tom E. Bogert on Surveys; Captain Corb S. Hoffman as Chief, Sub-Contracting Section. And a Purchasing Section, under Martin Sandler who fell heir to the berth once held by Ben Ayres; a Purchase Information Section bearing the Major William Ainsworth Eadie crest. Also in this group, the Board of Awards, formed back in January 1942—with H. Paul Gant, Martin Sandler, Solon Joe Whelan—and Mrs. Helen MacFarland, Secretary.

Still going down the column: H. Paul Gant is speeding up his Special Projects Section under Thomas S. Potts; Captain, then Lieutenant M. H. Patterson, a young man with a future in Ordnance, as Secretary, Machine Tool Committee; John Baizley, Machine Tool Consultant, and Major Brendan D. Walsh leading the Plans and Services Division. A Production Display Section is indicated under Major Michener. And, the late H. E. "Dick" Snyder, Chief, W. P. B. Liaison Section. A few changes over in the General Office Division: Captain David H. Robb, heading the Industrial Service Section of the Property Branch, and Lieutenant Philip J. Fields, spear-heading Mail and Records Section.

And the Co-ordinators are at work.

Into 1943—as of 17 April—and new names, new units, new procedures spring up overnight with mushroom alacrity. Lt. Colonel Robert G. Allen, successor to Captain Ogden, is Executive Officer. A Price Adjustment Section is feeling its oats. Under Charles P. Stokes, its Chief, appears an Administrative unit directed by Major, then Captain, W. Fred Feustel, a Reports Unit with T. H. Roth, and a Price Adjustment Board manned by J. H. Fassitt, Chairman, W. M. McKee, S. G. McNees and J. M. Taylor. And Director of Planning H. Paul Gant is finding plenty to keep him awake nights, with the help of Assistant Lieutenant Gene Uhler, who, with Lieutenant Tom Bogert, is running the Procurement Planning Section; Caleb F. Fox III, striving to match Warren Webster's record on Smaller War Plants; Captain W. S. Canning, directing traffic in the Transportation Section; Tom Potts sleuthing along with the Fire Control Unit, and J. P. Young taking care of Scrap Salvage.

The Industrial Service, now the Industrial Division, has added a bit of avoirdupois. R. W. Cook is listed as a Staff Member. Production

Director Guernsey has annexed Blythe Minnier as a Staff Member. Lew L. Rittenhouse has been assigned the Gage Laboratory post; Major, then Captain, Ed. Lafferty is making history in the Production Engineering Section; W. L. Weintz is head man in the Production Engineering Section; Special Assistance Section claims Robert F. Rundle; W. J. Jefferies now tagged Chief Metallurgist; Dan H. Bell is working miracles in the Conversion Engineering Section.

Now look what they've done to Major Paul Carlson: In addition to his duties as Executive Assistant to Lt. Colonel Seiler they have elected him Chief, Production Service Branch, with Robert Rundle in the No. 2 spot. Attached units include a C. M. P. (Controlled Materials Plan) and Priorities Section, with R. L. Kirk; a dangling Priorities Unit under J. S. Winslow; Statistics and Reports, navigated by Captain, then Neal W. Slack, another Princeton-Harvard product, succeeding Major Bill Lafean, who had been assigned Chief of the newly established P. O. D. Control Branch; Labor still a responsibility of Major Van Dusen; an Inspection Clerical Section all charmed up with Mrs. Bertha K. Berry, and, finally, the Technical Data Section now under the direction of K. E. Butler, succeeding Lieutenant Jilbert.

The Office of the Director of Purchase grows apace; Chief Martin Sandler has a high-pressure Assistant in Major, then Captain, Theodore C. Sheaffer. A Purchase Section led by Captain, then Lieutenant, J. Albury Fleitas is appended; and ditto for a Price Analysis Section with Major Joseph M. Baxter.

Other units included the now charted Intelligence Officer, Captain Morton H. Fetterolf; a Censorship Branch, with Major Lew Van Dusen ably assisted by Vrest Orton, Time Fuse editor, and, finally the Security Branch with Captain Robert Merz and Vermonter Major Robert W. Chutter.

Also added are a Packaging Section under paper merchant Captain Cecil Bentley, and a Procurement Liaison Director, Malcolm White, with a pendant Defense Plant Corporation and Facilities Section directed by F. D. Mensing.

Subsequent changes in 1943 include a shift in Public Relations: Captain David H. McIlvaine is transferred to the Pay and Travel Section of Fiscal. Vrest Orton puts up the P. R. O. sign. General Office Administrator O. Howard Wolfe has vanished from the chart—gone over to the Treasury Department—leaving Major Bill Lafean holding the bag, temporarily. Fred W. Harvey continues as Chief, Office Service Section. Following Mr. Wolfe's departure, various of the Sections break loose on their own, and the Division becomes a purely Administrative Branch, directed by Captain Lewis A. Smith, Jr., and made up of such units as the Communications Section (formerly Mail and Records), directed by Lieutenant Phil J. Fields; Office Service Section with Fred W. Harvey; Travel Section under Tom H. Lowry, and the Clerical Section responding to Anne M. Almeida. A Purchase-Terminations Division now appears; a merger of Purchase and Terminations with Martin Sandler as Chief, assisted by Lt. Colonel A. W. Gilmer, as Assistant in reference to Terminations, and Major Theodore C. Sheaffer in reference to Purchase. The Price Analysis Branch, out on the right wing, still hails Major Baxter as Chief. The Negotiation Branch, with Major J. A. Fleitas as Chief, is a consolidation of five units—Ammunition Section, with H. C. Middleton; Artillery Section with M. R. Gardner; Miscellaneous Materials Section with E. M. Chalikian; Small Arms Section under Harold Dripps, and Tank-Automotive Section under John Swartley.

The Miscellaneous Materials Branch is liquidated—the boss-man, Major Welles H. Denney going over to the Production Service Branch to assist Paul Carlson; Alfred R. Testa going to Production Equpment Section; Chester A. Elliott, Denney right-hand man, was rescued by Dan H. Bell in Conversion Engineering.

A change in January 1944, in Statistics and Reports: Captain Neal Slack has been assigned as Assistant to Lt. Colonel H. Ken Kelley, Chief, Property Disposal Branch; his place taken by Richard M. Keator. Lew Rittenhouse departs the Gage Section—now combining the Gage Section and Gage Laboratory—and Lieutenant Bob Watson is assigned. Major Carlson heads the Redistribution and Salvage Section of his Production Service Branch and Major Art Allison, in from the Regional Offices, is now steering the Production Equipment Section of the Branch.

The Board of Awards, Sales and Salvage looms, with H. Paul Gant, Chairman; and the following members: Lt. Colonel Arthur J. Seiler, Lt. Colonel Joseph A. Whelan, Lt. Colonel, then still Major, A. W. Gilmer, Major J. A. Fleitas, Martin Sandler and Malcolm R. White.

And the Control Board: the first panel, January 1944, with Major Wilbur Lafean as Control Officer;

H. Paul Gant, as Chairman, pointed with pride to the following members: Lt. Colonel Arthur J. Seiler, Lt. Colonel Joseph A. Whelan, Lt. Colonel Henry W. Gadsden, Major Joseph C. Hoffman, Major William L. Stephens, Jr., Captain John F. Carson, Martin Sandler and Malcolm R. White.

Legal still growing—Captain B. M. Zimmerman heads in.

October 1944, and charts are popping as thick and as fast as fleas on a yellow dog. Ordnance installations now in the chart business, "seems if," with Ordnance a sideline. Demand exceeds production as charts are obsoleted before the ink is dry.

We cannot possibly record all the changes that took place, for instance, between January and October of 1944. Placed side by side and compared unit for unit the charts for those months appear almost as strangers to each other. Let's see what has happened since January.

First off, Lt. Colonel Bob Allen is out in the Hawaiian Islands, and Lt. Colonel Henry W. Gadsden is signing "Executive Officer" to all pertaining documents. Captain Richard A. Line now is Chief of the two Sections—Intelligence and Public Relations. The Control Branch carries the name of George T. Francis, Jr., at the masthead, and clustered about him, the Statistics and Progress Section (another change of designation) with W. M. Kinney; the History Section with Robert T. Gebler, and the Library Section (something new) with Mrs. Elizabeth M. Graffen. Others to come into the Library Section were Anne M. Hayes, Sue Pantano and Alice Smith.

A few shifts in the Administration Branch where Captain Lew Smith was still wearing the mantle, assisted by Captain J. I. Spiegelhalter of the Travel Section; Lieutenant S. M. Levenson of Communications, Fred W. Harvey of the Office Service Section, and Anne M. Almeida master-minding the Clerical cohorts.

Changes on the Price Adjustment Board: T. G. Aspenwall, H. N. Rodenbaugh and H. G. Stewart came in; T. H. Roth, J. H. Fassitt, S. G. McNees and J. M. Taylor—missing. In Fiscal: Major Joseph Hoffman remains as Chief, Major Charles W. Sorber as Assistant. Lieutenant W. J. Crockett of the Payroll Section first appears. And comes a Purchase Action Section with Lieutenant J. F. Bush, Jr.

In the Industrial Division we find Assistant Chief, Major Ernest J. Langham as Chief of the

Production Service Branch (Major Carlson has departed for Baltimore). One change in the Branch was in the Material Control Section, when J. Ed. Moore had taken over the assignment previously held by R. L. Kirk. An RAD (Research and Development) Section is added, with Captain Tom E. Bogert assigned. An added attraction in the Division was the Executive Branch. In it, names you will recall from the chapter on Sub-Offices: Colonel Kelso, Chief; Major Ernest J. Langham in charge of Field Offices; Major Ed. W. Lafferty, on Technical Service; Captain Walter E. English, Property Disposal; French E. Dennison, Inspection, and W. E. Gilbert on Production.

A move in the Administration Branch brings in Lieutenant H. D. "Murf" Ginsburg to replace Captain John I. Spiegelhalter. In the Property Branch, A. J. Donahue now is heading the Traffic Section and in the Storage Section, Lieutenant S. B. Honour, up from Eddystone, is top man.

The complexion of the Purchase-Termination Division changes with the weather, there are those who will tell you. Of course, "Terminations" at this point was in a fair way of becoming big business—and eventually did. But no time like the early days to get set for the rush that would come. Reviewing the set-up in October 1944, we find Lt. Colonel Oscar M. Hansen, C. P. A. in New York and in Pennsylvania and licensed to practice Law in both states, and Major Joseph Baxter as assistants to the Division Chief, Martin Sandler. Lt. Colonel Gilmer still is heading the Terminations Branch, while Major Ted C. Sheaffer and Major J. A. Fleitas are holding the line at the top of the Purchase Branch.

The Property Disposal Branch now is part and parcel of the Purchase-Terminations Division. Its Chief, Lt. Colonel H. Ken Kelley, has supervision of these units: Control Section, with Major Denney, Redistribution and Salvage Officer; Operating Section, with Sidney S. Press, Chief; Ammunition Property Disposal Unit under Lieutenant Le Roy M. Bissett, well-known Sunbury Real Estate and Insurance specialist; Artillery-Small Arms Property Disposal Unit, with R. R. McKnight, and Tank-Automotive Unit under Lieutenant James H. Nisbett, down from the Production Service Branch. An attached Salvage Board carries the names of W. J. Jefferies, Major Arthur B. Allison, Leonard L. Eyster, C. W. Graves and H. B. LaRue.

The Units of the Terminations Branch appear this way: Miscellaneous Section, with Captain Phil M. Andress; Ammunition Section, with our old friend of the Statistics and Reports, Major Wilbur L. Lafean; Artillery-Small Arms Section, with Major Joseph I. Wexlin; Tank-Automotive Section with then Major Oliver C. Conger and a Production Service Section with then Major Art Allison.

The Units of the Purchase Branch of the Division line up about like this: Control Section, the responsibility of Captain Louis F. Unger, who came to P. O. D. in April 1941 and was first assigned to Procurement Planning; Ammunition Section, directed by H. C. Middleton, Lafayette athlete; Meredith I. Gardiner, World War I, Air Corps Lieutenant; Tank-Automotive Section with John C. Swartley, and a Gage Section navigated by W. S. Stokes. And out on the right wing of the chart—Captain William T. Young, University of Kentucky 1939, in charge Price Analysis Branch.

Captain Young was one of the District Chief Ingersoll's up-and-comers. Following a swing around the District in late 1944, when he was assigned to lend a hand in ironing out purchase and price analysis functions, there came back to P. O. D. paeans of high praise from such dignitaries as: Colonel K. B. Harmon, District Chief, San Francisco; Brigadier General G. H. Drewry, District Chief, Springfield, Mass.; Colonel Gilbert I. Ross, District Chief, New York; and Lt. Colonel Irving A. Duffy, Assistant, Office Chief of Ordnance.

One important development of this period was the distribution made of the activities of the Board of Awards, Sales and Salvage. To ease the burden of rapidly increasing responsibilities there was effected a three-way split, with the result, a separate Board of Awards, as before; a Board of Terminations and a Board of Sales. The Board of Awards continued H. Paul Gant at the head with assists by Colonel A. D. Kelso, Major Joseph A. Whelan, Martin Sandler and Major J. A. Fleitas, Contracting Officer. On the Board of Terminations, lead by Martin Sandler, there is listed Captain John R. Armstrong of Legal; Major Charles W. Sorber of Fiscal; H. Paul Gant, and Lt. Colonel A. W. Gilmer, Contracting Officer. Easing over to the Board of Sales, we find H. Paul Gant again at the lead with Major Roland C. Disney, Tank-Automotive Chief; Lt. Colonel Henry W. Gadsden, Executive Officer, Martin Sandler and Lt. Colonel H. Ken Kelley, Contracting Officer.

Enough for now.

Chapter LXI

THE CHARTS ARE COMING—AS THE DISTRICT BRANCHES OUT

NOW, through the storm of charts deep into 1945—we find ourself heading into June. Suddenly looms before us in the chair so recently occupied by C. Jared Ingersoll, the familiar figure of that good soldier, Colonel A. Donald Kelso; at his side the mace once so effectively wielded by his predecessor.

In the Executive Branch—one change with a double shift: Captain Dick Line has relinquished to "Tiny" Dan H. Shipley, his job as Intelligence Officer; and to Andrea Farnese, he bequeathed the Public Relations Office.

The Boards remained approximately as in late 1944. No change on the Control Board beyond the departure of Colonel Joseph Whelan. The Board of Sales and the Board of Terminations, as before. The Board of Awards also has said its farewell to Colonel Whelan, and to Colonel Kelso, and there have been added the names of Major Ernest J. Langham, Major Rutledge Slattery, Legal Chief, and Captain Bernard Zimmerman. The Administration Branch still doing business at the old stand and with the same crew except that Captain Smith has taken over the Office Service Section recently vacated by Fred W. Harvey. This change brought William Hart and Joseph Stone decidedly to the fore. The Property Branch, and the Civilian Branch where Sam McClenahan and his bowmen, John J. Wood and Howard W. Biles, both up from Eddystone, still were on the march as of old, except that Captain J. B. Jones, of Mobile Shop Depot fame, is sparking the Storage Section of the Property Branch and the Audit Section has gone over to W. A. McCracken.

A few changes are revealed in the Price Analysis Branch. Captain Bill Young remains as Chief, Lieutenant Edward J. Lynch, Assistant; W. A. Martel now heads the Ammunition Section; C. P. Webb on Artillery-Small Arms; S. D. Bass, Tank-Automotive Section, and Captain R. Paul Fugate, Price Revision Section. In the Purchase Branch of the Division, a Gage Section with F. A. Dubbs has

been added. Sid Press now is Chief, Property Disposal Branch, succeeding Lt. Colonel H. Ken Kelley, and Captain Neal W. Slack shows up as Assistant. All the old Sections of the Property Disposal Branch have disappeared. In their places: a Staff Section, with Lieutenant Earl H. Lentz, from the Oriole City, as Chief; a Termination Inventory Disposal Section, with Lieutenant Philip J. Fields; a Government Disposal Section, under Lieutenant J. H. Nisbet; a Service Section with Captain Howard S. Gallaher, and the Redistribution Center, at Pencoyd, the charge of Lieutenant Eugene Ayres, Bates College lad.

A Salvage Board, set up back in 1944, claimed W. J. Jeffries as Chairman, and serving with him, Captain J. P. Grimwade, C. W. Graves, R. W. James and Hugh B. LaRue.

The Executive Branch of the Industrial Division has enrolled Major Eugene H. Uhler, Major Welles H. Denney, Ed. T. Berdge and that master of figures, Ed. E. Clark. The names of Colonel Kelso and Captain Walter E. English no longer appear. A peek at the Production Service Branch reveals Captain Dick Furniss, down from the Bethlehem Regional Office, replacing Major Langham in the key post; the Production Equipment Section boasting no less a personality than Captain John P. Grimwade, down from the York Regional Office by way of Eddystone; Captain Cecil Bentley, topping the Packaging Section; Lieutenant Bob Watson still heading the Gage Section; Lieutenant Jack Walsh, doing the honors in the Labor Section; Procurement Planning Section answering to the call of Harvey R. Battersby, late of Smaller War Plants.

By 19 October 1945 the District was in a position to measure topside shrinkage. In the interim, many had checked out, for keeps. Units and Branches had been consolidated into more compact groups, here and there. The District was experiencing the sensation provided by a diminishing waist-line. Once familiar names have faded from the rolls—

Charles P. Stokes, H. Paul Gant, Martin Sandler, Major Harold Vennell, W. E. Gilbert, Major T. C. Sheaffer, Major J. Albury Fleitas, Major John H. Beyer, Lieutenant John I. Spiegelhalter, Major Paul H. Carlson, Captain William B. Wellborn, Captain John B. Jones, Major Charles T. Michener, Major Victor W. Smith, Lieutenant Maurice P. Felton, Captain Bernard Zimmerman, Major Oliver C. Conger, Captain Ross T. Henderson—gone, all gone, back to earlier scenes, time-scarred and paper-weary.

A few others whose names will be long remembered: Joseph K. Seidle, Lee C. Matter, James E. Tucker, Edward M. Chalikian, Roger L. Kirk, Fred A. Dubbs, Clifton H. Hendrix, Richard W. Myers, Howard W. Biles, Harvey R. Battersby, Jr., John E. Ryan, Merrill A. Conn, Robert E. Layton, George E. Layton, George D. Keller, Robert J. Bothwell, Elizabeth M. Graffen, Harold D. Hershberger, Marvin F. Seiffert, David P. McIntire, Charles W. Selden, Jr.—well, that will give the reader an idea.

Follow the pattern of organization now: Major Joseph C. Hoffman is Chairman of the Board of Awards and appears as Assistant Executive Officer and, at the same time as Chief of the Control Branch. Fellow members of the Board of Awards are Major Langham, Major Slattery, Major Sorber and Captain Louis F. Unger as Contracting Officer. On the Board of Terminations: Lt. Colonel Henry W. Gadsden, Chairman; his associates, Captain John R. Armstrong, Major Sorber, Sidney S. Press, and Lt. Colonel Gilmer as Contracting Officer.

Moving across the Board we discover Captain R. Paul Fugate in the former Michener post. Major Charles W. Sorber is riding high in Fiscal; Major Rutledge Slattery still at the wheel in Legal, a Branch distinguished by such names as those of Captains Armstrong, Pyle, Page, Grumbly, Burns, Haight, Durfee, Lentz, Carmen Saponari, Lt. Colonel Whelan, Lt. Colonel Gilmer and, of course, "Rut" himself.

The Purchase-Termination Division now is known as the Contract Settlement Division. The former Purchase Branch and the Price Analysis Branch have been consolidated, appearing as the Purchase Branch under Captain "Bill" Young. Lt. Colonel Gilmer heads the Division. Sid Press signs as Assistant Chief. Captains Phil M. Andress, and Paul B. Caldwell, University of Alabama, are named Assistants. The Salvage Board is no longer.

Further shifts in Contract-Settlement Division are: Lieutenant E. H. Lentz succeeding Lieutenant Eugene Ayres at the Redistribution Center. The Staff Section and the Service Section discontinued, and a Special Facilities Section added with John McDowell; and an RFC Liaison Section under Lieutenant Alexander Zeeve, Columbia 1938.

In the Industrial Division, Ed T. Berdge has succeeded Major Gene Uhler as Assistant to the Chief, who still reports to the Division as Assistant in Charge, Field Office Administration. Serving with him are Captain Thomas E. Bogert, as Assistant, in Charge Plant Clearance, and Richard M. Keator as Termination Liaison.

And that about does it for October.

It is the 2nd of January 1946. The line of departees grows longer and longer from one pay-period to another. We linger in the lobby of 150 South Broad Street and search in vain for faces so familiar only yesterday. "Where," we ask, "is Charles G. Blakelock of Bethlehem, W. B. Jones, Thomas G. Aspinwall, George MacCool, Captain Julius Mehalek, Captain Robert S. Gibson, Lieutenants Ed Klint, Thomas M. Browne, Ben M. Ingram, Jr., and Captain Dick Furniss? What has happened to Captain Dave McIlvaine, Lieutenant Bob Bernheim, Ralph Campbell once down at Baldwin's, Phil Rahaim from Cressona and John Lombardi of Pottstown Ordnance, Bert Krause of Berwick and Cressona.

And what of Captain Tom Bogert, Captain Bill Young, Captain Norman L. Cavedo and Lieutenant Jack Walsh? Too, we remember among so many others, Calvan P. Webb, John W. Brown of Richmond, Manuel Cole, Sam Marx, Captain E. C. Peterson, Captain James R. Stewart?

Nor are we forgetting that only a few hours ago as time is measured, we said a reluctant farewell to Colonel A. Donald Kelso, to Lt. Colonel Henry W. Gadsden, to Major Joseph I. Wexlin, to Major Howard P. Klair.

The Officers Club has gone the way of the just.

In the midst of our despair there came to the District in January 1946, a new Chief, Colonel John P. Harris, an Officer we quickly learned to admire and who went a long way to fill that void so often referred to as "aching." Colonel Harris arrived in the midst of a "reduction in force" program which was a pretty tough assignment for a man to whom the personalities and procedures of the District were so new. That he was able to encompass this situation and so promptly come up with right answers is to his eternal credit. We were not long to have this grand person for an associate. Came a fine day in May when he folded his papers and scampered back to his Eden— Picatinny.

All right, it's 2 January 1946. You want to know how the pattern has changed since October. Take the various Boards, for instance: The Board of Awards has lost a Langham and gained a Palmer— Captain R. G., Fiscal Chief; the Board of Terminations has lost a Gadsden and come up with a Pyle— John C., "Pride of Legal"—and again, a Palmer; the same. The Board of Sales is gone altogether. In its stead on the books, now a Property Disposal and Salvage Board—boasting in its membership such notables as Ed T. Berdge, Chairman, and William J. Jefferies, Richard M. Keator, Jacob M. Noll, Lieutenant Guy D. Beaumont, who presently also was doing his bit in the Government-Furnished Equipment Section of the Production Service Branch, and Lieutenant J. R. Aydelotte, Fort Scott, Kansas, lad who, in his short space in P.O.D., had played many parts—in Property Disposal, Ammunition Branch and so on . . . and so on.

Major Hoffman now is Executive Officer; Major Charles W. Sorber, Assistant. The Control Branch still wears the Hoffman "silks" with George T. Francis, Jr., looking on. Lieutenant A. T. Collins, the New York *Times* Washington Bureau man, down from Alaska, is heading up Public Relations. Shortly after, he too had gone, and Public Relations was made a History Section responsibility.

Major Slattery and Captain John Pyle now are directing Legal, in that order. In the Contract-Settlement Division it still is Lt. Colonel Gilmer and Sid Press, with Major Joseph Baxter and Lieutenant Paul B. Caldwell assisting. Paul Williams has replaced Major Wexlin as Chief, Artillery-Small Arms Termination Branch of the Division; Lieutenant Oliver K. Hearte, in Terminations from 15 January 1944, still in charge, Tank-Automotive Termination Branch. The Miscellaneous Terminations Branch no longer appears; but we do have now a Consolidated Termination Branch, the charge of Captain Jesse C. Jessen, the Camden lad who arrived in the Tank-Automotive Branch of P.O.D. via Drexel, Temple and Villanova.

The Industrial Division had some time since lost its Commodity Branches, and now appears with a Procurement and Production Branch with

Julius Gussman at the controls; an Inspection Branch set up under Ed T. Berdge, Industrial Division Chief; and the old Production Service Branch, with Lieutenant Ed T. Lynch in Captain Dick Furniss' cozy chair.

The Buying Section of the Procurement and Production Branch has been taken over by Herbert L. Wilson; there is a Production Section with Cyril P. Cosgrove, rounding out his seventh year in P.O.D., as Chief; and a Price Analysis Section under Ray Theuret.

In the Inspection Branch, there pops up, as it so often did, the name of John J. Target; this time, in Charge of the Ammunition Section; W. W. Henry, heading the Artillery-Small Arms Section, H. B. La Rue heading the Tank-Automotive Section; John Target, again, directing the Quality Control Section and Henry E. Marcus at the head of the Gage Section.

In the Production Service Branch, Lieutenant Guy D. Beaumont, as we noted higher up the page, in charge, Government-Furnished Equipment Section; Lieutenant John B. Adair, Dartmouth, at the high post of the Packaging Section; Julius Gussman directing the Engineering-Specifications Section; Gladys B Kovesy with a firm grip on matters in the Records-Statistics Section.

"Well," you say, "that's fine. Everything is all set. Every man in his place. No more changes. I can put this book back on the shelf. Anyone asks me who did what, I can come pretty close to telling him . . . etc., etc., etc."

You think so? Tell us, then, who is Chief of the Board of Awards and of the Board of Terminations: You are wrong, it's Captain Oliver C. Hearte.

On the Property Disposal and Salvage Board, it's Ed T. Berdge. Captain Lewis A. Smith, Jr., is Contracting Officer for all three Boards, and Ed Berdge is a member of each of the other Boards. On the Board of Awards we also discover Major Slattery and Charles Barnard who, with Bill Rathgeber, is running Fiscal. Charles Barnard again appears on the Board of Terminations, with Captain John C. Pyle. On the Property Disposal and Salvage Board who should turn up but Julius Gussman, Pennsylvania, and Emil Mathias, Villanova, 1938.

In May 1946, came down from Frankford Arsenal, to guide the District through its latter day processes, Colonel Gordon B. Welch. It was all so sudden. We were discussing with Colonel Harris the respective merits of "Red Hackles" and "Royal Coachmen" when of a sudden we looked around and there was Colonel Welch with his "papers"; and it seemed, when we again looked about, he was gone, and there was Lt. Colonel Tyler D. Barney, assigned from Rock Island following plenty of hot weather and tough going in New Guinea.

Though his time was short, Colonel Welch was long enough here to pin high honors on two men who had gloriously served P. O. D. and the Nation through the war years. They were H. Paul Gant and Martin Sandler. It was on the 17th of September, before many of their former associates.

Back to the rolls. W. J. Cowan is boss of the Audit Branch of Fiscal. Dan K. Betts is looking after the Traffic Branch of Property. The General Office Division, a new arrangement of the Administration Division, discloses Captain R. Paul Fugate in charge, and himself directing both the Military Personnel and Civilian Personnel Branches; Joseph Stone, that nimble manipulator of a multitude of duties, as Chief, Administration Branch and its pendant Office Service Section; Helen V. Meehan, in Charge Mail and Records Section, and in charge of the Library, once a Control Branch activity, Sue Pantano.

The Industrial Division has undergone a bit of shuffling since our last visit. The Ammunition Branch, the Artillery-Small Arms Branch and the Tank-Automotive Branch are back in the picture. The Production Service Branch and the Inspection Branch continue as major units.

The Ammunition Branch is under the Gussman banner, with H. L. Wilson in Charge of Purchase; Julius Gussman, Chief, Production Section; Paul

Lt. Col. Henry W. Gadsden

W. Williams in charge Contract-Settlement Section and Ray Theuret, heading Price Analysis Section. Carl L. Phillipi, one of Major Vic Smith's Regional Office boys Chief, Artillery-Small Arms Branch, and of the Production Section. The Tank-Automotive Branch under Hugh B. LaRue who also is Chief of the Branch Production Section. Contract-Settlement in all Commodity Branches is a Paul Williams responsibility; H. L. Wilson takes care of Purchase through all three Commodity Branches and R. Theuret looks after the Price Analysis Sections. The Inspection Branch has been taken over by Charles F. Kemper who distinguished himself as Chief Inspector in Ammunition. His first visit to Philadelphia—that was just prior to World War I—was in reference to inspection of ships at Hog Island. He was subsequently called to the Rochester Ordnance District, resigning some years later to join forces with Montgomery-Ward Company. Tiring of indoor work, he purchased a farm. This was going according to schedule, and might well have continued, had a call not come in 1939 for experienced Ordnance men. Charley, accepting the challenge again, joined up, and there you are, and here he is.

In the Production Service Branch of the Industrial Division, in order to complete the story, we discover Lieutenant John D. Adair usurping the post of Chief, formerly held by Lieutenant Lynch, from over on the Jersey side. The Gage Section now is a Henry Marcus operation. Operating the Engineering-Specifications and Drawings Section passes to Emil Mathias. Paul Williams who distinguished himself in many capacities in Ordnance during the war is assigned as Chief of the Contract Settlement Section—all that is left of the once large Contract-Settlement Division; and bringing up the Price Analysis Section is that very capable gentleman, Ray Theuret.

And this entire Industrial Division was being most efficiently administered by two good men who came to P. O. D. before we had entered the war and remained through the mopping-up period that followed—Ed T. Berdge, as Chief; John J. Target as Assistant Chief.

All of which about winds up the story of the Industrial Division phase of the narrative. Though June 1946 did not mark the end of Division activities—not by a jug-full—it did see the greater part of a great job accomplished, and on this note the chapter ends.

Chapter LXII

DISTRICT EXPANSION VIA FIELD OFFICES

OUT on the right wing of even the earliest charts are the Field Offices. Some originally were called Inspection Offices; later, Sub Offices; then, again, Field Offices and finally, Regional Offices. These were manifestations of the type of organization expanding from and around the Commodity Branch idea.

The establishment of the Regional Offices was in line with the general spirit of decentralization stemming all the way from across the Potomac. From 1938 and through 1941 these outposts of the P. O. D. central office were bursting into bloom in important industrial points throughout the District. They were the long arms of the District Office, expediting procurement, production, inspection; beating time to the punch; integrating orders and instructions from headquarters; plugging P. O. D. right into production lines.

At one time (1942) the charts disclosed nine Regional Offices—Baltimore, Berwick, Bethlehem, Eddystone, Philadelphia, Reading, Richmond, York and, for a limited period, the Autocar Company, which later, under the regime, beginning in October 1942, of "Mr." Kelso, was reclassified an Inspection Office, due to the fact that, though a sizable operation, it did not rate the appellation of Sub-office, or Regional Office.

It is difficult at this late moment to date the first of the Regional Offices to come into being. Bethlehem, for instance, first appears as a Field Office far back in December 1938 when Major Harry L. Koenig was assigned by the District Office to handle inspection at Bethlehem Steel Company of contracts placed by Picatinny Arsenal and Watertown Arsenal for bar and tool steel, and 37 mm. Breech Ring Forgings.

First quarters were opened in Bethlehem in the Fall of 1939. These were in the Main Laboratory Building of the Bethlehem Steel Company. The small inspection staff assigned Major Koenig was augmented in the Spring of 1940, when additional contracts came down from Picatinny Arsenal. These covered the procurement of 100 pound, 300 pound, 500 pound, 1,000 pound and 2,000 pound Demolition Bombs, and 105 mm. H.E. Shells. By July 1941 there were 70 contracts in force in the Bethlehem Sub-Office area. Educational Orders now in process in the area included one at Mack Manufacturing Corporation, Allentown, Pa., for Pilot T-3 Half Track Chassis.

As of 1 January 1942 the number of contracts under administration had risen to 175—and the Office now boasted 72 employees. Major Koenig resigned in May 1942 because of ill-health. Major, then Captain, J. I. "Watch-My-Dust" Wexlin took over. Lawrence A. Larson, who had been serving as Chief Inspector, requested transfer, George I. Tull succeeded him. In August 1942. George Tull was transferred to the Philadelphia Office, making room for Edmund L. Frank, who had been until this time Inspector-in-Charge at the Taylor-Wharton Steel Company. Came in at this time Lieutenant John R. Graf as Assistant Officer-in-Charge. As of the end of the year there were in effect in the Bethlehem area 104 prime contracts and 226 sub-contracts the former tagged at $100,000,000; the latter, at $25,000,000.

Limits of space do not permit recording of the many other accomplishments of contractors under jurisdiction of the Bethlehem Sub-Office. Two such are noteworthy: Lehigh Foundries, Inc., in converting from manganese bronze castings to malleable iron castings in the production of 75 mm., 3 in. 90 mm. and 105 mm. Dummy Practice Cartridge Cases, thus saving, on these items alone, 650 tons of copper, 235 tons of zinc, 50 tons of aluminum, 35 tons of manganese and 5 tons of tin. And credit to the Taylor-Wharton Iron and Steel Company coming up from many months behind schedule to a monthly production of 18,000 units of 155 mm., H.E. Shell. This company now had completed more than 200 years of manufacturing activity and over the span had produced

Ordnance items through every war in which the U. S. had a part.

Joe Wexlin carried on at Bethlehem for a month and a day. Came then World-War-I Major Timothy Van Alen, Williams 1908, and one time a District Manager for Mack-International Motor Truck Corporation; organizer and President, Farmers and Mechanics National Bank, Northumberland, Pennsylvania; Director, Sunbury Bridge Company; Member, Pennsylvania Legislature, and so on and so on ad infinitum. Shortly after Major Van Alen's ascension, Lieutenant James F. Bush, Jr., until then a Field Auditor in the Bethlehem Office, was reassigned as Assistant to the Officer-in-Charge. The chart of the period shows C. G. Blakelock as Production Chief; E. T. Frank, Inspection Chief, and George Baumer as Administration Chief.

It was during this period that the name of Lieutenant John R. Graf first is heard in the Bethlehem area. His first assignment had been to the Ammunition Branch. He arrived in the Regional Office 31 August 1942. During May, following, he was assigned to the Industry Integration Committee on 60 mm. and 81 mm. Mortar Shells, at Lehigh Foundries, Inc., Easton. Later in the month he moved down to United Specialties Company in Philadelphia. One year later he turns up with the Committee on M1A1, M1A2 and M3 Adapter Clusters at Armstrong Cork Company, Lancaster. In January 1945 he is at Reading Air Chutes, Inc., on the T-1 Parachute. He was promoted to Captain, 13 September 1945, and on 4 October received his discharge from the Army at Fort George G. Meade.

In August 1943, Major Van Alen was transferred to the Reading Regional Office and was succeeded at Bethlehem by Captain Arthur B. Allison, who had been in charge at Reading from early in 1941. "Art" was a Wheaton College luminary, with a University of Pennsylvania final polish as a prelude to a turn with Worth Steel Company and another with Lukens Steel Company. Captain Allison continued at Bethlehem to January 1944 when he was reassigned to the Philadelphia District Office as Chief of the Production Equipment Section and other currently active posts. Somewhat later, after a tour of duty overseas he was assigned to the Readjustment Branch under Brigadier General Hauseman in Pentagon.

On the heels of the Allison vanishing act followed one Major Harold L. Vennel, former Officer-in-Charge, Baltimore Regional Office. Harold Vennel

first was assigned to the Philadelphia Ordnance District, 19 August 1942. In September of the following year he received his commission as a Major. A few days later Major General Milton A. Reckford wrote from the Third Service Command to compliment the Major on a "great job" in putting over "This Is the Army"—a morale building movie. His tenure of office at Bethlehem was not for long. Late in January he was back in the District Office delivering terminations talks to the P. O. D. folk. In May, he was named Assistant to the Chief, Terminations Branch; was hospitalized early in July 1945, and by 23 July was out of the Army.

Succeeding Major Vennel, as Officer-in-Charge at Bethlehem, was Captain Richard A. "Dick" Furniss, who had come up through the ranks at Reading, beginning with a station with the Textile Machine Works of that city. Dick came out of the University of Michigan back in 1931 with honors in Mechanical Engineering which he promptly impacted upon the General Electric Company at Erie, and a bit later, S. S. Fretz, Jr., Incorporated of Philadelphia. P. O. D. bear-trapped him 7 June 1942. Indiantown Gap got him, 27 November 1945; but not before serving a round with the Bethlehem Inspection Office as Officer-in-Charge.

'Dick" Furniss no sooner is out of the way at Bethlehem than up pops Captain "Happy" Jack H. Derickson, Jr., of the Delaware area, Eastern Shore Dericksons. Jack, earlier, as Lieutenant John H. had been associated with Civilian Personnel with Captain John F. Carson. He went to Bethlehem, 12 July 1944, as Assistant to the Officer-in-Charge. On 18 December 1945 he moved to the post relinquished by Captain Furniss. Jack matriculated at Randolph-Macon College with A.B. (Atta Boy!) in 1927, joined up with the National City Company; and in his stride, measured with the best of them in the officers of Graham Parsons & Company, and E. H. Rollins & Sons. He had among his Assistants, at Bethlehem, Captain Richard A. Line, who had come from the Cincinnati District in December 1943 with Colonel Fred A. McMahon the then newly appointed District Chief. Dick Line, first as Aide, then as Intelligence and Censorship Officer, gave a good account of himself. In February 1946, Indiantown Gap added the Derickson scalp to its Collection.

All of which brings this tale to 6 February 1946, to the appointment as Officer-in-Charge of First Lieutenant Charles H. Stahl; and WOJG Frank

H. Maier as Assistant. Lieutenant Stahl entered active duty in P. O. D. 12 January 1945, and on 1st March was assigned as Assistant to the Officer-in-Charge. He had been associated for two years with the Cleveland Ordnance District following an imposing string of Army assignments, including Camp Euclid, Ohio, where he had been in charge of a unit of 42 men engaged with road, trail, wall and bridge construction. Following his final assignment at Bethlehem, where he did a commendable job in getting that office finally out of the war, he traveled the road that many had traveled before him, to Fort George G. Meade, where the record was closed, 3 September 1946.

The Eddystone Regional Office, another of the real old-timers, defies dating; its activity being practically inseparable from that of the Baldwin Locomotive Works. The first contract assigned by the War Department to Baldwin involved a small order for machining Base Rings for 5 in. Navy Guns; placed 16 February 1939, by Rock Island Arsenal.

On 22 December 1939, when the Baldwin Locomotive Works, affected as were many of our great industries by the industrial depression begun in 1929, the company accepted from the Ordnance Department its first major contract. This was a procurement for 22 Railway Mounts for 8 in. Guns, valued at $1,115,000. The order was placed by Watertown Arsenal which then was manufacturing Seacoast Defense Gun Carriages of a similar type.

The record reveals that Lt. Colonel H. W. Rehm of the Watertown Arsenal spent a considerable amount of time between 1 January 1940 and 1 March 1940 at Baldwin's advising that facility on production methods in order to give the contractor the benefit of Arsenal experience. At the same time Colonel Rehm, and Ed. T. Berdge, a Senior Inspector at Watertown, were on a similar mission at York Safe & Lock Company, both dividing their time between the two plants. Late in March, A. H. Austin and L. J. Luoma, Watertown Inspectors, were assigned to Baldwin's.

On 15 September 1940, Lt. Colonel Rehm was transferred to the then newly planned Detroit Tank Arsenal, leaving Ed Berdge in charge of the now termed Baldwin Inspection Office. On 16 November 1940, Second Lieutenant Arthur J. Seiler was named Army Inspector of Ordnance at the Baldwin plant, and Officer-in-Charge of the Inspection Office, taking an active part in the

setting up of both inspection and production methods for several large contracts awarded at about this time to the contractor. To 31 December 1940, awards to Baldwin had reached a total of $93,354,173.

In September 1940 the Philadelphia Ordnance District assumed responsibility for the administration and inspection of the Watertown contracts; and from that time the Baldwin Inspection Office functioned exclusively as a Branch-Inspection Office of P. O. D., later taking the designation of Eddystone Inspection Office.

The Reading Sub-Office slid down the ways as a full-feathered unit in September 1940 with Major, then Mr., Arthur B. Allison and an original force of one inspector and one typist, Miss Edith Spang, who remained until November 1940 when she was replaced by Miss Christine Borland, the first permanent clerk-typist to be assigned to this office. Charles Hahn was the Inspector. On 31 December, all work then being processed in plants within the area was brought under the administration of the Reading Office. The principal plants at that time were Parish Pressed Steel Company, Doehler Die Casting Company, Lebanon Steel Foundries and the Carpenter Steel Company. As of the end of this, the first year, seven inspectors had been assigned to the 105 prime and sub-contracts in production.

Reading was a fast-growing office. By 31 December 1941, the staff had expanded from a total in January of 9 persons to a year's end total of 47. The office entered 1943 with a personnel of 155 persons.

The York Regional Office also belongs to 1940 following Reading by one month. Originally, in 1938, there had been an Inspection Office in the York area—at York Safe & Lock Company, and, like Baldwin's during those early days, reporting to Watertown Arsenal. In March 1939 an Inspection Office was established in the plant of A. B. Farquhar Company, Ltd.; in December 1941, an Inspection Office was established in the Read Machinery Company, Inc., plant; others followed at Harrisburg Steel Corporation, Armstrong Cork Company and so on, in almost unending sequence. In June 1941 the Regional Office (Sub-Office, then) was set up to do business in eight counties, and absorbing all Inspection Offices operating at that time.

Following Lt. Colonel Rehm, who was in charge during the York Safe & Lock era, came Major, then Captain, Ed H. Cahill as Officer-in-Charge, arriving with the change of Office designation. In March 1941, Cap'n Ed stepped down to make way for Captain, then Lieutenant, Robert D. Scarlett.

The Berwick Regional Office reported 21 November 1941. Office Memorandum No. 135 turned the trick, and in short order the Berwick Office was pointing with pride to a staff of four Commissioned Officers and 148 Civilians, peopling the Engineering Division set up in the plant of American Car & Foundry Company, the Berwick Proof Range, and the various divisions of the Regional Office itself. And let it be noted that this was a 17-county-wide office—10,520 square miles, if you are a stickler for figures; but with Howard Pierson Klair, then a blushing Lieutenant in charge, one could venture the question, "So what?"

Production during the early "Klairvoyant" days around Berwick was of such items as 1000 lb. Demolition Bombs, M3; Light Tanks, M3, and Jettison Tanks, to mention a few. Before the Office was a year old it was tackling Shell, H.E., 105 mm., M1; Shot S. A. P., 3 in., M79; Proof Projectile, 8 in. 200 lb. Steel, T-9 and Shell, Q. F., H.E., 40 mm. By October '43 Berwick personnel was easing along toward a "400" of its own, and production

spreading over an increasing variety of items as new capacities were being turned up.

So on to Baltimore! The Regional Office in the city of Fort McHenry and the Star Spangled Banner came into existence with the award, 30 June 1940, to the Koppers Company of a contract for 500 units of 37 mm. A.A. Gun Carriages, M3, by Watertown Arsenal. On 3 July, Robert E. Layton, who remained with Ordnance to the Liquidation of the Baltimore Office was instructed to take over the duties and assume the responsibility for the establishment of the office, reporting five days later to the Koppers Company.

By December of 1940, the Baltimore organization had grown to a point where it was thought advisable by the Executive Officer of P. O. D., Major D. N. Hauseman, to install an Officer in this area. Consequently, on 18 December, Captain, then Lieutenant, Albert S. Branson was assigned as Officer-in-Charge. The Office at this time boasted 20 civilian inspectors and a clerical staff of two. The Office was coming of age. By January 1941 the Office had outgrown quarters at Koppers. Space was found in the Pennsylvania Railroad Building—1,300 feet of it. Not long thereafter, with business still "going like crazy," an Assistant

Major Charles T. Michener, Chief, Military Personnel Branch, initiates display to attract contractors to war production

to the Officer-in-Charge was found and placed in charge of production. He was Lieutenant Robert A. Scott, fresh in P. O. D. from the rolls of Bethlehem Steel Company at Sparrows Point, Maryland. Scott was a very handy man about the place; and a good thing, for those were the days when no one appeared to have all the answers. For instance, in the matter of the 37 mm. Gun Carriage, M3A1: beyond the 1,500 drawings originally provided, there were issued during the "change around" period, not less than 5,000 drawings, resulting in an inordinate volume of work in respect to purchase order cancellations, issuance of inspection requisitions, correspondence, contractual price changes and severe pains in executive necks. But that was war "they kept telling us down at the office." And there was much more of this, hither and yon, while we were getting our sights set.

By October 1941, pressure was on at Baltimore for more and more personnel. A large sub-contract for Flare Fuzes M111, complete, except for the clock mechanism, had been awarded Black & Decker Company of Towson, Maryland; and a prime contract to Chevrolet Motor Division for 491 Bomb-Service Trucks, explained the SOS that came winging its way to Civilian Personnel. By 1 December, one hundred persons were punching the clock at Baltimore.

The Declaration of War, 9 December 1941, found the Baltimore Office bearing down on production all along the line; some facilities on a 7-day week basis, and quotas upped from 40 per cent to 60 per cent. This was not strictly a Baltimore development. It was the same everywhere; in all Districts. Sky was the limit. In May 1942, the Baltimore Office still was bulging at the sides. New and larger space in which to grow was discovered at 11 East Mount Royal Avenue—3,500 square feet, this time. And this, too, was the general story—at Bethlehem, Reading, York, Philadelphia. And in this merry month of May, the Baltimore Office had under administration 125 prime contracts and 350 Sub-contracts—worth, all told, something in the neighborhood of $100,000,000.

An interesting procurement of this period was a rush order for 12-gauge shot guns. What practically was a door-to-door canvass of the area turned up 2,000 of the guns, all in good shape and acceptable to P. O. D. In August 1942, Lieutenant Branson was transferred to Field Service. Major, then Captain, Harold L. Vennell was assigned to succeed him.

October 1942 brought to the Baltimore Office added responsibilities growing out of the transfer to Ordnance of Quartermaster Corps Automotive contracts. Facilities were found in the Chevrolet plant, Watson Automotive Company and the Maryland Manufacturing Company. Personnel now had been pushed up to 240, and dollar value of production, as a result of the Quartermaster arrangement to $410,000,000.

By 31 December, the population of the Baltimore Office had grown to 205 persons, a group that had plenty of work to keep everyone busy, what with 338 prime contracts, 723 sub-contracts and 234 sub-sub-contracts. The business of the District was to climb to even larger totals, and there would be two more moves to gain space—one move to the Chevrolet Sales Rooms on West Mt. Royal Avenue, and a final move to downtown Baltimore.

On 30 May 1944, Major Paul H. Carlson came down from the P. O. D. Property Disposal Branch to succeed Major Vennel who had been transferred to Bethlehem. Paul acquired his "know-how" in the ice machinery business, but contracted none of its chill; he had warmth, this chap. He found on his arrival in the City of the Calverts such capable assistants as Lieutenant Mahlon C. Hoy, Ben Grier, R. E. "Bob" Layton. Later to appear, among others, in Baltimore were First Lieutenant Louis Rosenstein, C. W. Miller. Upon the separation from the Service, 1 October 1945, of Major Carlson, the laurel went to Lieutenant Hoy, who trailed along until March 1946. The last we saw of the energetic Lieutenant was in March of 1946. He had come up to P. O. D. with a shipment of files of which he was madly trying to make sense, while keeping one eye on a date with Fort George G. Meade.

It was Office Memorandum No. 136, dated 29 November 1941, which created the Philadelphia Regional Office, with Major, then Captain, Victor W. Smith in charge. The territory involved extended from Trenton on the north to Eddystone on the south; the Atlantic Ocean at the eastern extremity and Coatesville as the western limit. The Memorandum ordered that the new installation would administer all contracts within the prescribed area with the exception of Edward G. Budd Manufacturing Company, Philco Corporation, Standard Pressed Steel Company, Henry Disston & Sons, Inc., and Empire Ordnance Corporation.

While the Office Memorandum setting up the office bore the date of 29 November, the personnel realized that much confusion might result if a too speedy attempt were made to assume complete jurisdiction as of an arbitrarily established date. Consequently, the high command ordered a period of grace extending to 1 January 1942. Before the end of January, the Office, with the assistance of a number of inspectors who, to this time had formed the nucleus of the inspector unit of the District Office, was administering 150 contracts at 60 plants. Personnel rapidly had been expanded to a total of one Reserve Officer, 109 Civilian Men and 30 Females—all crowded into a space in the Mitten Building of 20 by 100 feet. To ease the pressure, an Inspection Office was established in Trenton to administer contracts in that area.

As time went on other Inspection Offices were established, and Resident Inspectors stationed in many plants of the area. For instance, Archie Borbeck, and later J. P. Werbickas, at J. G. Brill Company, P. H. Kizlin at H. W. Butterworth & Sons, J. F. Durning at Disston, W. H. McGrath, and, later, Lieutenant Phil Welch at Heintz Manufacturing; F. E. Feesley, H. A. Buskirk at Electric Service & Supplies; Lieutenant Julius Mehalek at Budd, Harry Allison at Lukens, and so on down the long list and through many changes.

Earliest Assistants to Major Victor W. Smith, who was transferred from his post of Chief, Executive Division of P. O. D. to direct the newly formed Philadelphia Regional Office were: Lieutenant H. C. Troth and Lieutenant W. H. Nichols. Hubert Troth was one of the very few P. O. Ders to report Stanford as his Alma Mater. He was assigned in February 1943 to the Industry Integration Committee for the M66A1 Fuze at Bulova Watch Company. In September 1944 he was assigned to the Chicago Ordnance District. Major Smith's Alma Mater was Alabama Poly, where he graduated in electrical and mechanical engineering in 1928, following which he spent the next dozen years with such industrial leaders as Frigidaire Division of General Motors, The York Company, and Peerless Company of Chicago.

Phil Welch, all Lehigh and a yard wide (not physically) went to work for P. O. D. in February 1942. Did a turn for Procurement Planning at the request of H. Paul Gant, Planning Director; followed by a month at Budd thence, 19 October 1942, joined forces with Major Smith. Marked up other performances, including a job on procurement of critical waterproofing materials that brought a bravo! from General Campbell. Went to Indian-

town Gap, 23 February 1946, for separation. Lieutenant Nichols was P. M. C.—and as good a soldier as he was a cadet. Arrived in P. O. D. for duty 6 February 1942. In October was assigned as Contracting Officer's Representative; later to Autocar Inspection Office; and sometime thereafter left the Service to resume direction of his own business.

Other Assistants to the Officer-in-Charge later to come into the Regional Office were Lieutenant Oren H. Persons, former team-mate of Captain Lewis A. Smith, Jr., on Priorities, Lieutenant Walter H. Vogelsberg, one time of the Gage Section and, finally, Lieutenant Paul E. Nieman, formerly Chief, P. E. P. Section and earlier of the Fuel Section.

The Philadelphia Regional Office grew to be the largest among the outposts. The District became accustomed to and soon seemed not particularly to note, except when the "heat was on" all over the District for reduction of personnel, such monthly totals as 517, 582 and 604. And within these totals many men, more than can be named individually in this narrative, who would make important and substantial contribution to the war effort in P. O. D. Came in time, as Executive Officer, Captain, then Lieutenant Robert D. Scarlett.

Who will not recall H. D. Goldberg, Carl L. Phillipi, on Inspection; W. S. Patterson, J. J. McNally, Harry V. Ayres, D. F. Feaster on Administration; L. V. Pettit and later, Captain, then Lieutenant, R. G. Palmer on Fiscal; R. G. Bothwell on Shipping, Packaging, Spare Parts, Traffic; and later J. Simkiss on Spare Parts; Lieutenant H. C. Troth and later W. E. Gilbert heading up Production; T. E. Marks, D. A. Duncan, R. L. Tatem, D. V. Feaster on Scrap and Salvage; O. D. Greenlee, Chief, Technical Division; J. H. Winslow on Machine Tools; the late H. E. "Dick" Snyder, as Executive Assistant; Lieutenant Herbert G. Geittman, Jr., Assistant, and Lieutenant Frank Kron and H. P. Patchett in a similar capacity.

Names without end: W. Stoever and S. Riggins, Inspectors; W. E. Holloway on Personnel; Christman, Fileccia, Franklin, Doling, White, Hatch, Kinney, Heindel, Gibson, Mullin, Wright, Newberry, Bertschy and on and on, "far into the night"— and into history. Then there was W. Jack Gilliford, who joined Vic Smith on Production, who later was wounded in the "Battle of the Bulge"—for which he received the Purple Heart, with citation.

Following discharge, he joined up with General Electric Company in Philadelphia.

In March 1943, the Office had placed under its jurisdiction the contracts at Standard Pressed Steel Company, Pennsylvania Manufacturing Company and R-S Products Company. Business was humming along with 305 prime contracts, 1730 sub-contracts—and to accomodate the increase larger space had to be found; and was, at 1420 Walnut Street. In December 1942 it was decided that the Office had now come of age and as a birthday gift Major Smith's boys were assigned the Autocar Company, E. G. Budd Manufacturing Company and the Empire Ordnance Corporation, the last of the Exempted Inspection Offices to be absorbed.

A story told of Major Victor Smith, was on the day he was lost on the way to De Long Hook & Eye Company with an "E" Award party. The Major was at the wheel. Somewhere on the way a detour threw him off the scent with the result that he soon was miles off the trail floundering in strange and forbidding neighborhoods. Nor was the crew he carried of particular assistance. By the time the convoy arrived at the plant, an hour behind schedule, the band had exhausted its repertoire, the guests were fidgeting and the plant force had reached the limit of endurance. Vic has a map, drawn in the Public Relations Section, which he cherishes as a memento of his far-flung journey uptown.

And so the Philadelphia Regional Office rode on to glory, with no small part in America's Victory. On 12 October 1945 Major Smith walked off his post for the last time and into Deshon General Hospital at Butler, Pennsylvania, for an overhaul job before his return to the world of common mortals. Captain Walter E. English, old-time Berwick, Baltimore and York Regional Office oracle, was named successor. In February 1946, Captain Walter moved on to Indiantown Gap, and Harry V. Ayres, long of Ordnance, took over, continuing to the time of his separation in April 1946 when Charles F. Kemper stepped into the gap to do the clean-up job and write finis to a great Ordnance installation.

Calling Richmond! the last of the Regional Offices. Early records do not clearly indicate when this organization actually was established. The first correspondence or record reveals that on or about 15 December 1941 desk space was provided in the Richmond Office of Production Management

(later to be known as the War Production Board) then located in the Johnson Publishing Company Building. Office Memorandum No. 6, issued by P. O. D., officially set 7 January 1942 as the natal day for Richmond. So let's take it from there.

The area assigned embraced Virginia, North Carolina and South Carolina. The first Officer-in-Charge was Major S. H. Franklin, Jr., who was assigned the assistance of A. J. Fitzgerald, the Chief Inspector at the Tredegar Iron Works, who at that time had, with the assistance of his organization of 18 Inspectors, handled all inspection assignments in the area. The Major checked in as Officer-in-Charge at Richmond, 2 March 1942.

The Office had a total of 40 contracts under inspection at this time; one very important contract was that with the Richmond Engineering Company who held a sub-contract with Baldwin Locomotive Works on an educational order for welded Tank Hulls. Another important contract of the period was one with the Molins Machine Company for the development of .50 Cal. Linking Machines.

In January 1942 the Office moved into larger quarters in the Mutual Building and a stenographer was temporarily transferred from Philadelphia. At the same time, V. R. Murphy came along to serve as Production Chief. The Office now definitely was emerging from the bush leagues. Number of contracts in force had grown to 63; among them, one at Solvay Process Company for Ammunition Nitrate; one at Wannamaker Chemical Company for Tetryl; and at Tredegar Iron Works, contracts for various sizes of Proof Projectiles.

In March 1943, Lieutenant Louis F. Unger was sent down from the P. O. D. Procurement Planning Section to do a turn as Assistant to the Officer-in-Charge. He continued at this post to 15 January 1944 and his reassignment to Philadelphia. Contracts now were to the number of 83; and procurement activities reaching for new highs, made necessary the use of additional space in the Mutual Building.

A particularly interesting procurement under the Unger regime was one placed with the Essex Corporation, Charlottesville, Virginia, for 1,000,000 PD M-64 Fuzes for 40 mm. Ammunition; a long step from the contractor's former business of manufacture of fountain pens and propelling pencils.

Business still swinging up the chart in June 1942, and the payroll growing in proportion, the Office went on a prowl for larger space; found it in the Grace Securities Building. It was about this time that DuVal S. Hughes came in as Administration Chief. In August came W. L. Worden to head up production. He was succeeded a month or so later by E. J. Busch, Jr. The Assistant Production Chief was R. F. Jones—come to remain long in Ordnance.

Midway of November, Major Franklin had re-assigned. To succeed this able officer came from Philadelphia Major, then Captain, John W. Ogden, P. O. D.'s Executive Officer, he of the Churchill-length cigars. Awaiting Ogdenian ministrations were 192 contracts (87 primes; 105 subs) with 70 contractors; and to a dollar value of $24,127,550.21. Conquering all current major problems in Richmond, John moved on to greater glory, 19 February 1943, to the Legal Branch, Smaller War Plants Division, O. C. O., in Washington. All of which gave Major, then Captain Oliver C. Conger, Pottstown agriculturist, his opportunity. On 27 March, the Office made its final move—to the Reynolds Metals Company Building. Ollie continued in command until 30 November when word came down that Baltimore needed him. Captain Dan H. Pletta, who had been navigating the Fuel Conservation Section in Philadelphia, was assigned as next-in-line, with Lieutenant William B. Wellborn of the Sub-Office Administration Division coming along as runner-up. On June 1944, Captain Pletta was selected by the Military Academy to fill a vacant faculty post. Captain Wellborn, the 'bama lad who made good, was assigned, continuing to September 1945, when Captain Charles A. Sinquefield, who first came to Richmond in March, following a tour of duty at the York Regional Office, assumed command. Another change in command in December 1945 when Charley Sinquefield "went to the showers" at Fort George G. Meade, brought First Lieutenant Donald B. Kimmell to the fore. Don, Purdue 1936, formerly had been in Property Disposal; later, Assistant-in-Charge at Richmond. In February 1946 Don came to Philadelphia as Assistant to the Industrial Chief as a stop-over on his way to duty overseas, the Richmond Regional Office meanwhile disappearing into the archives.

During the span of its existence the R. R. O. saw many good men come, and finally go. Among them, in addition to the Officers already named, Lieutenant A. D. Edwards, Lieutenant C. A. Kilgore, Lieutenant Edward L. Pearce, A. C.

Woolridge, J. McC. D. Greathead, C. W. Blanks, M. G. James, L. C. Purdey, F. D. Thornton, C. W. Selden, Jr., Spurgeon T. Ayscue, C. L. Powers, J. W. Brown, M. Lewis, E. Lynn, S. C. Schaaf, A. M. Griffin, J. E. Cleland, M. T. Gibson, W. G. Sloan, E. T. Von Pippen, W. A. Brownlee.

And what did they turn out down there? To mention a few items, M7 Grenades, trunnion bands, clay pigeons, fliers' armor, frag. bombs, mount telescope, practice rockets, boosters, cargo bodies, 6 Ton 6 by 6 Prime Movers, and so on and so on right down the Ordnance alphabet.

And what did it all add up to besides helping win the war? It proved beyond all question that the Industrial South was big enough to take on all comers.

Control of all the work in the Field was vested in the Sub-Office Administration Division back in P. O. D. This, the guiding influence of the far flung and expanding outposts, came into being without benefit of Directive or Office Memorandum.

By the fall of 1939 it had become a matter of extreme hardship for any one man to oversee the activities of all Field personnel. However, it was not until January 1941 that definite steps were taken to provide adequate supervision. At this time there was appointed a Chief Inspector, Joseph B. Anderson of "Anderson Hardware," York, Pennsylvania, who, shortly afterward, was succeeded by William I. Mirkil, and two assistants: one, W. H. Lownsbury on Inspection, and "grave-digging" Sam McClenahan in charge of Personnel.

In June 1941 the Sub-Office Division as P. O. D. later was to know it was given honorable existence by Office Memorandum No. 74, Subject: "Inspection of Sub-Offices and Resident Inspection Offices." From its inception, the Sub-Office Administration Division was purely an Administrative unit. It did not originate routines or procedures; it had no clear alignments with Commodity Branches or other P. O. D. divisions. Its whole concern was the efficient operation of Sub-Offices and Sub-Office routines and the standardization of Sub-Office organization and management. Production, Inspection, Fiscal and other units established in the Sub-Offices worked directly with the corresponding units in P. O. D. The Sub-Office Administration Division adhered to its one purpose of representing the Sub-Office in the District Office.

Major additions to the staff revealed by the

District Chart of 30 September 1942, were Harry V. Ayres, Virginia gentleman out of Washington and Lee, in to assist on the Administration job. Harry once played football. "All-American end," he said. "All the Americans ran around my end." Coached baseball for a time. Went out for the major leagues, but was set back by an accident to his throwing arm. Good salesman, too. And a good instructor. Harry tells of a talk he once gave to a group of new women inspectors, ". . . you must be regular in attendance," he told them, "else it will be necessary to separate you." One woman, with an expression of bewilderment, replied, "Ye gods, Mr. Ayres, do you mean to say I might get separated from my husband on account of this job?"

It was about the same time that Thomas P. "Jenkintown Ford Dealer" Lowry, rumored the best dressed man in P. O. D., according to Sam Marx, signed up as Production Chief. Tom later took over the Travel Section of P. O. D., succeeding Captain, then Lieutenant, John I. Spiegelhalter. Mrs. J. Bright appears now in charge of female inspectors. H. Spoll heads the Fiscal Unit. Edward E. Clark was a later acquisition.

Up from the War Production Board in October 1942 came "Mister" Albert Donald Kelso, to be assigned by Colonel Hauseman to the very tough job of straightening out procedures in the Sub-Offices, expedite operations generally, consolidate activities, put the bee on excessive paper-work, cut down personnel. What he accomplished on this crusade did him no harm when his name came up for the Legion of Merit Award. He got it—16 December 1945, the day of his fadeout from P.O.D.

Following his report to the Colonel on his crusade, his Majority order arrived in the District—and the success climb, as told elsewhere in this story, had begun—for it was just a matter of days before the newly labeled Major succeeded Captain Joe at the No. 1 Desk. Joe moved upstairs as Assistant to the Director of Planning. In August 1943 the Captain was assigned as Officer-in-Charge, Philadelphia Mobile Shop Depot. In September 1944, Captain Anderson was relieved at his own request to return to his business.

The Sub-Offices, now the Regional Offices, grew apace with the changing tides and tempo of the war. Sections were added from time to time as the need became pressing: Production, Inspection, Fiscal, Scrap Salvage, Priorities, Planning, Terminations, Packaging . . .

The trip made by Major Kelso over the Sub-Office route, paid out in rich dividends. At York he was able to effect a consolidation of the York Proof Range, York Safe & Lock Inspection Office and the York Regional Office. The consolidation was made 19 December 1942, and all activities set up in the York Regional Office, occupied at the time by Major, then Captain, Ernest J. Langham as Officer-in-Charge, Lieutenant J. P. Grimwade as Assistant, and a personnel staff of 46. Total P. O. D. employment in the area, including all Resident Inspectors and the York Safe & Lock group, was of 276 persons; down 23 from November. The consolidation was accomplished with both savings in personnel and marked increase in efficiency, the record says.

Major Kelso was a strategist of "the first water." He not only was able to inspire his people to greater achievement but was able quickly to select men for tasks they could most efficiently perform; for the work they best could do. Getting the right man into the right job at the right time represented the larger phase of his work. There was no doubt at any time that the esprit de corps engendered under his leadership paid dividends, not only throughout the field, but extended into contractors plants as well.

In his visits to Regional Offices and their pertaining facilities, Major Kelso was P. O. D.'s ambassador of good will. He was accompanied on one series of such visits by the District Chief, Mr. C. Jared Ingersoll; Major R. C. Disney of the Industrial Division; French E. Dennison, Chief of Inspection; W. E. Gilbert, Production Director, and members of the Public Relations Staff. These visits enabled Regional Office personnel to air their difficulties and peeves at the very foot of the throne. They felt good about the whole arrangement. So did the contractors visited.

On the Baltimore visit, a staff car carrying District Chief Ingersoll, Major Kelso, Major Disney and the Historian, and driven by Major Paul H. Carlson, the Officer-in-Charge at Baltimore, was stopped by two Military Police who, noting the speed of the car, whistled the vehicle to a curbside stop. Leaving the Baltimore Office "on the double," the otherwise painstakingly precise Major Carlson had forgotten his credentials. It looked like "curtains" until Major Disney, who had gone to high-school in Baltimore with just about everybody, recognized one of the MP's as an old school-mate. The MP immediately recognized th

Major; and just as immediately four very sagging jaws in the car quickly snapped to hilarious attention—and all was well with the world.

So it went, through 1943. Major Kelso at the throttle; his eye on the track and the signals all of the time, and everybody glad of it. However, as always, comes the shift somewhere along the line. In December 1943, Colonel Fred A. McMahon came on from Cincinnati to succeed Colonel Hauseman. Colonel McMahon, rated a pretty good production man, added to his duties that of Industrial Chief, releasing the incumbent Lt. Colonel Arthur J. Seiler for duty as Director of Production and Inspection. Major, now Lt. Colonel, Kelso was moved into the Industrial Division as Assistant, with the title Chief, Production-Inspection Control.

Early in January 1944 Colonel McMahon was transferred to Washington. C. Jared Ingersoll, once again, was named District Chief. It was shortly following this shift, in February 1944, that Colonel Kelso was assigned as Chief of the Industrial Division, with Major Langham as Assistant Chief. Major, then Captain, Eugene H. Uhler succeeded to Major Langham's old post.

It also was during the McMahon regime that the Sub-Offices, or Field Offices, became known chartwise as Regional Offices; and the Sub-Office Administration Division was discontinued as a separate unit and absorbed by the Office of the Executive Assistant — Field Office, Executive Branch, Industrial Division.

The Executive Branch of the Industrial Division under the leadership of the indomitable Lt. Col. Kelso was not long in setting up its own Academy of Immortals. Major Ernest J. Langham, fresh down from the York Regional Office, 21 January 1944, had been named Executive Assistant, Field Office-Executive Branch, and Chief, Production Service Branch. Major Langham's associates in the Executive Branch of the Division were Lt. Colonel H. K. Kelley, Chief, Property Disposal; E. W. Lafferty, Chief, Spare Parts; French E. Dennison, Inspection Director; W. E. Gilbert, Production Director, and Sam McClenahan, Administration.

Clicking to the generalship of Major Ernie in the Production Service Branch were Major Eugene H. Uhler, Chief, Planning-Engineering Section; Major Arthur B. Allison, Chief, Production Equipment Section; Captain Cecil Bentley, Chief, Packaging Section; Lieutenant R. O. Watson, Chief, Gage Section; Lieutenant Oren H. Persons,

on Material Control and Victor R. Strohlein, heading the Technical Data Section.

A chief responsibility of Major Langham through all this period was that of supervision of Field Offices (or Regional Offices) activities—with the assistance of as hard hitting a crew as ever trumped a partner's ace.

In July 1944, Sam McClenahan departed his post in the Executive Branch of the Division to succeed Captain Jack Carson as Chief, Civilian Personnel Branch, where he distinguished himself in assisting Lt. Colonel Henry W. Gadsden in recruiting personnel for the Ammunition drives, and later assisting that Officer in organizing an orderly retreat of that personnel.

In December 1944, Major Langham was selected to "quarterback" the Ammunition drive. He was named in addition to his other duties Chief, Ammunition Branch, with Major Ed Lafferty to assist on the heavy shell program. Also during December, Major Langham was named Assistant Industrial Chief.

In January 1945, Major Roland C. Disney came down from the Tank-Automotive Branch as Assistant to the Chief, Industrial Division, and Executive Assistant-Field Office-Executive Branch. Lieutenant Walter D. Gilbert also was assigned to the Branch about this time. In May, Major Welles H. Denney reported.

The following month, June 1945, brought many major changes. C. Jared Ingersoll, following a long period of illness, resigned. Colonel Kelso, with the recommendation of Mr. Ingersoll and the approval of General Campbell, was assigned the highest post the District had to offer—that of Chief. Major Langham was named Chief, Industrial Division. Major Disney was released for duty overseas.

Other changes of that period involved Ed T. Berdge, who was brought up from Eddystone as Executive Assistant, Field Office-Executive Branch; Major Lafferty as Assistant to the Chief, Industrial Division; Major Uhler as Assistant to the Chief-Field Office-Executive Branch. And still the changes come, and more changes. In September, Major Denney transferred to the post of Chief, cost-plus-a-fixed-fee Section, Termination Branch. Major Uhler was named Chief of the Field Office-Executive Branch Section.

During all these changes, the Regional Offices gradually were reducing ranks. The war pressures were off. Old routines and procedures were being put out to pasture. However, there still was much to be done, and good men were needed to crack the whip. In October 1945, for instance, Ed Berdge was appointed Assistant Chief, Industrial Division. One month later he made the final jump, taking the high command spot on the Industrial Division chart. In December, Lieutenant R. O. Watson, late of Gages, was named assistant to the Chief, continuing to the appointment, a few weeks later, in January 1946, when Lieutenant Philip J. Welch, was named Assistant, only to depart 1 April to make way for Lieutenant Don B. Kimmel, who on 12 July 1946 was relieved

for duty in ETO—all of which set the stage for John J. Target—P. O. D. 1938—who promptly nailed over his door the sign reading Assistant Chief.

Business at this time in the Field Offices was fast approaching the mists from which it had emerged 'way back when. Terminations work in the various Regional Office areas had got well over the peak. Only a few cases remained to be settled. The names of W. I. Mirkil and Joe Anderson had long since become part of the tradition. Thus do great enterprises grow . . . and thus having served the need that gave them being, disappear.

FINAL OFFICERS' MESS, 7 DECEMBER 1945, KENNEY'S CAFE, CAMDEN, N. J.
First row: Capt. Fugate, Major Slattery, Major Eadie, Major Case, Lt. Col. Michener, Major Stephens, Lt. Col. Hansen, Lt. Col. Gilmer, Col. Kelso, Lt. Col. Gadsden, Major Wexlin, Major Hoffman, Major Lafean, Major Feustel, Major Sorber, Major Carlson, Major Langham, Major Beyer. Second row: Capt. Chambers, W/O Stransky, Capt. Redmond, Lt. Lynch, Capt. Furniss, Capt. Smith, Lt. Stahl, Lt. Rosenstein, Capt. Stewart, Lt. Hoy, Capt. Fisher, Capt. English, Capt. MacIlvaine, Lt. Watson, Lt. Gilbert, Capt. Unger, Lt. Ginsburg, W/O Cohen, W/O Riddell, W/O Gillers, W/O Cohart, W/O Buchwald. Third row: Capt. Kron, Lt. Kimmel, Lt. Beaumont, Capt. Dilks, Major Lafferty, W/O Bell, Major Wilmsen, W/O Morgan, Capt. Armstrong, Capt. Felton, Lt. Griffin, Capt. Caldwell, Major Uhler, Lt. Law, Lt. Nieman, Major Baxter, Capt. Burns, W/O Brewer, Lt. Aydelotte, W/O Moroney, Capt. Andress, Capt. Fields, Lt. Watson, Lt. Nisbett, Capt. Pyle, Lt. Geraghty, Lt. Bennett, Capt. Feigley, Lt. Strachan, Lt. Hamilton, W/O Succop, Capt. Derickson, W/O Baummer, W/O Graham, W/O Neckowitz. Fourth row: W/O Silverman, Capt. Cavedo, Lt. Kilgore, Capt. Slack, Lt. Stein, Capt. Welch, Lt. Tabors, Lt. Spiegelhalter, Capt. Patterson, Lt. Smith, Capt. Hearte, Lt. Hinchman, Lt. Kaufman, Lt. Auger, Capt. Lee, Capt. Jessen, Capt. Mingle, Lt. Young, Lt. E. Hall, Major Scarlett, Capt. Buerger, W/O Swingley, W/O Schaffner, W/O Melnick, Capt. Edmonds, Lt. Jones, Capt. Persons

Addenda

THE RISE AND FALL OF CIVILIAN PERSONNEL IN P. O. D.

STRENGTH – APPOINTMENTS – SEPARATIONS – RECLASSIFICATIONS

	Personnel – Number (Excluding Term. Leave)	Appointments	Separations	Reclassifications
1940				
July............	115	95		
August..........	220	57		
September.......	225	17		
October.........	245	23		
November.......	284	50		
December.......	329	49	5	
1941				
January.........	420	136	5	
February........	532	116	7	
March..........	642	164	30	
April...........	769	187	35	
May............	846	138	27	
June...........	956	164	30	
July............	1104	222	35	
August..........	1208	178	31	
September.......	1368	212	29	
October.........	1482	178	25	
November........	1561	147	32	
December.......	1693	214	32	
1942				
January.........	1866	351	44	
February........	2150	318	64	
March..........	2413	400	51	
April...........	2616	283	63	
May............	2832	354	84	
June...........	3339	565	87	
July............	3712	427	119	
August..........	3879	294	126	180
September.......	3845	214	248	166
October.........	4149	418	114	325
November.......	4104	105	156	181
December.......	3856	176	182	300

1943

January	3370	25	319	575
February	3432	53	250	662
March	3139	100	173	227
April	3100	98	135	313
May	3039	76	135	261
June	3020	111	126	271
July	3039	123	110	294
August	3015	90	168	191
September	2930	69	120	463
October	2936	106	131	245
November	2914	96	124	271
December	2811	32	147	207

1944

January	2644	4	160	167
February	2609	70	108	101
March	2674	179	121	22
April	2686	134	126	775
May	2643	84	135	110
June	2677	136	96	127
July	2683	111	104	141
August	2710	138	128	116
September	2722	110	106	165
October	2804	180	98	218
November	2863	210	135	126
December	2888	117	85	174

1945

January	2986	254	95	138
February	3063	210	125	221
March	3298	109	133	126
April	3209	42	131	191
May	2784	15	180	156
June	2778	16	282	117
July	2508	23	293	168
August	2313	19	214	56
September	1635	15	693	22
October	1580	24	79	8

PRIME CONTRACTORS OF PHILADELPHIA
ORDNANCE DISTRICT

Among the long list of fine firms serving the District and the War effort, the historian is proud to include those following. One cannot praise too highly their superb performance, often in the face of serious bottlenecks, new and complicated processes necessarily to be made effective on the eve of deadlines, and critical shortages of materials, equipment and workers. All hail!

ACF–Brill Motors Company......................................Philadelphia, Pa.
Acme Tin Plate Roofing Supply Company....................Philadelphia, Pa.
Aeronautical Supplies, Inc.......................................Reading, Pa.
Air Shields, Incorporated......................................Hatboro, Pa.
Allen-Morrison Sign Company, Inc............................Lynchburg, Va.
Allied Chemical and Dye Corporation.......................New York, N. Y.
Allied Machine Tool Company................................Philadelphia, Pa.
Allied Metal Stamping Company............................Camden, N. J.
Alloy Rods Company..York, Pa.
Aluminum Company of America.............................Pittsburgh, Pa.
American Can Company.......................................Philadelphia, Pa.
American Car and Foundry Company.......................New York, N. Y.
American Chain and Cable Company, Inc..................New York, N. Y.
American Die and Tool Company............................Reading, Pa.
American Insulator Company...............................New Freedon, Pa.
American Instrument Company.............................Silver Springs, Md.
American Meter Company....................................Philadelphia, Pa.
American Pulley Company...................................Philadelphia, Pa.
American Standard Radiator & Sanitary Corporation.........Pittsburgh, Pa.
American Viscose Corporation...............................Wilmington, Del.
Anchor Packing Company....................................Manheim, Pa.
Anchor Post Fence Company.................................Baltimore, Md.
Andrews, Frank C. Company.................................Phoenixville, Pa.
Animal Trap Company of America, Ltd......................Lititz, Pà
Aristo Manufacturing Company.............................Berwick, Pa.
Armstrong Cork Company....................................Lancaster, Pa.
Arrow Safety Device Company..............................Mount Holly, N. J.
Art Metal Works, Inc...East Stroudsburgh, Pa.
Atlantic Elevator Company..................................Philadelphia, Pa.
Atlantic Products Corporation..............................Trenton, N. J.
Atlantic Refining Company..................................Philadelphia, Pa.
Atlas Fence Company...Mifflinburg, Pa.
Atlas Powder Company.......................................Wilmington, Del.
Autocar Company...Ardmore, Pa.
The Aviation Corporation....................................Williamsport, Pa.
Baker, Harold W. Company..................................Bryn Mawr, Pa.
Baldwin Locomotive Works..................................Eddystone, Pa.
Bally Case Cooler Company..................................Bally, Pa.
Barbizon Corporation..Scranton, Pa.
Barclay White Company......................................Philadelphia, Pa.
Barrett Division—Allied Chemical and Dye Company.........Philadelphia, Pa.

Beard, L. O. Tool Company . . . . Lancaster, Pa.
Bearings Company of America . . . . Lancaster, Pa.
Bendix Aviation Corporation . . . . Philadelphia, Pa.
Bethlehem Steel Company . . . . Bethlehem, Pa.
Bilgram Gear and Machine Works, Inc. . . . . Philadelphia, Pa.
Billard Machine Tool Company . . . . Mansfield, Pa.
Birdsboro Steel Foundry Company . . . . Birdsboro, Pa.
Black and Decker Manufacturing Company . . . . Towson, Md.
Bonney Forge and Tool Works . . . . Allentown, Pa.
Bonschur and Holmes Optical Company . . . . Philadelphia, Pa.
Bowers Battery & Spark Plug Company . . . . Reading, Pa.
Briddell, Charles D., Inc. . . . . Chrisfield, Md.
Brinton, H. Company . . . . Philadelphia, Pa.
Brown Instrument Company . . . . Philadelphia, Pa.
Brubaker, W. L. Brothers Company . . . . Millersburg, Pa.
Budd, Edward G. Manufacturing Company . . . . Philadelphia, Pa.
Bulova Watch Company . . . . Philadelphia, Pa.
Bunting Glider Company . . . . Philadelphia, Pa.
Burlington Mills Corporation . . . . Greensboro, N. C.
Butterworth, H. W. Sons Company . . . . Philadelphia, Pa.
Cameron Stove Corporation . . . . Richmond, Va.
Carey-McFall Company . . . . Philadelphia, Pa.
Carnell and Bradburn . . . . Philadelphia, Pa.
Carolina Truck and Trailer Company . . . . Charlotte, N. C.
Carpenter Steel Company . . . . Reading, Pa.
Carrier Corporation . . . . Syracuse, N. Y.
Castelli, F. C. Company . . . . Philadelphia, Pa.
Champion Blower and Forge Company . . . . Lancaster, Pa.
Chipman Knitting Mills . . . . Easton, Pa.
Cleveland Container Company . . . . Philadelphia, Pa.
Columbia Mills, Inc. . . . . Wilkes Barre, Pa.
Congoleum Nairn, Inc. . . . . Marcus Hook, Pa.
Container Corporation of America . . . . Philadelphia, Pa.
Continental Can Company . . . . New York, N. Y.
Coplay Cement Manufacturing Company . . . . Coplay, Pa.
Corbitt Company . . . . Henderson, N. C.
Crawford Manufacturing Company, Inc. . . . . Richmond, Va.
Crown Can Company . . . . Philadelphia, Pa.
Crown Cork and Seal Company . . . . Baltimore, Md.
Cutler Metal Products Company . . . . Camden, N. J.
Dana Tool-D Nast Machine Company . . . . Philadelphia, Pa.
Darling Valve Manufacturing Company . . . . Williamsport, Pa.
Day & Zimmermann, Inc. . . . . Philadelphia, Pa.
DeLong Hook and Eye Company . . . . Philadelphia, Pa.
Dienelt and Eisenhardt . . . . Philadelphia, Pa.
Disston, H. Sons, Inc. . . . . Philadelphia, Pa.
Doehler Die Casting Company . . . . Pottstown, Pa.
Du Pont de Nemours, E. I. Company . . . . Wilmington, Del.
Eastern Rolling Mill Company . . . . Baltimore, Md.
Edgemoor Iron Works . . . . Edgemoor, Del.
Electric Power Equipment Company . . . . Philadelphia, Pa.
Electric Storage Battery Company . . . . Philadelphia, Pa.

Empire Ordnance Corporation............................Philadelphia, Pa.
Everready Company, Inc...............................Frederick, Md.
Farquhar, A. B. Company.................................York, Pa.
Ferracute Machine Company........................Bridgeton, N. J.
Firestone Tire and Rubber Company....................Akron, Ohio
Foote Mineral Company............................Philadelphia, Pa.
Ford Motor Company...................................Chester, Pa.
Franklin Institute of Philadelphia....................Philadelphia, Pa.
Garrett, George K. Company, Inc......................Philadelphia, Pa.
General Steel Castings Company........................Eddystone, Pa.
Geroter May Corporation.............................Baltimore, Md.
Gilmer, L. H. Company...............................Philadelphia, Pa.
Girton Manufacturing Company..........................Milleville, Pa.
Grammes, L. F. Sons Company.........................Allentown, Pa.
Grimes, Bradley E. Company.......................Collingswood, N. J.
Gulf Oil Corporation...............................Philadelphia, Pa.
Habhegger, E. O....................................Philadelphia, Pa.
Hackney Brothers Body Company.........................Wilson, N. C.
Haines Gauge Company...............................Philadelphia, Pa.
Hamilton Watch Company...............................Lancaster, Pa.
Harrisburg Steel Company............................Harrisburg, Pa.
Heintz Manufacturing Company.......................Philadelphia, Pa.
Hendricks Manufacturing Company.....................Carbondale, Pa.
Hepler, T. W......................................Valley View, Pa.
Hercules Powder Company............................Wilmington, Del.
Hollingshead, R. M. Corporation......................Camden, N. J.
Hopkins, Johns University............................Baltimore, Md.
Houghton, E. F. Company.............................Philadelphia, Pa.
Hunter Manufacturing Company..........................Bristol, Pa.
International Chain Manufacturing Company.................York, Pa.
IX, Frank Sons, Inc.............................New Holland, Pa.
Jacquard Knitting Machine Company..................Philadelphia, Pa.
Kaiser Industries, Inc...............................Scranton, Pa.
Kennedy Van Saun Manufacturing & Engineering Company.......Danville, Pa.
Koppers Company—Bartlett-Hayward Division...............Baltimore, Md.
Krenz Machine Shop..............................Somers Point, N. J.
L. & S. Welding Company.............................Baltimore, Md.
Laros Textile Company..............................Bethlehem, Pa.
Laux Manufacturing Company.........................Wilkes Barre, Pa.
Lebanon Steel Foundry Company.........................Lebanon, Pa.
Lee Tire and Rubber Company......................Conshohocken, Pa.
Leeds and Northrup Company.........................Philadelphia, Pa.
Lehigh Foundries, Inc..............................Lancaster, Pa.
Lieberknecht, Karl, Inc.............................Reading, Pa.
Line Material Company of Pennsylvania............East Stroudsburg, Pa.
Link Belt Company..................................Philadelphia, Pa.
Lukenweld, Inc....................................Coatesville, Pa.
Machined Metals Company............................Norristown, Pa.
Mack Manufacturing Corporation......................New York, N. Y.
Mann Edge Tool Company..............................Lewistown, Pa.
Marco Company, Inc................................Wilmington, Del.
Martin, Glenn L. Company.........................Middle River, Md.

Martin and Schwartz, Inc................................Salisbury, Md.
Masland, C. H. Sons....................................Carlisle, Pa.
Mason Manufacturing Company, Inc.....................Newport News, Va.
May Oil Burner Corporation.............................Baltimore, Md.
McAleer, E. J. Company, Inc............................Philadelphia, Pa.
McKay Company.......................................York, Pa.
Metlab Company.......................................Philadelphia, Pa.
Middlesex Paper Tube Company.........................Trenton, N. J.
Midvale Company......................................Philadelphia, Pa.
Mifflinburg Body Works, Inc............................Mifflinburg, Pa.
Modern Tool and Die Company...........................Philadelphia, Pa.
Moistaire Cabinet Company.............................Philadelphia, Pa.
Motor Parts Company..................................Philadelphia, Pa.
Narrow Fabric Company................................York, Pa.
National Enameling & Stamping Company.................Baltimore, Md.
Nesbitt, John J., Inc...................................Philadelphia, Pa.
New England Auto Products Company....................Philadelphia, Pa.
Norris Tool and Machine Company.......................Philadelphia, Pa.
Null Screw Machine Works..............................Philadelphia, Pa.
Ocean City Manufacturing Company.....................Philadelphia, Pa.
Oehrle Brothers Company, Inc..........................Philadelphia, Pa.
Owens Illinois Can Company............................Baltimore, Md.
Parish Pressed Steel Company...........................Reading, Pa.
Peco Manufacturing Company...........................Philadelphia, Pa.
Penn Fishing Tackle Manufacturing Company.............Philadelphia, Pa.
Philadelphia Rust Proof Company........................Philadelphia, Pa.
Philco Corporation....................................Philadelphia, Pa.
Princeton University...................................Princeton, N. J.
Proctor and Schwartz, Inc..............................Philadelphia, Pa.
Quaker City Motor Parts Company.......................Philadelphia, Pa.
R-S Products Corporation...............................Philadelphia, Pa.
Raybestos-Manhattan, Inc..............................Manheim, Pa.
Read Machinery Company...............................York, Pa.
Reading Hardware Corporation..........................Reading, Pa.
Revere Copper and Brass Company.......................Baltimore, Md.
Reynolds Metals Company...............................Richmond, Va.
Rheem Manufacturing Company..........................Sparrows Point, Md.
Richmond Engineering Company..........................Richmond, Va.
Riverside Metal Company...............................Riverside, N. J.
Roberts and Mander Stove Company......................Hatboro, Pa.
Roebling, John A. Sons Company........................Trenton, N. J.
Rohm and Haas Company...............................Philadelphia, Pa.
Roller-Smith Company.................................Bethlehem, Pa.
Schramm, Inc..West Chester, Pa.
Sharples Chemicals, Inc................................Philadelphia, Pa.
SKF Industries, Inc...................................Philadelphia, Pa.
Slaymaker Lock Company...............................Lancaster, Pa.
Sloane Blabon Corporation.............................New York, N. Y.
Smith, S. Morgan Company.............................York, Pa.
Specialty Engineering Company.........................Philadelphia, Pa.
Standard Oil Company of New Jersey....................Jersey City, N. J.
Standard Pressed Steel Company........................Jenkintown, Pa.

Steel Heddle Manufacturing Company......................Philadelphia, Pa.
Stokes, F. J. Machine Company............................Philadelphia, Pa.
Stern, Edward Company, Inc..............................Philadelphia, Pa.
Stick Manufacturing Company.............................Philadelphia, Pa.
Taylor Wharton Iron & Steel Company.....................Easton, Pa.
Thomas, Perley A. Car Works.............................High Point, N. C.
Thorn, J. S. Company...................................Philadelphia, Pa.
Textile Machine Works..................................Reading, Pa.
Thornton Fuller Company................................Philadelphia, Pa.
Tredegar Company.......................................Richmond, Va.
Truitt Manufacturing Company...........................Greensboro, N. C.
Princeton University...................................Princeton, N. J.
University of Pennsylvania..............................Philadelphia, Pa.
United States Pipe & Foundry Company...................Burlington, N. J.
United Specialties Company.............................Philadelphia, Pa.
Van Dorn Electric Tool Company.........................Towson, Md.
Vance, J. A. Company...................................Winston Salem, N. C.
Vanity Fair Silk Mills.................................Reading, Pa.
Victory Parachutes, Inc................................Scranton, Pa.
Virginia Steel Company, Inc............................Richmond, Va.
Wald, John R. Company..................................Milton, Pa.
Wannamaker Chemical Company, Inc.......................Orangeburg, S. C.
Webster, Warren Company................................Camden, N. J.
Wheaton, T. C. Company.................................Milleville, N. J.
Wiedemann Machine Company..............................Philadelphia, Pa.
Wildman Manufacturing Company..........................Norristown, Pa.
Wood, John Manufacturing Company.......................Conshohocken, Pa.
York Corporation.......................................York, Pa.
York-Hoover Corporation................................York, Pa.
York Safe and Lock Company.............................York, Pa.
York-Shipley, Inc......................................York, Pa.
Young, L. A. Spring & Wire Company.....................Trenton, N. J.

ARMY AND NAVY "E" AWARDS IN THE PHILADELPHIA ORDNANCE DISTRICT

Philco Corporation	Philadelphia, Pa.	8/14/42
Autocar Company	Ardmore, Pa.	8/28/42
Ford Motor Company	Chester, Pa.	8/26/42
Parish Pressed Steel Company	Reading, Pa.	10/13/42
Solvay Process Company	Hopewell, Va.	11/11/42
Martin & Schwartz, Inc.	Salisbury, Md.	11/12/42
Mack Manufacturing Company	Allentown, Pa.	11/28/42
Heintz Manufacturing Company	Philadelphia, Pa.	11/28/42
Armstrong Cork Company	Lancaster, Pa.	11/30/42
Henry Disston & Sons, Inc.	Philadelphia, Pa.	12/ 1/42
United Specialties Corporation	Philadelphia, Pa.	12/ 3/42
Peco Manufacturing Company	Philadelphia, Pa.	12/11/42
Haines Gage Company	Philadelphia, Pa.	12/12/42
E. I. DuPont de Nemours, Inc., Repanno Works	Gibbstown, N. J.	12/18/42
Warren Webster Company	Camden, N. J.	1/ 4/43
Ocean City Manufacturing Company	Philadelphia, Pa.	1/19/43
Allied Chemical Company, Barrett Division	Philadelphia, Pa.	2/ 5/43
A. B. Farquhar Company, Ltd.	York, Pa.	2/ 8/43
Wannamaker Chemical Company	Orangeburg, S. C.	2/17/43
Fidelity Machine Company	Philadelphia, Pa.	2/20/43
Metlab Company	Philadelphia, Pa.	3/12/43
Hendrick Manufacturing Company	Philadelphia, Pa.	3/16/43
Hercules Powder Company	Hopewell, Va.	4/13/43
Animal Trap Company of America, Ltd.	Lititz, Pa.	4/15/43
Baldwin Locomotive Works	Philadelphia, Pa.	4/16/43
Lehigh Foundries, Inc.	Easton, Pa.	4/27/43
Lehigh Foundries (Merchant & Evans)	Lancaster, Pa.	4/29/43
Middlesex Paper Tube Company	Burlington, N. J.	5/18/43
Hamilton Watch Company	Lancaster, Pa.	6/16/43
DeLong Hook & Eye Company	Philadelphia, Pa.	6/17/43
E. I. DuPont de Nemours, Inc.	Moosic, Pa.	6/21/43
Lebanon Steel Company	Lebanon, Pa.	6/22/43
American Viscose Corporation	Marcus Hook, Pa.	7/14/43
Ace Manufacturing Company	Philadelphia, Pa.	7/20/43
Eastern Rolling Mills	Baltimore, Md.	7/24/43
Atlas Powder Company	Reynolds, Pa.	7/27/43
Multiplex Manufacturing Company	Berwick, Pa.	7/29/43
L. A. Young Spring & Wire Corporation	Trenton, N. J.	7/31/43
Smith, Drum & Company	Philadelphia, Pa.	8/12/43
American Car & Foundry Company	Berwick, Pa.	8/19/43
General Machine & Manufacturing Company	Berwick, Pa.	8/27/43
John R. Wald Company	Milton, Pa.	1/29/43
Line Material Company	East Stroudsberg, Pa.	10/ 7/43

American Viscose Corporation	Front Royal, Va.	10/13/43
Everedy Company	Frederick, Md.	10/19/43
Ordnance Gage Company	Philadelphia, Pa.	10/19/43
Read Machinery Company	York, Pa.	11/22/43
York Ice Machinery Company	York, Pa.	11/23/43
B. F. Goodrich Company	Oaks, Pa.	12/ 3/43
George K. Garrett Company	Philadelphia, Pa.	12/23/43
Kennedy-Van Saun Manufacturing & Engineering Co...	Danville, Pa.	12/28/43
Charles D. Briddell, Inc.	Chrisfield, Md.	1/ 4/44
Owens-Illinois Can Company	Baltimore, Md.	1/19/44
ACF—Brill Motors	Philadelphia, Pa.	1/25/44
Chipman Knitting Mills	Easton, Pa.	1/27/42
L. F. Grammes & Sons, Inc.	Allentown, Pa.	2/ 1/44
U. S. Asbestos Division Raybestos-Manhattan, Inc.	Manheim, Pa.	2/ 4/44
John J. Nesbitt, Inc.	Philadelphia, Pa.	2/11/44
Precision Manufacturing Company (E. J. Schoettle Paper Box Company)	Philadelphia, Pa.	2/25/44
Firestone Tire & Rubber Company	Gastonia, N. C.	3/27/44
Machined Metals Company	W. Conshohocken, Pa.	5/ 2/44
Argo Lamp Company	Philadelphia, Pa.	5/11/44
International Chain & Manufacturing Company	York, Pa.	5/20/44
Mathieson Alkali Works, Inc., Saltville Plant	Saltville, Va.	6/19/44
York-Shipley, Inc.	York, Pa.	6/28/44
York-Shipley, Inc., York Oil Burner Company	York, Pa.	6/28/44
Davison Chemical Corporation Curtis Bay Plant	Baltimore, Md.	7/ 5/44
Vanity Fair Silk Mills, Inc., Vanterial Corporation	Reading, Pa.	7/21/44
York Corrugating Company	York, Pa.	8/ 9/44
Bonschur & Holmes Company	Philadelphia, Pa.	8/22/44
Congoleum-Nairn Corporation	Marcus Hook, Pa.	8/25/44
Franklin Lamp Company	Philadelphia, Pa.	8/29/44
May Oil Burner Company	Baltimore, Md.	9/ 6/44
Standard Pressed Steel Company	Jenkintown, Pa.	10/17/44
American Meter Company	Philadelphia, Pa.	11/27/44
Cutler Metal Products Company	Camden, N. J.	11/30/44
Fred C. Good & Sons, Inc.	Philadelphia, Pa.	12/ 6/44
Harrisburg Steel Corporation	Harrisburg, Pa.	12/11/44
Reade Company	Lakehurst, N. J.	1/ 5/45
Wiedemann Machine Company	Philadelphia, Pa.	1/ 9/45
Bunting Glider Company	Philadelphia, Pa.	1/10/45
Pittsburgh Metallurgical Company	Charleston, S. C.	1/12/45
Coplay Cement Manufacturing Company, Machine Shop Division	Coplay, Pa.	1/30/45
Karl Lieberknecht, Inc.	Laureldale, Pa.	2/ 9/45
United States Rubber Company, Winnsboro Mills	Winnsboro, S. C.	2/15/45
Slaymaker Lock Company	Lancaster, Pa.	3/14/45
American Instrument Company, Plant No. 1	Silver Spring, Md.	5/28/45
Motor Parts Company	Philadelphia, Pa.	5/28/45
Firestone Tire & Rubber Company	Bennettsville, S. C.	6/ 5/45
Atlas Fence Company	Philadelphia, Pa.	6/26/45
Atlas Powder Company	White Haven, Pa.	6/28/45
Bulova Watch Company Fuze Division	Philadelphia, Pa.	7/ 2/45
General Aviation Equipment Company	Wilkes-Barre, Pa.	7/ 6/45

E. I. DuPont de Nemours Company Wilmington Shops	Wilmington, Del.	7/ 3/45
Pennsylvania Tool & Manufacturing Company	York, Pa.	7/ 9/45
National Waterproofing Company	Camden, N. J.	7/10/45
Proctor Electric Company, Proctor & Schwartz	Philadelphia, Pa.	7/11/45
Hill Independent Manufacturing Company	Philadelphia, Pa.	7/23/45
American Radiator and Standard Sanitary Corporation Baltimore Works	Baltimore, Md.	7/25/45
Carey-McFall Company, Tool Division	Philadelphia, Pa.	7/21/45
Hopkins Equipment Company	Hatfield, Pa.	8/ 2/45
Quality Knitting Company	Stowe, Pa.	8/ 3/45
Keystone Drawn Steel Company	Spring City, Pa.	8/ 6/45
D. Wilcox Manufacturing Company	Mechanicsburg, Pa.	8/ 8/45
Schlosser Manufacturing Company	Philadelphia, Pa.	8/ 9/45
Corbitt Company	Henderson, N. C.	9/ 4/45
Dienelt & Eisenhardt	Philadelphia, Pa.	9/ 5/45
Croessant Machine Works	Reading, Pa.	9/ 6/45
Phoenix Manufacturing Company Forging Division	Catasasqua, Pa.	9/ 7/45
Continental Can Company, Plant No. 55	Wilkes-Barre, Pa.	9/11/45
American Chain & Cable Company, Inc., Electric Welding Plant and Malleable Foundry	York, Pa.	9/14/45

ॐ

There were many other contractors who received "E" Awards, but those listed herein were substantially contractors to Ordnance. We have not listed those who contracted with other services in addition to Ordnance. Inclusion of their names would have been far beyond the intent of this volume.

ॐ

Summary of Activities—Board of Awards
Philadelphia Ordnance District

Month	Value	Cumulative	No. of Awards	Cumulative
1942				
January...............	$ 67,742,000	$	* 75	
February..............	46,921,000	114,663,000	*100	175
March................	58,472,000	173,135,000	*125	300
April.................	46,822,575	219,957,575	88	388
May..................	44,388,173	264,345,748	188	576
June.................	26,217,839	290,563,587	210	786
July.................	28,528,461	319,092,048	254	1040
August...............	154,512,660	473,604,708	220	1260
September............	83,063,181	556,667,889	208	1468
October..............	92,018,301	648,686,190	238	1706
November............	34,516,474	683,202,664	711	2417
December............	65,405,887	748,608,551	481	2898
1943				
January...............	113,823,108	862,431,659	498	3396
February..............	23,754,563	886,186,222	406	3802
March................	41,598,135	927,784,357	354	4156
April.................	26,594,201	954,378,558	452	4608
May..................	105,549,436	1,060,927,994	375	4983
June.................	229,834,492	1,290,762,486	432	5415
July.................	99,494,930	1,390,257,416	430	5845
August...............	101,016,505	1,491,273,921	430	6275
September............	173,754,161	1,665,027,082	393	6678
October..............	54,807,384	1,719,834,466	322	7000
November............	60,230,736	1,780,065,202	335	7335
December............	41,958,171	1,822,023,373	255	7590
1944				
January...............	22,536,387	1,844,559,760	261	7851
February..............	20,935,718	1,865,495,478	275	8126
March................	34,350,161	1,899,845,639	372	8498
April.................	48,493,980	1,948,339,619	341	8839
May..................	79,969,107	2,028,308,726	463	9302
June.................	109,745,127	2,138,053,853	497	9799
July.................	65,122,811	2,203,176,664	465	10264
August...............	71,144,383	2,274,321,047	543	10807
September............	70,676,447	2,344,997,494	444	11251
October..............	36,183,031	2,381,180,525	383	11634
November............	31,059,644	2,412,240,169	350	11984
December............	54,164,272	2,466,405,441	440	12424
1945				
January...............	122,366,932	2,588,772,373	517	12941
February..............	88,112,037	2,676,884,410	678	13619
March................	84,225,413	2,761,109,823	563	14182
April.................	38,273,182	2,799,383,005	474	14656
May..................	40,317,541	2,839,700,546	462	15118
June.................	31,820,451	2,871,520,997	399	15517
July.................	20,595,451	2,892,116,448	372	15889
August...............	6,546,554	2,898,663,002	160	16049
September............	584,598	2,899,247,600	31	16080
October..............	923,257	2,900,170,857	53	16133
November............	1,025,640	2,901,196,497	28	16161
December............	407,725	2,901,604,222	79	16240

Average: Value per month.......................$60,450,088
Value per award....................... 178,670
Awards per month.................... 339

*Estimated

[